Second Edition

Algebra I

Expressions, Equations, and Applications

Paul A. Foerster

Teacher's Edition

Addison-Wesley Publishing Company

Menlo Park, California • Reading, Massachusetts
New York • Don Mills, Ontario • Wokingham, England
Amsterdam • Bonn • Sydney • Singapore • Tokyo
Madrid • San Juan

To the women in my life:

My grandmother, Annie Higgins, whose foresight made teaching a feasible career.

My mother, Gladys Foerster, who inspired me by asking the right questions at the right time

My wife, Jo Ann, who makes it all worthwhile.

Paul A. Foerster has taught mathematics at Alamo Heights High School in San Antonio, Texas since 1961. In that same year he received his teaching certificate from Texas A&M University. His B.S. degree in Chemical Engineering and M.A. degree in Mathematics are from the University of Texas. Among many honors, he was awarded the Presidential Award for Excellence in Mathematics Teaching in 1983.

Design and cover: John Edeen
Illustrations: Irene Imfeld, Valerie Felts

ISBN-0-201-25074-8
BCDEFGHIJKL-KR-892109

Foreword to the Student

You are about to embark on the course which lays the foundation for virtually all of higher mathematics. In previous courses you have occasionally used a letter to stand for a number you seek to find. Now you will be less concerned about what number the letter represents, and will concentrate on things that are true just because it is a *number*.

The letters used will be called variables, because they can stand for different numbers at different times. Expressions containing these variables can represent quantities in the real world, such as how high a ball is above the ground at various times after it was thrown. By learning how to operate with such expressions, you will be able to predict such things as how high the ball is at a given time, how long it takes to reach a given height, and when it will be back down.

Some of the things you will learn may not seem to have any immediate practical use. Learn them anyway, and learn them well! They are all part of a big picture which becomes clear only after you have unveiled its various parts.

The way to learn mathematics is by practice. Some things may seem clear when your teacher explains them. But they will not become a part of you until you can *do* them. Do your homework only after you have worked the text examples. Then do the problems without looking at the examples. Sometimes you will be asked to read the book and work new problems on your own prior to classroom discussion. Keep asking yourself how new problems relate to the ones you have done before. You have a chance to gain self-reliance that will help you the rest of your life.

Neatness is an asset in algebra. Clear writing will help you avoid mistakes. There will be times when you cannot tell what step to take next in a problem until you have done the step before. It is less time-consuming in the long run to write carefully and get things right the first time than it is to save a few minutes, then have to redo the work. Developing the habit of neatness and of saying exactly what you mean will help you in other subjects as well as mathematics.

In conclusion, let me wish you the best as you start the course. Remember that mathematics is not a spectator sport. May your hard work cause you to progress toward better understanding of mathematics.

Paul A. Foerster

Foreword to the Teacher

Algebra I: Expressions, Equations, and Applications presents the normal content of first-year high school algebra. It is designed to prepare students for a subsequent course in either geometry or second-year algebra. The materials were written for use in the author's own classes, and have been refined following successful pilot tests in public and private schools across the United States.

The unifying theme is the concept of an *expression*. For increasingly complex expressions, students do these three things:

1. Write an expression representing a variable quantity in some real-world situation,
2. Find the value of the expression when x is known,
3. Find x when the value of the expression is known.

The first part of the book is carefully sequenced to lead to the Quadratic Formula by mid-year. This departure from the more traditional sequence of topics is made possible by technology, specifically, the use of calculators to evaluate radicals. As a result, students are able to work more realistic word problems in which answers are decimals. Students must check their answers based on whether or not they are reasonable, not because they came out as small, whole numbers.

The second part of the book allows more flexibility in selection of sequence and topics to fit students' needs and available time. Expressions with two variables, harder factoring problems, algebraic fractions, radical equations, and inequalities appear here. Students can also learn that the computer is appropriate for repetitive evaluation of expressions, while the calculator or the brain is more appropriate for single calculations. The final chapter introduces topics to which the students will spiral back in geometry, algebra II, and trigonometry.

The Second Edition differs from the first by inclusion of some more topics, resequencing of a few other topics, and expanding the treatment of several topics where students seem to need more practice. In Chapter 3, the three Equality Axioms and all Field Axioms except Closure are stated formally. The axioms are used to identify what was done in *familiar* transformations of expressions and equations, rather than for proving various (unfamiliar) other properties.

The properties are still introduced as *verbs* such as "commute" and "distribute." As a teacher for 28 years, I have found that students grasp the properties better if they first learn what it means to *do* these things. As a person with degrees and work experience in both mathematics and chemical engineering, I have found that a good grasp of theory is essential for the intelligent application of mathematics.

Chapter 4 on "Harder Equations" now has a section on literal equations and formulas. By solving for one variable in terms of others, students acquire skills helpful in science.

Chapter 8 on two-variable equations now contains a formal treatment of the *reverse* process of graphing a line. Specifically, students learn to find the equation of a line from given information about the graph, such as two points on it. In the problems, students practice drawing a line that reasonably fits scattered data.

Students are eased into operations with algebraic fractions less abruptly in the renumbered Chapter 11. Simplification of rational expressions comes first, then multiplication and division, then addition and subtraction. The combined operations still occur, but only after students have practiced the operations individually. The topic of probability is touched upon in connection with operations on fractions. The Density Axiom is treated in the problems.

The Inequalities chapter, now Chapter 13, has been moved closer to the end of the book. The move has two purposes. First, the work on algebraic fractions now comes earlier in the year, before students' attention is too much distracted by the approaching end of school. Second, the work on inequalities provides an excellent review to tie together solving and evaluating techniques before the final exam, without simply reworking old types of problems.

The last chapter now contains a formal treatment of linear functions. However, $f(x)$ terminology is deliberately avoided, in favor of two variables with *familiar* names, such as x and y. The students seem to understand a function as something that "tells how y is related to x" this way, rather than just as "that $f(x)$ thing!"

The main features of the First Edition remain intact. Word problems involve variables that really *vary*, rather than standing for unknown constants. The "hand- holding" phase at the beginning of the text has problems with multiple parts. Students are asked to define variables and to write expressions representing the quantities in the problem. Then students either evaluate expressions if a value of the variable is given, or solve for the variable if a value of the expression is given. Thus, students quick enough to do easy problems in their heads are forced to learn proper algebraic techniques, while those who might have trouble are given successful experience by following the instructions.

Toward the middle of the book the word problems look rather like those in any good algebra I text. Students are expected to know that they should define a variable, and write and solve equations. By Chapter 10 students enter the "no-holds-barred" phase. Here, clever short-cuts and trial-and-error techniques are encouraged, as well as the traditional algebraic techniques. Students thus practice problem solving as advocated by the National Council of Teachers of Mathematics. The experience helps prepare them for contests and standardized tests, where the emphasis is on getting the right answer quickly.

Pedagogically, the first two chapters start slowly for the benefit of students who have never encountered negative numbers or variables, or who just need time to get started at the beginning of the course. Classes with a stronger background can move rapidly here, allowing time for the more difficult problems later on, or for the advanced topics at the end.

Some sections, particularly at the beginnings of chapters, are for students to read and work on their own. This feature provides a worthwhile assignment to be given following a test. Each section contains Oral Practice problems, where appropriate. These problems are *lettered* rather than numbered, so that students will not work orals by mistake when you assign "Problems 1 through 10" on a particular page.

The examples in each section specify that the student cover the answers at the dotted lines, then work the example himself or herself. The answers are to be uncovered only after the student has done the work. The technique is very effective, but students must be trained to do the work, and not just to look at the solutions.

Paul A. Foerster

Acknowledgements

Thanks go to my students starting in 1980 for putting up with "all those ditto sheets!" In particular, thanks to Maria Flores and Gilbert Rios whose good class notes provided input for much of the First Edition. Special thanks go to Isabel Zsohar and Becky Wallace for ideas and materials that went into Chapters 3 and 11 in the Second Edition.

The following teachers pilot tested the materials for the First Edition or provided valuable input for the Second Edition.

Alamo Heights High School, San Antonio, Texas: Tammy Frietsch, Sharon Brassel, Bruce Fink, Kathy Schlosberg, Susan Thomas, Becky Wallace, Mercille Wisakowsky, Isabel Zsohar, Paul Foerster

Alamo Heights Junior School, San Antonio, Texas: Martha Jo Buckley

Eisenhower Middle School, San Antonio, Texas: Loren Caraway

John Evans Junior High, Greeley, Colorado: Gary Steward, Jack Pendar

Greenwich High School, Greenwich, Connecticut: Terry Lowe, William Bechem

Groton School, Groton, Massachusetts: Jonathan Choate

Lamar Middle School, Temple, Texas: Larry Scott, Mariella Morgan

Libertyville High School, Libertyville, Illinois: Barbara Schultz, Jack Zetterberg

Milwaukee Technical High School, Milwaukee, Wisconsin: Adele Hanson

Pan American University, Edinburg, Texas: Olga Ramirez, John Huber

Sandusky High School, Sandusky, Ohio: Paula Schmansky, Paul Dahnke

University of Massachusetts, Amherst, Massachusetts: Ron Narode, Jack Lochhead

Valley View Junior High, Omaha, Nebraska: David Thronson, Al Gloor

Westridge School for Girls, Pasadena, California: Jerry Pillsbury, Sandra Feeney

Thanks go to Jill Foerster for proofreading the original manuscript. Thanks also to Richard and Josephine Andree for letting their children Calvin Butterball and Phoebe Small join my own (the Dupp Family, etc.) in making the problems a bit more entertaining.

Photograph Acknowledgments

Cover: © 1982 Paul Jablonka/International Stock Photography Ltd.

Page 1:   Dana Gluckstein*

Page 42:   Keith H. Murakami/Tom Stack & Associates

Page 89:   Charlotte Pawel

Page 129:   © 1981 Ted Spiegel/Black Star

Page 104:   Charlotte Pawel*

Page 213:   Peter Southwick/Stock, Boston

Page 270:   Grant Heilman

Page 299:   Grant Heilman

Page 360:   Walter Spencer/U.S. Navy

Page 410:   © 1981 Howard Sochurek/Woodfin Camp & Associates

Page 455:   Wayland Lee*/Addison-Wesley Publishing Company

Page 520:   Alan Pitcairn/Grant Heilman

Page 568:   Dana Gluckstein*

Page 615:   © Jonathan Blair/Woodfin Camp & Associates

*Photographs provided expressly for the publisher.

Contents

1

Expressions and Equations

In this course you will work with quantities that can vary. For instance, if you mow lawns for $10 each, you will earn varying amounts depending on how many lawns you mow. One type of problem is: If you mow 3 lawns, how much money will you make? Another is: If you want to make $70, how many lawns must you mow? The answers, of course, are $30 and 7 lawns, respectively. In algebra you will learn to reduce complicated problems to easy ones like these. The name algebra comes from the Arabic word al-jabr. It is part of the title of the ninth century book hisab al-jabr wa'l muqabalah, meaning "the science of reduction and comparison." Letters are used to stand for quantities whose value varies, and expressions and equations are made using these variables.

<table>
<tr><td>1-1</td><td>OPERATIONS WITH NUMBERS</td></tr>
</table>

Time: 1 day

Possible to move faster... .

Chalkboard Examples:

1. Evaluate: 4 + (3 × 5)   Ans.: 19
     (4 + 3) × 5   Ans.: 35
   Conclusion: The answer depends on which
      operation is done first.
   Note: Use the format in text examples,
      starting with the given expression and
      writing steps *vertically,* putting = signs
      to connect one expression with the next.
      The = sign is a *verb* in a sentence that
      says that the original expression equals
      the final answer.

2. Evaluate: [(24 ÷ 3) × 4] + 2   Ans.: 34
     [24 ÷ (3 × 4)] + 2   Ans.: 4
     24 ÷ [3 × (4 + 2)]   Ans.: $1\frac{1}{3}$
     (24 ÷ 3) × (4 + 2)   Ans.: 48
   Conclusion: Do what is nested inside the
      innermost symbols of inclusion first.

3. Evaluate: $\frac{5 \times 8}{3 + 8}$ Ans.: $\frac{40}{11}$
   Conclusion: Bar (vinculum) is a symbol of
      inclusion.
   Note: Do not cancel the 8's!

Assignment:

1–31 odd or 2–32 even

An *operation* in mathematics is something you do to numbers, such as adding, subtracting, multiplying, or dividing. For instance, in

$$3 + 11,$$

the operation of addition is performed on the numbers 3 and 11. Difficulties may arise if there are several different operations. For example, what number does

$$3 + 2 \times 7$$

represent? If you add 3 and 2 first and then multiply by 7, you get

$$5 \times 7 = \underline{\underline{35}}.$$

But if you multiply 2 by 7 first, then add the result to 3, you get a different number:

$$3 + 4 = \underline{\underline{17}}.$$

To avoid this difficulty, **symbols of inclusion**—parentheses, ( ), or brackets, [ ]—are used to tell which operation to do first.

$$(3 + 2) \times 7 \quad \text{means} \quad 5 \times 7, \quad \text{or} \quad 35.$$
$$3 + (2 \times 7) \quad \text{means} \quad 3 + 14, \quad \text{or} \quad 17.$$
$$12 \div [2 \times 3] \quad \text{means} \quad 12 \div 6, \quad \text{or} \quad 2.$$

Another symbol of inclusion is the bar used in fractions, called a **vinculum.** For example, in

$$\frac{6 + 7}{2 \times 7}$$

the operations 6 + 7 and 2 × 7 are done *first,* giving

$$\frac{13}{14}.$$

Then 13 is divided by 14, giving about 0.929.

A collection of numbers, operation signs, and symbols of inclusion (parentheses, brackets, vinculums) is called an **expression.** Finding the value of an expression is called **evaluating** the expression. An expression such as

$$36 \div 3 \times 4 + 2$$

can have different values, depending on how the operations are grouped.

EXAMPLE 1

Evaluate $[(36 \div 3) \times 4] + 2$.

$$
\begin{aligned}
& [(36 \div 3) \times 4] + 2 \\
={} & [12 \times 4] + 2 \\
={} & 48 + 2 \\
={} & \underline{\underline{50}}
\end{aligned}
$$

Note that you do what is inside the *innermost* symbols of inclusion *first*.

EXAMPLE 2

Evaluate $[36 \div (3 \times 4)] + 2$.

$$
\begin{aligned}
& [36 \div (3 \times 4)] + 2 \\
={} & [36 \div 12] + 2 \\
={} & 3 + 2 \\
={} & \underline{\underline{5}}
\end{aligned}
$$

Objective:
Given an expression, be able to *evaluate* it.

As shown in the examples, you should do the following to evaluate an expression:

1. Write the given expression.
2. Do the innermost operation and write the result. Use an = sign to connect the new expression to the original one.
3. Keep doing operations until you reduce the expression to a *single* number. Use = signs to connect each expression to the one before, as shown in the examples.
4. Clearly indicate the answer by underlining or boxing it.

Now *you* work the examples on the next page. Put a piece of paper along the dotted lines. This will cover the answer, leaving only the original expression showing. (If the writing shows through, use more sheets of paper or an index card.) Then evaluate the expression. Last, uncover the answer in the book to make sure your *work* and your *answer* are right.

EXAMPLE 3

Evaluate $36 \div [3 \times (4 + 2)]$.

– – – – –   – – – – –

	Think These Reasons
$36 \div [3 \times (4 + 2)]$	Write the given expression.
$= 36 \div [3 \times 6]$	Do the *innermost* operation first.
$= 36 \div 18$	Do operations in parentheses or brackets next.
$= \underline{2}$	Do the arithmetic. Underline or box the answer.

Note: Be sure to write the given expression first and to use $=$ signs to connect each simplified expression to the one on the line above.

EXAMPLE 4

Evaluate $(36 \div 3) \times (4 + 2)$.

– – – – –   – – – – –

$(36 \div 3) \times (4 + 2)$	Write the given expression.
$= 12 \times 6$	Do what is inside parentheses first.
$= \underline{\underline{72}}$	Underline or box the answer.

As you read the above material, you found the words *operation, expression,* and *evaluate*. It is important for you to know exactly what these words mean. This is why mathematicians make precise *definitions* of the words they use. You should learn the following definitions.

DEFINITIONS

ARITHMETIC OPERATION
Addition, subtraction, multiplication, and division are called **arithmetic operations.**

EXPRESSION
An **expression** is a collection of numbers, operation signs, and inclusion symbols that stands for a number.

EVALUATING
To **evaluate an expression** means to find the number for which the expression stands.

EXERCISE 1-1

Evaluate the following expressions.

1. $(5 + 7) \times 8$ 96
2. $(4 + 9) \times 5$ 65
3. $5 + (7 \times 8)$ 61
4. $4 + (9 \times 5)$ 49
5. $9 - (4 \times 2)$ 1
6. $11 - (5 \times 2)$ 1
7. $(9 - 4) \times 2$ 10
8. $(11 - 5) \times 2$ 12
9. $[8 \times 7] - 13$ 43
10. $[7 \times 6] - 19$ 23
11. $9 \times [4 + 2]$ 54
12. $8 \times [2 + 5]$ 56
13. $(36 \div 2) \times 6$ 108
14. $(54 \div 3) \times 2$ 36
15. $36 \div (2 \times 6)$ 3
16. $54 \div (3 \times 2)$ 9
17. $[16 - (3 \times 2)] - 4$ 6
18. $[17 - (4 \times 3)] - 2$ 3
19. $16 - [(3 \times 2) - 4]$ 14
20. $17 - [(4 \times 3) - 2]$ 7
21. $(10 + 6) \times (11 - 3)$ 128
22. $(14 + 6) \times (9 - 2)$ 140
23. $10 + [6 \times (11 - 3)]$ 58
24. $14 + [6 \times (9 - 2)]$ 56
25. $100 \div [(20 \div 5) - 3]$ 100
26. $[800 \div (50 \div 2)] - 7$ 25
27. $100 \div [20 \div (5 - 3)]$ 10
28. $[(800 \div 50) \div 2] - 7$ 1
29. $\dfrac{63 - 8}{3 + 8} - 2$ 3
30. $19 - \dfrac{25 - 7}{5 + 4}$ 17
31. $5 \times \dfrac{19 - 7}{5 + 1}$ 10
32. $28 \div \dfrac{8 \times 6}{5 + 7}$ 7

1-2 | VARIABLES

In the last section you learned what it means to evaluate an expression such as

$$3 + (7 \times 9).$$

The answer is 66. Suppose that you are not told what one of the numbers in this expression is.

$$3 + (\underline{} \times 9)$$

The value of this expression *varies*, depending on what number you put in the blank space. Some examples are shown on the next page.

Time: 1 day

Chalkboard Examples:

1. Evaluate $x - 7$ if x is 15.   Ans.: 8
   Note: Use format shown in Examples 1 and 2. Have students write the expression with x on the first line and the expression $15 - 7$ on the next line to show physically the substitution of 15 for x. The answer is less important than the concept of substituting for x.

2. Evaluate $(30 - x) \times 2$ if x is 5.
   Ans.: 50

3. Write an expression for:
   a. the product of 9 and x
      Ans.: $9x$ or $9 \times x$
   b. 3 more than x
      Ans.: $3 + x$ or $x + 3$
   c. 8 less than x Ans.: $x - 8$ (only)
   Note: Occasionally, students substituting 7
      for x in $9x$ will write 97 instead of
      9×7, or 63. Make sure they know $9x$
      means 9 times x.

4. Write an expression for the length marked
   "?":   Ans.: $x + 8$

   Note: The skill acquired here is useful in
      problems later on involving diagrams
      with dimensions.

Assignment:

1–35 odd or 2–36 even

$$3 + (\underline{\ 2\ } \times 9)$$
$$= 3 + 18$$
$$= \underline{21}$$

$$3 + (\underline{100} \times 9)$$
$$= 3 + 900$$
$$= \underline{903}$$

$$3 + (\underline{5.7} \times 9)$$
$$= 3 + 51.3$$
$$= \underline{54.3}$$

It is customary to use a letter such as x, y, or z to stand for a number that can take on different values at different times. Instead of using a blank space, the expression above would be written

$$3 + (x \times 9).$$

A letter such as x is called a *variable*.

DEFINITION

> **VARIABLE**
> A **variable** is a letter that represents a number. (It can represent different numbers at different times, but it represents the *same* number each place it appears in an expression.)

To evaluate an expression containing a variable, you must be told what value to use for the variable. Then you *substitute* that number for the variable and evaluate the expression as before. Symbols such as 14, 7.8, or $\frac{3}{4}$, which stand for the *same* number *all* the time, are called **constants.**

DEFINITION

> **SUBSTITUTING**
> To **substitute** means to replace a variable with a constant (such as 3, 158, or 1001).

For each of the examples on the next page, put a piece of paper along the dotted lines to cover the answer. Work the example. Then uncover the answer to be sure you are right.

EXAMPLE 1

Substitute 4 for x and evaluate: $(15 - x) \times 3$

– – – – –   – – – – –

	Think These Reasons

$(15 - x) \times 3$	Write the given expression.
$= (15 - 4) \times 3$	Substitute 4 for x.
$= 11 \times 3$	Do what is inside the parentheses.
$= \underline{\underline{33}}$	Underline or box the answer.

Note: Be sure to use $=$ signs to say that the first expression is *equal* to the next, and so forth.

EXAMPLE 2

Substitute 9 for x and evaluate: $(15 - x) \times 3$

– – – – –   – – – – –

$(15 - x) \times 3$	Write the given expression.
$= (15 - 9) \times 3$	Substitute 9 for x.
$= 6 \times 3$	Do what is inside the parentheses.
$= \underline{\underline{18}}$	Underline or box the answer.

Note: The *same* expression has *different* values when different numbers are substituted for the variable.

It is possible to write an expression that fits a given description. For instance, "the sum of x and 7" is written

$$x + 7.$$

You should recall from previous courses what the words *sum, difference, product,* and *quotient* mean.

$11 + 3$ is an indicated *sum.*

$11 - 3$ is an indicated *difference.*

11×3 is an indicated *product.*

$11 \div 3$ is an indicated *quotient.*

The numbers in a sum, difference, and product have special names, as shown at the top of the next page.

$$11 + 3$$
$$11 - 3$$
Terms

$$11 \times 3$$
Factors

DEFINITION

TERMS AND FACTORS

Terms are numbers that are *added* to each other or *subtracted* from each other.

Factors are numbers that are multiplied together.

EXAMPLE 3

Cover the answers on the right. Write each expression described. Then uncover the answer to be sure that you are correct.

Question	*Possible Answer*
a. The sum of x, 5, and 2.	$x + 5 + 2$
b. The product of 2 and 11.	2×11
c. The difference 17 minus 4.	$17 - 4$
d. The quotient 13 divided by 7.	$13 \div 7 \left(\text{or } \dfrac{13}{7}\right)$
e. x decreased by 6.	$x - 6$
f. 10 more than y.	$y + 10$ or $10 + y$
g. 50 less than z.	$z - 50$

There are several ways to write the *product* of two numbers x and y:

$$x \times y \quad \text{or} \quad x \cdot y \quad \text{or} \quad (x)(y) \quad \text{or} \quad xy.$$

In the last two, there is no operation sign. So you must *understand* that multiplication is to be done. An expression such as

$$3x$$

means 3 *times* x.

Sometimes an expression may be described by a picture. For instance, the length marked by a question mark below is the *sum* of 3 and x.

You would write <u>3 + x</u> or <u>x + 3</u> to represent this length.

Cover the answers below as you work the next examples.

EXAMPLE 4

Find the length marked "?".

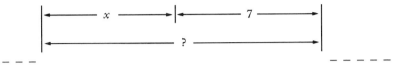

| Think These Reasons |

$\underline{x + 7}$ or $\underline{7 + x}$ x and 7 must be *added* to get the total length.

EXAMPLE 5

Find the length marked "?".

$\underline{29 - x}$ 29 is the *whole* length. x is *part* of that length. So $29 - x$ is what is *left* when x is taken away. Note that $x - 29$ would not be correct.

Objective:
Be able to write expressions from a verbal description and evaluate expressions by substituting a value for the variable.

EXERCISE 1-2

For Problems 1 and 2, write an expression representing the quantity described.

1. a. The product of 13 and 8.   b. The product of x and 8.
   c. The product of 13 and y.   d. The product of x and y.
   e. The sum of 3 and y.   f. The sum of x and 7.
   g. The difference x minus y.   h. The quotient x divided by y.
   i. 3 more than x.   j. 3 times as much as x.
   k. 5 less than y.   l. One-fifth of y.

2. a. The sum of 17 and 9.   b. The sum of x and 9.
   c. The sum of 17 and y.   d. The sum of x and y.
   e. The product of 9 and y.   f. The product of x and 2.

1. a. 13×8 b. $x \times 8$ or $8x$
    c. $13y$ d. xy
    e. $3 + y$ f. $x + 7$
    g. $x - y$ h. $x \div y$
    i. $x + 3$ j. $3x$
    k. $y - 5$ l. $y \div 5$
2. a. $17 + 9$ b. $x + 9$
    c. $17 + y$ d. $x + y$
    e. $9 \times y$ f. $x \times 2$
    g. $y - z$ h. $y \div z$
    i. $x + 2$ j. $2 \times x$
    k. $z - 8$ l. $\frac{1}{8}z$
(Other correct forms are o.k.)

g. The difference y minus z.   h. The quotient y divided by z.
i. 2 more than x.   j. 2 times as much as x.
k. 8 less than z.   l. One-eighth of z.

Problem Notes:

For Problems 3–14, students should write the given expression first for each part of the problem. Then they should show the step where the value is substituted for the variable. It is not necessary for students to copy the other problems.

For Problems 3 through 14, evaluate the expressions by substituting the given values of the variable.

3. $5 + x$, if:
   a. x is 4; 9
   b. x is 17. 22

4. $x + 7$, if:
   a. x is 8; 15
   b. x is 93. 100

5. $(24 \div y) - 1$, if:
   a. y is 4; 5
   b. y is 12. 1

6. $(72 \div z) + 5$, if:
   a. z is 6; 17
   b. z is 9. 13

7. $(z - 19) \times 2$, if:
   a. z is 100; 162
   b. z is 37; 36
   c. z is 19. 0

8. $(y - 31) \times 4$, if:
   a. y is 80; 196
   b. y is 57; 104
   c. y is 31. 0

9. $9x$, if:
   a. x is 4; 36
   b. x is 13. 117

10. $7x$, if:
    a. x is 8; 56
    b. x is 11. 77

11. $\dfrac{30}{x}$, if:
    a. x is 6; 5
    b. x is 90; $\frac{1}{3}$
    c. x is 45. $\frac{2}{3}$

12. $\dfrac{40}{x}$, if:
    a. x is 5; 8
    b. x is 80; $\frac{1}{2}$
    c. x is 60. $\frac{2}{3}$

13. $\dfrac{p + 5}{2}$, if:
    a. p is 11; 8
    b. p is 95; 50
    c. p is 0. $2\frac{1}{2}$

14. $\dfrac{k + 7}{3}$, if:
    a. k is 5; 4
    b. k is 53; 20
    c. k is 0. $2\frac{1}{3}$

For Problems 15 through 34, write an expression for the length marked "?."

15. $5 + 2$
16. $3 + 7$
17. $x + 4$
18. $5 + x$
19. $9 + y$
20. $y + 4$

15.
16.
17.
18.
19.
20.

21.

```
|←——— x ———→|←— y —→|
|←——————— ? ———————→|
```

22.

```
|←—— y ——→|←—— x ——→|
|←——————— ? ———————→|
```

23.

```
|←————— 15 —————→|
|←— 8 —→|←— ? —→|
```

24.

```
|←————— 13 —————→|
|← 5 →|←——— ? ———→|
```

25.

```
|←————— 7 —————→|
|← x →|←——— ? ———→|
```

26.

```
|←————— 12 —————→|
|← x →|←——— ? ———→|
```

27.

```
|←————— y —————→|
|←——— ? ———→|← 5 →|
```

28.

```
|←————— z —————→|
|←——— ? ———→|← 5 →|
```

29.

```
|←————— y —————→|
|←——— ? ———→|← x →|
```

30.

```
|←————— z —————→|
|← ? →|←——— y ———→|
```

31.

```
|←——————— ? ———————→|
|← 6 →|← y →|← x →|
```

32.

```
|←——————— ? ———————→|
|← 4 →|← x →|← z →|
```

33.

```
|←——————— 12 ———————→|
|←——— 7 ———→|←y→|←?→|
```

34.

```
|←——————— 25 ———————→|
|← 9 →|← x →|←— ? —→|
```

21.	$x + y$	22.	$y + x$
23.	$15 - 8$	24.	$13 - 5$
25.	$7 - x$	26.	$12 - x$
27.	$y - 5$	28.	$z - 5$
29.	$y - x$	30.	$z - y$
31.	$6 + y + x$	32.	$4 + x + z$
33.	$12 - 7 - y,$	34.	$25 - 9 - x,$
	$12 - (7 + y)$		$25 - (9 + x)$

Write expressions for the following quantities.

35. Les Moore is 57 years old.
    a. How old will he be in 4 years?   61 years
    b. How old will he be in y years? $57 + y$ years
    c. How old was he 8 years ago?   49 years
    d. How old was he z years ago? $57 - z$ years
    Manny Moore is x years old.
    e. How old will he be in 4 years? $x + 4$ years
    f. How old will he be in y years? $x + y$ years
    g. How old was he 8 years ago? $x - 8$ years
    h. How old was he z years ago? $x - z$ years

36. Stan Dupp is 127 cm tall.
   a. How tall will he be if he grows 7 cm?   134 cm
   b. How tall will he be if he grows y cm? $127 + y$ cm
   c. How tall was he when he was 13 cm shorter?   114 cm
   d. How tall was he when he was z cm shorter? $127 - z$ cm
   Phoebe Small is x cm tall.
   e. How tall will she be if she grows 3 cm? $x + 3$ cm
   f. How tall will she be if she grows y cm? $x + y$ cm
   g. How tall was she when she was 9 cm shorter? $x - 9$ cm
   h. How tall was she when she was z cm shorter? $x - z$ cm

1-3 | POWERS AND EXPONENTS

Time: 1 day

Chalkboard Examples:

1. Write in simpler form: $7 + 7 + 7$.
   Ans.: 3×7
   Write in simpler form: $7 \times 7 \times 7$.
   Ans.: 7^3
   Conclusion: Multiplication is repeated addition. Raising to powers is repeated *multiplication*. In both cases above, the 3 tells how many 7's to use.

2. Evaluate 7^3 Ans.: 343

3. Read: 7^2 Ans.: Seven squared.
      7^3 Ans.: Seven cubed.
      7^4 Ans.: Seven to the fourth power.

4. Write as a power:
   a. $4 \cdot 4 \cdot 4 \cdot 4 \cdot 4$ Ans.: 4^5
   b. $x \cdot x \cdot x$ Ans.: x^3
   c. $8 \cdot 8 \cdot 8 \cdot \ldots \cdot 8$ (x of them)
      Ans.: 8^x
   d. . . . . . Number of dots   Ans.: 5^2
      . . . . .
      . . . . .
      . . . . .
      . . . . .
   e. 243 as a power of 3   Ans.: 3^5
   Note: The Oral Practice is helpful in this section to convey the concepts before students start working the Examples or Exercise 1–3.

Assignment:

1–45 odd or 2–46 even

You know that multiplication can be thought of as a shorthand way of writing repeated addition. For instance,

$$5 + 5 + 5 \quad \text{is written} \quad 3 \times 5.$$

There is also a short way of writing repeated multiplication.

$$5 \times 5 \times 5 \quad \text{is written} \quad 5^3.$$

The expression 5^3 is read "5 cubed," or "5 raised to the third power," or "the third power of 5." Parts of 5^3 are given names.

5 is called the *base*.
3 is called the *exponent*.
5^3 is called a *power*.

DEFINITION

> **POWER, BASE, AND EXPONENT**
> In the expression x^y,
>
> x is called the **base**,
>
> y is called the **exponent**, and
>
> x^y is called a **power**.

Don't confuse the words *exponent* and *power*. The exponent 3 is just the number that tells how many 5s to multiply together. The power is the entire expression, 5^3. Power is similar in meaning to sum or product.

$5 + 3$ A *sum*.
$5 - 3$ A *difference*.
$5 \cdot 3$ A *product*.
$5 \div 3$ A *quotient*.
5^3 A *power*.

Objective :
Be able to evaluate a given power and write a number as a power.

To evaluate a power, you simply do the multiplication. In each of the following examples, put a piece of paper along the dotted lines to cover the answer. Work the examples. Then uncover the answers to make sure you are right.

EXAMPLE 1

Evaluate 5^3 (read "five cubed").

– – – – –   – – – – –

$$5^3$$
$$= 5 \cdot 5 \cdot 5$$
$$= \underline{\underline{125}}$$

Writing a number as a power might take some cleverness!

EXAMPLE 2

Write each of the following as a power.

Think These Reasons

a. 7 to the fourth power

– – – – –   – – – – –

$\underline{\underline{7^4}}$ The base is 7, exponent is 4.

b. 13 squared.

– – – – –   – – – – –

$\underline{\underline{13^2}}$ Squared means raised to the *second* power.

c. $x \cdot x \cdot x \cdot x \cdot x \cdot x$

– – – – –   – – – – –

$\underline{\underline{x^6}}$ There are *six* x's multiplied together.

d. $3 \cdot 3 \cdot 3 \cdots 3$ (x of them)

– – – – –   – – – – –

$\underline{\underline{3^x}}$ There are x 3s multiplied together.

e. 32 as a power of 2.

– – – – –   – – – – –

$\underline{\underline{2^5}}$ "As a power of 2" means 2 is the *base*.

Note: To find out how *many* 2s are multiplied together to give 32, do some "upside down repeated short dividing," as shown at the right. Then count the number of 2s.

$$\textit{Five } 2s \longrightarrow \begin{array}{l} 2\overline{)32} \\ 2\overline{)16} \\ 2\overline{)\;8} \\ 2\overline{)4} \\ \;\;2 \end{array}$$

Powers can represent geometrical ideas, such as area or volume.

EXAMPLE 3

How many dots are in this picture? Write the answer as a power.

- - - -   - - - -

$\underline{\underline{9^2}}$ 9 rows of 9 dots means 9×9 dots, and 9×9 is 9^2. You can check the answer by counting the dots. 9^2 is 81 and there are 81 dots.

ORAL PRACTICE

Evaluate.

A. 2^3 8   B. 3^2 9   C. 4^2 16   D. 3^3 27   E. 5^1 5   F. 1^{10} 1

Give these as powers.

G. $3 \cdot 3 \cdot 3 \cdot 3$ 3^4 H. $4 \cdot 4 \cdot 4$ 4^3 I. $x \cdot x \cdot x \cdot x \cdot x$ x^5 J.   7 7^1

Give the power represented.

K.   ⦂⦂⦂ Number of dots. 3^2 L.   [grid] Number of smallest squares. 3^2

Give the exponent needed.

M. $8 = 2^?$ 3   N. $16 = 2^?$ 4   O. $9 = 3^?$ 2   P. $25 = 5^?$ 2

EXERCISE 1-3

1. Evaluate.
    a. 2^7 128   b. 3^4 81   c. 4^3 64   d. 5^2 25
    e. 7^3 343   f. 10^5 100,000   g. 8^2 64   h. 0^4 0
    i. 13^1 13   j. 1^{1000} 1

2. Evaluate.
    a. 3^5 243   b. 2^6 64   c. 6^2 36   d. 5^4 625
    e. 11^3 1331   f. 10^7 10,000,000   g. 9^2 81   h. 0^6 0
    i. 17^1 17   j. 1^{200} 1

3. For the expression x^3.
    a. What is the 3 called?   Exponent   b. What is the x called?   Base
    c. Evaluate it if x is 6.   216   d. Evaluate it if x is 10.   1000
    e. Write two different ways x^3 could be read.   "x cubed" "x to the third
                                                          power"

4. For the expression z^4.
    a. What is the 4 called?   Exponent   b. What is the z called?   Base
    c. Evaluate it if z is 3.   81   d. Evaluate it if z is 10.   10,000
    e. Write two different ways z^4 could be read.   "x to the fourth" "the
                                                          fourth power of x"

For Problems 5 through 14, write a power representing the indicated quantity.

5.   Number of dots.   6.   Number of dots.
                                   6^2 7^2

7.   Number of
        smallest
        squares   8.   Number of
                                        smallest
                                        squares
                               4^2 5^2

9. 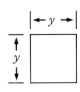 |← y →| Area. y^2 10.   Area. x^2
        y

Problem Notes:

Problems 9 and 10 generalize Problems 7 and 8, area of a square equals length squared.

Problems 13 and 14 generalize Problems 11 and 12, volume of a cube equals length cubed.

Problems 27–30—If a student is sharp enough to write something like $7 \cdot 7^5$ for 7^6, you may accept that answer.

11. 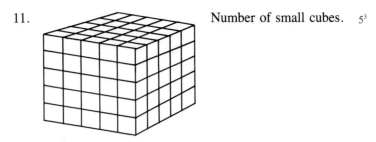 Number of small cubes. 5^3

12. 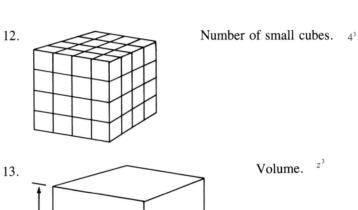 Number of small cubes. 4^3

13. Volume. z^3

14. 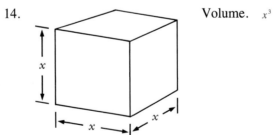 Volume. x^3

For Problems 15 through 26, write the expression as a power.

15. $6 \cdot 6 \cdot 6 \cdot 6$ 6^4 16. $9 \cdot 9 \cdot 9$ 9^3

17. $4 \cdot 4 \cdot 4 \cdot 4 \cdot 4 \cdot 4$ 4^6

18. $3 \cdot 3 \cdot 3 \cdot 3 \cdot 3 \cdot 3 \cdot 3 \cdot 3 \cdot 3$ 3^9

19. $x \cdot x \cdot x \cdot x \cdot x$ x^5 20. $y \cdot y \cdot y \cdot y$ y^4

21. $2 \cdot 2 \cdot 2 \cdot \ldots \cdot 2$ (11 of them) 2^{11}

22. $5 \cdot 5 \cdot 5 \cdot \ldots \cdot 5$ (13 of them) 5^{13}

23. $2 \cdot 2 \cdot 2 \cdot \ldots \cdot 2$ (y of them) 2^y

24. $5 \cdot 5 \cdot 5 \cdot \ldots \cdot 5$ (x of them) 5^x

25. $y \cdot y \cdot y \cdot \ldots \cdot y$ (z of them) y^z

26. $x \cdot x \cdot x \cdot \ldots \cdot x$ (y of them) x^y

For Problems 27 through 34, write the power as a product. For instance, $3^4 = 3 \cdot 3 \cdot 3 \cdot 3$.

27. 7^6 $7 \cdot 7 \cdot 7 \cdot 7 \cdot 7 \cdot 7$ 28. 8^7 $8 \cdot 8 \cdot 8 \cdot 8 \cdot 8 \cdot 8 \cdot 8$

29. z^5 $z \cdot z \cdot z \cdot z \cdot z$ 30. y^6 $y \cdot y \cdot y \cdot y \cdot y \cdot y$

31. 5^x $5 \cdot 5 \cdot 5 \cdot \ldots \cdot 5$ (x of them)   32. 6^z $6 \cdot 6 \cdot 6 \cdot \ldots \cdot 6$ (z of them)

33. z^x $z \cdot z \cdot z \cdot \ldots \cdot z$ (x of them)   34. y^z $y \cdot y \cdot y \cdot \ldots \cdot y$ (z of them)

For Problems 35 through 44, write the given number as a power with the given base. For instance, 8 as a power of 2 is 2^3.

35. 81 as a power of 3.   36. 64 as a power of 4.

37. 343 as a power of 7.   38. 36 as a power of 6.

39. 64 as a power of 2.   40. 625 as a power of 5.

41. 100,000 as a power of 10.   42. 1,000,000 as a power of 10.

43. 12 as a power of 12.   44. 8 as a power of 8.

45. *Calvin's Study-Time Problem*   Calvin Butterball studied algebra for 1 minute the first week of school. Then he studied 2 minutes the second week, 4 minutes the third week, 8 minutes the fourth week, and so on. Each week he doubled the number of minutes. If he keeps up this pattern, how many minutes will he study algebra the last week of an 18-week semester? Write the answer as a power.

46. *Ancestors Problem*   Your ancestors in the first, second, and third generations back are your natural parents, grandparents, and great-grandparents, respectively. You have had 2 parents, 4 grandparents, and 8 great-grandparents. How many ancestors do you have in the 10th generation back? Write the answer as a power.

35. 3^4 36. 4^3 37. 7^3 38. 6^2
39. 2^6 40. 5^4 41. 10^5 42. 10^6
43. 12^1 44. 8^1 45. 2^{17} min
46. 2^{10} ancestors

Problems 45 and 46 should count as bonus problems in any grading of homework. You should count on discussing these in class. In Problem 46, make sure students realize that it is the *natural* ancestors, not step-parents, and that it is not necessarily *living* ancestors. Projecting backwards to the year 1 AD, and assuming about 25 years per generation, you get about 2^{80} ancestors, which is more than the entire population of the world! This fact leads to the conclusion that there were *common* ancestors in times past.

1-4   ORDER OF OPERATIONS

You have learned that symbols of inclusion can be used to tell which operation is to be performed first in an expression. If there are more than three operations, there would be so many parentheses and brackets that the expression would look untidy, like this:

$$(4 + [(9 \times 3) \div 6]) + [(5 \times 8) - 7].$$

To avoid all this clutter, users of mathematics have *agreed* on an order in which operations are to be performed. Parentheses are used only to *change* this order.

If an expression has no parentheses to tell you otherwise, then you raise to powers first. For example,

$$3 \cdot 2^4 \quad \text{means} \quad 3 \cdot 16, \quad \text{or} \quad \underline{\underline{48}}.$$

If you want the multiplication to be done first, you have to use parentheses.

$$(3 \cdot 2)^4$$
$$= 6^4$$
$$= \underline{\underline{1296}}$$

Multiplication and division are done before addition and subtraction. For example,

$$13 - 2 \cdot 4 \quad \text{means} \quad 13 - 8, \quad \text{or} \quad \underline{\underline{5}}.$$
$$15 + 35 \div 5 \quad \text{means} \quad 15 + 7, \quad \text{or} \quad \underline{\underline{22}}.$$

Parentheses must be used if you want to do the addition or subtraction first.

$$(13 - 2) \cdot 4$$
$$= 11 \cdot 4$$
$$= \underline{\underline{44}}$$
$$(15 + 35) \div 5$$
$$= 50 \div 5$$
$$= \underline{\underline{10}}$$

If an expression has only multiplication and division or only addition and subtraction, then these operations are done in order, from left to right. For example,

$$48 \div 6 \times 2 \quad \text{means} \quad 8 \times 2, \quad \text{or} \quad \underline{\underline{16}};$$
$$17 - 5 + 3 \quad \text{means} \quad 12 + 3, \quad \text{or} \quad \underline{\underline{15}}.$$

Time: 1 or 2 days

Chalkboard Examples:

1. Evaluate: $5 \cdot 2^3$ Ans.: 40, not 1000
       $7 + 3^2$ Ans.: 16, not 100
   Conclusion: Evaluate powers *before* either multiplying or adding.

2. Evaluate: $15 - 3 \times 2$ Ans.: 9
       $12 + 8 \div 2$ Ans.: 16
       $12 \div 3 \times 2$ Ans.: 8
   Conclusions: Multiply and divide *before* adding or subtracting. Multiply and divide in the order in which the operations appear, left to right.

3. Evaluate: $3 + 5 - 2$ Ans.: 6
       $9 - 2 + 3$ Ans.: 10
   Conclusion: Add and subtract *last,* in the order in which the operations appear, left to right.
   Note: Parentheses may be used to *change* this order if that is what has to be done.
   The Oral Practice is most helpful here.

Assignments:

Day 1: 1–25 odd or 2–26 even
Day 2: selected problems from 1–26, if needed, and 27–39 odd or 28–40 even, and Exercise 1-5, #1–9 odd or 2–10 even (if possible)

Again, parentheses must be used if you are supposed to do the operations in a different order:

$$48 \div (6 \times 2) = 48 \div 12 = \underline{\underline{4}};$$
$$17 - (5 + 3) = 17 - 8 = \underline{\underline{9}}.$$

AGREEMENT

ORDER OF OPERATIONS
If there are no parentheses to tell you otherwise, operations are performed in the following order:

1.   Evaluate any *powers* first.
2.   After powers, *multiply* and *divide,* in order, from left to right.
3.   Last, *add* and *subtract,* in order, from left to right.

Objective :
Be able to evaluate expressions using the agreed-upon order of operations.

For each of the following examples, put a piece of paper along the dotted lines to cover up the answer. Evaluate the expression. Then uncover the answer to be sure you are right.

EXAMPLE 1
Evaluate $60 - 7(5 + 6 \div 2) + 2^4$.

– – – – – –   – – – – –

	Think These Reasons
$60 - 7(5 + 6 \div 2) + 2^4$	Write the given expression.
$= 60 - 7(5 + 3) + 2^4$	Inside the parentheses, divide *before* adding.
$= 60 - 7(8) + 2^4$	Do what is inside parentheses *first*.
$= 60 - 7(8) + 16$	Evaluate *powers* next.
$= 60 - 56 + 16$	Multiply *before* adding and subtracting.
$= 4 + 16$	Add and subtract, in order, from left to right.
$= \underline{\underline{20}}$	Answer.

At first it is safer to evaluate expressions *one* step at a time. Later you will learn ways to combine steps. You do *not* need to write down the reason for each step, but you should *think* of what the reason is.

If you are evaluating an expression containing a variable, you must substitute a value for the variable first.

EXAMPLE 2

Evaluate $3x^2 - 5x$ if x is 4.

- - - - -   - - - - -

	Think These Reasons
$3x^2 - 5x$	Write the given expression.
$= 3 \cdot 4^2 - 5 \cdot 4$	Substitute 4 for x, *both* places.
$= 3 \cdot 16 - 5 \cdot 4$	Raise to powers *before* multiplying.
$= 48 - 20$	Multiply *before* adding or subtracting.
$= \underline{\underline{28}}$	Answer.

ORAL PRACTICE

Evaluate:

A. $10 - 4 + 3$ 9   B. $10 - 4 - 3$ 3   C. $12 \div 4 + 2$ 5

D. $10 + 4 \div 2$ 12   E. $4 + 3 \cdot 5$ 19   F. $4 \cdot 3 + 5$ 17

G. $12 \div 6 \cdot 2$ 4   H. $12 \cdot 6 \div 2$ 36   I. $3 \cdot 2^2$ 12

J. $(3 \cdot 2)^2$ 36   K. $(3 + 2)^2$ 25   L. $3 + 2^2$ 7

M. $23 - 3(2)$ 17   N. $18 + 2(3)$ 24

O. $12 - 2(3 + 1)$ 4   P. $(12 - 2)(3 + 1)$ 40

EXERCISE 1-4

Problem Notes:

Problems 1–6 each involve the *same* numbers with *different* operations.

For Problems 1 through 26, evaluate the given expression.

1. a. $24 - 6 + 2$ 20   2. a. $36 - 9 + 2$ 29
    b. $24 - 6 \cdot 2$ 12   b. $36 - 9 \cdot 2$ 18
    c. $24 \cdot 6 - 2$ 142   c. $36 \cdot 9 - 2$ 322
    d. $24 \div 6 \cdot 2$ 8   d. $36 \div 9 \cdot 2$ 8
    e. $24 \div 6 \div 2$ 2   e. $36 \div 9 \div 2$ 2

3. a. $5 + 2 \cdot 4 + 3$ 16
    b. $(5 + 2) \cdot 4 + 3$ 31
    c. $5 + 2 \cdot (4 + 3)$ 19
    d. $(5 + 2) \cdot (4 + 3)$ 49

4. a. $6 + 4 \cdot 5 - 2$ 24
    b. $(6 + 4) \cdot (5 - 2)$ 30
    c. $6 + 4 \cdot (5 - 2)$ 18
    d. $(6 + 4) \cdot 5 - 2$ 48

5. a. $5 + 2^3$ 13
    b. $5 - 2^3$ -3
    c. $5 \cdot 2^3$ 40
    d. $(5 \cdot 2)^3$ 1000

6. a. $7 + 3^2$ 16
    b. $7 - 3^2$ -2
    c. $7 \cdot 3^2$ 63
    d. $(7 \cdot 3)^2$ 441

Problems 5b and 6b have negative answers.

7. $10 - 3(8 - 6)$ 4

8. $30 - 4(8 - 3)$ 10

9. $4 + 6(5 - 2)$ 22

10. $7 + 3(12 - 2)$ 37

11. $8 + 5 \cdot 4^3$ 328

12. $2 + 8 \cdot 3^2$ 74

13. $33 - 3 \cdot 2^3$ 9

14. $34 - 4 \cdot 2^3$ 2

15. $16 + 4(7 - 4 + 1)$ 32

16. $17 + 3(8 - 5 + 1)$ 29

17. $14 + 8 \div 2 - 1$ 17

18. $30 + 10 \div 5 - 3$ 29

19. $4 \cdot 9 + 7 \cdot 8$ 92

20. $9 \cdot 5 + 6 \cdot 7$ 87

21. $37 + 3[16 \div (2 \cdot 4)]$ 43

22. $48 + 2[12 \div (2 \cdot 3)]$ 52

Problems 21–26 are fairly complicated and may need to be discussed in class the following day.

23. $102 - 2(3^4 - 51)$ 42

24. $53 - 3(2^5 - 22)$ 23

25. $33 - 3[4 \cdot (7 - 5)] + 3^2$ 18

26. $74 - 4[3 \cdot (9 - 4)] + 5^2$ 39

For Problems 27 through 40, evaluate the expression for the given values of x.

27. x^3, if:
    a. x is 3;   27
    b. x is 5;   125
    c. x is 1.   1

28. x^4, if:
    a. x is 2;   16
    b. x is 3;   81
    c. x is 0.   0

Problems 27–40 reinforce the concept that variables can represent different numbers at different times.

29. 3^x, if:
    a. x is 2;   9
    b. x is 4;   81
    c. x is 1.   3

30. 2^x, if:
    a. x is 3;   8
    b. x is 5;   32
    c. x is 1.   2

31. $4x^2$, if:
    a. x is 3;   36
    b. x is 5;   100
    c. x is 0.   0

32. $6x^2$, if:
    a. x is 3;   54
    b. x is 4;   96
    c. x is 1.   6

33. $x^2 + 2x + 1$, if:
    a. x is 6;   49
    b. x is 4;   25
    c. x is 1.   4

34. $x^2 + 4x + 4$, if:
    a. x is 3;   25
    b. x is 5;   49
    c. x is 0.   4

35. $(x + 1)^2$, if:
    a. x is 6;   49
    b. x is 4;   25
    c. x is 1.   4

36. $(x + 2)^2$, if:
    a. x is 3;   25
    b. x is 5;   49
    c. x is 0.   4

37. $(3x)^2$, if:
    a. x is 1;   9
    b. x is 2;   36
    c. x is 0.   0

38. $(5x)^2$, if:
    a. x is 1;   25
    b. x is 2;   100
    c. x is 0.   0

39. $56 - 6x$, if:
    a. x is 8;   8
    b. x is 1;   50
    c. x is 0.   56

40. $108 - 8x$, if:
    a. x is 12;   12
    b. x is 1;   100
    c. x is 0.   108

1-5   EXPRESSIONS FROM WORD STATEMENTS

Time: 2 days, including test

Chalkboard Examples:

1. Subtract 7 from 50, then add 5.
   Ans.: $50 - 7 + 5$ (No parentheses needed.)

2. Subtract 7 from 50, then multiply by 5.
   Ans.: $(50 - 7) \times 5$ (Parentheses *are* needed.)

3. Add 5 to x, then cube the result.
   Ans.: $(5 + x)^3$ (Parentheses *are* needed.)

4. Add the cubes of 5 and x.   Ans.: $5^3 + x^3$ (No parentheses needed.)

5. The quantity a minus b, squared.
   Ans.: $(a - b)^2$ (Parentheses are needed because of "the quantity. . . .")

Assignments:

Day 1: 1–29 odd or 2–30 even (Some of these may have been assigned earlier with the second assignment of Section 1–4.)
Day 2: After test, assign: Study Section 1–6; Work 1–6 Problems 1, 2, 3, and 4.

In Section 1-2 you wrote expressions such as $x + 3$ to represent the sum of x and 3. In this section you will write expressions involving three or more numbers.

The expression

$$3 + 5x$$

means add 3 and the product of 5 and x. No parentheses are necessary since the multiplication, $5x$, is done before the addition. The expression

$$(3 + 5)x$$

is read "the *quantity* 3 plus 5, times x." The words "the quantity . . ." are used to say in English what the parentheses say in mathematics. The parentheses, of course, mean that the 3 and 5 are to be added *before* multiplying by x.

Objective :
Given a description of an expression, write that expression using parentheses only when necessary.

For each of the following examples, put a piece of paper along the dotted lines to cover the answers. Work the example. Then uncover the answer to make sure you are right and did not leave any unneeded parentheses.

EXAMPLE 1
Subtract 6 from 21, then add 3.

– – – – –   – – – – –

Think These Reasons

$\underline{21 - 6 + 3}$ No parentheses are needed, because addition and subtraction are done in order from left to right.

EXAMPLE 2

Subtract 6 from 21, then divide by 3.

$- - - - -$ $- - - - -$

$(21 - 6) \div 3$, or $\dfrac{21 - 6}{3}$ Parentheses or a vinculum *are* needed. Without them, the 6 would first be divided by the 3.

EXAMPLE 3

Add 3 to x, then square the result.

$- - - - -$ $- - - - -$

$(x + 3)^2$ Parentheses *are* needed. Without them, only the 3 would be squared.

EXAMPLE 4

The sum of the squares of x and 3.

$- - - - -$ $- - - - -$

$x^2 + 3^2$, or $x^2 + 9$ No parentheses are needed, because squaring is done *before* adding.

EXAMPLE 5

The quantity r minus s, cubed.

$- - - - -$ $- - - - -$

$(r - s)^3$ Parentheses *are* needed since "the quantity . . ." means that the subtraction must be done *first*.

EXERCISE 1-5

Write the expression described. Use parentheses only where necessary.

1. Subtract 2 from x, then add y. $x - 2 + y$

2. Add 5 to y, then multiply by x. $(y + 5) \cdot x$

3. Subtract the sum of 2 and y from x. $x - (2 + y)$

4. Add the product of 5 and y to x. $x + 5y$

5. Divide x by 3, then multiply by z. $\dfrac{x}{3} \cdot z$ or $x \div 3 \cdot z$

6. Multiply x by the sum of 7 and y. $x \cdot (7 + y)$

7. Divide x by the product of 3 and z. $x \div (3z)$ or $\dfrac{x}{3z}$

8. Multiply x by 7, then add y. $7x + y$

9. Multiply x by 3, then add y. $3x + y$

Problem Notes:

The instructions say, "Use parentheses only where necessary." You may want to allow students to use extra parentheses, in a correct manner, until they are comfortable writing the expressions.

10. Divide y by 7, then add z. $y \div 7 + z$ or $\frac{y}{7} + z$

11. Add x and 3, then multiply by y. $(x + 3) \cdot y$

12. Divide y by the sum of 7 and z. $y \div (7 + z)$ or $\frac{y}{7 + z}$

13. Add x and y, then square the result. $(x + y)^2$

14. Add 6 and x, then cube the result. $(6 + x)^3$

15. Add the squares of x and y. $x^2 + y^2$

16. Add the cubes of 6 and x. $6^3 + x^3$

17. Subtract the product of 5 and x from 7. $7 - 5x$

18. Subtract the product of 3 and y from 19. $19 - 3y$

19. Subtract the cube of z from 15. $15 - z^3$

20. Subtract the square of p from 18. $18 - p^2$

21. 5 more than the product of 3 and c. $3c + 5$

22. 6 more than the quotient 7 divided by j. $7 \div j + 6$ or $\frac{7}{j} + 6$

23. 13 less than the quotient 5 divided by p. $5 \div p - 13$ or $\frac{5}{p} - 13$

24. 17 less than the product of 9 and k. $9k - 17$

25. 4 times the sum of 10 and x. $4(10 + x)$

26. 11 times the quantity y minus 3. $11(y - 3)$

27. 5 divided by the quantity x minus 7. $5 \div (x - 7)$ or $\frac{5}{x - 7}$

28. 10 divided by the quantity r plus t. $10 \div (r + t)$ or $\frac{10}{r + t}$

29. The quantity $3x + 2$ divided by the quantity $1 - 3x$. $(3x + 2) \div (1 - 3x)$ or $\frac{3x + 2}{1 - 3x}$

30. The quantity $4x - 7$ divided by the quantity $1 + 4x$. $(4x - 7) \div (1 + 4x)$ or $\frac{4x - 7}{1 + 4x}$

1-6 | INTRODUCTION TO EQUATIONS

Time: 0 days (Combine with Section 1–7.)

Chalkboard Examples:

(See Section 1–7.)

Assignment:

Assign all four problems following the test on Sections 1 through 5. See Assignments, Section 1–5. All ten problems in Exercise 1–6 can be done as a classroom exercise in less than 15 minutes.

This section is intended for you to read by yourself, without help from your teacher. Read the material below, work the examples to see what is being asked for, and then work the assigned problems.

You have learned how to find the value of an expression when you know what x equals. Here, you will find the value of x when you know what the *expression* equals. For example, if the expression is $x + 5$ and you know that it equals 17, you could write

$$x + 5 = 17.$$

This is called an **equation.** The expression on the left side is called the **left member** and the expression on the right is called the **right member.**

To find what x equals, you must have x alone on one side of the equation. To do this you must get rid of the unwanted 5 in the left member. You can *subtract* 5 from *each* member, getting

$$x + 5 - 5 = 17 - 5.$$

Simplifying leads to

$$\underline{x = 12.}$$

As you can see, 12 + 5 really *does* equal 17!

Objective :
Given the value of an expression, be able to find the value of the variable.

For each of the following examples, put a piece of paper along the dotted lines to cover the answer. After you do one step, uncover the work down to the next set of dotted lines to be sure you are right.

EXAMPLE 1

For the expression $x - 7$, find x when the expression equals 15.
First, you write an equation.

– – – – –   – – – – –

$$x - 7 = 15$$

Then you figure out how to get rid of the unwanted 7 in the left member so that x will be alone. *Adding* 7 to each member will do the job.

– – – – –   – – – – –

$$x - 7 + 7 = 15 + 7$$

Finally, you do the operations.

– – – – –   – – – – –

$$\underline{\underline{x = 22}}$$

EXAMPLE 2

For the expression $\frac{1}{3}x$, find x if the expression equals 13.

Your thought process should be, "I want to get x by itself. So I must get rid of the $\frac{1}{3}$ in front of the x. To do this I can *multiply* each member by 3."

– – – –   – – – –

Think These Reasons

$\frac{1}{3}x = 13$ Write an equation.

$3 \cdot \frac{1}{3}x = 3 \cdot 13$ Multiply each member by 3.

$\underline{\underline{x = 39}}$ Do the operations to get x alone.
Underline or box the answer.

EXAMPLE 3

For the expression $7x$, find x when the expression equals 42.

– – – –   – – – –

$7x = 42$ Write an equation.

$\frac{7x}{7} = \frac{42}{7}$ *Divide* each member by 7 to get rid of the 7 that is multiplied by x.

$\underline{\underline{x = 6}}$ Do the operations to get x alone.

EXERCISE 1-6

Problem Notes:

These problems introduce the concept of *reversing* the evaluation process. Instead of substituting for x and evaluating the expression, students start with the value of the expression and go backwards to find x. The problems also reinforce the concept that a variable can stand for different numbers at different times by having students set the *same* expression equal to different numbers.

1. For the expression $x - 3$, find x when the expression equals:
    a. 7 10   b. 10 13   c. 20 23
    d. 100 103   e. 1998 2001

2. For the expression $x + 8$, find x when the expression equals:
    a. 10 2   b. 17 9   c. 35 27
    d. 107 99   e. 1776 1768

3. For the expression $\frac{1}{2}x$, find x when the expression equals:
    a. 5 10   b. 13 26   c. 50 100
    d. 111 222   e. 65 130

4. For the expression $5x$, find x when the expression equals:
    a. 10 2   b. 75 15   c. 1000 200
    d. 15 3   e. 27 5.4

1-7 SOLVING EQUATIONS

In the last section you learned how to find the value of x if you are given the value of an expression containing x. For instance, by subtracting 5 from each member of the equation

$$x + 5 = 17,$$

you found that

$$x = 12.$$

If you substitute the number 12 for x in the original equation, you get the *true* statement

$$12 + 5 = 17.$$

The number 12 in this example is called a *solution* of the equation. The process of finding all values of the variable that make the equation true is called *solving the equation*. Taking a step such as subtracting 5 from each member is called *transforming* the equation. Thus to solve an equation, all you need to do is *transform* it until it says

$$x = \text{some number.}$$

The particular transformation you pick is the one that gets the variable by itself by getting *rid* of unwanted numbers surrounding the variable.

$x - 2 = 7$ *Add* 2 to each member to get rid of the 2.

$x + 3 = 8$ *Subtract* 3 from each member to get rid of the 3.

$\frac{1}{5}x = 9$ *Multiply* each member by 5 to get rid of the $\frac{1}{5}$.

$6x = 2$ *Divide* each member by 6 to get rid of the 6.

EXAMPLE

Solve $x + 3 = 8$. Show the transformation.

- - - - -   - - - - -

Think These Reasons

$x + 3 = 8$ Write the given equation.

$x + 3 - 3 = 8 - 3$ Subtract 3 from each member.

$\underline{x = 5}$ Do the operations.

See the examples of Section 1-6 if you need more practice.

Objective :
Be able to solve equations by transforming them to the form $x =$ some number.

You can probably tell that a simple equation like $x + 5 = 17$ has 12 as its solution *without* doing any transformations. However, soon you will have to solve equations like

$$3x^2 - 4x - 2 = 7.$$

Time: 1 day, with Section 1–6

Chalkboard Examples:

1. Find x: $x - 8 = 17$ Ans.: $x = 25$
   Note: Although sharper students can see the answer mentally, make them display the step $x - 8 + 8 = 17 + 8$, and say, "Add 8 to each member." It is the *concept* that is important here rather than simply the answer.
   Note: Later on, students will write the answer as a solution set. That terminology is thought to be premature here, because it masks the idea of "finding x."

2. Find x: $x + 2 = 13$ Ans.: $x = 11$

3. Find x: $\frac{1}{3}x = 12$ Ans.: $x = 36$
   Note: At this point, it might be necessary to review $3(\frac{1}{3}) = 1$ and $1 \cdot x = x$.

4. Find x: $4x = 10$ Ans.: $x = 2\frac{1}{2}$ or $x = 2.5$
   Note: The Oral Practice is particularly effective here in making students verbalize things like, "Subtract 4 from each member" and in distinguishing between an expression and an equation.

Assignment:

1–39 odd or 2–40 even
Problems 41–50 can be assigned to stronger students or as part of a later assignment.

It is almost impossible to figure out that 2.5225881 is a solution of this equation without doing some transformations. So it is a good idea to get used to doing the transformations while the problems are still relatively easy.

A transformation such as adding 3 to each member can be thought of as adding equal weights to both sides of a balance. If it was balanced before, it will still balance afterward. But if you add weight to only *one* side, it no longer balances!

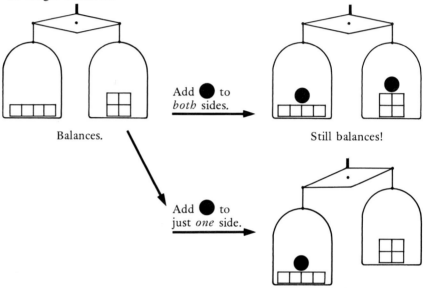

Balances.

Add ● to *both* sides.

Still balances!

Add ● to just *one* side.

Doesn't balance!!

You have read the words *equation, solution,* and *transform*. Here are formal definitions of these words.

DEFINITIONS

EQUATION
An **equation** is a sentence (such as $x + 3 = 5$) which says that one expression is equal to another expression.

SOLUTION
A **solution** of an equation is a number you can substitute for the variable that makes the sentence *true*. (For instance, 2 is a solution of $x + 3 = 5$ because $2 + 3$ equals 5.)

TRANSFORMING AN EQUATION
To **transform** an equation means to do the *same* operation to *each* member of the equation.

ORAL PRACTICE

Give the transformation needed to solve the equation.

A. $x + 4 = 13$ **B.** $x - 3 = 4$ **C.** $2x = 11$

D. $\frac{1}{6}x = 5$ **E.** $x - 5 = 6$ **F.** $\frac{1}{3}x = 9$

G. $7x = 5$ **H.** $x + 7 = 19$ **I.** $x - 7 = 4$

J. $x + 1 = 10$ **K.** $\frac{1}{4}x = 20$ **L.** $8x = 0$

Tell whether each is an equation or an expression.

M. $x + 6 - 8$ **N.** $x + 6 = 8$ **O.** $x = 4$

P. $x - 4$ **Q.** $3x \div 5$ **R.** $3x = 5$

S. $x^2 + 2x$ **T.** $x^2 = 2x$ **U.** $x^2 - 2x$

V. $2 = x + 3$ **W.** $2x = 3$ **X.** $2x + 3$

A. Subtract 4 from each member.
B. Add 3 to each member.
C. Divide each member by 2.
D. Multiply each member by 6.
E. Add 5 to each member.
F. Multiply each member by 3.
G. Divide each member by 7.
H. Subtract 7 from each member.
I. Add 7 to each member.
J. Subtract 1 from each member.
K. Multiply each member by 4.
L. Divide each member by 8.
M. Expr.   **N.** Eqn.   **O.** Eqn.
P. Expr.   **Q.** Expr.   **R.** Eqn.
S. Expr.   **T.** Eqn.   **U.** Expr.
V. Eqn.   **W.** Eqn.   **X.** Expr.

EXERCISE 1-7

Solve each equation. Show the transformation step.

1. $x - 10 = 17$ $x = 27$
2. $x - 8 = 13$ $x = 21$
3. $x + 4 = 13$ $x = 9$
4. $x + 9 = 21$ $x = 12$
5. $5x = 90$ $x = 18$
6. $6x = 72$ $x = 12$
7. $\frac{1}{3}x = 29$ $x = 87$
8. $\frac{1}{5}x = 23$ $x = 115$
9. $x - 16 = 7$ $x = 23$
10. $x - 17 = 8$ $x = 25$
11. $x - 32 = 95$ $x = 127$
12. $x - 45 = 89$ $x = 134$
13. $x + 58 = 74$ $x = 16$
14. $x + 43 = 91$ $x = 48$
15. $x + 91 = 247$ $x = 156$
16. $x + 79 = 422$ $x = 343$
17. $12x = 132$ $x = 11$
18. $15x = 210$ $x = 14$
19. $8x = 1000$ $x = 125$
20. $4x = 100$ $x = 25$
21. $\frac{1}{7}x = 68$ $x = 476$
22. $\frac{1}{9}x = 58$ $x = 522$
23. $\frac{1}{10}x = 100$ $x = 1000$
24. $\frac{1}{10}x = 1000$ $x = 10{,}000$

Problem Notes:

Students should write the given equation first, then do a transformation on it. This procedure helps reduce errors that arise from trying to do algebra while going from book to paper. For the time being, they should actually display the number added, multiplied, etc., to reinforce the concept. The technique is important rather than the answer.

Problems 25 and 26 have negative answers.

25. $x + 5 = 4$ $_{x = -1}$ 26. $x + 7 = 5$ $_{x = -2}$

27. $x - 94 = 362$ $_{x = 456}$ 28. $x - 61 = 365$ $_{x = 426}$

29. $x + 1984 = 2001$ $_{x = 17}$ 30. $x + 1066 = 1776$ $_{x = 710}$

31. $\frac{1}{3}x = 51$ $_{x = 153}$ 32. $\frac{1}{3}x = 57$ $_{x = 171}$

33. $3x = 51$ $_{x = 17}$ 34. $3x = 57$ $_{x = 19}$

35. $17x = 51$ $_{x = 3}$ 36. $19x = 57$ $_{x = 3}$

37. $\frac{1}{17}x = 51$ $_{x = 867}$ 38. $\frac{1}{19}x = 57$ $_{x = 1083}$

39. $6x = 2$ $_{x = \frac{1}{3}}$ 40. $8x = 4$ $_{x = \frac{1}{2}}$

Problems 41 through 50 involve fractions.

EXAMPLE

$$\frac{2}{3}x = 12 \qquad \text{Given equation.}$$

$$\frac{3}{2} \cdot \frac{2}{3}x = \frac{3}{2} \cdot 12 \qquad \textit{Multiply by the reciprocal of } \frac{2}{3}.$$

$$x = \underline{\underline{18}} \qquad \text{Do the operations.}$$

Problems 41–50 give students a review of fraction techniques. This review is badly needed for many students.

41. $\frac{2}{3}x = 6$ $_{x = 9}$ 42. $\frac{3}{2}x = 6$ $_{x = 4}$

43. $\frac{3}{5}x = 30$ $_{x = 50}$ 44. $\frac{4}{5}x = 20$ $_{x = 25}$

45. $\frac{7}{2}x = 28$ $_{x = 8}$ 46. $\frac{5}{3}x = 30$ $_{x = 18}$

47. $x + \frac{2}{3} = \frac{5}{3}$ $_{x = 1}$ 48. $x + \frac{3}{5} = \frac{13}{5}$ $_{x = 2}$

49. $x - \frac{3}{4} = 1\frac{3}{4}$ $_{x = 2\frac{1}{2}}$ 50. $x - \frac{2}{3} = 4\frac{2}{3}$ $_{x = 5\frac{1}{3}}$

1-8   PROBLEMS THAT LEAD TO EQUATIONS

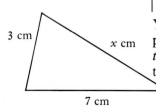

3 cm

x cm

7 cm

You have learned how to evaluate expressions and solve equations. Expressions can represent things in the real world. For instance, the *perimeter* of a figure is the *sum* of the lengths of its sides. In the triangle shown, the perimeter is the sum

$$x + 3 + 7, \quad \text{or} \quad x + 10.$$

If someone tells you that the perimeter is 18 centimeters (cm), you could write an equation stating this fact.

$$x + 10 \quad = \quad 18$$

The perimeter   is   18.

Then you could find the length of the variable side, x cm, by *solving* the equation. To isolate x you must get rid of the unwanted 10 on the left. So you subtract 10 from each member.

$$x + 10 = 18$$

$$x + 10 - 10 = 18 - 10$$

$$x = 8$$

Side is 8 cm.

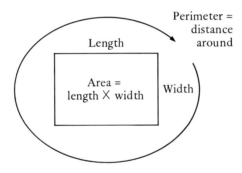

Perimeter =
distance
around

Length

Area =
length × width

Width

Objective :
Be able to write and solve equations representing real-world situations.

For the problems in this section, you must keep in mind the difference between perimeter and area. **Perimeter** is the *distance* around a figure. **Area** is a measure of the "space" inside a figure. For a rectangle, area equals length times width.

ORAL PRACTICE

For items A through G on the next page, give an expression for the perimeter or area.

Time: 1 day

Chalkboard Examples:

1. Write the perimeter of the triangle.
   Ans.: $x + 5 + 9$ or $x + 14$

2. Write the perimeter of the rectangle.
   Ans.: $2y + 10$, $y + 5 + y + 5$, etc.

3. Write the area of the rectangle.   Ans.: $5y$

Assignment:

1–21 odd or 2–20 even plus 21

Problem Notes:

Simplification of the expressions is optional at this stage. Accept correct answers in any form until students learn about commuting and associating.

Problem 21 has a circle of diameter exactly 2 centimeters. Students may already know how to find the circumference by multiplying by pi.

A.   Perimeter
     $x + 3 + x + 3$
     or $2x + 6$

B.   Area
     $3x$

C.   Perimeter
     $x + 8 + x + 8$
     or $2x + 16$

D.   Area
     $8x$

E.   Perimeter
     $x + 14$

F.   Area
     xy

G.   Perimeter
     $x + y + x + y$ or $2x + 2y$

EXERCISE 1-8

For Problems 1 through 10, write an expression for the perimeter of the figure.

1. $4 + 8 + 7$

2. $5 + 6 + 10$

3. $x + 20$

4. $x + 9$

5. $x + y + 14$

6. $x + y + 14$

7. $x + x + x$
     or $3x$

8. $x + x + x + x$
     or $4x$

9. $x + y + x + y$
     or $2x + 2y$

10. $x + y + x + y$
     or $2x + 2y$

11. a. Write an expression for the perimeter of this triangle. $x + 28$
     b. Write an equation stating that the perimeter equals 47. $x + 28 = 47$
     c. Find x by solving the equation. $x = 19$

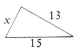

12. a. Write an expression for the perimeter of this triangle. $x + 43$
     b. Write an equation stating that the perimeter equals 62. $x + 43 = 62$
     c. Find x by solving the equation. $x = 19$

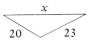

13. Find x if the perimeter of this triangle is 61. $x = 18$

14. Find x if the perimeter of this triangle is 56. $x = 9$

15. Find x if the perimeter of this figure is 30. $x = 5$

16. Find x if the perimeter of this figure is 28. $x = 4$

17. a. Write an expression for the area of this rectangle. $8x$
     b. Write an equation stating that the area is 584. $8x = 584$
     c. Find x by solving the equation. $x = 73$

18. a. Write an expression for the area of this rectangle. $7x$
     b. Write an equation stating that the area is 105. $7x = 105$
     c. Find x by solving the equation. $x = 15$

19. Find x if the area of this rectangle is 5. $x = 2\frac{1}{2}$

20. Find x if the area of this rectangle is 12. $x = 2\frac{2}{5}$

21. Although circles do not have sides, they do have "perimeters."
     a. What special name is given to the perimeter of a circle?   Circumference
     b. Measure the perimeter of this circle. Use centimeters. Find the
         answer correct to the nearest 0.1 cm. You must be very clever
         to figure out how to do this!   6.3 cm

1-9 | PROBLEMS THAT LEAD TO EXPRESSIONS AND EQUATIONS

Time: 4 days

Chalkboard Examples:
(First day)

1. *Pilot and Copilot Problem*—A pilot makes $20 per hour more than a copilot. Let x be the number of dollars per hour a copilot makes.
   a. Write an expression for the number of dollars per hour a pilot makes.
   Ans.: x = no. of $/h for copilot
   $x + 20$ = no. of $/h for pilot
   b. How much does a pilot make if a copilot makes $74 per hour?
   Ans.: $x + 20$
   $= 74 + 20$
   $= 94$
   $94 per hour
   c. Write an equation that says a pilot makes $115 per hour. Ans.:
   $x + 20 = 115$
   d. How much does a copilot make if a pilot makes $115 per hour?
   Ans.: $x + 20 - 20 = 115 - 20$
   $x = 95$
   $95 per hour

2. *Blond Hair Problem*—Assume that $\frac{1}{7}$ of all people have blond hair. Let x be the number of people in a given group.
   a. Write an expression for the number of blond-haired people in the group.
   Ans.: x = no. of people in the group.
   $\frac{1}{7}x$ = no. of blond-haired people.
   b. If there are 301 people in the group, how many will be blond?
   Ans.: 43 people
   c. Write an equation that says the number of blond-haired people in the group is 35.   Ans.: $\frac{1}{7}x = 35$
   d. Solve the equation to find out how many people there are in the group.
   Ans.: 245 people

For subsequent days, use homework problems or other problems from the text as examples. Spend enough time on these problems for students to overcome any inhibitions about word problems. Giving class time for working homework problems is one way that helps.

In the last section you saw how expressions could be used to represent things such as perimeter and area of a rectangle. Now you are ready to use expressions to represent other quantities. By evaluating the expression or by solving an equation involving the expression, you can get answers to problems from the real world.

EXAMPLE 1

A cook makes $16 per day more than a waiter makes. Let x be the number of dollars per day a waiter makes. Answer the following questions.

a.   Write an expression for the dollars per day a cook makes.

b.   If a waiter makes $35 per day, how much does a cook make?

c.   If waiters get a raise to $40 per day, how much will a cook make?

d.   If a cook makes $65 per day, how much does a waiter make?

	Think These Reasons
a. Waiter: x dollars per day	Write the given variable.
Cook: $x + 16$ dollars per day	Cook makes $16 *more*. So you add 16 to x.
b. $x + 16$	Write the expression from (a).
$= 35 + 16$	Substitute 35 for x.
$= 51$	Do the arithmetic.
Cook makes $51 per day.	Answer the question.
c. $x + 16$	Write the expression from (a).
$= 40 + 16$	Substitute 40 for x.
$= 56$	Do the arithmetic.
Cook makes $56 per day	Answer the question.
d. $x + 16 = 65$	Set cook's expression equal to 65.
$x + 16 - 16 = 65 - 16$	Subtract 16 from each member.
$x = 49$	Do the operations.
Waiter makes $49 per day.	Answer the question.

Objectives :
1.   Be able to write expressions representing things in the real world.
2.   Be able either to evaluate the expression or solve an equation containing the expression to answer a question about the real world.

For the following example, put a piece of paper along the dotted lines to cover the answer. Work each part. Then uncover the answer to be sure you are right before going on to the next part.

Assignments:

Day 1: 1 (in class), 2, and 3 (for homework). It is better to give a short assignment the students can do well than to have them become frustrated over a massive assignment the first day.

Day 2: 4, 5, and 6
Day 3: 7, 8, and 9
Day 4: 3 or 4 problems from numbers 10 through 15 as review for test

EXAMPLE 2

Genes Problem   If parents have a certain combination of genes, then about $\frac{1}{4}$ of their children will have light hair. Let x be the number of children born to a group of couples with these genes.

a.   Write an expression for the number of light-haired children.

b.   If these couples have a total of 532 children, about how many of them will be light-haired?

c.   About how many children would the couples need to have in order for there to be 240 light-haired children?

– – – –   – – – –

a.   Total number: x Write the given variable.

Light-haired: $\frac{1}{4}x$ "$\frac{1}{4}$ of" means "$\frac{1}{4}$ times."

– – – –   – – – –

b. $\frac{1}{4}x$ Write the expression from (a).

$= \frac{1}{4}(532)$ Substitute 532 for x.

$= 133$ Do the arithmetic.

133 children   Answer the question.

– – – –   – – – –

c. $\frac{1}{4}x = 240$ Write an equation.

$4\left(\frac{1}{4}x\right) = 4(240)$ Multiply each member by 4.

$x = 960$ Do the operations.

960 children   Answer the question.

ORAL PRACTICE

Give an expression representing each.

A. $\frac{1}{4}$ of x. $\frac{1}{4}x$ B.   7 less than x. $x - 7$

C. 5 more than x. D. 3 fewer than x.

E. 6 years older than x. F. 10 years younger than x.

G. 4 times x.

H. 30% of x (30% means $30 \div 100$, or 0.30).

I. 90% of x. J. 2.3 times as much as x.

EXERCISE 1-9

Problem Notes:

All problems have titles (e.g., "Freshman Problem") to make them more memorable to the students.

Students should write the definition of the variable on their papers, whether or not the problem calls for it. They should also tell in words what quantity the expression represents, as is done in the examples. In this way they can tell which thing stands for which quantity.

The problems call for the students to write an equation. This strategy gives you a response for students who want to do the whole problem in their heads. They must write the equation, because the question asks them to.

Students should use stack fractions, such as $\frac{1}{4}$ in the text, because they are easier to operate with than slash fractions such as 1/4.

Problems 5 on have i, ii, iii, iv, etc., for part numbers. These are lower-case Roman numerals.

1. *Freshmen Problem* Suppose that $\frac{1}{4}$ of the students in a school are freshmen. Let x stand for the total number of students.
    a. Write the definition of x. Then write an expression representing the number of freshmen. $\frac{1}{4}x$
    b. Write an equation stating that the number of freshmen is 312. $\frac{1}{4}x = 312$
    c. Find the number of students in the school. 1248 students

2. *Rain Problem* At Scorpion Gulch, it rains $\frac{1}{8}$ of the days. Let x stand for the total number of days that have passed.
    a. Write the definition of x. Then write an expression representing the number of days it rains. $\frac{1}{8}x$
    b. Write an equation stating that the number of days it rains is 31. $\frac{1}{8}x = 31$
    c. Solve the equation to find the total number of days that have passed. 248 days

3. *Sid's and Tip's Age Problem* Sid Upp is 4 years younger than his brother, Tip. Let x stand for Tip's age.
    a. Write the definition of x. Then write an expression for Sid's age. $x - 4$
    b. Write an equation stating that Sid's age is 76. $x - 4 = 76$
    c. Find Tip's age by solving this equation. Tip is 80.

4. *Tess and Clara's Allowance Problem* Tess T. Fye gets $3 less allowance each week than her older sister Clara. Let x stand for the number of dollars Clara gets a week.
    a. Write the definition of x. Then write an expression for the number of dollars Tess gets a week. $x - 3$
    b. Write an equation stating that Tess gets $11 per week. $x - 3 = 11$
    c. Find Clara's allowance by solving the equation. Clara gets $14.

5. *Rectangle Problem* The length of a rectangle is 7 cm more than its width. Let x be the number of cm in the width.
    a. Draw the rectangle. Then write an expression for its length. $x + 7$
    b. Find the length if the width is:
        i. 12 cm; 19 cm ii. 37 cm; 44 cm iii. 100 cm. 107 cm

   c. Write an equation stating that the length is 43 cm. Then solve the equation to find the width.   36 cm wide

   d. Repeat the procedure in part (c) to find the width if the length is:

      i. 91 cm;   84 cm   ii. 34 cm.   27 cm

6. *Age Problem*   Inda Cates is 5 years younger than her sister Cindy. Let x be Cindy's age.

   a. Write an expression for Inda's age. $x - 5$

   b. How old will Inda be when Cindy is:

      i. 17; 12   ii. 23; 18   iii. 100? 95

   c. Write an equation stating that Inda is 24. Then solve the equation to find Cindy's age.   29

   d. Repeat the procedure in part (c) to find Cindy's age when Inda is:

      i. 13; 18   ii. 72. 77

7. *Downstream Problem*   When you travel downstream, your actual speed is your speed through the water *plus* the speed of the current. The San Antonio River flows at about 3 kilometers per hour (km/h). Let x be the number of kilometers per hour you go through the water.

   a. Write an expression representing your actual speed downstream. $x + 3$

   b. How fast would you go downstream in:

      i. a pedalboat, which goes 5 km/h; 8 km/h

      ii. a rowboat, which goes 11 km/h; 14 km/h

      iii. a speedboat, which goes 42 km/h? 45 km/h

   c. Write an equation stating that your actual speed is 21 km/h. Then solve the equation to find your speed through the water.   18 km/h

   d. Repeat the procedure of part (c) to find your speed through the water if your actual speed is:

      i. 9 km/h; 6 km/h   ii. 65 km/h 62 km/h

8. *Upstream Problem*   When you travel upstream, your actual speed is your speed through the water *minus* the speed of the current. The current in Snake River is 7 kilometers per hour (km/h). Let x be your speed through the water in kilometers per hour.

   a. Write an expression for your actual speed upstream. $x - 7$

   b. Find the actual speed of:

      i. a canoe traveling 12 km/h through the water; 5 km/h

      ii. a salmon swimming 9 km/h through the water; 2 km/h

      iii. a sound wave traveling 2000 km/h through the water. 1993 km/h

   c. Write an equation stating that your actual speed is 15 km/h. Solve this equation to find your speed through the water.   22 km/h

   d. Repeat the procedure of part (c) to find your speed through the water if your actual speed is:

      i. 25 km/h; 32 km/h   ii. 8 km/h. 15 km/h

9. *Left-Handers' Problem*   About $\frac{1}{5}$ of all people are left-handed. Let x be the number of people in a particular group.
    a. Write an expression for the number of left-handed people in the group. $\frac{1}{5}x$
    b. Write an equation stating that the number of left-handers in a group is 47. Solve the equation to find the number of people in that group.   235 people
    c. Find the number of people in groups that have:
        i.   100 left-handers   500 people
        ii. 4000 left-handers.   20,000 people
    d. How many left-handers are there in a group of:
        i.   30 people;   6   ii.   100 people;   20
        iii. 5000 people?   1000

10. *Sale Problem*   When an item is on sale for $\frac{1}{3}$ off, the number of dollars you save is $\frac{1}{3}$ of the normal price. Let x dollars be the normal price.

    a. Write an expression for the number of dollars you save. $\frac{1}{3}x$
    b. A tag says, "Save $43.00 on this pair of binoculars!" Write an equation expressing this fact. Then solve the equation to find the normal price of the binoculars. $129
    c. Find the normal selling price of:
        i.   a tent, on which you save $37.00; $111
        ii. a scuba mask, on which you save $13.00. $39
    d. How much do you save on:
        i.   a watch, normally priced at $12.00? $4
        ii. a video tape recorder, normally priced at $837.00? $279

11. *Submarine Problem*   To go through the water most efficiently, a submarine should be built so that its length is 7 times its diameter. Let x be the diameter in meters (m).

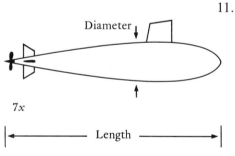

    a. Write an expression for the length. $7x$
    b. What should the length be if:
        i.   the diameter is 8 meters (m);   56 m
        ii. the diameter is 10 m?   70 m
    c. Write and solve equations to find out what the diameter should be if:
        i.   the length is 91 m;   13 m
        ii. the length is 50 m. $7\frac{1}{7}$ m

12. *Access Ramp Problem*   When an overpass is built on an expressway, the run should be 15 times the rise (see the diagram). Let x be the number of meters in the rise.

    a. Write an expression representing the run. $15x$
    b. Find the run if the rise is:
        i.   7 m;   105 m   ii.   20 m.   300 m
    c. Write and solve equations to find the rise if the run is:
        i.   195 m;   13 m   ii.   243 m.   16.2 m

13. *Profit Problem*   Mark Upp runs a retail store. On each item sold, he makes a profit of 20%, which means that he sells it for 1.2 times what he paid for it. Let x be the number of dollars he paid for an item.

   a.   Write an expression for the number of dollars for which he sells an item. $1.2x$

   b.   What is the selling price of:
   i.   a flag for which he paid $5.00; $6.00
   ii.   a skillet for which he paid $9.00; $10.80
   iii.   a desk for which he paid $140.00? $168.00

   c.   Find out how much Mark paid for:
   i.   a suitcase that he sells for $84.00; $70.00
   ii.   a clock that he sells for $13.20. $11.00

14. *Laborer Problem*   A construction company's rules say that a supervisor earns 1.5 times as much as a laborer. Let x be the number of dollars per hour a laborer earns.

   a.   Write an expression for the number of dollars per hour a supervisor earns. $1.5x$

   b.   Doug Upp is a laborer who earns $6.00 per hour. How much does his supervisor earn? $9.00

   c.   If Doug's pay is increased to $8.00 per hour, how much will the supervisor earn? $12.00

   d.   Suppose that a supervisor earns $9.60 per hour. How much does a laborer earn under these conditions? $6.40

15. *Challenge Problem*   Use the expression $2x + 5$.

   a.   Evaluate the expression if:
   i. x is 7;   19   ii. x is 13;   31   iii. x is 58.   121

   b.   Write an equation stating that the expression is 41. $2x + 5 = 41$

   c.   Solve the equation. Note that you will have to subtract *and* divide. See if you are clever enough to do these two transformations in the order that makes the problem the easiest! $x = 18$

1-10 | CHAPTER REVIEW AND TEST

In this chapter, you have used the two basic processes of algebra. If you are given an expression such as

$$x + 3$$

you should be able to do the following:

1.   Find out what the expression equals when you know the value of x.

2.   Find out what x equals when you know the value of the expression.

Time: 1 day

Test Suggestions:

Your test can be either a chapter test or a test strictly over word problems. The latter has the advantage that it forces students to learn to work word problems. Some students resist learning, rationalizing that they can score enough on other items to pass the test.

Assignment:

Section 2–1, Problems 1–33 (all) as preparation for the next day's class

The first is called *evaluating* an expression. The second is called *solving* an equation. Both processes are useful in solving problems from the real world.

One goal of your education should be to learn how to prepare for a test. Before you attempt the Chapter Test below, you should thumb through each section in this chapter and find the paragraph headed *Objective*. If you understand what the objective means, go right on to the next section and read its objective. If not, then look at the exercise for that section. If you still don't understand the objective, work examples in that section until you *do* get the idea.

CHAPTER TEST

T1. **a.** An expression just stands for a *number*.
   An equation says that an expression *equals* some number.
b. Evaluating means finding the expression's value when you know x. Solving means finding x's value when you know what the expression equals.
c. In $(3 + 4) \times 5$, the $3 + 4$ is done first.
   In $3 + 4 \times 5$, the 4×5 is done first.
d. A product is the result of multiplying two numbers, such as 3×4.
   A power is the result of *repeated* multiplication, such as $3^4 = 3 \cdot 3 \cdot 3 \cdot 3$.
e. A power is the "whole thing," such as 3^4. The exponent is just the 4 in 3^4.
f. Factors are numbers *multiplied* together.
   Terms are numbers *added* together (or subtracted).
g. The perimeter is the distance *around*. The area is a measure of the "space" inside.

T1. What is the difference in each case?
   a.   Expression and an equation.
   b.   Evaluating an expression and solving an equation.
   c.   Order of operations in $(3 + 4) \times 5$ and in $3 + 4 \times 5$.
   d.   Product and a power.
   e.   Power and an exponent.
   f.   Factors and terms.
   g.   Perimeter of a rectangle and area of a rectangle.

T2. Evaluate each expression.
   a. $30 + 5 \cdot 6 - 3$ 57
   b. $30 + 5 \cdot (6 - 3)$ 45
   c. $30 \cdot 5 + 6 \div 3$ 152
   d. $30 \cdot (5 + 6) \div 3$ 110
   e. $30 \div 5 \cdot 6 - 3$ 33
   f. $7 + 3^2$ 16
   g. $7 \cdot 3^2$ 63
   h. $7 \cdot (3^2)$ 63
   i. $62 - 2[24 - 5 \cdot 3]$ 44
   j. $5 + 5(11 \div 2^3)$ $11\frac{7}{8}$
   k. $\dfrac{30}{10} + \dfrac{6}{2}$ 6
   l. $\dfrac{30 + 6}{10 + 2}$ 3

T3. Evaluate $2x^2 + 7x - 4$ if:
   a. x is 3;   35
   b. x is 6.   110

T4. Evaluate each expression (i) if x is 35, and (ii) if x is 400.
   a. $x + 7$ i. 42   ii. 407
   b. $x - 16$ i. 19   ii. 384
   c. $\dfrac{1}{7}x$ i. 5   ii. $57\frac{1}{7}$
   d. $9x$ i. 315   ii. 3600

T5. Solve the equations.
   a. $x + 7 = 13$ $x = 6$
   b. $x - 16 = 59$ $x = 75$
   c. $\dfrac{1}{7}x = 19$ $x = 133$
   d. $9x = 54$ $x = 6$

T6.   Write each as a power.
   a. $12 \cdot 12 \cdot 12 \cdot 12 \cdot 12 \cdot 12 \cdot 12$ 12^7
   b.   243, with 3 as its base. 3^5
   c.   10,000, with 10 as its base. 10^4

T7. Write an expression for each of the following. Use parentheses only where necessary.
a. Eleven cubed. 11^3
b. The fifth power of y. y^5
c. The sum of 17 and x. $17 + x$
d. The product of 17 and x. $17x$
e. Add 8 to z; then multiply the result by x. $(z + 8) \cdot x$
f. Multiply 8 by z and add x to the result. $8z + x$
g. Divide the sum of r and s by the difference r minus s. $\dfrac{r + s}{r - s}$

T8. Write an expression for the length marked "?."

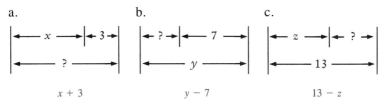

a.   b.   c.

$x + 3$ $y - 7$ $13 - z$

T9. *Savings Problem* When money is left in a savings account, it earns "simple interest." If the interest rate is 10% a year, you will have 1.1 times as much money at the end of 1 year as you had to start with. Each year the amount is multiplied by 1.1 again. If you start with $1, how much will you have at the end of 30 years? Write the answer as a power. 1.1^{30}

T10. *Thunder and Lightning Problem* The number of seconds it takes the thunder sound to reach you is 3 times the number of kilometers between you and the lightning. Let x be the number of kilometers.
a. Write an expression for the number of seconds the sound takes to reach you. $3x$
b. How long does it take the sound to reach you if the lightning is:
  i. 5 kilometers away; 15 sec
  ii. 2.8 kilometers away? 8.4 sec
c. Write an equation stating that the sound takes 12 seconds to reach you. Then solve it to find your distance from the lightning. 4 km

T11. *Bank Robbery Problem* Robin Banks robs a bank and takes off in the get-away car. Five minutes later, Willie Catchup starts after Robin. Let x be the number of minutes Robin has been driving.
a. Write an expression for the number of minutes Willie has been driving. $x - 5$
b. How long has Willie been driving when Robin has been going for:
  i. 13 minutes; 8 min   ii. 21 minutes? 16 min
c. How long has Robin been driving when Willie has been going for:
  i. 17 minutes; 22 min   ii. 24 minutes? 29 min

2

Operations with Negative Numbers

In the last chapter you learned how to write expressions representing such things as perimeter, area, dollars, and speed. In this chapter you will use the same techniques. But the answers will sometimes be negative *numbers. Negative numbers were invented to represent things like temperatures below freezing, overdrawn bank balances, and number of seconds ago. For instance, suppose you are riding a bike downhill and are gaining speed at $\frac{2}{3}$ mile per hour each second. If you are going 12 miles per hour now, positive values for time could be used to find your speed several seconds later. Negative values for time could be used to find your speed several seconds ago. In this chapter you will learn how to operate with negative numbers.*

Variable:

x Represents number of seconds later.

Expression:

$12 + \frac{2}{3}x$ Represents speed x seconds later.

x is -3 Represents 3 seconds *ago*.

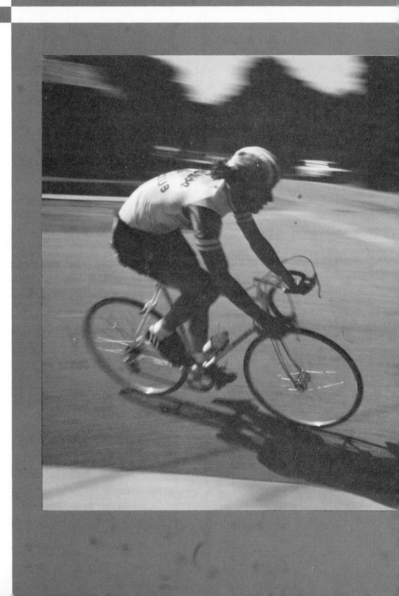

2-1 | INTRODUCTION TO NEGATIVE NUMBERS

This section is meant for you to read and work on your own. If you have worked with negative numbers before, this will be review. If not, this will be a chance for you to try learning something new before hearing about it in class.

Numbers were invented by people. Different kinds of numbers are used for different purposes. The *positive integers* 1, 2, 3, 4, 5, . . . were invented for counting. The *fractions* and *decimals,* such as $3\frac{1}{2}$ or 98.6, were invented for measuring. In order to express things like temperatures colder than 0°, overdrawn bank accounts, and speeds when going backwards, people invented negative numbers. Negative numbers are numbers that are less than zero.

One of the best ways for you to visualize negative numbers is to look at a number line.

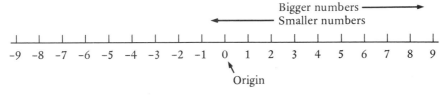

Each point on the line represents a number. The bigger the number, the farther it is to the *right*. Numbers to the left of 0 (the **origin**) are called *negative numbers*. The − sign is used to represent a negative number, as shown above. All numbers that have a place on the number line are called *real numbers*. These include decimals and fractions, both positive and negative.

To add two numbers such as 2 + 3, you start at 2 and move 3 spaces to the right, ending at 5.

Time: $\frac{1}{2}$ day, combined with Section 2–2 Possible to accelerate for those who know negative numbers already.

Chalkboard Examples:

Use the problems in Exercise 2–1 as the beginning of classwork. These problems may be used as oral exercises in which each student gives the answer to one problem. Raised ⁻ sign is not used.

Assignment:

All 33 problems already should have been assigned following the Chapter 1 test in preparation for your first class on Chapter 2. See assignments, Section 1–10.

2 + 3 = 5

To add a *negative* number to a positive number, such as 4 + (−3), you start at 4 and then count 3 spaces to the *left*, ending at 1.

4 + (−3) = 1

Objective :
Be able to discover something about the answers to addition problems of the forms

$$(\text{positive}) + (\text{negative}),$$
$$(\text{negative}) + (\text{positive}),$$
$$(\text{negative}) + (\text{negative}).$$

Working the following exercise should allow you to reach some conclusions.

EXERCISE 2-1

Problem Notes:

Problems 1–10 are all positive + negative.
Problems 11–20 are all negative + negative.
Problems 21–30 are all negative + positive.

Parentheses are used in 5 + (−2), for example, to separate two operation signs. The raised − sign is avoided in this text, because students are not always skillful enough in writing to make the distinction.

These problems can be used as Oral Practice, whether or not students have done them for homework.

Work the following addition problems. You may use a number line if necessary. You should work all 33 problems rather than just the odds or just the evens.

1. 5 + (−2)   3
2. 7 + (−3)   4
3. 6 + (−4)   2
4. 8 + (−7)   1
5. 2 + (−5)   −3
6. 9 + (−10)   −1
7. 13 + (−8)   5
8. 1 + (−4)   −3
9. 3 + (−7)   −4
10. 2 + (−11)   −9
11. −3 + (−2)   −5
12. −5 + (−1)   −6
13. −13 + (−4)   −17
14. −1 + (−6)   −7

15. $-4 + (-5)$ –9   16. $-2 + (-9)$ –11   17. $-8 + (-9)$ –17
18. $-1 + (-1)$ –2   19. $0 + (-3)$ –3   20. $-10 + (-10)$ –20
21. $-3 + 5$ 2   22. $-2 + 7$ 5   23. $-4 + 1$ –3
24. $-12 + 8$ –4   25. $-13 + 15$ 2   26. $-8 + 11$ 3
27. $-27 + 1$ –26   28. $-4 + 15$ 11   29. $-11 + 35$ 24
30. $-100 + 100$ 0

31. True or false?
   a. The sum of two negative numbers is always negative.   True
   b. A negative number plus a positive number is always negative.   False
   c. A positive number plus a negative number is always positive.   False

32. Adding a *negative* number to another number is the same as what *other* operation?   Subtraction

33. What is meant by:
   a. a negative number;   b. an integer;   c. a real number?

33.   a. A negative number is a number less than zero.
      b. An integer is a positive, negative, or zero "whole" number.
      c. A real number is any number that has a place on the number line.

2-2 | ADDING SIGNED NUMBERS

In the previous section, you added signed numbers on a number line. In this section, you will learn a quicker way.

Objective :
Be able to add positive and negative numbers *quickly*.

To accomplish this objective, you must first have two background concepts.

The first is that of *additive inverses (opposites):* Negative 5, written -5, is a number 5 units to the left of the origin on a number line. If you add 5 to it, the answer is 0.

$-5 + 5 = 0$

-5 0

Time: $\frac{1}{2}$ day, with Section 2–1

Chalkboard Examples:

1. $|6| = 6$
    $|-6| = 6$
    Conclusion: The absolute value of a number is the number of spaces between that number and the origin of the number line. Absolute value is introduced here only to be able to talk about the size of a number. A formal definition of absolute value is in Section 6–3.

2. Evaluate: $5 + (-3)$ Ans.: 2
                $5 + (-8)$ Ans.: -3
               $-4 + (-2)$ Ans.: -6
               $-4 + 7$ Ans.: 3
    Conclusion: (See text.)

Assignment:

1–59 odd or 2–60 even. (This is not as long an assignment as it sounds.)

Any two numbers that have a sum of zero are called *additive inverses,* or *opposites,* of each other.

DEFINITION

ADDITIVE INVERSES, OR OPPOSITES
Two numbers are **additive inverses,** or **opposites,** of each other if their *sum* equals *zero.* (For instance, -5 and 5 are additive inverses because $-5 + 5 = 0$.)

Because $-5 + 5$ equals 0, you can say that -5 is the opposite of 5 and that 5 is the opposite of -5. The opposite of -5 can be written $-(-5)$. So you can write

$$-(-5) = 5.$$

In general, for any real number x,

$$-(-x) = x$$

The second concept is **absolute value.** The *absolute value* of a number, written

$$|\text{number}|,$$

is its distance from the origin on a number line. Because 5 and -5 are both 5 spaces from the origin,

$$|-5| = 5 \quad \text{and} \quad |5| = 5.$$

As you can see, the absolute value of a number tells you its "size." For instance, -7 has a larger absolute value than does 3, because -7 is farther from the origin than 3.

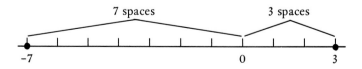

With these two concepts, you are ready to learn how to add negative numbers quickly. The following cases show how.

Case 1: Add 7 + (−4).

From the number line, the answer is 3.

$$7 + (-4) = 3$$

Quick way: 7 + (−4)

= 7 − 4 ← *Subtract* the numbers!

= <u>3</u>

Note that in expressions such as 7 + (−4), the parentheses are needed to separate the + and − signs. It is not correct notation to write two operation signs together without parentheses.

Case 2: Add 7 + (−9).

From the number line, the answer is −2.

$$7 + (-9) = -2$$

Quick way: 7 + (−9)

= 7 − 9   Subtract the *absolute values,* 9 and 7.

= <u>−2</u>   The answer is *negative* since the absolute value of 9 is greater than the absolute value of 7.

Case 3: Add −3 + (−4).

From the number line, the answer is −7.

$$-3 + (-4) = -7$$

Quick way: $-3 + (-4)$

$= \underline{\underline{-7}}$ ← *Add* the absolute values, 3 and 4. Then make the answer *negative*.

Case 4: Add $-3 + 4$.

From the number line, the answer is 1.

Quick way: $-3 + 4$

$= \underline{\underline{1}}$ ← *Subtract* the absolute values. The sign of the answer is the sign of the *greater* absolute value.

From these four cases, you can summarize the quick ways.

TECHNIQUE

TO ADD SIGNED NUMBERS:
1. If the two numbers have *opposite* signs:
   • *Subtract* the absolute values.
   • The answer has the sign of the term with the *greater* absolute value.

   Big minus small is *positive*.
   Small minus big is *negative*.

2. If the two numbers have the *same* sign:
   • *Add* the absolute values.
   • Use the sign of the two numbers for the answer.

   Positive plus positive is *positive*.
   Negative plus negative is *negative*.

You have read the words *positive number, negative number, integer,* and *real number.* Here are formal definitions of these sets of numbers.

DEFINITION

KINDS OF NUMBERS
Positive numbers are greater than zero.
Negative numbers are less than zero.
Integers are the numbers . . . −3, −2, −1, 0, 1, 2, 3, ... They
do *not* include the fractions in between.
Real numbers are *all* numbers on the number line, positive, negative,
and zero. They include fractions, decimals, etc., and fill the entire
number line, leaving no gaps.

ORAL PRACTICE

Evaluate the following.

A. $|-3|$ ₃   B. $|4|$ ₄   C. $|7.2|$ 7.2

D. $\left|\dfrac{-2}{3}\right|$ $\frac{2}{3}$ E. $|0|$ 0   F. $3 + (-5)$ −2

G. $8 + (-2)$ 6   H. $-6 + 1$ −5   I. $-3 + (-4)$ −7

J. $-3 + 4$ 1   K. $-2 + (-7)$ −9   L. $-(-4)$ 4

M. $-(-6.1)$ 6.1   N. $\left|-5\dfrac{1}{3}\right|$ $5\frac{1}{3}$ O. $-|-9|$ −9

P.   Tell why it would be bad form to write $3 + -7$.

P.   "3 + −7" is bad form because operation signs must be separated by parentheses, 3 + (−7).

Tell whether the parentheses are needed in each case.

Q. $6 + (-5)$ Yes   R. $-7 + (4)$ No   S. $-3 + (-1)$ Yes

T. $6.2 + (1.4)$ No   U. $-(-8)$ Yes

Give an example of each.

V. Negative number. −1   W. Positive number. 1

X.   Real number that is *not* an integer. $\frac{1}{2}$

Y.   Negative integer. -1

Z.   Negative real number that is not an integer. $-\frac{1}{2}$

EXERCISE 2-2

For Problems 1 through 40, evaluate the expression. Write both the given expression and the answer.

1. $12 + (-9)$ 3
2. $14 + (-6)$ 8
3. $8 + (-13)$ -5
4. $9 + (-19)$ -10
5. $-2 + (-16)$ -18
6. $-5 + (-11)$ -16
7. $-4 + 11$ 7
8. $-3 + 17$ 14
9. $-21 + 7$ -14
10. $-8 + 2$ -6
11. $-5 + (-8)$ -13
12. $-7 + (-9)$ -16
13. $5 + (-8)$ -3
14. $7 + (-9)$ -2
15. $-5 + 8$ 3
16. $-7 + 9$ 2
17. $-8 + 5$ -3
18. $-9 + 7$ -2
19. $-23 + (-15)$ -38
20. $-62 + (-38)$ -100
21. $-6.3 + 2.1$ -4.2
22. $-8.7 + 1.2$ -7.5
23. $5.8 + (-4.1)$ 1.7
24. $3.4 + (-2.1)$ 1.3
25. $-1.8 + (-7.3)$ -9.1
26. $-5.8 + (-7.4)$ -13.2
27. $\frac{5}{13} + \left(-\frac{2}{13}\right)$ $\frac{3}{13}$
28. $\frac{7}{11} + \left(-\frac{4}{11}\right)$ $\frac{3}{11}$
29. $-1\frac{5}{7} + \frac{2}{7}$ $-1\frac{3}{7}$
30. $-6\frac{4}{5} + \frac{3}{5}$ $-6\frac{1}{5}$
31. $|-7|$ 7
32. $|-6|$ 6
33. $-(-7)$ 7
34. $-(-6)$ 6
35. $-7 + 7$ 0
36. $-6 + 6$ 0
37. $-7 + (-7)$ -14
38. $-6 + (-6)$ -12
39. $-(-(-7))$ -7
40. $-(-(-(-6)))$ 6

Problem Notes:

Problems 39 and 40 have nested parentheses. Start from the inside and work out.

Problems 41–54 involve several terms. Students should take one step at a time, working from left to right, to minimize errors.

For Problems 55–60, make sure students distinguish between real number and integer.

For Problems 41 through 54, evaluate the expression. Recall the agreed-upon order of operations.

41. $14 + (-3) + (-6)$ 5
42. $21 + (-8) + (-7)$ 6
43. $2 + (-7) + (-10)$ -15
44. $5 + (-11) + (-2)$ -8

45. $-19 + 8 + (-4)$ -15 46. $-13 + 6 + (-1)$ -8

47. $-30 + 6 + 29$ 5 48. $-90 + 10 + 30$ -50

49. $-5 + (-12) + (-13)$ -30 50. $-4 + (-16) + (-27)$ -47

51. $5 + (-32) + 16 + (-8)$ -19 52. $12 + (-5) + 11 + (-29)$ -11

53. $-29 + 4 + (-15) + 40$ 0 54. $-17 + 6 + (-11) + 22$ 0

For Problems 55 through 60, tell what kind(s) of number is (are) given: real, positive, negative, or integer.

EXAMPLE

-8 <u>Real, negative, integer</u>

55. 13 Real, positive, integer   56. 7.2 Real, positive

57. -6.3 Real, negative   58. -11 Real, negative, integer

59. $\dfrac{3}{4}$ Real, positive   60. $1\dfrac{4}{5}$ Real, positive

---

2-3 | SUBTRACTING SIGNED NUMBERS

In the last section, you saw that addition of negative numbers can be turned into a subtraction problem. For example,

$$7 + (-3)$$
$$= 7 - 3$$
$$= \underline{\underline{4}}.$$

The reverse is also true. A subtraction problem can be turned into an addition problem. For instance,

$$7 - 3 = 7 + (-3).$$

This equation says

        7 *minus* 3 equals 7 *plus* the *opposite* of 3.

This idea can be used as a definition of subtraction.

DEFINITION

> **SUBTRACTION**
> Subtracting a number means adding its opposite. That is,
>
> $$x - y = x + (-y).$$

Time: $\frac{1}{2}$ day or 1 day, depending on prior knowledge of negative numbers

Chalkboard Examples:

(After presenting the definition of subtraction.)

Evaluate:	
$15 - 40$	Ans.: -25
$-7 - 3$	Ans.: -10
$20 - (-3) - 7$	Ans.: 16
$-4 - 9 - (-2)$	Ans.: -11

Assignment:

$\frac{1}{2}$ day on section:
  2–3 Problems 1, 5, 9, . . . , 49 or 2, 6, 10, . . . , 50; and 2–4 Problems 3, 7, 11, . . . , 51 or 4, 8, 12, . . . , 52

1 day on section:
  2–3 Problems 1–49 odd or 2–50 even

This definition is especially useful if you must subtract a *negative* number. The expression

$$9 - (-5)$$

can be written as

9 *plus* the *opposite* of -5.

Since the opposite of -5 is 5, you can write

$$9 - (-5)$$
$$= 9 + 5$$
$$= \underline{\underline{14}}.$$

Objective :
Be able to subtract positive and negative numbers.

The following rules can be used for quick subtraction of signed numbers.

TECHNIQUE

TO SUBTRACT SIGNED NUMBERS
1. Change subtracting to *adding* the *opposite*.
2. Follow the rules for *adding* signed numbers.

For each of the following examples, put a piece of paper along the dotted lines to cover the answer. Evaluate the expression. Then uncover the answer to be sure you are right.

EXAMPLE 1

Evaluate $13 - 29$.

- - - - -   - - - - -

	Think These Reasons
$13 - 29$	Write the given expression.
$= 13 + (-29)$	Change subtracting to adding the opposite.
$= \underline{\underline{-16}}$	*Subtract* the absolute values.

EXAMPLE 2

Evaluate $-4 - 3$.

- - - - -   - - - - -

$-4 - 3$ Write the given expression.

| $= -4 + (-3)$ | Change subtracting to adding the opposite. |
| $= \underline{\underline{-7}}$ | *Add* the absolute values. Make the answer *negative*. |

EXAMPLE 3

Evaluate $11 - (-3) - 4$.

- - - - -   - - - - -

$11 - (-3) - 4$	Write the given expression.
$= 11 + 3 - 4$	Change subtracting to adding the opposite. (The "−4" does not need to be changed yet.)
$= 14 - 4$	Add and subtract from left to right.
$= \underline{\underline{10}}$	Do the arithmetic.

EXAMPLE 4

Evaluate $-3 - 7 - (-2)$.

- - - - -   - - - - -

$-3 - 7 - (-2)$	Write the given expression.
$= -3 + (-7) + 2$	Change subtracting to adding the opposite.
$= -10 + 2$	*Add* the absolute values. Make the answer negative.
$= \underline{\underline{-8}}$	*Subtract* the absolute values. Make the answer negative.

ORAL PRACTICE

Give the value of each expression.

A. $5 - 7$ $_{-2}$ B. $-6 - 2$ $_{-8}$ C. $8 - (-5)$ $_{13}$

D. $7 - (-9)$ $_{16}$ E. $-3 - (-1)$ $_{-2}$ F. $-4 - 6$ $_{-10}$

G. $5 - (-2)$ $_{7}$ H. $7.3 - 9.8$ $_{-2.5}$ I. $6 + (-5)$ $_{1}$

J. $-2 + (-5)$ $_{-7}$

K. Tell why it would be bad form to write $3 - -7$.

K. "3 − −7" is bad form because it has two operation signs *not* separated by parentheses.

Tell whether or not the parentheses are needed in each case.

L. $6 - (-5)$ Yes   M. $-7 - (4)$ No   N. $-3 - (-1)$ Yes

O. $6.2 - (1.4)$ No   P. $0 - (2)$ No

Q. State the definition of subtraction.

Q. Subtracting a number means adding its opposite, or "$x - y = x + (-y)$."

EXERCISE 2-3

Evaluate.

1. $35 - 200$ -165
2. $144 - 441$ -297
3. $14 - (-17)$ 31
4. $15 - (-21)$ 36
5. $-11 - (-2)$ -9
6. $-34 - (-7)$ -27
7. $-99 - 59$ -158
8. $-40 - 30$ -70
9. $-241 - (-42)$ -199
10. $-300 - (-88)$ -212
11. $158 - (-115)$ 273
12. $135 - (-165)$ 300
13. $5.9 - 2.3$ 3.6
14. $6.7 - 4.1$ 2.6
15. $1.2 - 7.3$ -6.1
16. $2.5 - 6.7$ -4.2
17. $3.8 - (-2.7)$ 6.5
18. $5.4 - (-6.9)$ 12.3
19. $-\dfrac{5}{7} - \dfrac{2}{7}$ -1
20. $-\dfrac{13}{11} - \dfrac{9}{11}$ -2
21. $0 - (-15)$ 15
22. $0 - (-21)$ 21
23. $154 - (43 - 28)$ 139
24. $200 - (68 - 50)$ 182
25. $314 - (58 - 70)$ 326
26. $190 - (40 - 85)$ 235
27. $(33 - 45) - (64 - 78)$ 2
28. $(36 - 46) - (22 - 30)$ -2
29. $(13 - 5) - (-2 + 6)$ 4
30. $(33 - 13) - (-8 + 10)$ 18
31. $1066 - 1492 + 1984$ 1558
32. $1215 - 1776 + 2001$ 1440
33. $8 - (-3) - [4 - (-6)]$ 1
34. $-10 - 4 - [-6 - (-11)]$ -19
35. $1 - 2 + 4 - 8 + 16$ 11
36. $17 - 13 + 12 + 3 - 19$ 0
37. $45 - 7 - 58 + 11 - 21$ -30
38. $35 - 15 + 8 - 20 - 48$ -40
39. $19 - 2 + 23 - 54 + 34 - 29$ -9
40. $200 - 195 + 71 - 66 + 18 - 29$ -1

Problem Notes:

Problems 31 and 32 involve arithmetic on well-known dates.

For Problems 41–50, students must realize that operations inside absolute value signs must be done *first*.

For Problems 41 through 50, the operations inside the absolute value sign must be done first.

41. $|3 - 7|$ 4
42. $|2 - 9|$ 7
43. $|8 - (-11)|$ 19
44. $|6 - (-4)|$ 10
45. $|13 - 5| + 4$ 12
46. $|9 - 6| + 5$ 8
47. $|-17 + 2| - 2$ 13
48. $|-14 + 3| - 8$ 3
49. $-|-2 + 5| + 1$ -2
50. $-|-8 - (-5)| + 2$ -1

2-4 | MULTIPLYING SIGNED NUMBERS

You recall that multiplication can be thought of as repeated addition. For instance,

$$(4)(7) \quad \text{means} \quad 7 + 7 + 7 + 7, \quad \text{or} \quad 28.$$

Similarly,

$$(4)(-1) \quad \text{means} \quad (-1) + (-1) + (-1) + (-1), \quad \text{or} \quad -4.$$

Multiplying a number by -1 gives a special result. The answer is the *opposite* of the number multiplied. For example,

$$(13)(-1) = -13$$
$$(54)(-1) = -54$$
$$(1000)(-1) = -1000.$$

The two factors in a product can be written in either order. For example, $(5)(7)$ and $(7)(5)$ both equal 35. Therefore,

$$(-1)(13) = -13$$
$$(-1)(54) = -54$$
$$(-1)(1000) = -1000.$$

This fact is called the Multiplication Property of Negative One.

PROPERTY

> **MULTIPLICATION BY -1**
> -1 times a number equals the *opposite* of that number; that is, for any real number x,
>
> $$-1 \cdot x = -x.$$

The property is true if x itself is negative. For instance, $(-1)(-7)$ is the *opposite* of -7, which is 7. Similarly,

$$(-1)(-12) = 12$$
$$(-1)(-88) = 88$$
$$(-1)(-100) = 100.$$

In these examples, a *negative* number times a *negative* number gives a *positive* answer. This always happens, even when neither number is -1.

Time: $\frac{1}{2}$ day or 1 day, depending on prior experience with negative numbers

Chalkboard Examples:

(After deriving multiplication property of -1.)
1. Evaluate: $(-8)(-7)$ Ans.: 56
   $(-6)(9)$ Ans.: -54
   $(-4)(-5)(-6)$ Ans.: -120
   Conclusion: The sign of the answer depends on the number of *negative* factors.

2. Evaluate: $(-5)^3$ Ans.: -125
   $(-5)^2$ Ans.: 25
   -5^2 Ans.: -25
   Conclusion: The sign of the answer depends on the parity of the exponent.
   Conclusion: The exponent acts only on the symbol immediately to the left. For -5^2, therefore, only the 5 is squared, not -5.

Assignment:

$\frac{1}{2}$ day on section:
   (See Section 2–3 for the assignment from 2–3 and 2–4.)
1 day on section:
   2–4 Problems 1–51 odd or 2–52 even.

For example,

$$(-5)(-3) = 15$$
$$(-9)(-8) = 72$$
$$(-7)(-6) = 42.$$

You can remember these simple statements to help you multiply negative numbers.

> Negative times negative is *positive*.
> Positive times negative is *negative*.

Objective :
Be able to evaluate products that contain negative numbers.

Cover the answer as you work the example. Then uncover the answer to be sure you are right.

EXAMPLE 1

Evaluate $(-3)(-7)$.

- - - - -   - - - - -

	Think These Reasons
$(-3)(-7)$	Write the given expression.
$= \underline{\underline{21}}$	Negative times negative is *positive*.

EXAMPLE 2

Evaluate $(-5)(8)$.

- - - - -   - - - - -

$(-5)(8)$	Write the given expression.
$= \underline{\underline{-40}}$	Negative times positive is *negative*.

EXAMPLE 3

Evaluate $(-5)(-3)(-2)$.

- - - - -   - - - - -

$(-5)(-3)(-2)$	Write the given expression.
$= (15)(-2)$	Negative times negative is *positive*.
$= \underline{\underline{-30}}$	Positive times negative is *negative*.

EXAMPLE 4

Evaluate $(-3)(-8)(-2)(-1)$.

$- \; - \; - \; - \; -$ $- \; - \; - \; - \; -$

$\qquad (-3)(-8)(-2)(-1)$ Write the given expression.

$\qquad = (24)(-2)(-1)$ Negative times negative is *positive*.

$\qquad = (-48)(-1)$ Positive times negative is *negative*.

$\qquad = \underline{\underline{48}}$ Negative times negative is *positive*.

From these examples you should be able to see a shortcut for telling the *sign* of the answer. The product $(-5)(-3)(-2)$ has an *odd* number of negative factors and the answer is *negative*. The product $(-3)(-8)(-2)(-1)$ has an *even* number of negative factors and the answer is *positive*.

CONCLUSION

SIGN OF A PRODUCT
The sign of a product will be:
• *negative*, if it has an *odd* number of negative factors;
• *positive*, if it has an *even* number of negative factors.

The following examples involve *powers* of negative numbers.

EXAMPLE 5

Evaluate $(-2)^3$.

$- \; - \; - \; - \; -$ $- \; - \; - \; - \; -$

$\qquad (-2)^3$ Write the given expression.

$\qquad = (-2)(-2)(-2)$ Write the power as a product.

$\qquad = \underline{\underline{-8}}$ *Odd* number of negative factors.

EXAMPLE 6

Evaluate $(-2)^4$.

$- \; - \; - \; - \; -$ $- \; - \; - \; - \; -$

$\qquad (-2)^4$ Write the given expression.

$\qquad = (-2)(-2)(-2)(-2)$ Write the power as a product.

$\qquad = \underline{\underline{16}}$ *Even* number of negative factors.

EXAMPLE 7

Evaluate -2^4.

– – – – –   – – – – –

	Think These Reasons
-2^4	Write the given expression.
$= -(2)(2)(2)(2)$	Only *base* 2 is raised to the fourth power, not -2. You may think of -2^4 as meaning $(-1)(2^4)$.
$= \underline{\underline{-16}}$	Multiply *before* taking opposites.

The last three examples lead to a conclusion about the sign of a power.

CONCLUSION

SIGN OF A POWER OF A NEGATIVE NUMBER
(Negative number)$^{\text{even exponent}}$ is *positive*.
(Negative number)$^{\text{odd exponent}}$ is *negative*.

Note: An expression like -3^4 is *not* a power of a negative number, since taking the power is done *before* taking the opposite.

$$-3^4 \quad \text{equals} \quad -(3)(3)(3)(3), \quad \text{or} \quad -81.$$

ORAL PRACTICE

Evaluate.

A. $(-4)(6)$ -24 B. $(3)(-8)$ -24 C. $(-2)(-8)$ 16

D. $(7)(-1)$ -7 E. $(-9)(0)$ 0   F. $(-8)(-7)$ 56

G. $(-1)(-9)$ 9   H. $(4)(-8)$ -32 I. $(6)(7)$ 42

J. $(1)(-27)$ -27

Give the sign of the answer.

EXAMPLES

		Answers	
i.	$(-2)(-3)$	i.	Positive.
ii.	$(-2)(3)$	ii.	Negative.

K. $(-462)(-291)$ +   L. $(55)(-2)(-18)$ +

M. $(-73)(-54)(-66)$ –   N. $(-200)(35)(68)$ –

O. $(-2)(-3)(-4)(-5)(-6)$ –   P. $(-1)(2)(-3)(4)(-5)(-6)$ +

Q. $(-75)^2$ +   R. $(-51)^3$ –   S. $(-85)^{19}$ –

T. $(-21)^{100}$ +   U. -44^6 –   V. -26^{10} –

Evaluate.

W. $(-1)^{70}$ 1   X. $(-1)^{53}$ –1   Y. -1^{28} –1   Z. 0^{35} 0

EXERCISE 2-4

For Problems 1 through 40, evaluate the expression.

Problem Notes:

For problems involving powers, recommend that the students write out the power as a product first. When they see the pattern, they can use a short cut.

1. $(10)(-7)$ –70

2. $(-8)(-6)$ 48

3. $(-5)(-9)$ 45

4. $(-3)(12)$ –36

5. $(-6)(8)$ –48

6. $(4)(-7)$ –28

7. $(-1.2)(-5)$ 6

8. $(10)(-3.4)$ –34

9. $\left(-\dfrac{2}{3}\right)(6)$ –4

10. $\left(\dfrac{3}{4}\right)(-12)$ –9

11. $(-72)(1)$ –72

12. $(-1)(54)$ –54

13. $(-1)(-200)$ 200

14. $(1)(-300)$ –300

15. $(-53)(0)$ 0

16. $(-82)(0)$ 0

17. $(-3)(-5)(-7)$ –105

18. $(-2)(-4)(-6)$ –48

19. $(-2)(5)(-8)$ 80

20. $(-3)(5)(-10)$ 150

21. $(4)(-7)(2)$ –56

22. $(7)(-4)(3)$ –84

23. $(-1)(5)(-3)(-2)$ –30

24. $(-6)(-1)(5)(-3)$ –90

25. $(-4)^3$ –64

26. $(-5)^3$ –125

27. $(-4)^4$ 256

28. $(-5)^4$ 625

29. -4^4 –256

30. -5^4 –625

31. $(-1)^{15}$ –1

32. $(-1)^{22}$ 1

33. $(-1)^{18}$ 1

34. $(-1)^{21}$ –1

35. -1^{18} –1

36. -1^{20} –1

37. $(-1)(-3)^4$ –81

38. $(-1)(-2)^4$ –16

39. $(-3)^2(-2)^3$ –72

40. $(-2)^4(-3)^3$ –432

For Problems 41 through 50, evaluate the expression for the given values of the variable.

41. $(-5)^x$, if:
    a. x is 3; -125
    b. x is 2; 25
    c. x is 1. -5

42. $(-4)^x$, if:
    a. x is 3; -64
    b. x is 2; 16
    c. x is 1. -4

43. -5^x, if:
    a. x is 3; -125
    b. x is 2. -25

44. -4^x, if:
    a. x is 3; -64
    b. x is 2. -16

45. $(-x)^4$, if:
    a. x is 2; 16
    b. x is 1; 1
    c. x is 0. 0

46. $(-x)^2$, if:
    a. x is 3; 9
    b. x is 1; 1
    c. x is 0. 0

47. $-x$, if:
    a. x is 5; -5
    b. x is -3; 3
    c. x is -1. 1

48. $-x$, if:
    a. x is 8; -8
    b. x is -5; 5
    c. x is 0. 0

49. $-1 \cdot x$, if:
    a. x is 5; -5
    b. x is -3; 3
    c. x is -1. 1

50. $-1 \cdot x$, if:
    a. x is 8; -8
    b. x is -5; 5
    c. x is 0. 0

51. **51.** False! $-x$ is negative only if x is *positive*. $-(-3) = 3$, a *pos.* no., if x is -3.

51. From the answers to Problems 47 through 50, you can see that $-x$ and $-1 \cdot x$ always stand for the *same* number. True or false: Does the expression $-x$ always stand for a *negative* number? Explain.

52. **52.** $-x^2$ means $-(x)(x)$. The *mult.* is done *first*. $(-x)^2$ means $(-x)(-x)$. The *opposite* of x is taken first.

52. Explain the difference in meaning between $-x^2$ and $(-x)^2$.

2-5 | DIVISION OF SIGNED NUMBERS

Time: 1 day

Chalkboard Examples:

(After definition of division.)

1. Evaluate: $\dfrac{56}{-7}$ Ans.: -8

   $\dfrac{-56}{7}$ Ans.: -8

   $\dfrac{-56}{-7}$ Ans.: 8

   $-\dfrac{-56}{-7}$ Ans.: -8

You have learned that two numbers with a sum of 0 are called *additive inverses,* or opposites, of each other. There is a similar relationship applying to multiplication. For example,

$$\frac{2}{3} \cdot \frac{3}{2} = 1.$$

Any two numbers whose product is 1 are called *multiplicative inverses,* or *reciprocals,* of each other. Some other examples are

$$4 \text{ and } \tfrac{1}{4};$$

$$-\tfrac{3}{5} \text{ and } -\tfrac{5}{3};$$

$$-1 \text{ and } -1.$$

The symbols

$$\frac{1}{x} \quad \text{or} \quad 1/x$$

are used for the reciprocal of x. Note that 0 has *no* reciprocal, since there is no number for which

$$0 \cdot number = 1.$$

DEFINITION

MULTIPLICATIVE INVERSE, OR RECIPROCAL
Two nonzero numbers are **multiplicative inverses,** or **reciprocals,** of each other if their *product* equals 1. (For instance, $\tfrac{2}{3}$ and $\tfrac{3}{2}$ are reciprocals since $\tfrac{2}{3} \cdot \tfrac{3}{2} = 1$.)
Note: Zero has *no* reciprocal.

One-fourth *of* 20 means $\tfrac{1}{4}$ *times* 20, which equals 5. The 5 can be found by *dividing* 20 by 4. This fact provides a means of defining division in terms of multiplication.

$$20 \div 4 \quad \text{means} \quad 20 \cdot \frac{1}{4}.$$

DEFINITION

DIVISION
Dividing by a number means *multiplying* by its *reciprocal.* That is, for any real numbers x and y with $y \neq 0$,

$$x \div y = x \cdot \frac{1}{y}$$

or

$$\frac{x}{y} = x \cdot \frac{1}{y}$$

or

$$x/y = x \cdot \frac{1}{y}.$$

---

2. Evaluate: $\dfrac{0}{8}$ Ans.: 0

$\dfrac{8}{0}$ Ans.: None
(undefined quantity)

Assignment:

1–55 odd or 2–56 even. (Takes about 35 to 40 minutes for average students.)

Because 0 has no reciprocal, division by 0 is *undefined*. The expression

$$\frac{3}{0} \quad \text{means} \quad 3 \cdot \frac{1}{0},$$

which does not equal a real number. However, division *of* 0 *by* another number *is* defined. For example,

$$\frac{0}{5} = 0 \cdot \frac{1}{5} = 0.$$

With this definition of division, the properties of multiplying by negative numbers carry over directly to division. For example, consider $(-15) \div (-5)$.

$$\frac{-15}{-5}$$

$$= (-15)\left(-\frac{1}{5}\right) \qquad \text{Definition of division.}$$

$$= \underline{\underline{3}} \qquad \qquad \text{Negative times negative is positive.}$$

To find this quotient, you must realize that the reciprocal of -5 is $-\frac{1}{5}$, because $(-5)(-\frac{1}{5}) = 1$.

You can remember the sign of a quotient as follows.

> Negative divided by negative is *positive*.
> Positive divided by negative is *negative*.
> Negative divided by positive is *negative*.

Later in your mathematical career you will be able to *prove* these properties. For the time being, you will be required only to *remember* them and use them.

Objective:
Be able to evaluate quotients involving negative numbers.

Cover the answer as you work the example. Then uncover the answer to be sure you are right.

EXAMPLE

Evaluate $\dfrac{-54}{x}$ if:

a. x is 6;   b. x is -3;   c. x is 0.

		Think These Reasons

a. $\dfrac{-54}{x}$ Write the given expression.

$= \dfrac{-54}{6}$ Substitute 6 for x.

$= \underline{\underline{-9}}$ Negative divided by positive is *negative*.

b. $\dfrac{-54}{x}$ Write the given expression.

$= \dfrac{-54}{-3}$ Substitute -3 for x.

$= \underline{\underline{18}}$ Negative divided by negative is *positive*.

c. $\dfrac{-54}{x}$

$= \dfrac{-54}{0}$ Undefined.

Reason: Division by zero is undefined. Simply mark out the expression $-\frac{54}{0}$ and write the word *undefined*.

ORAL PRACTICE

Evaluate.

A. $\dfrac{24}{-6}$ -4 B. $\dfrac{-30}{10}$ -3 C. $\dfrac{-8}{-2}$ 4

D. $\dfrac{15}{-3}$ -5 E. $\dfrac{-20}{-2}$ 10 F. $\dfrac{-42}{3}$ -14

G. $\dfrac{5}{-4}$ -1.25 H. $\dfrac{-7}{-1}$ 7 I. $\dfrac{-12}{1}$ -12

J. $\dfrac{10}{-1}$ -10 K. $\dfrac{0}{-6}$ 0 L. $\dfrac{-4}{0}$ Undefined

Give the sign of the answer.

M. $\dfrac{-547}{261}$ $-$ N. $\dfrac{-82.8}{-0.03}$ $+$ O. $\dfrac{3840}{-125}$ $-$

P. $\dfrac{-6}{-100}$ $+$ Q. $\dfrac{41}{37}$ $+$

Tell the reciprocal of the given number.

X. Dividing by a number means multiplying

by its reciprocal, or "$x \div y = x \cdot \dfrac{1}{y}$" or

"$\dfrac{x}{y} = x \cdot \dfrac{1}{y}$."

R. 5 $\frac{1}{5}$ S. $\dfrac{2}{3}$ $\frac{3}{2}$ T. $-\dfrac{3}{5}$ $-\frac{5}{3}$

U. -1 -1 V. 1 1 W. 0   None

X.   State the definition of division.

EXERCISE 2-5

For Problems 1 through 40, evaluate the expression.

1. $\dfrac{-21}{7}$ -3 2. $\dfrac{35}{-5}$ -7 3. $\dfrac{21}{-7}$ -3

4. $\dfrac{-35}{5}$ -7 5. $\dfrac{-21}{-7}$ 3 6. $\dfrac{-35}{-5}$ 7

7. $-\dfrac{-21}{-7}$ -3 8. $-\dfrac{-35}{-5}$ -7 9. $-\dfrac{21}{-7}$ 3

10. $-\dfrac{-35}{5}$ 7 11. $-\dfrac{-21}{7}$ 3 12. $-\dfrac{35}{-5}$ 7

13. $\dfrac{-26}{2}$ -13 14. $\dfrac{-38}{2}$ -19 15. $\dfrac{51}{-3}$ -17

16. $\dfrac{57}{-3}$ -19 17. $\dfrac{-55}{-11}$ 5 18. $\dfrac{-39}{-13}$ 3

19. $\dfrac{1000}{-10}$ -100 20. $\dfrac{200}{-200}$ -1 21. $\dfrac{7-19}{-3}$ 4

Problem Notes:

Problems 23–26 have some tempting
"canceling" that produces wrong answers.
  Problems 27–30 can be done by canceling
first.
  Problems 31–40 will cause division-by-zero
errors for some students in spite of all you
have said in class.

22. $\dfrac{13-37}{-2}$ 12 23. $\dfrac{45}{5-14}$ -5 24. $\dfrac{200}{-50+10}$ -5

25. $\dfrac{32-4}{8-15}$ -4 26. $\dfrac{6-21}{6-1}$ -3 27. $\dfrac{(8)(-3)}{-6}$ 4

28. $\dfrac{(4)(-6)}{2}$ -12 29. $\dfrac{(-3)(10)}{5}$ -6 30. $\dfrac{(-14)(6)}{-3}$ 28

31. $\dfrac{10}{-1}$ -10 32. $\dfrac{20}{-1}$ -20 33. $\dfrac{-10}{-1}$ 10

34. $\dfrac{-20}{1}$ $\quad$ −20 $\qquad$ 35. $\dfrac{0}{10}$ $\quad$ 0 $\qquad$ 36. $\dfrac{20}{0}$ $\quad$ Undefined

37. $\dfrac{0}{-10}$ $\quad$ 0 $\qquad$ 38. $\dfrac{0}{20}$ $\quad$ 0 $\qquad$ 39. $\dfrac{10}{0}$ $\quad$ Undefined

40. $\dfrac{0}{-20}$ $\quad$ 0

For Problems 41 through 50, evaluate the expression for the given values of x.

41. $\dfrac{15}{x}$, if:

   a. x is 5; $\quad$ 3
   b. x is −3; $\quad$ −5
   c. x is 0. $\quad$ Undefined

42. $\dfrac{-45}{x}$, if:

   a. x is −5; $\quad$ 9
   b. x is 3; $\quad$ −15
   c. x is 0. $\quad$ Undefined

43. $\dfrac{x}{-30}$, if:

   a. x is 5; $\quad$ $-\frac{1}{6}$
   b. x is −3; $\quad$ $\frac{1}{10}$
   c. x is 0. $\quad$ 0

44. $-\dfrac{x}{15}$, if:

   a. x is −5; $\quad$ $\frac{1}{3}$
   b. x is 3; $\quad$ $-\frac{1}{5}$
   c. x is 0. $\quad$ 0

45. $\dfrac{45}{x^2}$, if:

   a. x is −3; $\quad$ 5
   b. x is 5; $\quad$ 1.8
   c. x is −1. $\quad$ 45

46. $\dfrac{75}{x^2}$, if:

   a. x is −5; $\quad$ 3
   b. x is 3; $\quad$ $8\frac{1}{3}$
   c. x is −1. $\quad$ 75

47. $\dfrac{x + 5}{x + 3}$, if:

   a. x is −2; $\quad$ 3
   b. x is 5; $\quad$ 1.25
   c. x is −3. $\quad$ Undefined

48. $\dfrac{x - 5}{x - 3}$, if:

   a. x is 5; $\quad$ 0
   b. x is 3; $\quad$ Undefined
   c. x is 0. $\quad$ $1\frac{2}{3}$

49. $\dfrac{5 - x}{3 - x}$, if:

   a. x is 2; $\quad$ 3
   b. x is 5; $\quad$ 0
   c. x is −3. $\quad$ $1\frac{1}{3}$

50. $\dfrac{3 - x}{5 - x}$, if:

   a. x is 6; $\quad$ 3
   b. x is 5; $\quad$ Undefined
   c. x is 3. $\quad$ 0

51. Explain why 0 has *no* reciprocal.

52. Explain why division by 0 is undefined, but division of 0 by a non-zero number is defined.

For Problems 53 and 54, write the reciprocal of each given number in the simplest possible form.

53. a. $7 \dfrac{1}{7}$ $\qquad$ b. 5/9 $\quad$ $\frac{9}{5}$ $\qquad$ c. $-\dfrac{2}{3}$ $\quad$ $-\frac{3}{2}$

    d. −1 $\quad$ −1 $\qquad\qquad$ e. 0.25 $\quad$ 4 $\qquad$ f. 0 $\quad$ None

In Problem 45, watch for the errors $\dfrac{1}{3} = .3$ and $\dfrac{5}{15} = 3$.

Problems 45 and 46 require students to realize that, for example, if −3 is substituted for x, they should write $(-3)^2$. Otherwise they may make the mistake $-3^2 = -9$, which is correct in itself but is not the answer to these questions.

For Problems 53 and 54, students should write just the answer. Be alert for incorrect statements such as $7 = \dfrac{1}{7}$.

51. There is no number such that $0 \cdot \text{number} = 1$.

52. Division *by* 0: $\dfrac{5}{0} = 5 \cdot \dfrac{1}{0}$, and $\dfrac{1}{0}$ is undefined. Division *of* 0: $\dfrac{0}{5} = 0 \cdot \dfrac{1}{5} = 0$, which *is* defined.

54.   a. 13 $\frac{1}{13}$ b. $1/3$ 3 c. $-\frac{3}{5}$ $-\frac{5}{3}$

d. 1 1 e. -0.5 -2 f. 0 None

For Problems 55 and 56, change the division to multiplication by the reciprocal.

55.   a. $x \div y$ $x \cdot \frac{1}{y}$ b. $\frac{a}{3}$ $a \cdot \frac{1}{3}$ c. $\frac{7}{p}$ $7 \cdot \frac{1}{p}$

d. $m \div \frac{2}{3}$ $m \cdot \frac{3}{2}$

56.   a. $k \div j$ $k \cdot \frac{1}{j}$ b. $4/t$ $4 \cdot \frac{1}{t}$ c. $\frac{c}{8}$ $c \cdot \frac{1}{8}$

d. $5 \div \frac{1}{x}$ $5x$

2-6 | COMMUTING AND ASSOCIATING

It is obvious that $5 + 3$ and $3 + 5$ are equal to each other because they each equal 8. The process of reversing the two terms in a sum is called *commuting* them.

DEFINITION

> **COMMUTE**
> To **commute** two numbers in an expression means to interchange their positions.

Since you can commute two terms in a sum without changing the answer, addition is said to be a *commutative* operation. So is multiplication. For example,

$$3 \cdot 7 \text{ and } 7 \cdot 3 \text{ each equal } 21.$$

CONCLUSION

> **COMMUTING TERMS AND FACTORS**
> You can commute the terms in a sum or the factors in a product. That is, if x and y are real numbers, then
> $$x + y = y + x \qquad x \cdot y = y \cdot x$$

Time: 3 days, including test

Chalkboard Examples:

First day:
1. Evaluate: $2 + 7 = 9$
   $7 + 2 = 9$
   $2 \times 7 = 14$
   $7 \times 2 = 14$
   Conclusion: Addition and multiplication can be commuted.

2. Evaluate: $2 - 8 = -6$
   $8 - 2 = 6$
   $2 \div 8 = 0.25$
   $8 \div 2 = 4$
   $2^8 = 256$
   $8^2 = 64$
   Conclusion: Subtraction, division, and exponentiation (raising to powers) *cannot* be commuted.

3. Evaluate: $(2 + 5) + 8 = 15$
   $2 + (5 + 8) = 15$
   $(2 \times 5) \times 8 = 80$
   $2 \times (5 \times 8) = 80$
   Conclusion: Addition and multiplication can be associated either way.

Not all operations are commutative. Commuting the numbers in a difference, a quotient, or a power *changes* the value of the expression.

Subtraction:

$$7 - 2 \qquad\qquad\qquad 2 - 7$$

$$= 5 \quad \longleftarrow \text{ Different! } \longrightarrow \quad = -5$$

Division:

$$6 \div 3 \qquad\qquad\qquad 3 \div 6$$

$$= 2 \quad \longleftarrow \text{ Different! } \longrightarrow \quad = 0.5$$

Power:

$$2^3 \qquad\qquad\qquad 3^2$$

$$= 8 \quad \longleftarrow \text{ Different! } \longrightarrow \quad = 9$$

Addition and multiplication are **binary** operations. This means that numbers are added or multiplied only *two* at a time. If a sum has three terms, such as

$$3 + 5 + 9,$$

it has been agreed to add in order from left to right. But the answer is the same no matter which order you add the terms.

$$(3 + 5) + 9 \qquad\qquad\qquad 3 + (5 + 9)$$

$$= 8 + 9 \qquad\qquad\qquad\qquad = 3 + 14$$

$$= 17 \quad \longleftarrow \text{ The same! } \longrightarrow \quad = 17$$

The process of grouping two numbers in an expression is called *associating* them.

DEFINITION

> **ASSOCIATE**
> To **associate** two of the numbers in an expression means to *group* them with parentheses (without changing their positions) so that the operation between them is done *first*.

Since you can associate any two terms in a sum without changing the answer, addition is said to be an *associative* operation. Multiplication is also an associative operation. For example,

4. Evaluate: $(20 - 10) - 2 = 8$
$\qquad\qquad 20 - (10 - 2) = 12$
$\qquad\qquad (20 \div 10) \div 2 = 1$
$\qquad\qquad 20 \div (10 \div 2) = 4$
$\qquad\qquad (3^2)^3 = 729$
$\qquad\qquad 3^{(2^3)} = 6561$

Conclusion: Subtraction, division, and exponentiation must be associated the way intended.

5. Simplify: $5 + 3x - 7$ Ans.: $3x - 2$
Note: The Oral Practice here is especially effective for getting students to say the words *commute* and *associate*.

Second Day:
Students put problems on the board. Make sure they say the words *commute* and *associate* as they present their solutions.

Assignments:

Day 1: 1–39 odd or 2–40 even
Day 2: Selected problems of opposite parity from the first assignment, including some from 41 through 50, in preparation for test.
Day 3: Following test, assign: Study Section 2–7; Work the examples, and Problems 1–7 odd or 2–8 even.

$$(2 \cdot 3) \cdot 5 \qquad\qquad 2 \cdot (3 \cdot 5)$$
$$= 6 \cdot 5 \qquad\qquad = 2 \cdot 15$$
$$= 30 \quad \longleftarrow \text{ The same! } \longrightarrow \quad = 30$$

CONCLUSION

> **ASSOCIATING TERMS AND FACTORS**
> You can associate any two terms in a sum or any two factors in a product. That is, if x, y, and z are real numbers, then
> $$(x + y) + z = x + (y + z)$$
> $$(x \cdot y) \cdot z = x \cdot (y \cdot z).$$

Again, subtraction, division, and raising to a power are *not* associative operations.

Subtraction:

$$(12 - 7) - 2 \qquad\qquad 12 - (7 - 2)$$
$$= 5 - 2 \qquad\qquad = 12 - 5$$
$$= 3 \quad \longleftarrow \text{ Different! } \longrightarrow \quad = 7$$

Division:

$$(24 \div 6) \div 2 \qquad\qquad 24 \div (6 \div 2)$$
$$= 4 \div 2 \qquad\qquad = 24 \div 3$$
$$= 2 \quad \longleftarrow \text{ Different! } \longrightarrow \quad = 8$$

Power:

$$(2^3)^2 \qquad\qquad 2^{(3^2)}$$
$$= 8^2 \qquad\qquad = 2^9$$
$$= 64 \quad \longleftarrow \text{ Different! } \longrightarrow \quad = 512$$

Commuting and associating can be used to simplify expressions containing variables. Any subtraction or division must be changed to addition or multiplication before you commute or associate.

Objective:
Be able to simplify expressions by commuting and associating.

Cover the answer as you work the example. Then uncover the answer to be sure you are right.

EXAMPLE 1

Simplify $3 + 2x + 7$.

- - - - -

	Think These Reasons
$3 + 2x + 7$	Write the given expression.
$= 2x + 3 + 7$	Commute the $2x$ and the 3.
$= \underline{2x + 10}$	Associate the 3 and the 7 and add.

Note: In the given expression, $2x$ is the variable term and 3 and 7 are constant terms. The idea is to commute and associate the *constant* terms to simplify the expression. If you like, you can commute and associate at the same time. The minimum you should write is the given expression and the answer.

EXAMPLE 2

Simplify $7 - x - 12$.

- - - - -   - - - - -

$7 - x - 12$	Write the given expression.
$= 7 + (-x) + (-12)$	Change subtracting to adding the opposite.
$= -x + 7 + (-12)$	Commute $-x$ and 7.
$= -x + (-5)$	Associate 7 and -12 and simplify.
$= \underline{-x - 5}$	Change adding the opposite back to subtracting.

Note: The form $-x - 5$ is considered to be simpler than $-x + (-5)$ because it has fewer symbols of inclusion.

EXAMPLE 3

Simplify $12x \cdot \frac{1}{4}$.

- - - - -   - - - - -

$12x \cdot \frac{1}{4}$	Write the given expression.
$= 12 \cdot \frac{1}{4} \cdot x$	Commute x and $\frac{1}{4}$.
$= \underline{\underline{3x}}$	Associate 12 and $\frac{1}{4}$ and simplify.

EXAMPLE 4

Simplify $\dfrac{-7x}{-7}$.

— — — — —   — — — — —

	Think These Reasons

$\dfrac{-7x}{-7}$ Write the given expression.

$= -7x \cdot \left(-\dfrac{1}{7}\right)$ Change dividing to multiplying by the reciprocal.

$= -\dfrac{1}{7} \cdot (-7x)$ Commute $-7x$ and $-\dfrac{1}{7}$.

$= 1 \cdot x$ Associate $-\dfrac{1}{7}$ and -7 and simplify.

$= \underline{\underline{x}}$ Replace $1 \cdot x$ with x.

Note: x is considered to be simpler than $1 \cdot x$. The expression $1 \cdot x$ equals x because 1 times any number equals that number.

ORAL PRACTICE

Tell what was done to transform the expression on the left to the one on the right.

EXAMPLES

Answers

i. $5 + x + 3 = 5 + (x + 3)$ i. Associate the x and the 3.

ii. $x - 7 = x + (-7)$ ii. Change subtracting 7 to adding -7.

iii. $x + (-7) = -7 + x$ iii. Commute the x and the -7.

A. Commute x and 5.
B. Commute x and 5.
C. Associate 3 and x.
D. Associate x and 6.
E. Commute 1 and $-x$.
F. Commute 3 and $-x$.
G. Associate 2 and 7.
H. Associate 4 and 5.

A. $5 + x = x + 5$ B. $x \cdot 5 = 5x$

C. $3 + x + 4 = (3 + x) + 4$ D. $5 + x + 6 = 5 + (x + 6)$

E. $1 + (-x) = -x + 1$ F. $3 + (-x) = -x + 3$

G. $(x + 2) + 7 = x + (2 + 7)$ H. $4 + (5 + x) = (4 + 5) + x$

I. $x \cdot 3 = 3x$

J. $x + 7 = 7 + x$

K. $3(4x) = (3 \cdot 4)x$

L. $2(6x) = (2 \cdot 6)x$

M. $x - 2 = x + (-2)$

N. $5 - x = 5 + (-x)$

O. $x - 3 = -3 + x$

P. $x - 9 = -9 + x$

Q. $x \div 4 = x \cdot \dfrac{1}{4}$

R. $\dfrac{x}{7} = x \cdot \dfrac{1}{7}$

S. $\dfrac{1}{4}(4x) = \left(\dfrac{1}{4} \cdot 4\right)x$

T. $\dfrac{1}{7}(7x) = \left(\dfrac{1}{7} \cdot 7\right)x$

U. $5 + x + 7 = x + 5 + 7$

V. $3 + x + 4 = x + 3 + 4$

W. $x + 5 + 7 = x + (5 + 7)$

X. $x + 3 + 4 = x + (3 + 4)$

Y. $5 + x - 7 = 5 - 7 + x$

Z. $4 - x + 6 = 4 + 6 - x$

I. Commute x and 3.
J. Commute x and 7.
K. Associate 3 and 4.
L. Associate 2 and 6.
M. Change subtracting 2 to adding -2.
N. Change subtracting x to adding $-x$.
O. Commute x and -3.
P. Commute x and -9.
Q. Change dividing by 4 to multiply by $\frac{1}{4}$.
R. Change dividing by 7 to multiply by $\frac{1}{7}$.
S. Associate $\frac{1}{4}$ and 4.
T. Associate $\frac{1}{7}$ and 7.
U. Commute 5 and x.
V. Commute 3 and x.
W. Associate 5 and 7.
X. Associate 3 and 4.
Y. Commute x and -7.
Z. Commute $-x$ and 6.

EXERCISE 2-6

For Problems 1 through 40, commute and associate the constants to simplify the expression as much as possible.

1. $4 + x + 3$ $x + 7$

2. $5 + x + 4$ $x + 9$

3. $6 + x + 7$ $x + 13$

4. $8 + x + 13$ $x + 21$

5. $5 + x - 3$ $x + 2$

6. $7 + x - 9$ $x - 2$

7. $-8 + x + 4$ $x - 4$

8. $-3 + x + 11$ $x + 8$

9. $15 - x + 9$ $24 - x$

10. $16 - x + 5$ $21 - x$

11. $6 - x - 37$ $-x - 31$

12. $12 - x - 15$ $-x - 3$

13. $-19 - x - 22$ $-x - 41$

14. $-2 - x - 71$ $-x - 73$

15. $9 - x - 9$ $-x$

16. $-13 - x + 13$ $-x$

17. $9 + 7x + 3$ $7x + 12$

18. $14 + 3x + 21$ $3x + 35$

19. $-18 - 3x + 7$ $-3x - 11$

20. $8 - 5x - 13$ $-5x - 5$

21. $5x \cdot 7$ $35x$

22. $7x \cdot 9$ $63x$

23. $(3x)(-8)$ $-24x$

24. $(5x)(-13)$ $-65x$

25. $20x \cdot \dfrac{1}{5}$ $4x$

26. $30x \cdot \dfrac{1}{6}$ $5x$

27. $-\dfrac{1}{8} \cdot 56x$ $-7x$

28. $-\dfrac{1}{3} \cdot 21x$ $-7x$

29. $9x \cdot \dfrac{1}{9}$ x

30. $\dfrac{1}{3}x \cdot 3$ x

Problem Notes:

Some students already will be able to simplify these expressions in their heads. If so, the minimum they can write is the given expression and the answer. However, when they present problems at the board, writing

$4 + x + 3$
$= x + 7,$

they should be able to say words such as, "I commuted the 4 next to the 3, associated them, and added."

31. $\dfrac{54x}{9}$ $6x$

32. $\dfrac{86x}{2}$ $43x$

33. $-88x \div 11$ $-8x$

34. $-18x \div 9$ $-2x$

35. $\dfrac{1000x}{-10}$ $-100x$

36. $\dfrac{100x}{-5}$ $-20x$

37. $-37x \div (-1)$ $37x$

38. $-x \div (-1)$ x

39. $\dfrac{-19x}{-19}$ x

40. $\dfrac{-25x}{-25}$ x

41. In $2 + 3x$, the multiplication must be done *before* the addition. Calvin *added* first!

42. Since subtraction does not commute, Phoebe must consider
$$-7 - x + 7$$
to be
$$-7 + (-x) + 7$$
before commuting. The $-$ sign goes along with the x, giving $-x$.

43. a. i. $6 + x + 7$
$= (6 + x) + 7$ Associate 6 and x.
$= (x + 6) + 7$ Commute 6 and x.
$= x + (6 + 7)$ Associate 6 and 7.
$= \underline{x + 13}$ Do the arithmetic.
ii. $6 + x + 7$
$= 6 + (x + 7)$ Associate x and 7.
$= 6 + (7 + x)$ Commute x and 7.
$= (6 + 7) + x$ Associate 6 and 7.
$= \underline{13 + x}$ Do the arithmetic.
b. Commute 13 and x in $13 + x$ to get $x + 13$.

44. a. i. $6x \cdot 7$
$= x \cdot 6 \cdot 7$ Commute 6 and x.
$= x(6 \cdot 7)$ Associate 6 and 7.
$= \underline{x \cdot 42}$ Do the arithmetic.
ii. $6x \cdot 7$
$= 6 \cdot 7 \cdot x$ Commute x and 7.
$= (6 \cdot 7)x$ Associate 6 and 7.
$= \underline{42x}$ Do the arithmetic.
b. Commute x and 42 in $x \cdot 42$ to get $42x$.

45. For example,
$(2 + 3) + 4 = 5 + 4 = 9$, and
$2 + (3 + 4) = 2 + 7 = 9$.
But $(2 - 3) - 4 = -1 - 4 = -5$, and
$2 - (3 - 4) = 2 - (-1) = 3$, not -5.

46. For example, $(2 \cdot 3) \cdot 4 = 6 \cdot 4 = 24$, and
$2 \cdot (3 \cdot 4) = 2 \cdot 12 = 24$.

But

$2 \div (3 \div 4) = 2 \div \dfrac{3}{4} = 2 \times \dfrac{4}{3} = \dfrac{8}{3}$;

but

$(2 \div 3) \div 4 = \dfrac{2}{3} \div 4 = \dfrac{2}{3} \cdot \dfrac{1}{4} = \dfrac{2}{12}$

$= \dfrac{1}{6}$, not $\dfrac{8}{3}$.

41. Calvin Butterball simplifies the expression $2 + 3x$. He associates the 2 and 3, gets $5x$, and loses points on a test. Tell Calvin what he did wrong.

42. Phoebe Small simplifies the expression $-7 - x + 7$ by commuting and associating the -7 and the 7, getting x for the answer. Explain to Phoebe what mistake she made.

43. You can simplify $6 + x + 7$ either of two ways.

i. $6 + x + 7$ ii. $6 + x + 7$
$= (6 + x) + 7$ $= 6 + (x + 7)$
$= (x + 6) + 7$ $= 6 + (7 + x)$
$= x + (6 + 7)$ $= (6 + 7) + x$
$= \underline{x + 13}$ $= \underline{13 + x}$

a. For each way, write each step and write what was done at that step. For instance, in the second line of the first way, you would write

$= (6 + x) + 7$ Associate the 6 and the x.

b. Tell in words how $13 + x$ (from the second way) can be transformed into $x + 13$ (from the first way).

44. You can simplify $6x \cdot 7$ either of two ways.

i. $6x \cdot 7$ ii. $6x \cdot 7$
$= x \cdot 6 \cdot 7$ $= 6 \cdot 7 \cdot x$
$= x(6 \cdot 7)$ $= (6 \cdot 7)x$
$= \underline{x \cdot 42}$ $= \underline{42x}$

a. For each way, write each step and write what was done at that step. For instance, in the second line of the first way, you would write

$= x \cdot 6 \cdot 7$ Commute the 6 and the x.

b. Tell in words how $x \cdot 42$ (from the first way) can be transformed into $42x$ (from the second way).

45. Give examples showing why addition *is* an associative operation but subtraction is *not*.

46. Give examples showing why multiplication *is* an associative operation but division is *not*.

47. Give examples showing why multiplication *is* a commutative operation but division is *not*.

48. Give examples showing why addition *is* a commutative operation but subtraction is *not*.

49. Give examples showing why raising to a power (*exponentiation*) is *not* a commutative operation.

50. Explain why raising to a power (*exponentiation*) is *not* an associative operation.

47. For example, $2 \cdot 3 = 6$, and $3 \cdot 2 = 6$ also. But $2 \div 3 = \frac{2}{3}$ and $3 \div 2 = 1.5$, not $\frac{2}{3}$.

48. For example, $2 + 3 = 5$ and $3 + 2 = 5$ also.
But $2 - 3 = -1$ and $3 - 2 = 1$, not -1.

49. For example, $2^3 = 8$, but $3^2 = 9$, not 8.

50. For example, $4^{(3^2)} = 4^9 = 262{,}144$, but $(4^3)^2 = 64^2 = 4096$.

2-7 | EQUATIONS THAT NEED TWO TRANSFORMATIONS

You have solved equations by adding (or subtracting) a number to (or from) each member. You have also solved equations by multiplying (or dividing) each member by a number. Some equations require *both* transformations. For example, to solve

$$\frac{1}{5}x + 4 = 13,$$

you would first subtract 4 from each member, getting

$$\frac{1}{5}x + 4 - 4 = 13 - 4$$

$$\frac{1}{5}x = 9.$$

From here on, the equation is just like those you have solved before. Multiplying each member by 5 gives

$$5 \cdot \frac{1}{5}x = 5 \cdot 9$$

$$\underline{x = 45}.$$

To make sure you are correct, you can check the solution by substituting the value of x into the left member of the original equation and showing that you get the right member for the answer.

Check: $\frac{1}{5}x + 4$

$= \frac{1}{5}(45) + 4$

$= 9 + 4$

$= 13$ Correct.

Time: 1 or 2 days

Chalkboard Examples:

Solve and check:
1. $3x + 7 = 25$ Ans.: $x = 6$
    Check: $3x + 7$
           $= 3(6) + 7$
           $= 25$

2. $25 = 10 - \frac{1}{5}x$ Ans.: $x = -75$
    Check: $10 - \frac{1}{5}x = \ldots = 25$

3. $5 - 7p = 33$ Ans.: $p = -4$
    Check: $5 - 7p = \ldots = 33$

4. $\frac{3}{5}x - 8 = 22$ Ans.: $x = 50$
    Check: $\frac{3}{5}x - 8 = \ldots = 22$

Assignments:

(Assumes 1–7 or 2–8 were assigned prior to starting this section.)
One day on section:
   11–29 odd or 12–30 even
Two days on section:
   Day 1: 2–20 even or 1–19 odd
   Day 2: 11–33 odd or 12–34 even

The secret to solving these equations is to do whatever is needed to get the variable *by itself* on one side of the equation.

Objective :

Be able to solve equations that require more than one transformation.

Cover up the answer at the dotted lines as you work these examples.

EXAMPLE 1

Solve and check: $2x + 3 = 19$.

– – – – –   – – – – –

$2x + 3 = 19$	Write the given equation.
$2x + 3 - 3 = 19 - 3$	Subtract 3 from each member.
$2x = 16$	Associate and do the operations.
$\dfrac{2x}{2} = \dfrac{16}{2}$	Divide each member by 2.
$\underline{x = 8}$	Do the operations.

Check:

$2x + 3$	
$= 2(8) + 3$	Substitute 8 for x.
$= 16 + 3$	Do the operations.
$= 19$ ✔	The "✔" shows that you have looked to see that the answer you get is the right member of the original equation.

EXAMPLE 2

Solve and check: $13 = 9 - \dfrac{1}{3}x$.

– – – – –   – – – – –

$13 = 9 - \dfrac{1}{3}x$	Write the given equation.
$13 - 9 = 9 - \dfrac{1}{3}x - 9$	Subtract 9 from each member.
$4 = -\dfrac{1}{3}x$	Do the operation on the left. Commute and associate 9 and -9 on the right.

$$-3 \cdot 4 = -3\left(-\frac{1}{3}x\right)$$ Multiply each member by -3.

$$\underline{\underline{-12 = x}}$$ Do the operation on the left. Associate -3 and $-\frac{1}{3}$ on the right.

Check: $9 - \frac{1}{3}x$

$$= 9 - \frac{1}{3}(-12)$$ Substitute -12 for x in the right member.

$$= 9 + 4$$ Do the operations.

$$= 13 \ \text{✔}$$ Show that you got the correct left member.

EXAMPLE 3

Solve and check: $5 - 3c = 17$.

– – – – –   – – – – –

$$5 - 3c = 17$$ Write the given equation. (The variable is c this time!)

$$5 - 3c - 5 = 17 - 5$$ Subtract 5 from each member.

$$-3c = 12$$ Do the operation on the right. Commute and associate 5 and -5 on the left. Remember $5 - 3c - 5$ is $5 - 3c + (-5)$.

$$\frac{-3c}{-3} = \frac{12}{-3}$$ Divide each member by -3.

$$\underline{\underline{c = -4}}$$ Do the arithmetic.

Check: $5 - 3c$

$$= 5 - 3(-4)$$ Substitute -4 for c in the left member.

$$= 5 - (-12)$$ Do the arithmetic.

$$= 17 \ \text{✔}$$ Correct!

EXAMPLE 4

Solve and check: $\frac{3}{2}x + 4 = -9$.

– – – – –   – – – – –

$$\frac{3}{2}x + 4 = -9$$ Write the given equation.

$$\frac{3}{2}x + 4 - 4 = -9 - 4$$ Subtract 4 from each member.

$$\frac{3}{2}x = -13 \qquad\qquad \text{Associate; do the arithmetic.}$$

$$\frac{2}{3} \cdot \frac{3}{2}x = \frac{2}{3} \cdot (-13) \qquad \text{Multiply each member by } \frac{2}{3}, \text{ the}$$

$$\textit{reciprocal of } \frac{3}{2}.$$

$$1 \cdot x = -\frac{26}{3} \qquad\qquad \text{Associate; multiply.}$$

$$x = -\frac{26}{3} \qquad\qquad 1 \cdot x = x.$$

Check: $\quad \dfrac{3}{2}x + 4$

A. Subtract 3 from each member.
B. Add 7 to each member.
C. Add 5 to each member.
D. Subtract 4 from each member.
E. Add 2 to each member.
F. Subtract 1 from each member.

$$= \frac{3}{2}\left(-\frac{26}{3}\right) + 4 \qquad \text{Substitute } -\frac{26}{3} \text{ for } x.$$

$$= -13 + 4 \quad \text{Multiply the fractions.}$$

$$= -9 \quad \text{✔ Correct!}$$

ORAL PRACTICE

Tell what transformation is to be done *first* for each equation.

EXAMPLE

$\dfrac{1}{4}x + 6 = 19 \qquad$ *Answer:* Subtract 6 from each member.

G. Multiply each member by 3.
H. Divide each member by 4.
I. Subtract 5 from each member.
J. Subtract 6 from each member.
K. Add 2 to each member.
L. Add 6 to each member.
M. Divide each member by 3.
N. Divide each member by 5.
O. Subtract 0.7 from each member.
P. Subt.act 4.6 from each member.
Q. Subtract $\frac{4}{7}$ to each member.
R. Add $\frac{2}{9}$ to each member.
S. Multiply each member by $\frac{3}{2}$.
T. Multiply each member by $\frac{4}{5}$.
U. Subtract 6 from each member.
V. Subtract 5 from each member.
W. Add 3 to each member.
X. Divide each member by -5.
Y. Multiply (or divide) each member by -1.
Z. Multiply (or divide) each member by -1.

A. $\dfrac{1}{5}x + 3 = 7$ **B.** $\dfrac{1}{8}x - 7 = 45$ **C.** $2x - 5 = 9$

D. $6x + 4 = 7$ **E.** $4c - 2 = -1$ **F.** $5p + 1 = -13$

G. $\dfrac{1}{3}x = 5$ **H.** $4x = 7$ **I.** $5 + 2x = 3$

J. $6 + 7x = 4$ **K.** $-2 + 3x = 8$ **L.** $-6 + 5x = 2$

M. $3x = 10$ **N.** $5x = 8$ **O.** $3x + 0.7 = 4$

P. $4.6 + 5x = -9$ **Q.** $3x + \dfrac{4}{7} = 9$ **R.** $5x - \dfrac{2}{9} = 1$

S. $\dfrac{2}{3}x = 5$ **T.** $\dfrac{5}{4}x = 2$ **U.** $6 - x = 4$

V. $5 - x = -7$ **W.** $-3 + 5x = 0$ **X.** $-5x = 1$

Y. $-x = 8$ **Z.** $-x = -\dfrac{2}{3}$

EXERCISE 2-7

Solve the following equations. Then check the solution by substituting it into one member and showing that you get the other member.

1. $\frac{1}{3}x + 5 = 7$ $x = 6$

2. $\frac{1}{5}x + 3 = 9$ $x = 30$

3. $\frac{1}{2}x - 8 = 3$ $x = 22$

4. $\frac{1}{4}x - 7 = 2$ $x = 36$

5. $5x + 4 = 39$ $x = 7$

6. $6x + 5 = 53$ $x = 8$

7. $3a - 7 = 26$ $a = 11$

8. $2r - 13 = 95$ $r = 54$

9. $-\frac{1}{6}x + 5 = 8$ $x = -18$

10. $-\frac{1}{3}x + 6 = 10$ $x = -12$

11. $-\frac{1}{4}x - 9 = 17$ $x = -104$

12. $-\frac{1}{2}x - 7 = 23$ $x = -60$

13. $13 - 4y = 25$ $y = -3$

14. $5 - 3t = 56$ $t = -17$

15. $8 - \frac{1}{7}v = -19$ $v = 189$

16. $11 - \frac{1}{9}d = -45$ $d = 504$

17. $53 = 5x + 11$ $8.4 = x$

18. $22 = 4 + 5x$ $3.6 = x$

19. $17 - x = 25$ $x = -8$

20. $15 - x = 41$ $x = -26$

21. $71 = 4 - x$ $-67 = x$

22. $13 = 17 - x$ $4 = x$

23. $\frac{2}{3}x + 6 = 18$ $x = 18$

24. $\frac{3}{4}x + 12 = 36$ $x = 32$

25. $0.9 + 3x = 6$ $x = 1.7$

26. $1.6 + 4x = 8$ $x = 1.6$

27. $-21 + 4p = 10$ $p = 7.75$

28. $-8 + 3f = 6$ $f = 4\frac{2}{3}$

29. $-\frac{4}{3} - x = -\frac{1}{3}$ $x = -1$

30. $-\frac{2}{5} - x = \frac{1}{5}$ $x = -\frac{3}{5}$

31. Faye Doubt transforms $5 - x = 11$ by subtracting 5 from each member, getting $x = 6$. Explain to Faye what she did wrong.

32. Ann X. Kewse solves $-3 - 4x = 8$ by adding 3 to each member, getting $4x = 11$. Explain to Ann what she did wrong.

33. Noah Vail transforms $3 + 4x = 21$ by associating the 3 and the 4, getting $7x = 21$. Tell Noah why he is wrong.

34. Iddy Ottic transforms $13 - 3x = 40$ by associating the 13 and the -3, getting $10x = 40$. Tell Iddy why what he did violates the order of operations.

Problem Notes:

This is the first time students have been asked to check their solutions. The format chosen for the check reinforces the concept of evaluating an expression as the inverse of the process of solving an equation. Present the check as an *opportunity* rather than a chore!

In problems such as 13, where $13 - 4y = 25$, the most common error is losing the $-$ sign in front of $-4y$ when subtracting 13 from each member. A mathematically honest way to explain what happens is to point out that subtraction does not commute or associate. Therefore, in

$13 - 4y - 13 = 25 - 13$

the subtraction must be changed to adding the opposite,

$13 + (-4y) + (-13) = 25 - 13$

before the left member can be simplified. Eventually, students should learn that the $-$ sign always goes along with the term to its right.

In Problem 21, for example, $71 = 4 - x$, subtracting 4 produces $67 = -x$. Students often stumble here till they realize first that they are not yet finished and second that the coefficient of x is -1. The last step is either multiplying or dividing by -1.

31. Faye forgot the $-$ sign in front of the x in $5 - x = 11$.

32. Ann forgot the $-$ sign in front of the $4x$ in $-3 - 4x = 8$.

33. Noah *added* before *multiplying* in $3 + 4x = 21$.

34. Iddy *subtracted* before *multiplying* in $13 - 3x = 40$.

2-8 | PROBLEMS THAT LEAD TO TWO-TRANSFORMATION EQUATIONS

Time: 5 days

Chalkboard Examples:

Day 1:
Gasoline Problem—A local gas station charges $1.10 per gallon (you may substitute a more current number) if you also pay $4.00 for a car wash.

a. Define a variable for the number of gallons you buy, then write an expression for the total number of dollars you pay.
   Ans.: x = no. of gallons (Students should write this.)
   $1.1x + 4$ = no. of dollars

b. How much, total, would you pay if you bought:
   i. 12 gallons;
      Ans.: $17.20
   ii. 20 gallons?
      Ans.: $26.00
      (Technique: Evaluate an expression.)

c. Suppose that your total bill was $13.57. How many gallons of gas did you get?
   Ans.: $1.1x + 4 = 13.57$
   $x = 8.7$
   8.7 gallons

Then have students do Exercise 2–8, Problem 2, in class.

Subsequent days: Homework problems or selected problems from Exercise 2–8.

Assignments:

Day 1: 1 and 3 (Note that it is better at first to assign just one or two problems and have students do a good job on those rather than overwhelming them with many problems.

Day 2: Classwork: Problem 4
       Homework: Problems 5, 6, and perhaps 7

Day 3: Select one problem for classwork and 3 more for homework.

Day 4: Select one problem for classwork and 3 more for homework.

Day 5: Work on Exercise 2–9 in preparation for test.

Now that you know how to solve slightly tougher equations, you can use these equations to solve more complicated problems.

Suppose that it takes 4 minutes to cook a batch of pancakes. Cooking 3 batches would take $4 \cdot 3$ minutes, or 12 minutes. Cooking x batches would take $4x$ minutes. In each case, you multiply the number of batches by 4. However, it usually takes some time beforehand to mix the batter and warm up the pan. If it takes 10 minutes to do these things, then the total time would be

$$4x + 10 \text{ min.}$$

In this expression, x is the number of batches. To find the time for 7 batches, you would substitute 7 for x.

$$4x + 10$$
$$= 4 \cdot 7 + 10$$
$$= 28 + 10$$
$$= 38$$

$$\underline{38 \text{ minutes}}$$

To find out how many batches you could cook in 30 min, you set $4x + 10$ equals 30 and solve the equation for x.

$$4x + 10 = 30$$
$$4x + 10 - 10 = 30 - 10$$
$$4x = 20$$
$$\frac{4x}{4} = \frac{20}{4}$$
$$x = 5$$

$$\underline{5 \text{ batches}}$$

The key to solving problems like this is to let a variable stand for one quantity, such as the number of batches. Then you write an expression for a related quantity, such as the number of minutes. The problem can then be answered either by evaluating the expression or by solving an equation.

Objective :
Be able to write an expression representing a variable quantity and use this expression to answer questions.

For the following example, put a piece of paper along the dotted lines to cover the answer. Work each part. Then uncover the answer to be sure you are right.

EXAMPLE

Pedalboat Problem   Flo Tilla is pedalboating on the lake. She starts back toward the dock, which is 800 yards away. She goes at a rate of 50 yd per minute toward the dock.

a.   Draw a picture showing the place Flo starts, the dock 800 yards away, and Flo somewhere in between.

b.   How far has Flo gone after:

   i.   1 minute;   ii.   2 minutes;   iii.   5 minutes?

c.   How far is Flo from the dock after:

   i.   1 minute;   ii.   2 minutes;   iii.   5 minutes?

d.   Let x be the number of minutes since Flo started for the dock. Write an expression in terms of x for:

   i.   the distance Flo has gone;

   ii.   the distance she is from the dock.

   Write these expressions on the diagram.

e.   Write an equation stating that Flo has reached a point 150 yards from the dock. Then solve the equation to find out *when* she is 150 yards from the dock.

– – – –   – – – – –

a.

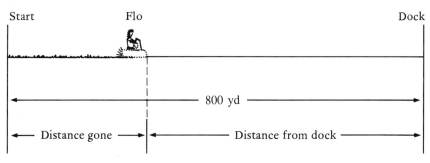

– – – –   – – – – –

Think These Reasons

b.   i.   50 yards   She goes 50 yd *per minute*.

   ii.   50(2) = 100   She goes 50(2) yd in 2 min.
         100 yards   Write the answer.

iii. $50(5) = 150$
        250 yards

She goes $50(5)$ yd in 5 min.
Write the answer.

_ _ _ _ _   _ _ _ _ _

c.   i. $800 - 50 = 750$

There were 800 yards to go, and
she has gone 50 yards. So
there are still $800 - 50$ yards
left to go.

          750 yards

Write the answer.

    ii. $800 - 100 = 700$
          700 yards

    iii. $800 - 250 = 550$
          550 yards

_ _ _ _ _   _ _ _ _ _

d.   i. x = number of minutes
           $50x$ = number of yards gone

Write the definition of x.
She goes $50(x)$ yards in x
minutes.

    ii. $800 - 50x$ = number of
                     yards from
                     dock

She has already gone $50x$ of the
800 yards. So $800 - 50x$ is
left.

_ _ _ _ _   _ _ _ _ _

e. $800 - 50x = 150$

Write an equation.

     $800 - 50x - 800 = 150 - 800$

Subtract 800 from each member.

              $-50x = -650$

Commute, associate, and do the
operations.

$$\frac{-50x}{-50} = \frac{-650}{-50}$$

Divide each member by -50.

                $x = 13$

Do the operations.

After 13 minutes.

Answer the question.

Note that the distance Flo travels, $50x$, is her *rate* multiplied by her *time*.
This is an example of the *distance-rate-time formula*.

FORMULA

> **DISTANCE-RATE-TIME FORMULA**
>
> $$\text{Distance} = (\text{rate})(\text{time})$$
>
> or
>
> $$d = rt$$

ORAL PRACTICE

Give an expression representing each of the following.

EXAMPLE

Spend $50 per day for x days, plus $230. How much do you spend?
Answer: $50x + 230$

A. Make 5 dollars per hour for x hours, plus $7.50. How many dollars
    do you make? $5x + 7.50$

B. Spend 65 cents per carton of milk for x cartons of milk, plus 80
    cents. How many cents do you spend? $65x + 80$

C. Go 40 miles per hour for x hours, then go 70 miles further. How
    many miles have you gone? $40x + 70$

D. Fly 600 miles per hour for x hours, then fly 1000 miles further. How
    many miles have you flown? $600x + 1000$

E. Earn $6 per hour for x hours, then pay back $10. How much do you
    have? $6x - 10$ dollars

F. Go 80 feet per minute for x minutes, then go back 30 feet. How
    many feet are you from where you started? $80x - 30$

G. Start with 50 grapes and eat 3 grapes per minute for x minutes. How
    many grapes are left? $50 - 3x$

H. Start with 100 quarters and spend 2 quarters per minute for x
    minutes. How many quarters are left? $100 - 2x$

I. Start 20 miles from home. Walk 4 miles per hour toward home for x
    hours. How far are you from home? $20 - 4x$ miles

J. Start 20 miles from home. Ride your bike 9 miles per hour away
    from home for x hours. How far are you from home? $20 + 9x$ miles

For Problems I and J, the *units* must be given since the question says "How far . . . " rather than "How many units . . . ."

EXERCISE 2-8

Problem Notes:

The problems here are broken down into easy steps involving writing an expression then using it in both directions to evaluate the expression and solve for x. Thus, the problems tie together the two most fundamental concepts of the course.

x donuts
20 cents each

15 cents for the box

1. b. iii. You must assume that the box is big enough to hold 100 donuts.

x cubic feet
$ .50 each

Plus $6.00 to deliver.

Spend enough time on this section so that students can get over any fear they still may have of word problems. If you do, you and your students will be rewarded with a better understanding later on in the course when the problems are less structured.

BILL

x hr. @ $42/hr. . . _____

Service . . . . . . _____

Total . . . . _____

1. *Donuts Problem*   Drenchin Donuts sells donuts for 20 cents each, plus 15 cents for the box in which they come. So the total number of cents you pay is 20 times the number of donuts, plus 15. Let x be the number of donuts.
   a. Write the definition of x on your paper. Then write an expression for the number of cents you pay for x donuts. $20x + 15$
   b. How much will you pay for:
      i.   12 donuts; $2.55
      ii. 100 donuts? $20.15
      iii. What assumption must you make about the box in order for the answer to (ii) to be reasonable?
   c. Write an equation stating that the number of cents you pay is 355. Then solve the equation to find out how many donuts you get for $3.55.   17 donuts

2. *Delivery Problem*   Bill Dupp's Lumber Yard charges $.50 for each cubic foot (ft^3) of sand you buy, plus $6.00 to deliver the sand. So the total number of dollars you pay is 0.50 times the number of cubic feet, plus 6. Let x be the number of cubic feet.
   a. Write the definition of x on your paper. Then write an expression for the number of dollars you pay for x ft^3 of sand, delivered. $0.5x + 6$
   b. How much would you pay to get 258 ft^3 delivered? $135
   c. Write an equation stating that you pay $17.50 to get x ft^3 of sand delivered. Then solve the equation for x.   23 ft^3
   d. How much sand could you get, delivered, for $100?   188 ft^3

3. *Plumbers' Wages Problem*   Drane & Route Plumbing Co. charges $42 per hour, plus $35 for the service call. Let x be the number of hours they work.
   a. Write the definition of x. Then write an expression for the number of dollars you must pay if they work for x hours. $42x + 35$
   b. How much would you pay for:
      i.   3 hours; $161   ii. $4\frac{1}{2}$ hours? $224
   c. Write an equation stating that the amount you pay is $140. Then solve the equation to find out how long they worked. $2\frac{1}{2}$ hours
   d. How long did they work if the bill is $56? $\frac{1}{2}$ hour

4. *Taxi Fare Problem* When the meter in a taxi is first turned on, it reads $1.20. As the taxi travels, $1.60 is added for each mile driven. Let x be the number of miles driven.

Problems 1–6 ask the students to write the definition of x on their papers. They also should write words describing the expression. This way they can quickly find out which is which in later parts of the problem. Later problems do not call for them to write the definition of x, but they are expected to do it without being told.

   a. Write the definition of x. Then write an expression for the number of dollars the meter reads after x mi. $1.20 + 1.60x$
   b. How much would you pay to ride:
       i. 5 mi; $9.20   ii. 13 mi? $22.00
   c. Write an equation stating that you paid $12.40. Then solve the equation to find out how far you rode.   7 miles
   d. How far could you ride for $33.20?   20 miles

5. *Dump Truck Problem* Doug Upp must shovel a pile containing 50 ft^3 of sand into a dump truck. With each scoop, he decreases the size of the pile by $\frac{1}{6}$ ft^3. Let x be the number of scoops he has shoveled.
   a. Write the definition of x. Then write an expression for the number of cubic feet of sand left in the pile after x scoops. $50 - \frac{1}{6}x$
   b. How much sand is left after:
       i. 12 scoops; 48 ft^3 ii. 100 scoops? $33\frac{1}{3}$ ft^3
   c. Doug takes a rest when 20 ft^3 of sand remain. Write an equation stating that 20 ft^3 remain. Then solve the equation to find out how many scoops Doug has shoveled before he rests.   180 scoops

6. *Gasoline Consumption Problem* Suppose that the gas tank of a car holds 12 gallons, and that the car uses $\frac{1}{20}$ of a gallon per mile. Let x be the number of miles the car has gone since the tank was filled.
   a. Write the definition of x. Then write an expression for the number of gallons left after x miles. $12 - \frac{1}{20}x$
   b. How many gallons are left after:
       i. 100 mi; 7 gal   ii. 170 mi? $3\frac{1}{2}$ gal
   c. Write an equation stating that 5 gallons are left. Then solve it to find out how far the car has gone when 5 gallons remain.   140 mi
   d. How far has the car gone when it runs out of gas?   240 mi

7. *Food Consumption Problem* According to studies conducted during World War II, a working person consumes 30 fewer calories (cal) per day for each 1° rise in the Celsius temperature. Suppose that a person consumes 3600 cal per day at 0°C.

Problem 7 uses the fact that more food must be consumed in cold weather to make up for loss of body heat to the surroundings.

   a. How many calories would the person consume at:
       i. 1°C; 3570 cal
       ii. 5°C; 3450 cal
       iii. T°C, where T is a variable? $3600 - 30T$ cal

b. Evaluate the expression you wrote in (iii) of part (a) if:
    i. *T* is 21; 2970 cal   ii. *T* is −10. 3900 cal
c. Write an equation stating that the consumption is 2400 cal. Then solve it to find the temperature. 40°C
d. At what temperature would the person consume 4200 cal? −20°

Problem 8—You may need to explain to students what an expansion gap is and why it gets *smaller* as the bridge expands.

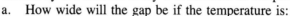

→ ||← Gap width

8. *Expansion Gap Problem* When bridges are built in expressways, a small gap is left between the bridge sections so that the bridge will have room to expand. That is why a car goes "bump-bump, bump-bump" as it goes across a bridge. As the temperature goes up, the bridge sections expand and the width of the gap goes down. Suppose that the gap is 21 millimeters (mm) at a temperature of 0°C and decreases by 0.4 mm for every 1°C increase in temperature.
    a. How wide will the gap be if the temperature is:
        i. 1°C; 20.6 mm   ii. 5°C; 19 mm
        iii. *T*°C? $21 - 0.4T$ mm
    b. Evaluate the expression you wrote in (iii) of part (a) if:
        i. *T* is 30; 9 mm   ii. *T* is 17; 14.2 mm
        iii. *T* is −10. 25 mm
    c. Write an equation which says that the gap is 7 mm. Then find the temperature at which the gap is 7 mm. 35°C
    d. At what temperature will the gap be:
        i. 23 mm; −5°   ii. completely closed? 52.5°C

9. *Weight Reduction Problem* Calvin Butterball weighs 250 pounds. He goes on a diet and loses 3 pounds per week.
    a. Write an expression representing his weight after *x* weeks. $250 - 3x$
    b. Find his weight after:
        i. 7 weeks; 229 lb   ii. 1 year. 94 lb
    c. How long will it take for him to get down to:
        i. 160 pounds; 30 weeks   ii. 150 pounds? $33\frac{1}{3}$ weeks
    d. What assumption do you have to make in order for the answers to parts (b) and (c) to be meaningful? He must keep losing at the same rate for the answers to be meaningful.

10. *Weight Increase Problem* Phoebe Small weighs 97 pounds. She goes on an eating spree, gaining $\frac{1}{4}$ pound per day.
    a. Write an expression representing her weight after *x* days. $97 + \frac{1}{4}x$
    b. How much will she weigh after:
        i. 12 days; 100 lb   ii. 4 weeks? 104 lb
    c. How long will it take her to reach:
        i. 150 pounds; 212 days   ii. 160 pounds? 252 days

11. a.

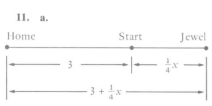

Home   Start   Jewel

11. *Cycling Problem Number 1* Jewel Case is at a point 3 miles from her home. She rides her bike at $\frac{1}{4}$ mile per minute *away* from home.
    a. Draw a picture showing home, Jewel's starting point 3 miles from home, and Jewel some distance *beyond* the starting point.

b. Jewel rides for *x* minutes. Write expressions for:
   i. the number of miles Jewel has ridden (recall that distance = (rate)(time)); $\frac{1}{4}x$
   ii. the number of miles Jewel is away from home. $3 + \frac{1}{4}x$
   Write these expressions on your diagram.
c. How far is Jewel from home after:
   i. 20 minutes; 8 mi
   ii. 1 hour? 18 mi
d. When will she be 10 miles from home? 28 min

12. **Cycling Problem Number 2** Justin Case (Jewel's brother) is at a point 3 miles from home. He starts riding his bike at $\frac{1}{4}$ mile per minute *toward* home.

12. a.

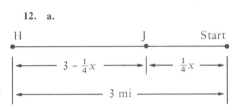

   a. Draw a picture showing home, Justin's starting point 3 miles from home, and Justin somewhere *between* start and home.
   b. Justin rides for *x* minutes. Write expressions for:
      i. the number of miles he has ridden (recall that distance = (rate)(time)); $\frac{1}{4}x$
      ii. the number of miles he is away from home. $3 - \frac{1}{4}x$
      Write these expressions on your diagram.
   c. How far is he from home after 8 minutes? 1 mi
   d. When will he be:
      i. $\frac{1}{2}$ mile from home; 10 min
      ii. at home? 12 min

13. **Downhill Speed Problem** As you coast downhill on your bike, you find that the speed increases by $\frac{2}{3}$ mi/h each second. When you are going 12 mi/h you start a stopwatch.
    a. Define a variable for the number of seconds that have passed since you started the stopwatch. Then write an expression for the speed you are going. $12 + \frac{2}{3}x$
    b. How fast will you be going after 15 sec? 22 mi/h
    c. What will the stopwatch read when you are going 18 mi/h? 9 sec
    d. How long *before* you started the stopwatch did you start coasting down the hill? 18 sec before

14. **Celsius and Fahrenheit Temperature Problem** To convert Celsius temperature to Fahrenheit temperature, you multiply the Celsius temperature by $\frac{9}{5}$, then add 32. Let *C* be the number of Celsius degrees.
    a. Write an expression representing the number of Fahrenheit degrees. $\frac{9}{5}C + 32$
    b. Find the Fahrenheit temperature for:
       i. 35° Celsius; 95°F
       ii. −20° Celsius. −4°F
    c. Write and solve equations to find *C* if the Fahrenheit temperature is:
       i. 59°; 15°C
       ii. 14°. −10°C

15. **Temperature Inside the Earth Problem** The temperature inside the earth is assumed to increase by about 10° Celsius for every kilometer

Problem 15—Some students wonder why caves are often cold if the temperature increases with depth. The reason is because caves stay near the *average* yearly surface temperature, which is usually colder than the good weather in which most people visit caves. Temperatures at the bottom of deep oil wells are hot enough to cause very viscous oil to flow easily.

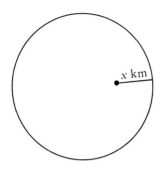

x km

beneath the surface. Suppose that the temperature at the surface is 24°C. Let x be the number of kilometers beneath the surface.

a.   Write an expression for the number of degrees at a depth of x kilometers. $24 + 10x$

b.   Find the temperature inside a coal mine 1.3 kilometers deep.   37°C

c.   Find the temperature at the bottom of an oil well 5 km deep.   74°C

d.   Write an equation stating that the temperature at the bottom of a diamond mine is 61°C. Then solve the equation to find the depth of the mine.   3.7 km

e.   At what depth would water boil (100°C)?   7.6 km

2-9   CHAPTER REVIEW AND TEST

Time: 1 day

Test Suggestions:

You might consider giving a test that consists exclusively of word problems. The knowledge that the test will be this way can motivate students to learn to do the problems. Some might otherwise feel they could score enough to pass the test without mastering these problems. The best kind of problem is the kind you make up yourself, involving local situations with which students are familiar. Some teachers even use their students' names on the test.

Assignment:

Following the test, study Section 3–1 and work all ten problems in Exercise 3–1.

In this chapter you have studied negative numbers. You added, subtracted, multiplied, and divided them, solved equations with them, and used them for such things as time *before* the present and temperatures *colder* than zero.

You also extended your equation-solving ability to equations like

$$7 + 5x = 3,$$

where *two* transformations are needed. You subtracted 7 from each member:

$$7 + 5x - 7 = 3 - 7.$$

Then you used the definition of subtraction to write

$$7 + 5x + (-7) = 3 - 7.$$

Then you *commuted* and *associated* the 7 and −7, and added them (getting 0); this left

$$5x = -4.$$

From here on it was an old problem. Dividing each member by 5 gave

$$x = -0.8.$$

You should now be able to appreciate the meaning of the word *algebra,* the "science of reduction and comparison." To solve a new problem, you *reduce* it to an old problem!

One thing you should teach yourself is how to review for a test. Something to try is making a list of key words. Before you attempt to work the following test, skim through the chapter and write down any word that sounds important. After you have made the list, write a phrase telling what each word means. For instance, if you have written

commute,

you might say:

to switch the numbers in a sum or a product.

If you cannot think of what to say, go back and look up the word. The index at the back of the book may help you locate the word.

The following test should take you about 45 minutes. For the most realistic practice, try putting yourself under "test conditions" and working the whole test without stopping. See if you really *can* do it in 45 minutes!

CHAPTER TEST

T1.   What is the difference in meaning in each case?
   a.   Negative number and positive number.
   b. -2^4 and $(-2)^4$.
   c. $\dfrac{5}{0}$ and $\dfrac{0}{5}$.
   d.   Commute and associate.
   e. $0 \cdot x$ and $1 \cdot x$.

T2.   Write each of the following.
   a.   The definition of integer.
   b.   The definition of real number.
   c.   The definition of subtraction.
   d.   The definition of division.
   e.   The multiplication property of -1.

T3.   Answer the following questions.
   a.   Is a negative number a real number? Explain.
   b.   Why does 0 have no reciprocal?
   c.   How many members does the equation $5 + 8x + 7 = 12$ have?
   d.   Write an equation relating rate, distance, and time.
   e.   Why is subtraction *not* associative?
   f.   Why is division *not* commutative?
   g.   Why must there be parentheses in $5 + (-3)$?

T4.   Evaluate each expression.
   a. $\dfrac{-52}{-4}$ 13
   b. -2^4 -16

T1.   a. A negative number is less than 0. A positive number is greater than 0.
   b. $-2^4 = -(2)(2)(2)(2) = -16$. $(-2)^4 = (-2)(-2)(-2)(-2) = 16$.
   c. $5/0$ is not a real number. $0/5$ equals zero.
   d. Commute means switch positions. Associate means group together (without switching positions).
   e. $0 \cdot x = 0$, and $1 \cdot x = x$.

T2.   a. An integer is a positive, negative, or zero whole number, ... $-3, -2, -1, 0, 1, 2, 3, ...$
   b. A real number is any number on the number line.
   c. $x - y = x + (-y)$.
   d. $x \div y = x \cdot \dfrac{1}{y}$.
   e. $-1 \cdot x = -x$.

T3.   a. Negative nos. *are* real nos. because they can be graphed on a number line.
   b. 0 has no reciprocal because there is no number that can be multiplied by 0 to give 1 for the answer.
   c. $5 + 8x + 7 = 12$ has 2 members, a left one and a right one.
   d. $d = rt$.
   e. Subtraction is *not* associative because, for example, $(2 - 3) - 4 = -1 - 4 = -5$, while $2 - (3 - 4) = 2 - (-1) = 3$.
   f. Division is *not* commutative because, for example, $12 \div 3 = 4$, but $3 \div 12 = \dfrac{1}{4}$.
   g. Operation and sign must be separated.

c. $(-2)^4$ 16   d. $(-2)^3$ -8

e. $(-2)(-3)(-4)$ -24 f. $(-1)(-5)(6)$ 30

g. $(-3)^2(-4)^3$ -576 h. $20 - (-3)$ 23

i. $20 - 60$ -40 j. $-6 - 8$ -14

k. $-9 - (-3 + 5)$ -11 l. $|-4|$ 4

m. $|4 - 7|$ 3

T5. Evaluate each expression if $x = -3$.

     a. $-x$ 3   b. x^2 9   c. x^3 -27

     d. $-x^2$ -9 e. $7x^2$ 63   f. $4x^2 - 5x$ 51

T6. Simplify by commuting and associating the constants.

     a. $-13 - 7x - 8$ $-21 - 7x$ b. $(4x)(-9)$ $-36x$

     c. $50x \cdot \dfrac{1}{5}$ $10x$

T7. Solve and check.

     a. $9 - 7x = 51$ $x = -6$ b. $13 = 25 - \dfrac{1}{4}x$ $48 = x$

     c. $5t + 34 = -9$ $t = -8.6$

T8. *Fried Chicken Problem*   A fried-chicken dealer makes boxes of chicken with various numbers of pieces. He charges 40 cents for each piece of chicken, plus a fixed charge of 55 cents for the box, the rolls, the service, and so on.

     a. Write an expression for the number of cents charged for a box containing x pieces of chicken. $40x + 55$

     b. Write an equation stating that a box containing x pieces costs $3.35. Then solve the equation to find the number of pieces in the box.   7 pieces

     c. How much would you pay for:

         i. a 5-piece box; $2.55   ii. a dozen-piece box? $5.35

Problem Notes:

Problem T9 involves a practical situation, slope of a hill, in which negative values of the variable are meaningful.

T9. *Speed on a Hill Problem*   On level ground (0 degrees slope), a car can go a top speed of 132 kilometers per hour (km/h). For each degree of uphill slope, the top speed is *decreased* by 11 km/h.

     a. Write an expression for the top speed on an uphill slope of x degrees. $132 - 11x$

     b. How fast can the car go on an uphill slope of 7 degrees?   55 km/h

     c. A 3 degree *down*hill slope can be thought of as a -3 degree *up*hill slope. How fast could the car go on a 3 degree downhill slope?   165 km/h

     d. Write an equation stating that the top speed is 187 km/h. Then solve it to find out how steep the hill is. Is it an *up*hill or a *down*hill slope? Explain.   5 degrees *down*hill, because value of x is negative.

     e. If the top speed is 0 km/h, the hill is so steep that the car cannot go up it. How steep would that be?   12 degrees

3

Distributing:
Axioms and
Other Properties

You have learned what it means to commute and associate numbers in a sum or product. In this chapter you will learn other properties for transforming expressions. Some of the properties, called axioms, *are assumed to be true without proof. Other properties can be proved by starting with the axioms. In the next chapter these properties will be used to reduce complicated expressions and equations to simpler ones you already know how to evaluate and solve.*

Expression:
$3(x - 7)$
Expression transformed by distributing:
$3x - 21$

3-1 | DISTRIBUTING

Time: $\frac{1}{2}$ day, with Section 3–2

Chalkboard Examples:

See Section 3–2 for examples for both sections.

Assignment:

All ten problems already should have been assigned following the Chapter 2 test in preparation for your first class on Chapter 3. See assignments, Section 2–9.

This section is meant for you to read and work on your own before the topic is discussed in class.

According to the agreed-upon order of operations, expressions such as

$$5(4 + 7)$$

should be evaluated by doing the operation inside parentheses *first:*

$$5(4 + 7)$$
$$= 5 \cdot 11$$
$$= 55.$$

However, if the operation inside is addition and the operation outside is multiplication, there is another way to get the right answer. You can multiply *each* number inside the parentheses by 5 and then add the answers.

$$5(4 + 7)$$
$$= 5 \cdot 4 + 5 \cdot 7$$
$$= 20 + 35$$
$$= 55$$

To see why this result is reasonable, think of $(4 + 7)$ as the length of a rectangle and 5 as its width (see the figure). The area of the rectangle is its width times its length, or

$$5(4 + 7).$$

But the area of the largest rectangle is also the *sum* of the areas of the smaller rectangles,

$$5 \cdot 4 + 5 \cdot 7.$$

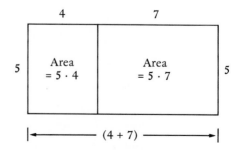

A 5 seems to be "passed out" to each number inside the parentheses. The 5 "goes over" the addition sign to get to the second term.

Goes over

$$5(4 + 7) = 5 \cdot 4 + 5 \cdot 7$$

Because of this property, multiplication is said to *distribute over addition*.

In algebra this property is most useful for simplifying expressions that contain variables, such as

$$3(x + 5) + 7.$$

The parentheses in $(x + 5)$ mean to do the addition *first*. But this is impossible until you know what number to substitute for x. However, you can *distribute* the 3 to the x and 5, getting

Distribute

$$3(x + 5) + 7$$

$= 3x + 3 \cdot 5 + 7$	Distribute 3 to x and 5.
$= 3x + 15 + 7$	Multiply before adding.
$= 3x + 22$	Associate 15 and 7.

The expression $3x + 22$ is *simpler* than the original expression.

Objective:

Be able to simplify expressions by distributing multiplication over addition.

Cover the answers as you work these examples.

EXAMPLE 1

Simplify $5(x + 2) + 9$.

- - - - -   - - - - -

	Think These Reasons
$5(x + 2) + 9$	Write the given expression.
$= 5x + 5 \cdot 2 + 9$	Distribute 5 to x and 2.
$= 5x + 10 + 9$	Multiply before adding.
$= 5x + 19$	Associate 10 and 9.

Think These Reasons

EXAMPLE 2

- - - - -   - - - - -

Simplify $4(3x + 7) - 50$.

$4(3x + 7) - 50$	Write the given expression.
$= 4 \cdot 3x + 4 \cdot 7 - 50$	Distribute 4 to $3x$ and 7.
$= 12x + 28 - 50$	Multiply before adding or subtracting.
$= \underline{\underline{12x - 22}}$	Associate the 28 and -50.

EXAMPLE 3

- - - - -   - - - - -

Simplify $7 + 3(2x + 8)$.

$7 + 3(2x + 8)$	Write the given expression.
$= 7 + 3 \cdot 2x + 3 \cdot 8$	Distribute 3 to $2x$ and 8.
$= 7 + 6x + 24$	Multiply before adding. (*Don't* add 7 and 3 before you multiply!)
$= \underline{\underline{6x + 31}}$	Commute and associate 7 and 24.

EXERCISE 3-1

Problem Notes:

Students who have worked the examples should have no trouble with the problems. Those who have not worked the examples may have trouble starting at Problem 5, where in $2(3x + 8) + 40$ they might do things like distributing the 2 to both the 3 and the x. In Problem 8, the unwary student may try $30 + 2(x + 8)$ by adding the 30 and the 2 first. In your follow-up presentation, you should be sure that they realize the order-of-operations requirement that multiplication must be done before addition.

Simplify by distributing, commuting, and associating.

1. $3(x + 5) + 11$ $\quad 3x + 26$
2. $4(x + 3) + 20$ $\quad 4x + 32$
3. $7(6 + x) + 8$ $\quad 7x + 50$
4. $5(3 + x) - 9$ $\quad 5x + 6$
5. $2(3x + 8) + 40$ $\quad 6x + 56$
6. $8(5x + 7) - 60$ $\quad 40x - 4$
7. $9(4 + 8x) - 6$ $\quad 72x + 30$
8. $30 + 2(x + 8)$ $\quad 2x + 46$
9. $100 + 6(4x + 9)$ $\quad 24x + 154$
10. $-15 + 9(5 + 8x)$ $\quad 72x + 30$

3-2   DISTRIBUTING MULTIPLICATION OVER SUBTRACTION

Time: $\frac{1}{2}$ day, with Section 3–1

Chalkboard Examples:

1. Distribute: $5(2x + 3)$ Ans.: $10x + 15$
   $-3(2 - 4x)$ Ans.: $-6 + 12x$

In the last section you learned that multiplication distributes over addition. For instance,

Distribute

$5(\overset{\frown}{x} + 3)$

$$= 5x + 5 \cdot 3$$

$$= 5x + 15$$

Multiplication also distributes over *subtraction*. For instance, the parentheses in $5(7 - 3)$ mean, "Subtract 3 from 7 and then multiply by 5." However, you get the same answer by distributing.

Operation in parentheses first	Distribute first.
$5(7 - 3)$	$5(7 - 3)$
$= 5(4)$	$= 5 \cdot 7 - 5 \cdot 3$
	$= 35 - 15$
$= 20$ ⟵ The same! ⟶ $= 20$	

The fact that multiplication distributes over addition and subtraction are called *properties*. Some properties are called *axioms*. An axiom is a property that is used as a starting point in the mathematics of real numbers. No attempt is made to *prove* an axiom. It is just assumed to be true.

DEFINITIONS

PROPERTY AND AXIOM

A **property** of a mathematical system is a fact that is true concerning that system.

An **axiom** is a property that forms the basis of a mathematical system. It is assumed to be true without proof.

The facts that multiplication distributes over addition and that multiplication distributes over subtraction are both *properties*. The first one is an *axiom* that is assumed to be true. The second one is not an axiom. It can be proved using the first one.

For future reference, here are formal statements of these two distributive properties.

THE DISTRIBUTIVE AXIOM

Multiplication distributes over addition.

That is, for real numbers x, y, and z,

$$x(y + z) = xy + xz.$$

---

2. Simplify: $-1(x - 5) - 7$ Ans.: $-x - 2$
   Note: $-x$ is simpler than $-1x$.
   $6 - 2(4x + 3)$ Ans.: $-8x$
   Note: Don't do $6 - 2$ first!
   Don't lose the $-$ sign in front of the $-8x$!

Assignment:

1–39 odd or 2–40 even

PROPERTY

> **MULTIPLICATION DISTRIBUTES OVER SUBTRACTION**
> For real numbers x, y, and z,
> $$x(y - z) = xy - xz.$$

Objective :
Be able to simplify expressions by distributing multiplication over addition and subtraction.

Cover the answers as you work these examples.

EXAMPLE 1

Distribute $3(4x - 2)$.

	Think These Reasons
$3(4x - 2)$	Write the given expression.
$= \underline{\underline{12x - 6}}$	Distribute 3 to $4x$ and 2. (Do the computation in your head!) Write the subtraction sign.

EXAMPLE 2

Simplify $5 + 4(7x - 6)$.

$5 + 4(7x - 6)$	Write the given expression.
$= 5 + 28x - 24$	Distribute 4 to $7x$ and 6. Write the subtraction sign.
$= \underline{\underline{28x - 19}}$	Commute; then associate 5 and -24.

EXAMPLE 3

Simplify $9 - 2(x - 4)$.

$9 - 2(x - 4)$	Write the given expression.
$= 9 - 2x + 8$	Think of $9 - 2(x - 4)$ as $9 + (-2)(x - 4)$. Distribute -2 to x and 4. Then rewrite $9 + (-2x) - (-8)$ as $9 - 2x + 8$.
$= \underline{\underline{17 - 2x}}$	Commute; then associate 9 and 8.

ORAL PRACTICE

Distribute the multiplication over the addition or subtraction.

EXAMPLES

Answers

i. $2(7 - 4)$
ii. $-3(6 - 4)$

i. $14 - 8$
ii. $-18 + 12$

A. $3(4 + 7)$ $12 + 21$

B. $6(3 + 8)$ $18 + 48$

C. $7(-9 + 3)$ $-63 + 21$

D. $9(-8 + 1)$ $-72 + 9$

E. $-4(2 + 10)$ $-8 - 40$

F. $-3(9 + 11)$ $-27 - 33$

G. $5(9 - 2)$ $45 - 10$

H. $4(7 - 2)$ $28 - 8$

I. $-4(3 - 10)$ $-12 + 40$

J. $-5(3 - 13)$ $-15 + 65$

K. $-2(-7 + 5)$ $14 - 10$

L. $-1(-6 - 8)$ $6 + 8$

EXERCISE 3-2

For Problems 1 through 20, distribute the multiplication over the addition or subtraction. Simplify, leaving no parentheses.

1. $3(x + 7)$ $3x + 21$

2. $8(x + 4)$ $8x + 32$

3. $7(3x - 8)$ $21x - 56$

4. $6(2x - 7)$ $12x - 42$

5. $x(3 + y)$ $3x + xy$

6. $x(5 + z)$ $5x + xz$

7. $-5(6 - x)$ $-30 + 5x$

8. $-2(11 - y)$ $-22 + 2y$

9. $-1(x - y)$ $-x + y$

10. $-1(a - b)$ $-a + b$

11. $x(x + 9)$ $x^2 + 9x$

12. $x(10 + x)$ $10x + x^2$

13. $6(9 + 7x)$ $54 + 42x$

14. $5(7x + 2)$ $35x + 10$

15. $\dfrac{1}{3}(12x - 15y)$ $4x - 5y$

16. $\dfrac{1}{6}(30x - 42y)$ $5x - 7y$

17. $28\left(\dfrac{1}{4}z + \dfrac{1}{7}\right)$ $7z + 4$

18. $24\left(\dfrac{1}{12} + \dfrac{1}{3}y\right)$ $2 + 8y$

19. $\dfrac{2}{3}\left(4x + \dfrac{3}{4}\right)$ $\dfrac{8}{3}x + \dfrac{1}{2}$

20. $\dfrac{3}{5}\left(2x - \dfrac{2}{3}\right)$ $\dfrac{6}{5}x - \dfrac{2}{5}$

Problem Notes:

For Problems 1–20, the minimum amount the students should write is the given expression, the answer, and an $=$ sign between them. The sooner they learn to leave out the middle step, the better. Middle steps should be put in only until students learn to do the work in their heads.

  Problems 9 and 10 have answers $-x + y$ and $-a + b$, respectively. Students should not leave answers in forms involving $-1 \cdot x$ or $-1 \cdot a$.

  Problems 15–20 and 39 and 40 are intended to drill students on operations with fractions.

For Problems 21 through 40, simplify the expression by distributing, commuting, and associating. Leave no parentheses.

21. $3(4x + 7) - 2$ $12x + 19$ 22. $5(3x + 2) - 7$ $15x + 3$

23. $7(3x - 5) + 20$ $21x - 15$ 24. $4(2x - 7) + 40$ $8x + 12$

25. $8(1 - 2x) + 5$ $13 - 16x$ 26. $9(4 - 5x) + 3$ $39 - 45x$

27. $-5(2 + 3x) + 7$ $-15x - 3$ 28. $-6(3 + 4x) + 8$ $-24x - 10$

29. $-1(x - 9) - 10$ $-x - 1$ 30. $-1(x - 2) - 7$ $-x - 5$

31. $4 + 3(2x - 9)$ $6x - 23$ 32. $7 + 3(5x - 1)$ $15x + 4$

33. $6 + 7(3x + 2) + 8$ $21x + 28$ 34. $10 + 2(6x + 3) + 4$ $12x + 20$

35. $8 - 5(4 - 6x)$ $30x - 12$ 36. $5 - 3(9 - 7x)$ $21x - 22$

37. $11 - 1(5x + 3)$ $8 - 5x$ 38. $21 - 1(3x + 8)$ $13 - 3x$

39. $7 + \dfrac{3}{5}(10 + 35x)$ $21x + 13$ 40. $11 + \dfrac{3}{2}(8 + 12x)$ $18x + 23$

Tell in words what was done.

41. $5(2x + 3) = 10x + 15$ 42. $7(5 + 4x) = 35 + 28x$

43. $9(4x - 5y) = 36x - 45y$ 44. $8(3z - 7a) = 24z - 56a$

45. $-4(5 - 7p) = -20 + 28p$ 46. $-3(18m - 10) = -54m + 30$

47. $5 + 3x + (-4) = 5 + (-4) + 3x$

48. $6p + 2 + 11 = 6p + (2 + 11)$

49. $6 + 5 + k = (6 + 5) + k$

50. $-3c + 4 + 5c = 4 + (-3c) + 5c$

Solve the equation.

51. $3x + 71 = 44$ 52. $5x - 19 = 44$

53. $0.4x - 9 = 13$ 54. $0.3x + 13 = 46$

55. Write the equation in the distributive axiom.

56. Write the equation in the distributive property of multiplication over subtraction.

3-3 | MORE DISTRIBUTIVE PROPERTIES

In Sections 3-1 and 3-2 you learned that multiplication distributes over addition and subtraction. For example,

$$5(x + 3) \quad \text{and} \quad 7(2x - 4)$$
$$= 5x + 15 \qquad\qquad = 14x - 28$$

In this section you will learn some more distributive properties.

If a sum or difference is divided by a number, you can distribute the division over the addition or subtraction.

Distributing division over addition:

$$\frac{10 + 16}{2} \quad \text{Add first.} \qquad = \frac{10 + 16}{2} \quad \text{Distribute first.}$$

$$= \frac{26}{2} \qquad\qquad\qquad = \frac{10}{2} + \frac{16}{2}$$

$$\qquad\qquad\qquad\qquad\qquad = 5 + 8$$

$$= 13 \longleftarrow \text{The same!} \longrightarrow = 13$$

Distributing division over subtraction:

$$\frac{12 - 27}{3} \quad \text{Subtract first.} \qquad \frac{12 - 27}{3} \quad \text{Distribute first.}$$

$$= \frac{-15}{3} \qquad\qquad\qquad = \frac{12}{3} - \frac{27}{3}$$

$$\qquad\qquad\qquad\qquad\qquad = 4 - 9$$

$$= -5 \longleftarrow \text{The same!} \longrightarrow = -5$$

These properties are true because division by a number can be changed into multiplication by the reciprocal of that number. For instance,

$$\frac{10 + 16}{2}$$

$$= (10 + 16) \cdot \frac{1}{2} \qquad \text{Change division by 2 to multiplication by } \frac{1}{2}.$$

$$= 10 \cdot \frac{1}{2} + 16 \cdot \frac{1}{2} \qquad \text{Distribute multiplication over addition.}$$

$$= 5 + 8 \qquad\qquad \text{Do the multiplication.}$$

$$= 13 \qquad\qquad\quad \text{Do the addition.}$$

This is the answer as above.

Time: 1 or 2 days

Chalkboard Examples:

Distribute:
1. $2x(x - 7)$ Ans.: $2x^2 - 14x$

2. $\dfrac{8x - 12y + 20}{4}$ Ans.: $2x - 3y + 5$

3. $(5 + 2x - 7y)(-3)$
   Ans.: $-15 - 6x + 21y$

4. $-(4 - x)$ Ans.: $-4 + x$
   Note: Although it is not strictly correct, you can say, "Distribute the minus sign."

Assignments:

1 day on section:
  1–49 odd or 2–50 even (A long but not unreasonable assignment.)
2 days on section:
  Day 1: 1–39 odd or 2–40 even
  Day 2: 12–50 even and 51 or 11–51 odd

From the second to the third line, the factor $\frac{1}{2}$ was distributed from the *right* side of the expression. If you have doubts that this is legal, just commute the two factors first.

$$(10 + 16) \cdot \frac{1}{2}$$

$$= \frac{1}{2} \cdot (10 + 16) \qquad \text{Commute } (10 + 16) \text{ and } \frac{1}{2}.$$

$$= 5 + 8 \qquad \text{Distribute } \frac{1}{2} \text{ from the } \textit{left}.$$

$$= 13 \qquad \text{Do the addition.}$$

If a sum or difference of *three* or more terms is multiplied or divided by a number, you can still distribute.

Distributing multiplication over three terms:

$2(4 + 5 - 6)$	Operations in	$= 2(4 + 5 - 6)$	Distribute first.
$= 2(9 - 6)$	parentheses first	$= 2 \cdot 4 + 2 \cdot 5 - 2 \cdot 6$	
$= 2(3)$		$= 8 + 10 - 12$	
$= 6$	—— Same —→	$= 6$	

Distributing division over three terms:

$\dfrac{15 - 35 + 60}{5}$	Add and subtract first.	$\dfrac{15 - 35 + 60}{5}$	Distribute first.
$= \dfrac{-20 + 60}{5}$		$= \dfrac{15}{5} - \dfrac{35}{5} + \dfrac{60}{5}$	
$= \dfrac{40}{5}$		$= 3 - 7 + 12$	
		$= -4 + 12$	
$= 8$	—— Same —→	$= 8$	

The above work leads to the following conclusions.

CONCLUSION

DISTRIBUTING
Multiplication or division distribute over addition or subtraction of two or more terms from the left or from the right.

In this section you will use these properties to simplify expressions that contain variables.

Objective :
Be able to use the distributive properties to transform expressions containing variables.

Cover the answer as you work the example.

EXAMPLE 1

- - - - -   - - - - -

Distribute $x(3x - 5)$.

	Think These Reasons
$x(3x - 5)$	Write the given expression.
$= x \cdot 3x - x \cdot 5$	Distribute the x.
$= 3x^2 - 5x$	Commute and associate. Remember $x \cdot x$ equals x^2.

EXAMPLE 2

- - - - -   - - - - -

Simplify $\dfrac{45 + 12x - 3y}{3}$.

$\dfrac{45 + 12x - 3y}{3}$	Write the given expression.
$= \dfrac{45}{3} + \dfrac{12x}{3} - \dfrac{3y}{3}$	Distribute the division over the addition and subtraction.
$= 15 + 4x - y$	Divide.

EXAMPLE 3

- - - - -   - - - - -

Simplify $-(x - 5)$.

$-(x - 5)$	Write the given expression.
$= -1 \cdot (x - 5)$	Multiplication property of -1.
$= -1 \cdot x - (-1)(5)$	Distribute -1 over the subtraction.
$= -x + 5$	$-1 \cdot x = -x$ and $-(-5) = +5$

ORAL PRACTICE

Distribute.

EXAMPLES

Answers:

i. $(4 - 5)(6)$ i. $24 - 30$

ii. $\dfrac{20 + 30 - 40}{-10}$ ii. $-2 - 3 + 4$

A. $(3 - 7)(5)$ $15 - 35$

B. $-2(4 - 7)$ $-8 + 14$

C. $3(4 + 5 + 6)$ $12 + 15 + 18$

D. $\dfrac{8 + 12}{4}$ $2 + 3$

E. $\dfrac{30 - 10}{5}$ $6 - 2$

F. $\dfrac{10 + 12 + 14}{2}$ $5 + 6 + 7$

G. $(2 - 4 + 5)(3)$ $6 - 12 + 15$

H. $-4(5 - 3 + 1)$ $-20 + 12 - 4$

I. $-1(7 - 9)$ $-7 + 9$

J. $-(5 - 2)$ $-5 + 2$

K. $\dfrac{12 + 15 - 6}{-3}$ $-4 - 5 + 2$

L. $\dfrac{3 - 5 + 7}{-1}$ $-3 + 5 - 7$

M.   State the definition of axiom.

N.   State the distributive axiom.

M.   An axiom is a basic assumption about a mathematical system. It is a property that is assumed to be true without proof.

N.   Multiplication distributes over addition. That is, $x(y + z) = xy + xz$.

EXERCISE 3-3

For Problems 1 through 50, transform the expression by distributing the multiplication or division over addition or subtraction. Simplify the answers.

1. $9(x - 8)$ $9x - 72$

2. $7(x - 9)$ $7x - 63$

3. $5(3x - 2)$ $15x - 10$

4. $6(8x - 7)$ $48x - 42$

5. $x(4 + z)$ $4x + xz$

6. $x(5 + y)$ $5x + xy$

7. $c(x + y)$ $cx + cy$

8. $r(x - y)$ $rx - ry$

9. $(-5 + y)(10)$ $-50 + 10y$

10. $(-10 + z)(13)$ $-130 + 13z$

11. $-7(x - 8)$ $-7x + 56$

12. $-4(x - 7)$ $-4x + 28$

13. $-(r - s)$ $-r + s$

14. $-(a - b)$ $-a + b$

15. $-(x + y)$ $-x - y$

16. $-(p + z)$ $-p - z$

17. $(x - 4)(x)$ $x^2 - 4x$

18. $(x + 5)(x)$ $x^2 + 5x$

19. $\frac{1}{4}(20x + 12)$ $5x + 3$ 20. $\frac{1}{3}(18x + 27)$ $6x + 9$

21. $(100x + 35)\left(\frac{1}{5}\right)$ $20x + 7$ 22. $(200x + 150)\left(\frac{1}{10}\right)$ $20x + 15$

23. $-\frac{1}{9}(-54x - 63)$ $6x + 7$ 24. $-\frac{1}{7}(-63x - 42)$ $9x + 6$

25. $21\left(\frac{1}{3} - \frac{1}{7}x\right)$ $7 - 3x$ 26. $45\left(\frac{1}{9} - \frac{1}{5}x\right)$ $5 - 9x$

27. $\frac{32 + 4x}{4}$ $8 + x$ 28. $\frac{56 + 8x}{8}$ $7 + x$

29. $\frac{15 - 21x}{3}$ $5 - 7x$ 30. $\frac{20 - 4x}{2}$ $10 - 2x$

31. $\frac{24x - 18}{-2}$ 32. $\frac{33x - 66}{-11}$

33. $9(2x + 3y + 4)$ 34. $8(5x + 4y + 3)$

35. $-2(5c - 2 + 7d)$ 36. $-3(6r - 5 + 9s)$

37. $-(6 + 3x - 4y)$ 38. $-(x - 7 + 2y)$

39. $(x + 2y - z)(-4)$ 40. $(3x + y - z)(-5)$

41. $x(2x - 4y + 7)$ 42. $x(3x + 4y - 13)$

43. $\frac{8x + 72 + 64c}{8}$ 44. $\frac{7x + 63 - 14d}{7}$

45. $\frac{-30 - 65r + 100s}{-5}$ 46. $\frac{-9 - 12x + 30z}{-3}$

47. $0.6(1.2 + 5x - 4y)$ 48. $0.8(1.3 - 3x + 5y)$

49. $(12x - 18y + 6)\left(\frac{2}{3}\right)$ 50. $(15 + 30x - 45y)\left(\frac{3}{5}\right)$

31. $-12x + 9$ **32.** $-3x + 6$
33. $18x + 27y + 36$ **34.** $40x + 32y + 24$
35. $-10c + 4 - 14d$ **36.** $-18r + 15 - 27s$
37. $-6 - 3x + 4y$ **38.** $-x + 7 - 2y$
39. $-4x - 8y + 4z$ **40.** $-15x - 5y + 5z$
41. $2x^2 - 4xy + 7x$ **42.** $3x^2 + 4xy - 13x$
43. $x + 9 + 8c$ **44.** $x + 9 - 2d$
45. $6 + 13r - 20s$ **46.** $3 + 4x - 10z$
47. $0.72 + 3x - 2.4y$ **48.** $1.04 - 2.4x + 4y$
49. $8x - 12y + 4$ **50.** $9 + 18x - 27y$

For Problems 51 through 60, tell in words what was done.

51. $3(x + y - z) = 3x + 3y - 3z$

52. $(a - b + c)(4) = 4a - 4b + 4c$

53. $\frac{1}{10}(20 + 15x) = 2 + 1.5x$ 54. $\frac{1}{c}(x - y) = \frac{x}{c} - \frac{y}{c}$

55. $(3x + 5)(7) = 7(3x + 5)$ 56. $5y(7 + 2x) = 5y(2x + 7)$

57. $3x - (-2x) = 3x + 2x$ 58. $12x \div \frac{2}{3} = 12x \cdot \frac{3}{2}$

59. $(5 - 9)x = 5x - 9x$ 60. $(7 + 3)x = 7x + 3x$

51. Distribute 3 to x, y, and $-z$.
52. Distribute 4 to a, $-b$, and c.
53. Distribute $\frac{1}{10}$ to 20 and $15x$.
54. Distribute $\frac{1}{c}$ to x and $-y$, then use definition of division.
55. Commute $(3x + 5)$ and 7.
56. Commute 7 and $2x$.
57. Use definition of subtraction.
58. Use definition of division.
59. Distribute x to 5 and -9.
60. Distribute x to 7 and 3.

Problem Notes:

Problem 62 can be done as an oral exercise in class or as a written classroom quiz.

61. 7776 = 7776

62. a. $x(y - z) = xy - xz$

b. $\dfrac{x + y}{z} = \dfrac{x}{z} + \dfrac{y}{z}$

c. $w(x + y + z) = wx + wy + wz$

d. $(x + y)z = xz - yz$

e. $x(y + z) = xy + xz$

f. $(x \cdot y) \cdot z = x \cdot (y \cdot z)$

g. $x + y = y + x$

63. A property is a fact that is true about a mathematical system. An axiom is a property that is assumed to be true without proof.

Time: 2 days

Chalkboard Examples:

Day 1:
1. Combine like terms:
   $5x + 7x$ Ans.: $12x$
   $8x - 11x$ Ans.: $-3x$
   $4x - x$ Ans.: $3x$
   Watch for the common error $4x - x = 4$.

$2🍎 + 3🍎 = 5🍎$

2. Factor:
   $4x + 8y$ Ans.: $4(x + 2y)$
   $3x - ax$ Ans.: $x(3 - a)$
   $x^2 + 7x$ Ans.: $x(x + 7)$

Day 2:
Simplify:
   $4x + 6(x - 5)$ Ans.: $10x - 30$
   $8 - 5(2x - 7)$ Ans.: $43 - 10x$
   $4x - (9 - 2x)$ Ans.: $6x - 9$
A quiz or test at this point is important. Otherwise, students tend to forget the technique of distributing while they are learning the proofs in Section 3–5.

Assignments:

Day 1: 1–39 odd
Day 2: 41–69 odd (and 22–40 even, if needed for review)

61. Show that

$$(2 \cdot 3)^5 \quad \text{equals} \quad 2^5 \cdot 3^5$$

by evaluating each expression using the agreed-upon order of operations. What property seems to relate the operations of multiplication and exponentiation (raising to a power)?

62. Using variables for the numbers, write an equation expressing each property:

a. Multiplication distributes over subtraction.
b. Division distributes over addition.
c. Multiplication distributes over a sum of three terms.
d. Multiplication distributes over addition from the right.
e. The distributive axiom
f. Multiplication is associative.
g. Addition is commutative.

63. Tell the difference between an axiom and any other property.

3-4	LIKE TERMS AND COMMON FACTORS

Grade school children learn that two apples plus three apples is five apples. It sounds reasonable that two x's plus three x's equals five x's, or more precisely,

$$2x + 3x = 5x.$$

Now that you know the distributive properties you can see *why* this is true. The expression

$$2x + 3x$$

looks like the *answer* to the problem

$$(2 + 3)x = 2x + 3x.$$

Since the $=$ sign can be read either way, the expression $2x + 3x$ can be transformed as follows:

$2x + 3x$ Write the given expression.

$= (2 + 3)x$ Use the distributive properties "backwards" to factor out x.

$= 5x$ Do the addition.

Therefore,

$2x + 3x = 5x$ The first expression equals the last one.

The two terms $2x$ and $3x$ are alike except for the constant. If the variables in two terms are exactly alike, the terms are said to be *like* terms, or *similar* terms. So $2x$ and $3x$ are like terms. Other examples of like terms are

$$5y \quad \text{and} \quad -13y$$
$$2x^5 \quad \text{and} \quad 7x^5$$
$$x \quad \text{and} \quad 8x$$
$$6z \quad \text{and} \quad 6z$$
$$4xy \quad \text{and} \quad -7xy.$$

DEFINITION

> **LIKE TERMS**
> Two terms in an expression are called **like terms** (or **similar terms**) if they have the *same* variable(s) raised to the *same* powers.

The constant multiplied by the variable is called the *numerical coefficient,* or simply the *coefficient.* For instance, in $3x^2$, 3 is the coefficient of x^2.

DEFINITION

> **NUMERICAL COEFFICIENT**
> The **numerical coefficient** of a term is the constant that is multiplied by the variables. (For example, in $5xy$, 5 is the numerical coefficient of xy.)

The transformation

$$3x + 2x = 5x$$

is called *combining like terms.* So to combine like terms, you simply add their numerical coefficients.

In the expression $3x + 2x$, each term has x as a factor. So x is said to be a *common factor.* Similarly, in

$$4x + 4y, \quad 4 \text{ is the common factor,}$$
$$3x - 6y, \quad 3 \text{ is the common factor,}$$

$$5x^2 - 7x, \quad x \text{ is the common factor,}$$

$$3x + 2y, \quad \text{there are } no \text{ common factors.}$$

DEFINITION

> **COMMON FACTOR**
> In an expression, c is a **common factor** if c is a factor of *each term* in that expression.

The process of using the distributive property backwards, as in

$$4x + 4y = 4(x + y)$$

is called *factoring out a common factor*.

Objective :
Be able to transform expressions by combining like terms or by factoring out common factors.

Cover the answers as you work the examples.

EXAMPLE 1

– – – – –   – – – – –

Simplify $7z - 5z$.

	Think These Reasons
$7z - 5z$	Write the given expression.
$= \underline{\underline{2z}}$	Combine like terms by subtracting the coefficients.

EXAMPLE 2

– – – – –   – – – – –

Factor out the common factor(s): $3x + 12y$.

$3x + 12y$	Write the given expression.
$= \underline{\underline{3(x + 4y)}}$	3 is a factor of each term.

EXAMPLE 3

- - - - -   - - - - -

Factor out the common factor(s): $5x^2 - 15x$.

$5x^2 - 15x$	Write the given expression.
$= \underline{\underline{5x(x - 3)}}$	5 and x are each common factors of $5x^2$ and $15x$.

EXAMPLE 4

- - - - -   - - - - -

Simplify $7x + x(4x + 3)$.

$7x + x(4x + 3)$	Write the given expression.
$= 7x + 4x^2 + 3x$	Distribute x.
$= 4x^2 + 7x + 3x$	Commute so that like terms are together.
$= \underline{\underline{4x^2 + 10x}}$	Associate and combine like terms.

Note: $4x^2$ and $10x$ are *not* like terms, because the powers of the variables are not alike.

EXAMPLE 5

- - - - -   - - - - -

Simplify $3(5x - 7) - 2(x + 8)$.

$3(5x - 7) - 2(x + 8)$	Write the given expression.
$= 3(5x - 7) + (-2)(x + 8)$	Change subtracting to adding the opposite.
$= 15x - 21 - 2x - 16$	Distribute 3 and -2.
$= 15x - 2x - 21 - 16$	Commute $-2x$ and -21 so that like terms are together.
$= \underline{\underline{13x - 37}}$	Associate and combine like terms.

EXAMPLE 6

- - - - -   - - - - -

Simplify $7(x + 3) - (x - 9)$.

$7(x + 3) - (x - 9)$	Write the given expression.
$= 7(x + 3) + (-1)(x - 9)$	Rewrite subtracting $(x - 9)$ as adding $(-1)(x - 9)$.
$= 7x + 21 - x + 9$	Distribute 7 and -1.
$= 7x - x + 21 + 9$	Commute $-x$ and 21.
$= \underline{\underline{6x + 30}}$	Combine like terms.

ORAL PRACTICE

Combine like terms.

A. $7x + 2x$ $9x$

B. $3a + 4a$ $7a$

C. $8x - 3x$ $5x$

D. $6b - 11b$ $-5b$

E. $8r - r$ $7r$

F. $5x^2 + 8x^2$ $13x^2$

G. $10bc - 4bc$ $6bc$

H. $3x + 5y$ Won't simplify

Factor out the common factor(s):

I. $4x + 4y$ $4(x + y)$

J. $9x - 9y$ $9(x - y)$

K. $5b + 20$ $5(b + 4)$

L. $8c - 4d$ $4(2c - d)$

M. $8c - 4$ $4(2c - 1)$

N. $x^2 + 5x$ $x(x + 5)$

O. $6x^2 - 6x$ $6x(x - 1)$

P. $3x + 5y$ Won't factor

EXERCISE 3-4

Problem Notes:

For Problems 1–20 and 41–70, the order of the terms in the final answer is immaterial. Some teachers prefer variables first, then constants, while others prefer an order that avoids starting with a − sign. It is suggested that you accept any correct form of the answer.

For Problems 1 through 20, combine like terms.

1. $5x + 9x$ $14x$

2. $6x + 5x$ $11x$

3. $8p - 3p$ $5p$

4. $7k - 5k$ $2k$

5. $9xy - 8xy$ xy

6. $10yz - 9yz$ yz

7. $6x - x$ $5x$

8. $4y - y$ $3y$

9. $3x + 7x + 8$ $10x + 8$

10. $5x + 8x + 3$ $13x + 3$

11. $5y + 9 + 7y$ $12y + 9$

12. $4y + 10 + 6y$ $10y + 10$

13. $3z - 2 - 8z$ $-5z - 2$

14. $5z - 7 - 9z$ $-4z - 7$

15. $-4 - 5x + 11x$ $6x - 4$

16. $-6 - 2x + 9x$ $7x - 6$

17. $-6c + 13 - 7c$ $13 - 13c$

18. $-7d + 4 - 9d$ $4 - 16d$

19. $4.5x - 7.1x + 11.6$ $11.6 - 2.6x$

20. $3.1x - 8.5x + 2.4$ $2.4 - 5.4x$

For Problems 21 through 40, factor out the common factor(s).

21. $3x + 3y$ $3(x + y)$

22. $5x + 5y$ $5(x + y)$

23. $5a - 5b$ $5(a - b)$

24. $7p - 7f$ $7(p - f)$

25. $7c - 14$ $7(c - 2)$

26. $3a - 6$ $3(a - 2)$

27. $16d - 8$ $8(2d - 1)$

28. $20r - 10$ $10(2r - 1)$

29. $6x + 8y$ $2(3x + 4y)$

30. $12x + 8y$ $4(3x + 2y)$

31. $3ab - 3ac$ $3a(b - c)$

32. $5bx - 5bz$ $5b(x - z)$

33. $4ax + 12bx$ $4x(a + 3b)$

34. $3cx + 15dx$ $3x(c + 5d)$

35. $x^2 - 9x$ $x(x - 9)$

36. $x^2 - 4x$ $x(x - 4)$

37. $7x^2 + 7x$ $7x(x + 1)$

38. $3x^2 + 3x$ $3x(x + 1)$

39. $3x + 3y - 6z$ $3(x + y - 2z)$

40. $2x - 2y + 10z$ $2(x - y + 5z)$

In Problems 41–70, simplify the expression by distributing, commuting, associating, and combining like terms.

41. $5x + 3(x - 2)$

42. $3x + 7(x - 9)$

43. $7 - 4(2x + 5)$

44. $13 - 2(3x + 4)$

45. $6x - (x - 1)$

46. $7x - (x - 2)$

47. $2(3x + 4) - 5x$

48. $5(3x + 4) - 15x - 20$

49. $-8(9x - 7) + 72x - 57$

50. $-7(6x - 4) + 41x$

51. $4(3x + 2) + 6(5x + 8)$

52. $5(2x + 6) + 3(6x + 7)$

53. $2(x - 5) + 5(4 - 2x)$

54. $4(x - 3) + 2(6 - 5x)$

55. $8(2x + 3) - 4(3x + 6)$

56. $8(3x + 2) - 4(7x + 4)$

57. $3(6 + 5x) - 7(2x - 1)$

58. $3(6 + 7x) - 5(4x + 9)$

59. $-6(x - 5) - 2(7 - 3x)$

60. $-3(4x - 5) - 6(7 - 2x)$

61. $8(x + 4) - (x - 5)$

62. $7(x + 2) - (x - 3)$

63. $5(2x - 3y + 7) - 4(3y + 5x - 1)$

64. $4(7x - 2y + 3) - 5(6x + 5y - 1)$

65. $3x + x(5 - 2x)$

66. $6x - x(4x + 1)$

67. $\frac{1}{4}(12x + 20) - \frac{1}{5}(30 - 15x)$

68. $\frac{1}{3}(15x - 21) - \frac{1}{4}(18 + 30x)$

69. $0.3(5x - 7) - 0.2(3x + 4)$

70. $0.4(2x - 9) - 0.6(4x + 5)$

41. $8x - 6$

42. $10x - 63$

43. $-8x - 13$

44. $5 - 6x$

45. $5x + 1$

46. $6x + 2$

47. $x + 8$

48. 0

49. -1

50. $28 - x$

51. $42x + 56$

52. $28x + 51$

53. $10 - 8x$

54. $-6x$

55. $4x$

56. $-4x$

57. $x + 25$

58. $x - 27$

59. 16

60. -27

61. $7x + 37$

62. $6x + 17$

63. $-10x - 27y + 39$

64. $2x - 33y + 17$

65. $8x - 2x^2$

66. $5x - 4x^2$

67. $6x - 1$

68. $-2.5x - 11.5$

69. $0.9x - 2.9$

70. $-1.6x - 6.6$

For Problems 71 through 74, solve the equation.

71. $x = 19.8$ **72.** $x = 12$

73. $x = -2.75$ **74.** $x = -33$

71. $5x - 23 = 76$ **72.** $84 = 6x + 12$

73. $14 = 3 - 4x$ **74.** $11 - x = 44$

For Problems 75 through 80, write an expression for the quantity indicated.

75. $5x + 3$ **76.** $\dfrac{f - 5}{4}$

77. $d^2 + e^2$ **78.** $15(3x - 7)$

79. $15y - 3$ **80.** $\dfrac{u}{3} - 14$

75. Five times the quantity x plus 3

76. The quotient of the quantity f minus 5, and 4

77. The sum of the squares of d and e

78. The product of 15 and the quantity $3x$ minus 7

79. Three less than the product of 15 and y

80. The quotient of u and 3, diminished by 14

Time: 3 days

3-5 | **AXIOMS FOR ADDING AND MULTIPLYING**

Chalkboard Examples:

1. Tell the definition, axiom, or other property illustrated:
   a. $-3x + 3x = 0$
      Additive inverse axiom
   b. $0 + 3x = 3x$
      Additive identity axiom
   c. $0 \cdot 3x = 0$ Multiplication property of 0
   d. $8 + (9 + 2x) = (8 + 9) + 2x$
      Associative axiom for addition
   e. $5 \cdot x \cdot 7 = 5 \cdot 7 \cdot x$
      Commutative axiom for mult.
   f. $3x + 4 - x = 3x + 4 + (-x)$
      Definition of subtraction
2. Tell the definition, axiom, or other property that justifies each step in this transformation.
   $3x + 4 - x$
   $= 3x + 4 + (-x)$
      a. Definition of subtraction
   $= 3x + (-x) + 4$
      b. Commutative axiom for addition
   $= [3x + (-x)] + 4$
      c. Associative axiom for addition
   $= [3x + (-1)x] + 4$

You have learned the words "commute," "associate," and "distribute" as *verbs*. They pertain to things you can do to change the form of an expression. For instance, commuting the terms in $2 + 5$ gives $5 + 2$. The fact that both expressions stand for the same number, 7, is an example of a *property* called the "commutative property for addition." The word "commutative" is the adjective that comes from "commute."

This commutative property is an *axiom*. It is a fact that is used as a basis for the system of real numbers. You can write an equation to express this fact in general, using variables for the numbers.

$$x + y = y + x$$

There are two commutative axioms, one for addition and one for multiplication.

There are also two *associative* axioms. They express the fact that you can associate the terms in a sum or the factors in a product any way you like, and still get the same answer. An equation for the associative axiom for addition is

$$(x + y) + z = x + (y + z).$$

A fifth axiom is the *distributive* axiom. An equation is

$$x(y + z) = xy + xz.$$

These five axioms are summarized in the following table.

AXIOMS

SOME AXIOMS FOR ADDITION AND MULTIPLICATION
In all the axioms, x, y, and z stand for real numbers.

Commutative axiom for addition

$$x + y = y + x$$

Commutative axiom for multiplication

$$xy = yx$$

Associative axiom for addition

$$(x + y) + z = x + (y + z)$$

Associative axiom for multiplication

$$(xy)z = x(yz)$$

Distributive axiom for multiplication over addition

$$x(y + z) = xy + xz$$

---

d. Multiplication property of -1
$$= [3 + (-1)]x + 4$$
e. Distributive axiom (in reverse?)
$$= 2x + 4$$
f. Arithmetic

Assignments:

Day 1: Memorize names and statements of the axioms and other properties.
   3-5 Problems 1 through 31 odd
   3-4 Two or three selected problems not previously assigned

Day 2: 3-5 Problems 2 through 32 even, and 33 through 41 odd
   3-4 Two or three selected problems not previously assigned

Day 3: 3-5 Problems 34 through 42 even, and 51 through 61 odd
   3-4 Two or three selected problems not previously assigned
   2-8 (possibly) One word problem not previously assigned

There are four other axioms for adding and multiplying. You have been using these axioms, perhaps without realizing it. They concern the numbers 0 and 1.

If you add 0 to a number or multiply a number by 1, the answer is *identical* to the original number. For instance,

$$3 + 0 = 3$$
$$7 \cdot 1 = 7$$

The axioms that express these facts are called the *identity* axioms.

If you add 5 and -5, you get 0. If you multiply $\frac{2}{3}$ by $\frac{3}{2}$, you get 1. The axioms that express these facts are called the *inverse* axioms. Formal statements of these axioms are in the box below.

AXIOMS

SOME MORE AXIOMS FOR ADDITION AND MULTIPLICATION
In all the axioms, x stands for a real number.

Additive Identity Axiom
Zero added to any number gives that number. That is,

$$x + 0 = x.$$

Multiplicative Identity Axiom
One times any number gives that number. That is,

$$x \cdot 1 = x.$$

Additive Inverses Axiom
Any number x has an opposite, $-x$, for which

$$x + (-x) = 0.$$

Multiplicative Inverses Axiom
Any number x (except for 0) has a reciprocal, $\dfrac{1}{x}$ for which

$$x \cdot \frac{1}{x} = 1.$$

There are two other important properties of multiplication. They tell what happens when you multiply a number by -1 or by 0. In Chapter 2 you learned that if a number is multiplied by -1, the result is the *opposite* of that number. For instance,

$$-1 \cdot 5 = -5, \quad \text{and} \quad -1 \cdot (-7) = 7.$$

This fact is named the *multiplication property of* -1. The fact that multiplying a number by 0 gives 0 for the answer is called the *multiplication property of 0*. For instance,

$$0 \cdot \left(-\frac{2}{3}\right) = 0.$$

Both properties can be proved using the other axioms, as you will learn in later courses. So these two are not called axioms.

PROPERTIES

x stands for a real number.

MULTIPLICATION PROPERTY OF −1
−1 times a number equals the *opposite* of that number.
That is,

$$-1 \cdot x = -x.$$

MULTIPLICATION PROPERTY OF 0
0 times a number equals 0. That is,

$$0 \cdot x = 0.$$

It will be your goal in this section to learn what these axioms and properties say by using them in various ways.

Objective :
Given a step in a computation, tell which axiom or other property justifies
that step.

Cover the answers as you work these examples.

EXAMPLE 1

Tell which axiom or property justifies the fact that the expression on the
right is equal to the expression on the left.

Think These Reasons

a. $\dfrac{3x}{2} \cdot \dfrac{2}{3x} = 1$

— — — — —   — — — — —

Multiplicative inverses axiom   A number multiplied by its
                                    multiplicative inverse
                                    (reciprocal) is 1.

b. $(x + 3y) = 1 \cdot (x + 3y)$

— — — — —   — — — — —

Multiplicative identity axiom   Multiplying by 1 gives an
                                    identical number for the answer.

c. $5 \cdot (3x) = (5 \cdot 3)x$

$- \ - \ - \ - \ -$ $- \ - \ - \ - \ -$

Associative axiom for multiplication   The 5 and 3 were associated.

d. $7(2 + 4x) = 14 + 28x$

$- \ - \ - \ - \ -$ $- \ - \ - \ - \ -$

Distributive axiom   The 7 was distributed.

e. $7 + (x + 5) = (x + 5) + 7$

$- \ - \ - \ - \ -$ $- \ - \ - \ - \ -$

Commutative axiom for addition   The 7 and $(x + 5)$ were
                                            commuted.

f. $-(x + 5) = -1 \cdot (x + 5)$

$- \ - \ - \ - \ -$ $- \ - \ - \ - \ -$

Multiplication Property of -1 The opposite of a number equals
                                            -1 times that number.

EXAMPLE 2

Write the axiom, definition, etc., justifying each step:

$$
\begin{aligned}
&7(3 + x) - 5 \\
&= 21 + 7x - 5 \qquad &\text{a.} \\
&= 21 + 7x + (-5) \qquad &\text{b.} \\
&= 21 + (-5) + 7x \qquad &\text{c.} \\
&= [21 + (-5)] + 7x \qquad &\text{d.} \\
&= \underline{\underline{16 + 7x}} \qquad &\text{e.}
\end{aligned}
$$

$- \ - \ - \ - \ -$ $- \ - \ - \ - \ -$

$$
\begin{aligned}
&7(3 + x) - 5 \\
&= 21 + 7x - 5
\end{aligned}
$$
a. *Distributive axiom*

$- \ - \ - \ - \ -$ $- \ - \ - \ -$

$= 21 + 7x + (-5)$ b. *Definition of subtraction*

$- \ - \ - \ - \ -$ $- \ - \ - \ -$

$= 21 + (-5) + 7x$ c. *Commutative axiom for addition*

$- \ - \ - \ - \ -$ $- \ - \ - \ - \ -$

$= [21 + (-5)] + 7x$ d. *Associative axiom for addition*

$- \ - \ - \ - \ -$ $- \ - \ - \ - \ -$

$= \underline{\underline{16 + 7x}}$ e. *Arithmetic*

ORAL PRACTICE

Name the axiom or definition illustrated:

A. $4 + x = x + 4$ B. $3(y + 7) = 3y + 21$

C. $1x = x$ D. $x \div \left(\dfrac{2}{3}\right) = x \cdot \left(\dfrac{3}{2}\right)$

E. $3c + 0 = 3c$ F. $ab = ba$

G. $\left(\dfrac{5}{8}\right) \cdot \left(\dfrac{8}{5}\right) = 1$ H. $-\dfrac{2}{7} + \dfrac{2}{7} = 0$

I. $5x - (-3x) = 5x + 3x$ J. $5(3x) = (5 \cdot 3)x$

K. $5x + 3x = (5 + 3)x$ L. $5x + 3x = 3x + 5x$

M. $\dfrac{x}{y} = x \cdot \dfrac{1}{y}$ N. $3x \cdot 0 = 0$

O. $-1 \cdot xy = -xy$

EXERCISE 3-5

For Problems 1 through 30, name the axiom, other property, or definition which justifies that the expression on the left is equal to the expression on the right. Do not abbreviate! You must show that you know how to spell the words!!

1. $x + y = y + x$ 2. $rs = sr$

3. $x - y = x + (-y)$ 4. $c \div d = c \cdot \dfrac{1}{d}$

5. $a + (b + c) = a + (c + b)$ 6. $p(mt) = p(tm)$

7. $a + (b + c) = (a + b) + c$ 8. $p(mt) = (pm)t$

9. $3x + 4x = (3 + 4)x$ 10. $7k + 7j = 7(k + j)$

11. $5m + 5n = 5(m + n)$ 12. $6r + 9r = (6 + 9)r$

13. $k \cdot 5 = 5k$ 14. $a + 5 = 5 + a$

15. $1 \cdot (4p - 2) = 4p - 2$ 16. $0 + 3t = 3t$

17. $2n - 5 \cdot 3 = 2n + (-5 \cdot 3)$ 18. $8f \div \left(\dfrac{2}{3}\right) = 8f \cdot \left(\dfrac{3}{2}\right)$

Oral Practice

A. Commutative axiom for addition
B. Distributive axiom for multiplication over addition
C. Multiplicative identity axiom
D. Definition of division
E. Additive identity axiom
F. Commutative axiom for multiplication
G. Multiplicative inverses axiom
H. Additive inverses axiom
I. Definition of subtraction
J. Associative axiom for multiplication
K. Commutative axiom for multiplication, Distributive axiom for multiplication over addition
L. Commutative axiom for addition
M. Definition of division
N. Multiplication property of 0
O. Multiplication property of −1

Exercise 3-5

1. Commutative axiom for addition
2. Commutative axiom for multiplication
3. Definition of subtraction
4. Definition of division
5. Commutative axiom for addition
6. Commutative axiom for multiplication
7. Associative axiom for addition
8. Associative axiom for multiplication
9. Distributive axiom for mult. over add.
10. Distributive axiom for mult. over add.
11. Distributive axiom for mult. over add.
12. Distributive axiom for mult. over add.
13. Commutative axiom for multiplication
14. Commutative axiom for addition
15. Multiplicative identity axiom
16. Additive identity axiom
17. Definition of subtraction
18. Definition of division

19. Multiplicative inverses axiom
20. Additive inverses axiom
21. Definition of division
22. Definition of subtraction
23. Multiplicative identity axiom
24. Multiplicative inverses axiom
25. Commutative axiom for multiplication
26. Associative axiom for addition
27. Commutative axiom for multiplication
28. Commutative axiom for addition
29. Multiplication property of 0
30. Multiplication property of −1
31. a. Dist. axiom
    b. Arithmetic
32. a. Dist. axiom
    b. Arithmetic
33. a. Def. of sub.
    b. Comm. for add.
34. a. Comm. for add.
    b. Def. of sub.
35. a. Dist. axiom
    b. Assoc. for add.
    c. Comm. for add.
    d. Assoc. for add.
    e. Arithmetic
36. a. Dist. axiom
    b. Assoc. for add.
    c. Comm. for add.
    d. Assoc. for add.
    e. Arithmetic
37. a. Def. of sub.
    b. Dist. axiom
    c. Arithmetic
    d. Def. of sub.
38. a. Def. of sub.
    b. Dist. axiom
    c. Arithmetic
    d. Def. of sub.
39. a. Def. of sub.
    b. Assoc. for add.
    c. Comm. for add.
    d. Assoc. for add.
    e. Factor out common factors
    f. Arithmetic
40. a. Def. of sub.
    b. Assoc. for add.
    c. Comm. for add.
    d. Assoc. for add.
    e. Factor out common factors
    f. Arithmetic
    g. Def. of sub.

19. $\dfrac{11}{b} \cdot \dfrac{b}{11} = 1$

20. $0.3 + (-0.3) = 0$

21. $\dfrac{11}{b} = 11 \cdot \dfrac{1}{b}$

22. $0.3 + (-0.3) = 0.3 - 0.3$

23. $\dfrac{11}{b} \cdot 1 = \dfrac{11}{b}$

24. $0.3\left(\dfrac{1}{0.3}\right) = 1$

25. $4(pt) = 4(tp)$

26. $3 + (k + 2n) = (3 + k) + 2n$

27. $4(pt) = (pt) \cdot 4$

28. $(3 + k) + 2n = 2n + (3 + k)$

29. $2001x \cdot 0 = 0$

30. $-1 \cdot ahs = -ahs$

For Problems 31 through 50, copy the steps shown. Then name the axiom, definition, etc., which justifies each step. You may abbreviate the names.

31.　　$3y + 4y$

$= (3 + 4)y$　　　　a.

$= 7y$　　　　b.

32.　　$\dfrac{2}{3}x + \dfrac{11}{3}x$

$= \left(\dfrac{2}{3} + \dfrac{11}{3}\right)x$　　　a.

$= 4x$　　　　b.

33.　　$9 - 7x$

$= 9 + (-7x)$　　　a.

$= -7x + 9$　　　b.

34.　　$-5 + 2y$

$= 2y + (-5)$　　　a.

$= 2y - 5$　　　b.

35.　　$4(3 + x) + 7$

$= 12 + 4x + 7$　　　a.

$= 12 + (4x + 7)$　　b.

$= 12 + (7 + 4x)$　　c.

$= (12 + 7) + 4x$　　d.

$= 19 + 4a$　　　e.

36.　　$8 + 6(x + 4)$

$= 8 + 6x + 24$　　　a.

$= (8 + 6x) + 24$　　b.

$= (6x + 8) + 24$　　c.

$= 6x + (8 + 24)$　　d.

$= 6x + 32$　　　e.

37.　　$7[x - 8]$

$= 7[x + (-8)]$　　　a.

$= 7x + 7(-8)$　　　b.

$= 7x + (-56)$　　　c.

$= 7x + 56$　　　d.

38.　　$[p - 5](3)$

$= [p + (-5)](3)$　　　a.

$= 3p + (-5)(3)$　　　b.

$= 3p + (-15)$　　　c.

$= 3p - 15$　　　d.

39.　　$5x + 13 - 2x$

$= 5x + 13 + (-2x)$　　　a.

$= (5x + 13) + (-2x)$　　b.

$= (13 + 5x) + (-2x)$　　c.

$= 13 + [5x + (-2x)]$　　d.

$= 13 + [5 + (-2)]x$　　e.

$= 13 + 3x$　　　f.

40.　　$11e - 7 - 3e$

$= 11e + (-7) + (-3e)$　　　a.

$= 11e + [(-7) + (-3e)]$　　b.

$= 11e + [(-3e) + (-7)]$　　c.

$= [11e + (-3e)] + (-7)$　　d.

$= [11 + (-3)]e + (-7)$　　e.

$= 8e + (-7)$　　　f.

$= 8e - 7$　　　g.

41. $8n \div 4$

$= 8n \cdot \dfrac{1}{4}$ a.

$= 8\left(n \cdot \dfrac{1}{4}\right)$ b.

$= 8\left(\dfrac{1}{4} \cdot n\right)$ c.

$= \left(8 \cdot \dfrac{1}{4}\right)n$ d.

$= 2n$ e.

42. $51t \div 17$

$= 51t \cdot \dfrac{1}{17}$ a.

$= 51\left(t \cdot \dfrac{1}{17}\right)$ b.

$= 51\left(\dfrac{1}{17} \cdot t\right)$ c.

$= \left(51 \cdot \dfrac{1}{17}\right)t$ d.

$= 3t$ e.

41.   a. Def. of div.
    b. Assoc. for mult.
    c. Comm. for mult.
    d. Assoc. for mult.
    e. Arithmetic

42.   a. Def. of div.
    b. Assoc. for mult.
    c. Comm. for mult.
    d. Assoc. for mult.
    e. Arithmetic

43. $11x + 5 - 11x$

$= 11x + 5 + (-11x)$ a.

$= 11x + [5 + (-11x)]$ b.

$= 11x + [(-11x) + 5]$ c.

$= [11x + (-11x)] + 5$ d.

$= 0 + 5$ e.

$= 5$ f.

44. $3 - 7.1a - 3$

$= 3 + (-7.1a) + (-3)$ a.

$= 3 + [(-7.1a) + (-3)]$ b.

$= 3 + [(-3) + (-7.1a)]$ c.

$= [3 + (-3)] + (-7.1a)$ d.

$= 0 + (-7.1a)$ e.

$= -7.1a$ f.

43.   a. Def. of sub.
    b. Assoc. for add.
    c. Comm. for add.
    d. Assoc. for add.
    e. Combine like terms
    f. Add. ident.

44.   a. Def. of sub.
    b. Assoc. for add.
    c. Comm. for add.
    d. Assoc. for add.
    e. Arithmetic
    f. Add. ident.

45. $\dfrac{12x}{x}$

$= 12x \cdot \dfrac{1}{x}$ a.

$= 12\left(x \cdot \dfrac{1}{x}\right)$ b.

$= 12 \cdot 1$ c.

$= 12$ d.

46. $\dfrac{4f}{f}$

$= 4f \cdot \dfrac{1}{f}$ a.

$= 4\left(f \cdot \dfrac{1}{f}\right)$ b.

$= 4 \cdot 1$ c.

$= 4$ d.

45.   a. Def. of div.
    b. Assoc. for mult.
    c. Mult. inv.
    d. Mult. ident.

46.   a. Def. of div.
    b. Assoc. for mult.
    c. Mult. inv.
    d. Mult. ident.

47. $6u - u$

$= 6u - (1u)$ a.

$= 6u + (-1u)$ b.

$= [6 + (-1)]u$ c.

$= 5u$ d.

48. $n - 7n$

$= 1n - 7n$ a.

$= 1n + (-7n)$ b.

$= [1 + (-7)]n$ c.

$= -6n$ d.

47.   a. Mult. ident.
    b. Def. of sub.
    c. Factor out common factors
    d. Arithmetic

48.   a. Mult. ident.
    b. Def. of sub.
    c. Factor out common factors
    d. Arithmetic

49. $5 - [x + 2]$

$= 5 - 1[x + 2]$ a.

$= 5 + (-1)[x + 2]$ b.

$= 5 + [(-x) + (-2)]$ c.

$= 5 + [(-2) + (-x)]$ d.

$= [5 + (-2)] + (-x)$ e.

$= 3 + (-x)$ f.

$= 3 - x$ g.

50. $7 - [k + 3]$

$= 7 - 1[k + 3]$ a.

$= 7 + (-1)[k + 3]$ b.

$= 7 + [(-k) + (-3)]$ c.

$= 7 + [(-3) + (-k)]$ d.

$= [7 + (-3)] + (-k)$ e.

$= 4 + (-k)$ f.

$= 4 - k$ g.

49.   a. Mult. ident.
    b. Def. of sub.
    c. Dist.
    d. Comm. for add.
    e. Assoc. for add.
    f. Arithmetic
    g. Def. of sub.

50.   a. Mult. ident.
    b. Def. of sub.
    c. Dist.
    d. Comm. for add.
    e. Assoc. for add.
    f. Arithmetic
    g. Def. of sub.

For Problems 51 through 60, if it is an expression, simplify it; if it is an equation, solve it.

51. $3x - 7 + 4$ $3x - 3$ **52.** $5x - 8 = 3$ $S = \left\{\dfrac{11}{5}\right\}$

53. $7x + 9 = 2$ $S = \{-1\}$ **54.** $9x + 7 - 13$ $9x - 6$

55. $x = 10$ **56.** $x - 8$
57. $-2x - 38.8$ **58.** $x = -15.95$
59. $S = x = -2.5$ **60.** $55x + 3$

61. Commutative and associative axioms for multiplication
62. The opposite of 0 is 0.

55. $3x - 10 = 2x$ **56.** $4x - 8 - 3x$

57. $3.1 - 2x - 41.9$ **58.** $1.7 - 2x = 33.6$

59. $5(3x + 8) = -x$ **60.** $7(8x + 3/7) - x$

61. The order of operations says multiplication such as $3 \cdot 2 \cdot 7$ should be done from left to right. What axiom says that you get the same answer if you multiply from right to left?

62. A problem on an algebra test says,

"Justify this statement: $-1 \cdot 0 = 0$."

Wanda Ngo says, "Multiplication Property of -1." Her sister Juana says, "Multiplication property of 0." Explain why *both* answers are right.

3-6 | **PROPERTIES OF EQUALITY**

Time: 3 days

Chalkboard Examples:

1. Name the definition, axiom, or other property that justifies the following:
   a. $5x = 100$,
      so $(0.2)(5x) = (0.2)(100)$.
      Mult. prop. of equality
   b. $5x - 100$
      $= 5x + (-100)$
      Definition of subtraction
   c. $5x = 100$,
      so $100 = 5x$ Symmetric axiom of equality
   d. $5x = 5x$ Reflexive axiom of equality
   e. $5x = (x)(5)$ Commutative axiom of multiplication
   f. If $5x = 100$, and $100 = 3y$,
      then $5x = 3y$.
      Transitive axiom of equality
2. Name the definition, axiom, or other property that justifies each step in solving the equation.
   $13 = 19 - 4x$
   $13 = 19 + (-4x)$
      a. Definition of subtraction
   $-19 + 13 = -19 + [19 + (-4x)]$
      b. Addition property of equality
   $-6 = -19 + [19 + (-4x)]$
      c. Arithmetic
   $-6 = [-19 + 19] + (-4x)$

In the last section you learned names for some properties of multiplication and addition. In this section you will learn names for some of the properties that apply to the "=" sign.

When you evaluate an expression, you write something like this:

$$3(5 - 1) + 7$$
$$= 3(4) + 7$$
$$= 12 + 7$$
$$= 19.$$

What you really want to say is that the original expression equals the final one,

$$3(5 - 1) + 7 = 19.$$

The property that allows you to connect the first expression to the last is called the *transitive axiom of equality*. The word "transit" comes from the Latin *transire*, meaning "to go across." The equality goes across from the first number to the last one.

A second axiom of equality expresses the fact that, for example, $x = 5$ and $5 = x$ both say the same thing. It is called the *symmetric axiom of equality*. The name can be remembered because the "=" sign looks the same from either side. It is "symmetric." So it doesn't matter which direction you read an equation, left to right, or right to left.

The third axiom expresses the fact that a variable stands for the same number, no matter where it appears in an expression or equation. When you check an equation such as

$$3x + 20 = x,$$

you must substitute the *same* number for x in both places. The property is called the *reflexive axiom of equality*. The equation expressing this axiom is

$$x = x.$$

You can remember the name by thinking that x sees its own "reflection" when it looks into an "=" sign.

These three axioms are stated formally below.

AXIOMS OF EQUALITY

x, y, and z stand for real numbers.

TRANSITIVE AXIOM OF EQUALITY
If the first number equals a second number, and the second number equals a third number, then the first number equals the third number. That is,

$$\text{If } x = y \quad \text{and} \quad y = z, \quad \text{then} \quad x = z.$$

SYMMETRIC AXIOM OF EQUALITY
The two members of an equation can be reversed without affecting their equality. That is,

$$\text{If } x = y, \quad \text{then} \quad y = x.$$

REFLEXIVE AXIOM OF EQUALITY
A number equals itself. That is,

$$x = x.$$

Besides these three axioms, there are other properties which express the fact that you can add the same number to each member of an equation, or multiply each member by the same number. For instance,

if $5x - 3 = 17$ is true, then so is $5x - 3 + 3 = 17 + 3$.

This fact is called the *addition property of equality*. The same fact for multiplying is called the *multiplication property of equality*. For instance,

d. Associative axiom for addition
$$-6 = 0 + (-4x)$$
e. Additive inverse axiom
$$-6 = -4x$$
f. Additive identity axiom
$$1.5 = x$$
g. Multiplication property of equality (mult. by -0.25)
$$x = 1.5$$
h. Symmetric axiom of equality

Assignments:

Day 1: Memorize the names and statements of the properties.
3-6 Problems 1 through 41 odd
Day 2: 3-6 Problems 4, 8, 16, . . . , 42, plus 43 through 53 odd
Day 3: 3-6 Problems 44 through 60 even, plus 61 through 69 odd

Problem Notes:

Problems 1 through 40 involve just *one* reason.

Problems 41 through 50 show solutions of entire equations. The steps in the solutions are ones the students have been using somewhat intuitively up to now. By working the problems, students should see that their intuition can be backed up by facts.

For Problems 51 through 56 it is important for students to realize that they have actually *proved* some properties. Here is a chance for you to sharpen their understanding of the distinction between axioms, which are not proved, and other properties, which can be proved. Actual memorization of the proofs is not necessary at this stage of your students' mathematical careers.

Problems 61 through 70 are more of the "simplify it or solve it" problems designed to distinguish between expressions and equations.

$$\text{if } 5x = 20 \text{ is true, then so is } 5x \cdot \left(\frac{1}{5}\right) = 20 \cdot \left(\frac{1}{5}\right).$$

These properties are stated formally below.

PROPERTIES FOR TRANSFORMING EQUATIONS

x, y, and z stand for real numbers.

ADDITION PROPERTY OF EQUALITY

If $x = y$,   then $x + z = y + z$.

MULTIPLICATION PROPERTY OF EQUALITY

If $x = y$,   then $xz = yz$.

Objective:

Learn the axioms and properties of equality well enough so that you can tell which property you are using at each step in solving an equation.

Cover the answers as you work these examples.

EXAMPLE 1

Name the axiom, other property, or definition that justifies the following:

> **Think These Reasons**

a. $3x + 5 = 14$
   $\therefore 3x + 5 + (-5) = 14 + (-5)$

(The 3-dot symbol "$\therefore$" stands for "therefore.")

- - - - -   - - - - -

Addition property of equality   You added the same number to each member of the equation.

b. $13 = 13$

- - - - -   - - - - -

Reflexive axiom of equality   13 sees its reflection in the "$=$" sign.

c. $8 + 12 = 20$, and $20 = 23 - 3$
   $\therefore 8 + 12 = 23 - 3$

- - - - -   - - - - -

Transitive axiom of equality   The first number, $8 + 12$, is equal to the last one, $23 - 3$.

d. $7x = 28$

$\therefore 7x \cdot \left(\dfrac{1}{7}\right) = 28 \cdot \left(\dfrac{1}{7}\right)$

- - - - -   - - - - -

Multiplication property of equality   Each member of the equation was
multiplied by the same number.

e. $6x + 17 = 89$
$\therefore 6x = 72$

- - - - -   - - - - -

Addition property of equality -17 was added to each member
of the equation. (Some associating
and arithmetic were also done.)

f. $19 + 5x + 11$
$= 5x + 19 + 11$

- - - - -   - - - - -

Commutative axiom of addition   The $5x$ and 19 were commuted.
(Note that this is a property of
addition, not equality!)

EXAMPLE 2

Name the axiom, other property, or definition that justifies each step.

$15 = 8 + 2x$
$8 + 2x = 15$ a.
$8 + 2x + (-8) = 15 + (-8)$ b.
$2x + 8 + (-8) = 15 + (-8)$ c.
$2x + [8 + (-8)] = 15 + (-8)$ d.
$2x + 0 = 15 + (-8)$ e.
$2x = 15 + (-8)$ f.
$2x = 15 - 8$ g.
$2x = 7$ h.
$x = 3.5$ i.

- - - - -   - - - - -

$15 = 8 + 2x$
$8 + 2x = 15$ a. Symmetric axiom of equality
$8 + 2x + (-8) = 15 + (-8)$ b. Addition property of equality
$2x + 8 + (-8) = 15 + (-8)$ c. Commutative axiom for addition
$2x + [8 + (-8)] = 15 + (-8)$ d. Associative axiom for addition
$2x + 0 = 15 + (-8)$ e. Additive inverse axiom
$2x = 15 + (-8)$ f. Additive identity axiom
$2x = 15 - 8$ g. Definition of subtraction
$2x = 7$ h. Arithmetic.
$x = 3.5$ i. Multiplication property of equality
(Each member was multiplied by $\frac{1}{2}$).

EXAMPLE 3

State the addition property of equality.

– – – – –   – – – – –

If a = b, then a + c = b + c.   "Stating" a property means telling what
it *says*. You may use any variables you
like, but you should not use constants.

Oral Practice

A.   Transitive axiom of equality
B.   Symmetric axiom of equality
C.   Addition property of equality
D.   Reflexive axiom of equality
E.   Commutative axiom for addition
F.   Definition of subtraction
G.   Associative axiom for addition
H.   Definition of division
I.   Multiplication property of equality
J.   Distributive axiom for multiplication over
          addition
K.   Commutative axiom for addition
L.   Commutative axiom for multiplication
M.   Reflexive axiom of equality

ORAL PRACTICE

Tell which axiom, other property, or definition was used.

A. $2 + 3 = 5$ and $5 = 4 + 1$
$\therefore 2 + 3 = 4 + 1$

B. $2 + 3 = 5$
$\therefore 5 = 2 + 3$

C. $2 + 3 = 5$
$\therefore 2 + 3 + (-3) = 5 + (-3)$

D. $2 + 3 = 2 + 3$

E. $2 + 3 = 3 + 2$

F. $2 + (-3) = 2 - 3$

G. $2 + 3 + 4 = 2 + (3 + 4)$

H. $2 \div 3 = 2 \cdot (1/3)$

I. $2 \cdot 3 = 6$
$\therefore 2 \cdot 3 \cdot \left(\frac{1}{3}\right) = 6 \cdot \left(\frac{1}{3}\right)$

J. $2(3 + 4) = 6 + 8$

K. $2(3 + 4) = 2(4 + 3)$

L. $2(3 + 4) = (3 + 4)(2)$

M. $2(3 + 4) = 2(3 + 4)$

Exercise 3-6

1.   Symmetric axiom of equality
2.   Reflexive axiom of equality
3.   Distributive axiom for multiplication over
          addition
4.   Commutative axiom for multiplication
5.   Commutative axiom for addition
6.   Associative axiom for addition
7.   Reflexive axiom of equality
8.   Transitive axiom of equality
9.   Additive inverses axiom
10. Additive identity axiom
11. Multiplicative inverses axiom

EXERCISE 3-6

For Problems 1 through 40, name the axiom, other property, or definition
that justifies the statement.

1. If $19 = 5x + 3$, then $5x + 3 = 19$.

2. $5x + 3 = 5x + 3$

3. $5(x + 3) = 5x + 15$

4. $5(x + 3) = (x + 3)(5)$

5. $5(x + 3) = 5(3 + x)$

6. $5 + (x + 3) = (5 + x) + 3$

7. $x + 3 = x + 3$

8. If $p = a$ and $a = f$, then $p = f$.

9. $w + (-w) = 0$

10. $w + 0 = w$

11. $w \cdot \dfrac{1}{w} = 1$

12. $w \cdot 0 = 0$

13. $-1 \cdot 3t = -3t$

14. $1x = x$

15. $0x = 0$

16. $1066x + 2001x = (1066 + 2001)x$

17. $1492w + 1492v = 1492(w + v)$

18. $3c \div 3 = 3c\left(\dfrac{1}{3}\right)$

19. $3(50 \cdot 90) = (3 \cdot 50) \cdot 90$

20. $3(50 + 90) = 3 \cdot 50 + 3 \cdot 90$

21. $3(50 + 90) = (50 + 90)3$

22. $3(50 + 90) = 3(90 + 50)$

23. $3 + (50 + 90) = (3 + 50) + 90$

24. $3 - 50 = 3 + (-50)$

25. $3 - 50 = -47$, and $-47 = -40 - 7$, so $3 - 50 = -40 - 7$.

26. $-1 \cdot 3 = -1 \cdot 3$

27. $0 \cdot x = x \cdot 0$

28. Since $3x + 5x = 8x$, $8x = 3x + 5x$.

29. $3x + 5x = (3 + 5)x$

30. If $3x = 5x + 7$, then $3x + (-5x) = 5x + 7 + (-5x)$.

31. If $\left(\dfrac{2}{3}\right)x = 12$, then $\left(\dfrac{2}{3}\right)x \cdot \left(\dfrac{3}{2}\right) = 12 \cdot \left(\dfrac{3}{2}\right)$.

32. If $x = 7$ and $7 = z$, then $x = z$.

33. If $14x = 28$, then $x = 2$.

34. If $13 + t = 43$, then $t = 30$.

35. If $14x + 28 = n$, then $28 + 14x = n$.

36. If $13 \cdot t = 43$, then $t \cdot 13 = 43$.

37. $-d + d = 0$

38. $1p = p$

39. $d - d = d + (-d)$

40. $d\left(\dfrac{1}{d}\right) = 1$

12. Multiplication property of zero
13. Multiplication property of -1
14. Multiplicative identity axiom
15. Multiplication property of zero
16. Distributive axiom
17. Distributive axiom
18. Definition of division
19. Associative axiom of multiplication
20. Distributive axiom
21. Commutative axiom for multiplication
22. Commutative axiom for addition
23. Associative axiom of addition
24. Definition of subtraction
25. Transitive axiom of equality
26. Reflexive axiom of equality
27. Commutative axiom for multiplication
28. Symmetric axiom of equality
29. Distributive axiom
30. Addition property of equality
31. Multiplication property of equality
32. Transitive axiom of equality
33. Multiplication property of equality
34. Addition property of equality
35. Commutative axiom for addition
36. Commutative axiom for multiplication
37. Additive inverse axiom
38. Multiplicative identity axiom
39. Definition of subtraction
40. Multiplicative inverses axiom

For Problems 41 through 50, copy the steps in the solution of the equation. For each step, name the axiom, other property, or definition which justifies that step.

41. $x + 3 = 8$
    $(x + 3) + (-3) = 8 + (-3)$ a.
    $x + [3 + (-3)] = 8 + (-3)$ b.
    $x + 0 = 8 + (-3)$ c.
    $x = 8 + (-3)$ d.
    $x = 5$ e.

41. a. Addition property of equality
    b. Associative axiom of addition
    c. Additive inverse axiom
    d. Additive identity axiom
    e. Arithmetic

42. a. Addition property of equality
     b. Associative axiom of addition
     c. Additive inverse axiom
     d. Additive identity axiom
     e. Arithmetic

42. $k + 8 = 3$
     $(k + 8) + (-8) = 3 + (-8)$ a.
     $k + [8 + (-8)] = 3 + (-8)$ b.
     $k + 0 = 3 + (-8)$ c.
     $k = 3 + (-8)$ d.
     $k = -5$ e.

43. a. Multiplication property of equality
        and definition of division
     b. Arithmetic
     c. Definition of division
     d. Associative axiom for multiplication
     e. Commutative axiom for multiplication
     f. Associative axiom for multiplication
     g. Multiplicative inverses axiom
     h. Multiplicative identity axiom

44. a. Multiplication property of equality
        and definition of division
     b. Arithmetic
     c. Definition of division
     d. Associative axiom for multiplication
     e. Commutative axiom for multiplication
     f. Associative axiom for multiplication
     g. Multiplicative inverses axiom
     h. Multiplicative identity axiom

43. $3m = 21$
     $3m \div 3 = 21 \div 3$ a.
     $3m \div 3 = 7$ b.
     $3m \cdot \dfrac{1}{3} = 7$ c.
     $3\left(m \cdot \dfrac{1}{3}\right) = 7$ d.
     $3\left(\dfrac{1}{3} \cdot m\right) = 7$ e.
     $\left(3 \cdot \dfrac{1}{3}\right)m = 7$ f.
     $1m = 7$ g.
     $m = 7$ h.

44. $8m = 63$
     $8m \div 8 = 63 \div 8$ a.
     $8m \div 8 = 9$ b.
     $8m \cdot \dfrac{1}{8} = 9$ c.
     $8\left(m \cdot \dfrac{1}{8}\right) = 9$ d.
     $8\left(\dfrac{1}{8} \cdot m\right) = 9$ e.
     $\left(8 \cdot \dfrac{1}{8}\right)m = 9$ f.
     $1m = 9$ g.
     $m = 9$ h.

45. a. Addition property of equality
     b. Arithmetic
     c. Associative axiom of addition
     d. Additive inverses axiom
     e. Additive identity axiom
     f. Multiplication property of equality
     g. Arithmetic
     h. Associative axiom for multiplication
     i. Multiplicative inverses axiom
     j. Multiplicative identity axiom

45. $4v + 21 = 3$
     $(4v + 21) + (-21) = 3 + (-21)$ a.
     $(4v + 21) + (-21) = -18$ b.
     $4v + [21 + (-21)] = -18$ c.
     $4v + 0 = -18$ d.
     $4v = -18$ e.
     $\left(\dfrac{1}{4}\right)(4v) = \left(\dfrac{1}{4}\right)(-18)$ f.
     $\left(\dfrac{1}{4}\right)(4v) = -4.5$ g.
     $\left(\dfrac{1}{4} \cdot 4\right)v = -4.5$ h.
     $1v = -4.5$ i.
     $v = -4.5$ j.

46. a. Addition property of equality
     b. Arithmetic
     c. Associative axiom of addition
     d. Additive inverses axiom
     e. Additive identity axiom
     f. Multiplication property of equality
     g. Arithmetic
     h. Associative axiom for multiplication
     i. Multiplicative inverses axiom
     j. Multiplicative identity axiom

46. $5y + 37 = 11$
     $(5y + 37) + (-37) = 11 + (-37)$ a.
     $(5y + 37) + (-37) = -26$ b.
     $5y + [37 + (-37)] = -26$ c.
     $5y + 0 = -26$ d.
     $5y = -26$ e.
     $\left(\dfrac{1}{5}\right)(5y) = \left(\dfrac{1}{5}\right)(-26)$ f.
     $\left(\dfrac{1}{5}\right)(5y) = -5.2$ g.

$$\left(\frac{1}{5} \cdot 5\right)y = -5.2$$

$1y = -5.2$

$y = 5.2$

<table>
<tr><td></td><td>h.</td></tr>
<tr><td></td><td>i.</td></tr>
<tr><td></td><td>j.</td></tr>
</table>

47. $10x - 31 = 45$

$10x = 76$ a.

$x = 7.6$ b.

48. $7x + 12 = 1$

$7x = -11$ a.

$x = -1.5714\ldots$ b.

49. $3x + 15 = 5x - 7$

$-2x + 15 = -7$ a.

$-2x = -22$ b.

$x = 11$ c.

50. $9x - 14 = 5x + 26$

$4x - 14 = 26$ a.

$4x = 40$ b.

$x = 10$ c.

47. a. Addition property of equality and arithmetic

    b. Multiplication property of equality and arithmetic

48. a. Addition property of equality and arithmetic

    b. Multiplication property of equality and arithmetic

49. a. Addition property of equality and combining like terms

    b. Addition property of equality and arithmetic

    c. Multiplication property of equality and arithmetic

50. a. Addition property of equality and combining like terms

    b. Addition property of equality and arithmetic

    c. Multiplication property of equality and arithmetic

51. a. Definition of subtraction

    b. Distributive axiom for multiplication over addition

    c. Positive times negative is negative

    d. Definition of subtraction

    e. Transitive axiom of equality

52. a. Definition of division

    b. Distributive property for multiplication over addition from the right

    c. Definition of division

    d. Transitive axiom of equality

Problems 51 through 56 show steps in proofs of some properties. Write the reasons that justify the steps.

51. *Multiplication Distributes over Subtraction*

Prove that $x(y - z) = xy - xz$.

PROOF:

$x(y - z)$

$= x[y + (-z)]$ a.

$= xy + x(-z)$ b.

$= xy + (-xz)$ c.

$= xy - xz$ d.

$\therefore x(y - z) = xy - xz$ e.

52. *Division Distributes over Addition*

Prove: If x, y, and z are any real numbers, $z \neq 0$, then

$$\frac{x + y}{z} = \frac{x}{z} + \frac{y}{z}.$$

PROOF:

a. $\dfrac{x + y}{z}$ a.

b. $= (x + y) \cdot \dfrac{1}{z}$ b.

c. $= x \cdot \dfrac{1}{z} + y \cdot \dfrac{1}{z}$ c.

d. $= \dfrac{x}{z} + \dfrac{y}{z}$ d.

e. $\therefore \dfrac{x + y}{z} = \dfrac{x}{z} + \dfrac{y}{z}$ e.

53.
   a. Associative axiom for addition
   b. Distributive axiom of multiplication over addition
   c. Distributive axiom of multiplication over addition
   d. Transitive axiom of equality

53.   *Multiplication Distributes over a Sum of Three Terms*

Prove: For any four real numbers w, x, y, and z,

$$w(x + y + z) = wx + wy + wz.$$

PROOF:

$w(x + y + z)$

$= w[x + (y + z)]$ a.

$= wx + w(y + z)$ b.

$= wx + wy + wz$ c.

$\therefore w(x + y + z) = wx + wy + wz$ d.

Hint: In (a), there are just *two* terms inside the parentheses, x and $(y + z)$. Thus you can use the distributive axiom in the next step.

54.
   a. Commutative axiom for multiplication
   b. Distributive axiom of multiplication over addition
   c. Commutative axiom for multiplication
   d. Transitive axiom of equality
   e. Symmetric axiom of equality

54.   *Combining Like Terms*

Copy the steps in the following proof that you can combine like terms by adding their coefficients. Then supply a reason for each step.

Prove: For any real numbers a, b, and x, $ax + bx = (a + b)x$.

PROOF:

$(a + b)x$

$= x(a + b)$ a.

$= xa + xb$ b.

$= ax + bx$ c.

$\therefore (a + b)x = ax + bx$ d.

$\therefore ax + bx = (a + b)x$ e.

55.
   a. Multiplication property of -1
   b. Distributive axiom of multiplication over addition
   c. Multiplication property of -1
   d. Definition of subtraction
   e. Transitive axiom of equality

55.   *Property of the Opposite of a Sum:*   The following is a proof that a "$-$" sign can distribute over addition. Name the axiom, other property, or definition which justifies each step.

PROOF:

$-(x + y)$

$= -1 \cdot (x + y)$ a.

$= -1x + (-1y)$ b.

$= -x + (-y)$ c.

$= -x - y$ d.

$\therefore -(x + y) = -x - y$ e.

56. *Multiplication Property of −1*

Prove that $-1x = -x$.

PROOF:

$$-1x + x$$
$$= -1x + 1x \qquad\qquad \text{a.}$$
$$= (-1 + 1)x \qquad\qquad \text{b.}$$
$$= 0x \qquad\qquad\qquad\quad \text{c.}$$
$$= 0 \qquad\qquad\qquad\quad\; \text{d.}$$
$$= x + (-x) \qquad\qquad \text{e.}$$
$$\therefore -1x + x = x + (-x) \qquad \text{f.}$$
$$\therefore -1x + x = -x + x \qquad \text{g.}$$
$$\therefore -1x = -x \qquad\qquad\quad \text{h.}$$

56. a. Multiplicative identity axiom
    b. Distributive property of multiplication over addition from the right
    c. Additive inverses axiom
    d. Multiplication property of 0
    e. Additive inverses axiom
    f. Transitive axiom of equality
    g. Commutative axiom for addition
    h. Addition property of equality ($-x$ was added to each member.)

57. What is wrong with this reasoning?

$$5 \cdot 0 = 0 \qquad\quad \text{Multiplication property of 0}$$
$$0 = 3 \cdot 0 \qquad\quad \text{Multiplication property of 0}$$
$$\therefore 5 \cdot 0 = 3 \cdot 0 \qquad \text{Transitive axiom of equality}$$
$$\therefore 5 = 3 \qquad\qquad\;\; \text{Multiplication property of equality}$$

57. The multiplication property of equality is true for real numbers, not for $\frac{1}{0}$.

58. One of these is an example of a commutative axiom. The other is an example of the symmetric axiom. Which is which?

If $3d + 5 = 14$,   then $14 = 3d + 5$.
If $3d + 5 = 14$,   then $5 + 3d = 14$.

58. symmetric
    commutative

59. State the axiom:
    a. Symmetric axiom of equality
    b. Reflexive axiom of equality
    c. Transitive axiom of equality
    d. Commutative axiom of multiplication
    e. Additive inverse axiom
    f. Multiplicative identity axiom

59. a. If $x = y$, then $y = x$.
    b. $x = x$
    c. If $x = y$ and $y = z$, then $x = z$.
    d. $xy = yx$
    e. $x + (-x) = 0$
    f. $x \cdot 1 = x$

60. State the property or definition:
    a. Addition property of equality
    b. Multiplication property of equality
    c. Multiplication property of −1
    d. Multiplication property of 0
    e. Definition of division
    f. Definition of subtraction

60. a. If $x = y$, then $x + z = y + z$.
    b. If $x = y$, then $xz = yz$.
    c. $-1 \cdot x = -x$
    d. $x \cdot 0 = 0$
    e. $\dfrac{x}{y} = x \cdot \dfrac{1}{y}$
    f. $x - y = x + (-y)$

For Problems 61 through 70, if it is an equation, solve it. If it is an expression, simplify it.

61. $5x - 7 = -34$

62. $3x - 5 + 7x$

63. $13 - x + 4x$

64. $8 - x = 51$

61. $S = \left\{-5\frac{2}{5}\right\}$

62. $10x - 5$

63. $13 + 3x$

64. $S = \{-43\}$

65. $15x - 2$ 66. $x = -32$
67. $x = 0.4$ 68. $-19x + 12$
69. $30x$ 70. $x^2 + 22x$

65. $4x - (2 - 11x)$ 66. $5x = 4(x - 8)$

67. $21 = 5(2x + 4) - 3$ 68. $2x + 3(4 - 7x)$

69. $(5)(3 \cdot 2x)$ 70. $x(x + 5) + 17x$

3-7   CHAPTER REVIEW AND TEST

Time: 1 day

Test Suggestions:

The chapter test should consist primarily of the technique of distributing. Make sure students have not forgotten this while proving properties. The daily practice problems at the ends of the problem sets should have helped. Do not expect mastery of the theorems by all students.

Assignment:

Following the test, study Section 4–1 and work Exercise 4–1, Problems 1–19 odd or 2–20 even.

In this chapter you have learned an important new technique—distributing. Distributing multiplication over addition, such as in

$$3(x + y) = 3x + 3y,$$

is an *axiom*. Other distributive properties, such as

$$3(x - y) = 3x - 3y$$

or

$$3(x + y + z) = 3x + 3y + 3z,$$

can be *proved* from the axioms. The distributive properties were used for two other types of transformation, collecting like terms and factoring out common factors.

Like terms: Common factors:

$4x + 3x - 5$ $4x - 12y$

$= 7x - 5$ $= 4(x - 3y)$

The chapter test below is one that you should be able to complete in 45 minutes. You will get the most benefit from it if you put yourself under test conditions (quiet room, no TV, etc.!). Don't just look at the problems and say, "Oh, I could do that." Actually write the problems and answers neatly and accurately as though it were a real test! Time yourself. When you finish, check the answers at the end of the book to see how well you did. If you do these things, you should be in good shape for the test your teacher will give you in class.

CHAPTER TEST

For Problems 1 through 20, simplify the expression by distributing, commuting, associating, and collecting like terms.

1. $7(9x - 8)$ $63x - 56$ 2. $(3x + 5)(8)$ $24x + 40$

3. $\dfrac{72a - 36b}{-12}$ $-6a + 3b$ 4. $x(x + 9)$ $x^2 + 9x$

5. $-42\left(\frac{1}{3}x - \frac{1}{7}y\right)$ $-14x + 6y$ 6. $-(x - 2)$ $-x + 2$

7. $5x + 7x + 11$ $12x + 11$ 8. $10 + 5r - 2r$ $10 + 3r$

9. $6 - 4x + 5x$ $6 + x$ 10. $7x - 5 - 4x$ $3x - 5$

11. $3x - x$ $2x$ 12. $4(x - 3) + 10x$ $14x - 12$

13. $3(x + 5) + 2(4x - 7)$ $11x + 1$ 14. $-4(3x - 9) + 6(2x + 7)$ 78

15. $5(x + 3) - (x - 7)$ $4x + 22$ 16. $6 + 4(x + 5) - x$ $3x + 26$

17. $7x + x(2 - 5x)$ $9x - 5x^2$

18. $\frac{1}{5}(35x - 50y) - \frac{1}{4}(24x - 20y)$ $x - 5y$

19. $0.4x + 0.7(x - 3)$ $1.1x - 2.1$ 20. $\frac{3}{4}(20x - 1) - 14x$ $x - \frac{3}{4}$

For Problems 21 through 26, factor out the common factor(s).

21. $5x + 10y$ $5(x + 2y)$ 22. $6p - 9j$ $3(2p - 3j)$

23. $rx + rz$ $r(x + z)$ 24. $12x + 18$ $6(2x + 3)$

25. $5x^2 - 3x$ $x(5x - 3)$ 26. $4x + 4y - 8z$ $4(x + y - 2z)$

27. The expressions $3(4 + x)$ and $3(4 \cdot x)$ are the same except for the operation between 4 and x. Simplify each expression. Then tell in words the difference between what you did for the two expressions.

28. Explain the difference between an axiom and any other property.

29. Write a statement of each of the following.
   a.   The commutative axiom for addition
   b.   The associative axiom for multiplication
   c.   The transitive axiom of equality
   d.   The definition of subtraction
   e.   The reflexive axiom of equality

30. Copy the steps in the following solution. Then supply a reason justifying each step.

   $29 = 5 - 3x$
   $5 - 3x = 29$ a.
   $5 + (-3x) = 29$ b.
   $-3x + 5 = 29$ c.
   $(-3x + 5) + (-5) = 29 + (-5)$ d.
   $(-3x + 5) + (-5) = 24$ e.
   $-3x + [5 + (-5)] = 24$ f.
   $-3x + 0 = 24$ g.
   $-3x = 24$ h.

27. $3(4 + x)$
    $= 12 + 3x$ Distribute the 3.
    $3(4 \cdot x)$
    $= 12x$ Associate the 3 and 4.

28. An axiom is a property that is assumed to be true without proof. Other properties can be proved from the axioms.

29. a. $x + y = y + x$
    b. $(xy)z = x(yz)$
    c. If $x = y$ and $y = z$, then $x = z$.
    d. $x - y = x + (-y)$
    e. $x + z = x + z$

30. a. Symmetric axiom of equality
    b. Definition of subtraction
    c. Commutative axiom of addition
    d. Addition property of equality
    e. Arithmetic
    f. Associative axiom of addition
    g. Additive identity axiom
    h. Additive identity axiom
    i. Multiplication property of equality
    j. Arithmetic
    k. Associative axiom of multiplication
    l. Multiplicative inverses axiom
    m. Multiplicative identity axiom

$$\left(-\frac{1}{3}\right)(-3x) = \left(-\frac{1}{3}\right)(24) \qquad \text{i.}$$

$$\left(-\frac{1}{3}\right)(-3x) = -8 \qquad \text{j.}$$

$$\left[\left(-\frac{1}{3}\right)(-3)\right]x = -8 \qquad \text{k.}$$

$$1x = -8 \qquad \text{l.}$$

$$x = -8 \qquad \text{m.}$$

31.

a. Write one member of the desired equation.

b. Definition of division

c. Commutative axiom for ·

d. Associative axiom for +

e. Distributive axiom for · over +

f. Distributive axiom for · over +

g. Commutative axiom for ·

h. Definition of division

i. Transitive axiom for =

31. Copy the steps in the following proof. Then supply a reason justifying each step.

Prove: For all real numbers w, x, y, and z, $\dfrac{w + x + y}{z} = \dfrac{w}{z} + \dfrac{x}{z} + \dfrac{y}{z}$.

PROOF:

a. $\quad \dfrac{w + x + y}{z}$

b. $\quad = (w + x + y) \cdot \dfrac{1}{z}$

c. $\quad = \dfrac{1}{z}(w + x + y)$

d. $\quad = \dfrac{1}{z}[(w + x) + y]$

e. $\quad = \dfrac{1}{z}[w + x] + \dfrac{1}{z} \cdot y$

f. $\quad = \dfrac{1}{z} \cdot w + \dfrac{1}{z} \cdot x + \dfrac{1}{z} \cdot y$

g. $\quad = w \cdot \dfrac{1}{z} + x \cdot \dfrac{1}{z} + y \cdot \dfrac{1}{z}$

h. $\quad = \dfrac{w}{z} + \dfrac{x}{z} + \dfrac{y}{z}$

i. $\quad \therefore \dfrac{w + x + y}{z} = \dfrac{w}{z} + \dfrac{x}{z} + \dfrac{y}{z}$

4

Harder Equations

In the last chapter you learned the distributive properties. These properties are useful in simplifying expressions such as 3(x + 5) − 7. They also allow you to simplify expressions like 4x + 7x + 8 by combining like terms. In this chapter you will solve equations that have expressions like these in one or both members. These expressions could represent things in the real world such as the amount of work done by construction crews that start at different times.

Variable:

x Number of days first crew has worked.

Expression:

$x - 2$ Number of days second crew has worked.

Expressions:

$9x$ Amounts of work
$12(x - 2)$ each crew has done.

Equation:

$9x = 12(x - 2)$ Says that each crew has done the same amount of work.

Time: $\frac{1}{2}$ day, with Section 4–2

4-1 | EQUATIONS WITH LIKE TERMS

Chalkboard Examples:

Solve and check.
$5x - 7 + 4x = 20$
Ans.: $x = 3$
Chk.: $20 = 20$
See Section 4–2 for other examples.

Assignment:

Problems 1–19 odd or 2–20 even should have been assigned following the Chapter 3 test in preparation for your first class on Chapter 4.

This section is meant for you to read and work on your own. If you have understood what you have learned so far, you should be able to do this without prior classroom discussion.

You have learned how to solve equations like

$$3x + 5 = 17.$$

You also know how to simplify expressions such as

$$3x - 7 + 5x,$$

which have like terms. Now you are ready to put together these two techniques and solve equations that look like this:

$$3x - 7 + 5x = 25.$$

In such equations, the variable appears more than once.

Objective:
Be able to solve equations that have like terms in one member.

The secret in working a new problem such as this is changing it to an old problem. The equation

$$3x - 7 + 5x = 25$$

can be transformed by combining like terms on the left. You get

$$8x - 7 = 25.$$

From here on, this is an old problem.

$$8x - 7 + 7 = 25 + 7 \qquad \text{Add 7 to each member.}$$

$$8x = 32 \qquad \text{Do the operations.}$$

$$\frac{8x}{8} = \frac{32}{8}$$ Divide each member by 8.

$$x = 4$$ Do the division.

Note: You can do some of the steps for solving this kind of equation in your head. For instance, you could write

$$8x - 7 = 25$$

$$8x = 32$$ Add 7 to each member.

$$\underline{\underline{x = 4}}$$ Divide each member by 8.

Cover the answers as you work these examples.

EXAMPLE
- - - - -   - - - - -

Solve and check: $2x - 8 + 7x = 19$.

	Think These Reasons

$2x - 8 + 7x = 19$ Write the given equation.

$9x - 8 = 19$ Combine like terms.

$9x - 8 + 8 = 19 + 8$ Add 8 to each member.

$9x = 27$ Do the operations.

$$\frac{9x}{9} = \frac{27}{9}$$ Divide each member by 9.

$$\underline{\underline{x = 3}}$$ Do the operations.

Check: $2x - 8 + 7x$ Write the left member.

$= 6 - 8 + 21$ Substitute 3 for x.

$= 19$ ✔   Do the arithmetic. The answer checks.

EXERCISE 4-1

For Problems 1 through 20, solve the equation and check your answer.

1. $2x + 6x = 56$ $x = 7$

2. $5x + 4x = 45$ $x = 5$

3. $7x - 4x = 15$ $x = 5$

4. $8x - 3x = 35$ $x = 7$

5. $3x + 4x + 8 = 22$ $x = 2$

6. $6x + 2x + 7 = 31$ $x = 3$

Problem Notes:

This type of problem is duplicated in Problems 1–20 of Section 4–2. If students need a few more of this type of assignment to gain confidence, you may assign problems from 4–2. The additional problems in 4–1 serve as a back-up in case of emergency need.

7. $10x - 7x + 18 = 6$ $x = -4$ 8. $7x - 4x + 21 = 15$ $x = -2$

9. $5x - 7x + 21 = 27$ $x = -3$ 10. $6x - 10x + 2 = 22$ $x = -5$

11. $7x + 3 + 3x = 63$ $x = 6$ 12. $2x + 3 + 5x = 31$ $x = 4$

13. $9x - 14 - 5x = -10$ $x = 1$ 14. $8x - 4 - 2x = -10$ $x = -1$

15. $10x - x = 90$ $x = 10$ 16. $6x - x = 30$ $x = 6$

17. $7x - 4 - 6x = 5$ $x = 9$ 18. $9x - 3 - 8x = 7$ $x = 10$

19. $2x + 3x + 4 + 5x = 34$ $x = 3$

20. $3x + 4 + 5x + 6x = 32$ $x = 2$

Problems 21 through 30 review other techniques.

21. Simplify: $3x - 4 + 5x$ $8x - 4$

22. Evaluate: $0.3 + 4.7(2)$ 9.7

23. Evaluate $3x + 4.9$ if x is 5. 19.9

24. Simplify: $4 - (2x - 11)$ $15 - 2x$

25. Evaluate: $|4 - 13|$ 9

26. Evaluate $\left(\dfrac{2}{3}\right)x - 10$ if x is 24. 6

27. Write an expression for twelve less than x. $x - 12$

28. Write an expression for the product of 6 and x, increased by 5. $6x + 5$

29. Name the axiom: $(ab)c = a(bc)$ Associative axiom of multiplication.

30. Name the axiom: If $a = b$, then $b = a$.   Symmetric axiom of equality.

4-2	EQUATIONS WITH LIKE TERMS AND DISTRIBUTING

Time: $\frac{1}{2}$ day or $1\frac{1}{2}$ days, with Section 4–1

Chalkboard Examples:

1. Present one problem assigned from Exercise 4–1.

2. Solve and check:
   $7(x + 3) - 2x = 11$ Ans.: $x = -2$
   Chk.: $11 = 11$
   $-8 = 4(x + 1) - 3(5x - 7)$ Ans.: $3 = x$
   Chk.: $-8 = -8$

In the last section you solved equations in which the left member has like terms. Equations such as

$$3x - 7 + 5x = 25$$

can be transformed into more familiar equations, like

$$8x - 7 = 25,$$

by combining like terms. In this section you solve more equations like this. You also solve equations such as

$$6(x - 2) + 5x = 43,$$

in which you must *distribute* before you can combine like terms.

Objective :
Be able to solve equations with like terms in one member, some of which
require distributing before like terms can be combined.

Assignments:

One day on Sections 4–1 and 4–2:
  21–39 odd or 22–40 even
  Selected problems from Section 3–4.
  Review on "simplify."
Two days on Sections 4–1 and 4–2:
  Day 1: 11–29 odd or 12–30 even
  Day 2: 22–44 even or 21–43 odd
  Selected problems from Section 3–4.

Cover the answers as you work these examples.

EXAMPLE 1

Solve and check: $6(x - 2) + 5x = 43$.

– – – – –   – – – – –

Think These Reasons

$6(x - 2) + 5x = 43$ — Write the given equation.

$6x - 12 + 5x = 43$ — Distribute 6 to x and to -2.

$11x - 12 = 43$ — Commute and combine like terms.

$11x = 55$ — Add 12 to each member.

$x = 5$ — Divide each member by 11.

Check: $6(x - 2) + 5x$ — Write the left member.

$= 6(5 - 2) + 25$ — Substitute 5 for x.

$= 6(3) + 25$ — Do the arithmetic.

$= 18 + 25$ — Do more arithmetic.

$= 43$ ✔ — The answer checks.

Some equations may require distributing more than once or may have the
variable in the right member instead of in the left.

EXAMPLE 2

Solve and check: $-1 = 5(x - 6) + 4(2 - 3x)$.

– – – – –   – – – – –

$-1 = 5(x - 6) + 4(2 - 3x)$ — Write the given equation.

$-1 = 5x - 30 + 8 - 12x$ — Distribute 5 and 4.

$-1 = -7x - 22$ — Combine like terms.

$21 = -7x$ — Add 22 to both members.

$-3 = x$ — Divide both members by -7.

Check: $5(x - 6) + 4(2 - 3x)$ — Write the right member of the equation.

$= 5(-3 - 6) + 4(2 + 9)$ — Substitute -3 for x.

$= 5(-9) + 4(11)$ — Do the arithmetic.

$= -45 + 44$ Do more arithmetic.

$= -1$ ✔   The answer checks.

ORAL PRACTICE

Tell what equation you get after the distributive step.

EXAMPLES

Answers

i. $3(7 - 2x) + 4x = 19$ i. $21 - 6x + 4x = 19$

ii. $5x - 2(3x - 7) = -13$ ii. $5x - 6x + 14 = -13$

A. $24x + 42 + 2x = 9$

B. $10x - 15 + 4x = 11$

C. $12y + 20 - 2y = 6$

D. $18z - 12 - 5z = 1$

E. $-8x - 6 + 5x = 7$

F. $-24 + 16x + 4x = 10$

G. $5x + 18 + 3x = -4$

H. $4x - 6x - 14 = 8$

I. $6x - 4 + 2x = 7$

J. $6x - 5x + 8 = 7$

A. $6(4x + 7) + 2x = 9$ B. $5(2x - 3) + 4x = 11$

C. $4(3y + 5) - 2y = 6$ D. $6(3z - 2) - 5z = 1$

E. $-2(4x + 3) + 5x = 7$ F. $-8(3 - 2x) + 4x = 10$

G. $5x + 3(6 + x) = -4$ H. $4x - 2(3x + 7) = 8$

I. $6x - 1(4 - 2x) = 7$ J. $6x - (5x - 8) = 7$

EXERCISE 4-2

Solve and check.

Problem Notes:

Problems 1–20 are similar to those in Section 4–1, except a few have variables other than x. Problems 21–40 involve distributing before like terms can be combined. Problems 41–44 can be regarded as bonus problems in which the students must figure out what happens when the variable is on *both* sides or when the variable disappears. These problems anticipate the work of Section 4–3, next.

1. $7x + 3x = 40$ $x = 4$ 2. $9x + 4x = 65$ $x = 5$

3. $4x - 11x = 105$ $x = -15$ 4. $7x - 11x = 60$ $x = -15$

5. $16x + 3 + 4x = 103$ $x = 5$ 6. $18x + 7 + 7x = 107$ $x = 4$

7. $7r - 8 - 4r = 25$ $r = 11$ 8. $10s - 7 - 3s = 84$ $s = 13$

9. $-5c + 17 - 8c = 56$ $c = -3$ 10. $-3t + 19 - 5t = 91$ $t = -9$

11. $58 = 6 - 14x + 12x$ $-26 = x$ 12. $65 = 5 - 8x + 2x$ $-10 = x$

13. $8t + 5 - 7t = 22$ $t = 17$ 14. $9r + 7 - 8r = 24$ $r = 17$

15. $20x + 84 - 8x = 0$ $x = -7$ 16. $13x + 105 - 8x = 0$ $x = -21$

17. $x + 21 + 4x = -33$ $x = -10.8$ 18. $9x + 33 + x = -93$ $x = -12.6$

19. $2x - 5x + 13 + 9x = 67$ $x = 9$ 20. $3x - 7x + 15 + 6x = 41$ $x = 13$

21. $5(x + 3) - 2x = -21$ $x = -12$ 22. $6(x + 2) - 4x = 48$ $x = 18$

23. $2(3x - 7) + 4x = 26$ $x = 4$ 24. $3(2x - 5) + 2x = -7$ $x = 1$

25. $5x + 3(x + 4) = 28$ $x = 2$ 26. $6x + 3(x + 7) = -15$ $x = -4$

27. $7x - 4(2 - 3x) = -27$ $x = -1$ 28. $5x - 2(6 - 5x) = 18$ $x = 2$

29. $7x - (5 + 6x) = 4$ $x = 9$ 30. $4x - (3x + 11) = -11$ $x = 0$

31. $12 - 7(x - 4) + x = -2$ $x = 7$ 32. $17 - 7(x - 3) + x = 86$ $x = -8$

33. $2(x + 3) - 5(x - 1) = 32$ $x = -7$34. $3(x + 4) - 5(x - 1) = 5$ $x = 6$

35. $55 = 3(2x - 1) + 2(x + 5)$ $6 = x$36. $66 = 4(2x - 3) + 2(x + 4)$ $7 = x$

37. $0 = 4(6 - x) + 7x$ $-8 = x$ 38. $0 = 5(7 - x) + 12x$ $-5 = x$

39. $3(a + 2) - (a - 1) = 17$ $a = 5$ 40. $4(c + 3) - (c - 1) = 64$ $c = 17$

Problems 41 through 44 require clever transformations or have surprising answers!

41. $9x + 35 = 4x$ $x = -7$ 42. $8x + 21 = 5x$ $x = -7$

43. $3(4x + 5) - 2(6x - 1) = 17$ 44. $3(4x + 5) - 2(6x - 1) = 18$
     x can be *any real number*.   No solution

Problems 45 through 50 review other techniques.

45. What property is this? $-1 \cdot s = -s$ Multiplication property of -1.

46. Evaluate $5x^2$ if x is 3.   45

47. Simplify: $19 - 9(2x - 4)$ $55 - 18x$

48. Evaluate: $\dfrac{2}{3} + \dfrac{5}{6}$ $1\frac{1}{2}$

49. Simplify: $-(-14x + 3) - 7$ $14x - 10$

50. What property is this? $(x)\left(\dfrac{1}{x}\right) = 1$ Multiplicative inverses axiom.

4-3 | **EQUATIONS WITH VARIABLES IN BOTH MEMBERS**

The equations of Sections 4.1 and 4.2 had all the variable terms in either the left member or the right member. Equations such as

$$7x = 5x + 18$$

have variable terms in *both* members. These equations can readily be transformed so that all variable terms are in *one* member.

Time: 2 days

Chalkboard Examples:

Day 1:
Solve and check:
$7x - 4 = 5x - 22$ Ans.: $x = -9$
                         Chk.: $-67 = -67$
$5(x - 3) = 2 - 3(x - 2) - 2$
                         Ans.: $x = \frac{21}{8}$
                         Chk.: $-1\frac{7}{8} = -1\frac{7}{8}$

Day 2:
Solve and check:

$6x + 5 = 2(3x - 1)$
$6x + 5 = 6x - 2$
$5 = -2$ Ans.: No solution.
                      No check
                      possible.

$5(x + 3) = 2x + 3(x + 5)$
$5x + 15 = 5x + 15$
$5x = 5x$ or $15 = 15$ Ans.: Any number.
                            (identity)
                         Checking is
                         impractical.

The Oral Practice problems of this section are quite helpful in conveying the concepts. They take 10 to 15 minutes and can save an evening of frustration for the students!

Assignments:

Day 1: 1–19 odd or 2–20 even
Day 2: 21–43 odd or 22–44 even (fairly long)

$7x = 5x + 18$	Write the given equation.
$7x - 5x = 5x + 18 - 5x$	Subtract $5x$ from each member.
$2x = 18$	Combine like terms on the left. Commute and associate $5x$ and $-5x$ on the right.
$\underline{\underline{x = 9}}$	Divide each member by 2.

By getting rid of the variable term in the right member, you have changed this new problem into an old problem. From there on, you use familiar techniques to solve the equation.

The check for such an equation is most easily done by substituting the solution into *both* members of the equation.

$7(9) \stackrel{?}{=} 5(9) + 18$	Substitute 9 for x.
$63 \stackrel{?}{=} 45 + 18$	Do the arithmetic.
$63 = 63$ ✔	The answer checks.

The $\stackrel{?}{=}$ sign asks: *Are* these equal?

Objective :
Be able to solve equations with variables in both members.

Cover the answers as you work these examples.

EXAMPLE 1

Solve and check: $3x + 55 = 8x$.

– – – – –   – – – – –

	Think These Reasons
$3x + 55 = 8x$	Write the given equation.
$3x + 55 - 8x = 8x - 8x$	Subtract $8x$ from each member.
$-5x + 55 = 0$	Combine like terms.
$-5x = -55$	Subtract 55 from each member.
$\underline{\underline{x = 11}}$	Divide each member by -5.

Check:

$3(11) + 55 \stackrel{?}{=} 8(11)$	Substitute 11 for x.
$33 + 55 \stackrel{?}{=} 88$	Do the arithmetic.
$88 = 88$ ✔	Checks!

Sometimes there are surprises when you try to solve this kind of equation. For example, the equation

$$x = x + 5$$

has *no* solutions. It says that a number is 5 more than *itself*. If you try to solve such an equation, you get the following result.

$x = x + 5$	Write the given equation.
$x - x = x + 5 - x$	Subtract x from each member.
$0 = 5$	Combine like terms.
<u>No solutions.</u>	Write a conclusion.

The impossible statement $0 = 5$ indicates that there are *no* solutions. So you write a conclusion stating this fact.

Another surprise results from solving an equation like this:

$$2x + 3x + 7 = 5x + 1 + 6.$$

Upon combining like terms, you get

$$5x + 7 = 5x + 7.$$

The two expressions are identical. The equation is therefore true for *all* values of x. For instance, $5(3) + 7 = 5(3) + 7$, since both equal 22, and $5(-2) + 7 = 5(-2) + 7$, since both equal -3.

Such an equation is called an *identity*. The equations you have solved so far are called *conditional equations*, because they are true only under the condition that the variable has the "right" value.

DEFINITION

IDENTITIES AND CONDITIONAL EQUATIONS
An **identity** is an equation that is true for *all* values of the variable.

A **conditional equation** is one that is true for some value(s) of the variable and not true for other values of the variable.

If you try to solve the identity above, you get the following result.

$5x + 7 = 5x + 7$	
$5x + 7 - 5x = 5x + 7 - 5x$	Subtract $5x$ from each member.
$7 = 7$	Combine like terms.
<u>Any number (identity).</u>	Write a conclusion. The statement $7 = 7$ is *always* true, so the equation is an identity.

CONCLUSION

> The following examples show what is true if the variable *disappears* from an equation.
>
> $0 = 5$ *Never* true. *No* solutions
>
> $7 = 7$ *Always* true. Any number is a solution.
>   (Equation is an *identity*.)

The next two examples illustrate these ideas.

EXAMPLE 2

Solve $5 - 9x = 9x$.

– – – – –   – – – – –

$$5 - 9x = -9x$$ Write the given equation.

$$5 - 9x + 9x = -9x + 9x$$ Add $9x$ to each member.

$$5 = 0$$ Combine like terms.

No solutions.   Write a conclusion.

EXAMPLE 3

Solve $4(x + 3) = 3x + 12 + x$.

– – – – –   – – – – –

$4(x + 3) = 3x + 12 + x$ Write the given equation.

$4x + 12 = 4x + 12$ Distribute on the left. Combine like terms on the right.

Any number (identity).   Write a conclusion.

Note: It is not necessary for you to do any more steps once you have shown that the two members of the equation are exactly the same.

ORAL PRACTICE

Tell what you would do to get rid of the variable in the right member.

EXAMPLES

		Answers		
i.	$3x + 8 = 5x$		i.	Subtract $5x$ from each member.
ii.	$2x = 3 - 7x$		ii.	Add $7x$ to each member.
iii.	$x = 4x - 8$		iii.	Subtract $4x$ from each member.

A. $9x - 2 = 4x$

B. $6x + 5 = -3x$

C. $4 - 2x = 7x$

D. $5x = 2 + 8x$

E. $7x = 5 - 9x$

F. $-10x = -4x + 3$

G. $-2x = 5 - x$

H. $5x - 4 = 3x + 7$

I. $2 + 8x = 5 - 7x$

J. $3 - 2x = -11x + 4$

K. Tell what $\overset{?}{=}$ means.

L. Give the definition of identity.

M. Give the definition of conditional equation.

A. Subtract $4x$ from each member.
B. Add $3x$ to each member.
C. Subtract $7x$ from each member.
D. Subtract $8x$ from each member.
E. Add $9x$ to each member.
F. Add $4x$ to each member.
G. Add x to each member.
H. Subtract $3x$ from each member.
I. Add $7x$ to each member.
J. Add $11x$ to each member.
K. "Is . . . equal to . . .?"
L. An identity is an equation that is true for *all* values of the variable.
M. A conditional equation is an equation that is true for some value(s) of the variable and not true for other values of the variable.

The last step in solving an equation is given below. Tell whether the equation is *conditional*, is an *identity*, or has *no* solution.

EXAMPLES

		Answers		
i.	$4 = 0$	i.	No solution
ii.	$5 = 5$	ii.	Identity
iii.	$x = 7$	iii.	Conditional

N. $x = 3$ Conditional   O. $7 = 7$ Identity   P. $8 = x$ Conditional

Q. $8 = 7$ No solution   R. $8 = 8$ Identity   S. $x = x$ Identity

T. $x = 0$ Conditional   U. $0 = 0$ Identity

EXERCISE 4-3

For Problems 1 through 20, solve and check.

1. $5x + 27 = 2x$ $x = -9$

2. $7x + 66 = 4x$ $x = -22$

3. $6x - 28 = 8x$ $x = -14$

4. $5x - 39 = 8x$ $x = -13$

5. $9x = 4x - 65$ $x = -13$

6. $8x = 2x - 60$ $x = -10$

7. $55 - 3x = 8x$ $5 = x$

8. $54 - 5x = 4x$ $6 = x$

9. $5x = 48 - x$ $x = 8$

10. $3x = 40 - x$ $x = 10$

11. $10c - 51 = 7c$ $c = 17$

12. $9j - 75 = 6j$ $j = 25$

13. $29y + 56 = 27y$ $y = -28$

14. $14b + 30 = 16b$ $b = 15$

15. $-6a = a - 70$ $a = 10$

16. $-a = 7a - 48$ $a = 6$

17. $9x = 34 + 8x$ $x = 34$

18. $7x = 45 - 2x$ $x = 5$

19. $7z = -16 - 9z$ $z = -1$

20. $11y = -400 - 9y$ $y = -20$

Problem Notes:

You can tell whether the student has checked the answer correctly by looking at the last line of the check. Both expressions must have the same value. That value, however, is not obvious to the student until the check has actually been done. It is satisfactory for students to show only this last step.

Problems 1–20 are straightforward, involving only combining like terms. Problems 21–44 bring in equations with no solutions and identities as well as transformations requiring distributing.

1.	$-18 = -18$	2.	$-88 = -88$
3.	$-112 = -112$	4.	$-104 = -104$
5.	$-117 = -117$	6.	$-80 = -80$
7.	$40 = 40$	8.	$24 = 24$
9.	$40 = 40$	10.	$30 = 30$
11.	$119 = 119$	12.	$150 = 150$
13.	$-756 = -756$	14.	$240 = 240$
15.	$-60 = -60$	16.	$-6 = -6$
17.	$306 = 306$	18.	$35 = 35$
19.	$-7 = -7$	20.	$-220 = -220$

For Problems 21–44, solve and check. If the equation is an identity or has no solution, write an appropriate conclusion.

21. No solution
22. $x = 0$
23. $x = 0$
24. No solution
25. $x = -9$
26. $a = -9$
27. All real numbers (identity)   28. $x = -2$
29. $x = 13$
30. Identity
31. $6 = x$
32. $x = -30$
33. $-3 = x$
34. $r = -1$
35. $20 = s$
36. $t = 4$
37. No solution
38. Identity
39. Identity
40. No solution
41. $x = -2$
42. $-7 = x$
43. $x = -5\frac{1}{2}$
44. $x = 28$

Checks:

21. —
22. $7 = 7$
23. $8 = 8$
24. —
25. $-23 = -23$
26. $-39 = -39$
27. —
28. $10 = 10$
29. $59 = 59$
30. —
31. $36 = 36$
32. $-210 = -210$
33. $60 = 60$
34. $21 = 21$
35. $3 = 3$
36. $26 = 26$
37. —
38. —
39. —
40. —
41. $2 = 2$
42. $-18 = -18$
43. $-6.5 = -6.5$
44. $228 = 228$
45. $12x - 6.9y + 2z$ 46. $4x$
47. 12.2
48. 120
49. $4x - 25.3$
50. $4 + 3 + x$

21. $4u = 37 + 4u$
22. $5x + 7 = 4x + 7$
23. $5x + 8 = 7x + 8$
24. $5x + 7 = 5x + 8$
25. $2x - 5 = 3x + 4$
26. $4a - 3 = 5a + 6$
27. $5 - 2x = 3 - 2x + 2$
28. $4 - 3x = 5 - 6x - 7$
29. $6x + 7 - 2x = 3 + 5x - 9$
30. $5 + 2x - 9 = 7x - 4 - 5x$
31. $4(x + 3) = 6x$
32. $7x = 5(x - 12)$
33. $5(9 - x) = 4(x + 18)$
34. $7(2 - r) = 3(r + 8)$
35. $3s + 3(1 - s) = s - 17$
36. $2(5 - t) + 6t = t + 22$
37. $4x - 2(1 - x) = 2(3x - 2)$
38. $3(x - 4) - x = 2(x - 6)$
39. $4(r + 1) = 6 - 2(1 - 2r)$
40. $x + 2(x + 4) = 1 + 3(x + 2)$
41. $2[1 - 3(x + 2)] = -x$
42. $3(1 + x) = 2[3(x + 2) - (x + 1)]$
43. $6(x + 4) - (x + 3) = x - 1$
44. $3(3x + 1) - (x - 1) = 6(x + 10)$

Problems 45 through 50 review other techniques.

45. Distribute: $3\left(4x - 2.3y + \frac{2}{3}z\right)$

46. Simplify: $5x - x$

47. Evaluate $11 - 4x$ if x is -0.3.

48. Find 30% of 400.

49. Simplify: $4(3x - 7) - (8x - 2.7)$

50. Commute the x and the 3: $4 + x + 3$

Time: 2 or 3 days, including test or quiz

4-4

EQUATIONS THAT INVOLVE DECIMALS

Chalkboard Examples:

Day 1:
Solve and check:
$29x + 47 = 129$ Ans.: $x = 2.82758...$
$x \approx 2.83$
Chk.: $129 = 129$

Until now the equations you have solved have "come out nicely." The answers were usually *integers*. As you recall from Section 2.2, the integers are the whole numbers 0, 1, 2, 3, . . . and their opposites, -1, -2, -3, ... They are used to mark the scale on the number line.

In most problems from the real world, the answers are *not* integers. For instance, if you drive for 258 mi between fill-ups and buy 13.8 gal of gas, then you mileage is

$$\frac{258}{13.8} \text{ miles per gallon (mpg).}$$

Dividing by calculator gives approximately

$$18.69565217 \text{ mpg.}$$

Normally, such numbers would be rounded, for example, to

$$18.7 \text{ mpg.}$$

In this section you will solve equations whose solutions turn out to be "untidy decimals" like this.

Objective :
Be able to find approximate solutions for equations involving decimals.

Cover the answers as you work these examples.

EXAMPLE 1

Solve $17x + 38 = -24$. Round off to two decimal places. Check your answer.

– – – – –   – – – – –

	Think These Reasons
$17x + 38 = -24$	Write the given equation.
$17x = -62$	Subtract 38 from both members.
$x = -\dfrac{62}{17}$	Divide each member by 17.
$x = -3.64705$	Use a calculator. (Save this value in memory for use in the check.)
$x \approx -3.65$	Round off to two decimal places.

Check:

$17(-3.647 \ldots) + 38 \overset{?}{=} -24$ Recall the value of x from memory.

$-24 = -24$ Do the operations. The answer checks.

$3.4x + 13.7 = 0.58x - 35.2$
  Ans.: $x = -17.34042 \ldots$ $x \approx -17.34$
Chk.: $-45.25 \ldots = -45.25 \ldots$
$4.3x - 7.1 = 3.8(5x + 0.4)$
  Ans.: $x = -0.58639 \ldots$ $x \approx -0.59$
Chk.: $-9.62 \ldots = -9.62 \ldots$

Day 2: Homework problems at the board. You should consider giving a test or quiz on Day 2 or Day 3. In this way, students will be motivated to learn the techniques before embarking on the word problems in Section 4–6.

Assignments:

Two days on section:
  Day 1: 1–19 odd or 2–20 even
  Day 2: following quiz, work 18 and 20 or
    17 and 19
Three days on section:
  Day 1: 1–13 odd
  Day 2: 2–20 even
  Day 3: following quiz, work 17 and 19
  Note: Unless your students are unusually strong, it is advisable *not* to have them try to work ahead in the word problems of Section 4–5.

Notes:

1. The symbol $\approx$ means *is approximately equal to*.
2. The round off to two decimal places, you (mentally) put a mark after the *second* digit to the *right* of the decimal point, like this:

$$-3.64{\mid}7058824.$$

Next, circle the two digits on either side of the mark.

$$-3.6 \textcircled{4{\mid}7} 058824$$

Then ask, "Is 47 closer to 40 or closer to 50?" Since it is closer to 50, you rounded off *upward,* getting

$$-3.65.$$

3. A number ending in 5 should be rounded off *upwards* unless there is a reason for doing otherwise. Thus

$$2.975,$$

when rounded off to two decimal places, becomes

$$2.98.$$

4. Because of round-off inside some calculators, the check may show a number only approximately equal to -24, such as -23.9997.

EXAMPLE 2

Solve $5.2x - 26.3 = 0.47x - 8$. Round off to two decimal places. Check your answer.

$- - - - -$ $- - - - -$

$5.2x - 26.3 = 0.47x - 8$	Write the given equation.
$5.2x - 0.47x = -8 + 26.3$	Add 26.3 to and subtract $0.47x$ from each member.
$4.73x = 18.3$	Combine like terms.
$x = \dfrac{18.3}{4.73}$	Divide each member by 4.73.
$x = 3.86892 \ldots$	Use a calculator. (Save this value in memory for use in the check.)
$x \approx 3.87$	Round off to two decimal places.

Check: $5.2(3.868 \ldots) - 26.3 \overset{?}{=} 0.47(3.868 \ldots) - 8$

$$-6.1816 \ldots = -6.1816 \ldots \quad \checkmark$$

Note: $0.47x$ could be written $.47x$. However, the leading zero helps you avoid losing the decimal point and thinking that the number is $47x$.

EXAMPLE 3

Solve $5.3x + 11.82 = 4.2(3.1x - 7.5)$. Round to two decimal places.
Check your answer.

_ _ _ _ _   _ _ _ _ _

$5.3x + 11.82 = 4.2(3.1x - 7.5)$	Write the given equation.
$5.3x + 11.82 = 13.02x - 31.50$	Distribute 4.2.
$5.3x - 13.02x = -31.50 - 11.82$	Subtract 11.82 and $13.02x$ from each member.
$-7.72x = -43.32$	Combine like terms.
$x = \dfrac{-43.32}{-7.72}$	Divide each member by -7.72.
$x = 5.61139\ldots$	Use a calculator. (Save this value in memory for use in the check.)
$\underline{\underline{x \approx 5.61}}$	Round to two decimal places.

Check: $5.3(5.611\ldots) + 11.82 \overset{?}{=} 4.2(3.1(5.611\ldots) - 7.5)$

$41.5604\ldots = 41.5604\ldots$ ✔

Note: In checking, the entire calculation for each member can be done on the calculator *without* writing intermediate values! You should write down the *last* line of the check to show that the two members really are equal.

ORAL PRACTICE

Round off to two decimal places.

EXAMPLES

		Answers	
i.	0.293	i.	0.29
ii.	-5.407	ii.	-5.41
iii.	3.698241	iii.	3.70

A.   3.127   3.13   B.   48.582   48.58

C.   0.587   0.59   D.   -1.094   -1.09

E.   3.52831   3.53   F.   6.497   6.50

Problem Notes:

Rounding off to two decimal places is reasonable at this stage of a student's development. Once the student is comfortable rounding off numbers, the stage will be set for later introduction to significant digits in Section 9–6.

Students may do the entire check on a calculator. To make sure they have done it correctly, have the students write at least the last line of the check. Make sure they save the answer in memory without round-off, or the check will be somewhat inaccurate.

All problems in this section are straightforward in that none are identities or empty solution sets. Problems 12 and 15 have *exact* answers.

G. -9.4308 $_{-9.43}$ H. 0.057 $_{0.06}$

I. -99.699 $_{-99.70}$ J. 0.535 $_{0.54}$

Use a calculator to find each quotient. Round off approximate answers to two decimal places.

K. $\dfrac{3.7}{1.3}$ $_{2.85\,\uparrow\,*}$ L. $\dfrac{6.8}{1.4}$ $_{4.86\,\uparrow}$ M. $\dfrac{4.2}{9.7}$ $_{0.43\,\downarrow}$

N. $\dfrac{-5.4}{0.7}$ $_{-7.71\,\downarrow}$ O. $\dfrac{0.7}{-3.7}$ $_{-0.19\,\uparrow}$ P. $\dfrac{5.1}{1.7}$ $_{3(\text{exact})}$

Q. $\dfrac{4.03}{0.65}$ $_{6.2(\text{exact})}$ R. $\dfrac{3.76}{2.09}$ $_{1.80\,\uparrow}$ S. $\dfrac{0}{5.9}$ $_{0(\text{exact})}$

T. $\dfrac{3.8}{0}$ $_{\text{Undefined}}$

*Arrows indicate which direction the (absolute) value is rounded.

EXERCISE 4-4

For Problems 1 through 20, solve the equation. Round off the answer to two decimal places. Check and write the last line of the check.

Checks:

1. $x \approx 5.29\,\uparrow$ 1. $63.42\ldots = 63.42\ldots$
2. $x \approx 4.46\,\downarrow$ 2. $66.92\ldots = 66.92\ldots$
3. $x \approx 2.88\,\downarrow$ 3. $19.52\ldots = 19.52\ldots$
4. $x \approx 4.29\,\uparrow$ 4. $45.57\ldots = 45.57\ldots$
5. $x \approx -2.62\,\downarrow$ 5. $-8.36\ldots = -8.36\ldots$
6. $x \approx -4.39\,\downarrow$ 6. $-17.99\ldots = -17.99\ldots$
7. $c \approx -6.79\,\downarrow$ 7. $-10.53\ldots = -10.53\ldots$
8. $d \approx -2.74\,\downarrow$ 8. $-7.84\ldots = -7.84\ldots$
9. $x \approx 5.09\,\downarrow$ 9. $-32.17\ldots = -32.17\ldots$
10. $x \approx 9.51\,\uparrow$ 10. $-40.33\ldots = -40.33\ldots$
11. $x = 1.5(\text{exact})$ 11. $1.6 = 1.6$
12. $x = -0.2(\text{exact})$ 12. $0.42 = 0.42$
13. $x \approx -1.98\,\downarrow$ 13. $0.71\ldots = 0.71\ldots$
14. $x \approx 2.20\,\downarrow$ 14. $-0.30\ldots = -0.30\ldots$
15. $s = 4.25(\text{exact})$ 15. $11.4 = 11.4$
16. $t \approx 4.92\,\downarrow$ 16. $-2.46\ldots = -2.46\ldots$
17. $x \approx 9.76\,\downarrow$ 17. $84.39\ldots = 84.39\ldots$
18. $x \approx 11.55\,\uparrow$ 18. $96.01\ldots = 96.01\ldots$
19. $z \approx 30.67\,\uparrow$ 19. $2.38 = 2.38$
20. $y \approx -6.94\,\downarrow$ 20. $6.1725 = 6.1725$

1. $12x = 5x + 37$

2. $15x = 2x + 58$

3. $57 - 13x = 4x + 8$

4. $67 - 5x = 9x + 7$

5. $3.2x = 7.1x + 10.2$

6. $4.1x = 9.5x + 23.7$

7. $0.3c - 8.5 = 1 + 1.7c$

8. $0.2d - 7.3 = 2 + 3.6d$

9. $4.5 - 7.2x = 3.4x - 49.5$

10. $5.3 - 4.8x = 1.3x - 52.7$

11. $0.3x + 0.4 + 0.5x = 0.6x + 0.7$

12. $0.4x + 0.5 = 0.6x + 0.7 + 0.8x$

13. $3(2.4x + 5) = x + 2.7$

14. $2(3.7x + 8) = x + 1.9$

15. $6.3 + 1.2s = 4(7.1 - s)$

16. $5.9 - 1.7t = 3(4.1 - t)$

17. $2.4(3.1x + 4.9) = 75.9 + 0.87x$

18. $3.7(2.1x + 1.7) = 86.2 + 0.85x$

19. $0.72z - 19.7 = 0.3(0.2z + 1.8)$

20. $1.8 - 0.63y = 0.7(0.3y + 10.9)$

Problems 21 through 30 review other techniques.

21. Factor completely: $24x + 36y$

22. Add the fractions: $\dfrac{3}{4} + \dfrac{7}{8}$

23. Find 60% of 300.

24. Write the statement of the addition property of equality.

25. Associate the 4 and the y: $3x + 4 + y$

26. Simplify: $-(3 - 4x) + 17x$

27. Simplify the fraction: $\dfrac{27}{81}$

28. Simplify: $3(4x - 7) - 2(5x - 13)$

29. Write 64 as a power that has 4 as its base.

30. Bonnie starts working 3 hours after Clyde. Clyde has been working for x hours. Write an expression for the number of hours Bonnie has been working.

21. $12(2x + 3y)$
22. $1\frac{5}{8}$
23. 180
24. For real numbers x, y, and z, if $x = y$, then $x + z = y + z$.
25. $3x + (4 + y)$
26. $-3 + 21x$
27. $\frac{1}{3}$
28. $2x + 5$
29. 4^3
30. $x - 3$

4-5   LITERAL EQUATIONS AND FORMULAS

You have been solving equations in which there is one variable and several constants, such as

$$3x + 91 = 44.$$

If a letter is used to stand for one or more of the constants, as in

$$3x + a = 44,$$

the equation is said to be a *literal equation*. The word "literal" comes from the Latin word "littera," which means "letter."

If you solve a literal equation, the value of x comes out in terms of the other letters. In the above equation, subtracting a from each member gives

$$3x = 44 - a.$$

Dividing by 3 gives

$$x = \left(\frac{1}{3}\right)(44 - a).$$

The result is called a *formula* for x in terms of a. In this section you will solve some literal equations, and evaluate formulas for given values of the literal constants.

Time: 2 days

Chalkboard Examples:

1. Solve $3x + 4y = 150$ for x in terms of y.
    Solution:
    $3x + 4y = 150$
    $3x = 150 - 4y$
    $x = 50 - \dfrac{4}{3}y$

2. The volume of a cone is given by $V = \frac{1}{3}\pi r^2 h$, where V stands for volume, r stands for radius, and h stands for altitude ("height"), and π (or pi) is approximately 3.14. Evaluate this formula for a cone of radius 7 inches and altitude 11 inches.
    Solution:
    $V = \dfrac{1}{3}(3.14)(7^2)(11)$
    $V = 564.1533 \ldots$
    $V \approx 564.15$ cubic inches.

The oral practice problems on page 147 are helpful for this topic.

Assignments:

Day 1: 4-5 Problems 1 through 29 odd
         4-4 Selected problems not previously
         assigned
Day 2: 4-5 Problems 2 through 30 even, plus
         31 or 32
         3-6 Selected problems not previously
         assigned

Objectives :

1. Given a literal equation, solve it for the variable.
2. Given a formula, evaluate it for various values of the literal constants.

Cover the answers as you work these examples.

EXAMPLE 1

Solve $5y + 3c = 17$ for y in terms of c.

	Think These Reasons
$5y + 3c = 17$	Write the given equation.
$5y = 17 - 3c$	Subtract $3c$ from each member.
$y = \dfrac{(17 - 3c)}{5}$	Divide each member by 5. (You could multiply by $\frac{1}{5}$).

EXAMPLE 2

Solve $A = LW$ for L in terms of W.

$A = LW$	Write the given equation.
$\dfrac{A}{W} = L$	Divide each member by W.
$L = \dfrac{A}{W}$	Use the symmetric axiom so that the desired variable is on the left.

EXAMPLE 3

The length, L, of a rectangle is given in terms of the area, A, and width, W, by the formula $L = \frac{A}{W}$. Find the length if:
a. A is 300 in^2 and W is 8 in.
b. A is 0.4 square miles, and W is 0.025 square miles.

a. $L = \dfrac{A}{W}$	Write the formula.
$L = \dfrac{300}{8}$	Substitute for A and W.
$L = 37.5$	Arithmetic
Length is 37.5 in.	Write the answer.

b. $L = \dfrac{A}{W}$ Write the formula.

   $L = \dfrac{0.4}{0.025}$ Substitute for A and W.

   $L = 16$ Arithmetic

   <u>16 mi</u>   Write the answer.

EXAMPLE 4

The definition of rate of speed is distance divided by time. Let r stand for rate, d stand for distance, and t stand for time.

a. Write a formula for r in terms of d and t.
b. Solve for d in terms of r and t.
c. Evaluate d when the speed is 55 miles per hour and the time is 4.2 hours.

– – – – –   – – – – –

a. $r = \dfrac{d}{t}$ Get the formula from the words.

– – – – –   – – – – –

b. $rt = d$ Multiply each member by t.
   <u>$d = rt$</u>   Use the symmetric axiom to write the desired variable on the left.

– – – – –   – – – – –

c. $d = (55)(4.2)$ Substitute for r and t.
   <u>$d = 231$</u>   Arithmetic. (Since the question just asked you to evaluate d, you do not need to write that the distance is 231 miles.)

ORAL PRACTICE

Evaluate the formula for the given value of the literal constant.

$x = 9g$:   A. $g = 5$ B. $g = 200$ C. $g = 0.7$

$y = 7p$:   D. $p = 8$ E. $p = -4$ F. $p = 1000$

$z = 3a + 4$:   G. $a = 2$ H. $a = 2.5$ I. $a = 0$

Solve the literal equation for x:

J. $5x = k$ K. $cx = 92$ L. $fx = t$

M. $x + e = 1$ N. $x - 7 = r$ O. $w + x = n$

P. $\dfrac{x}{3} = c$ Q. $\dfrac{u}{x} = 5$

R.   What is the origin of the word "literal?"

Oral Practice

A. 45   B. 1800   C. 6.3
D. 56   E. -28 F. 7000
G. 10   H. 11.5   I. 4

J. $x = \dfrac{k}{5}$ K. $x = \dfrac{92}{c}$ L. $x = \dfrac{t}{f}$

M. $x = 1 - e$ N. $x = r + 7$
O. $x = n - w$ P. $x = 3c$

Q. $x = \dfrac{u}{5}$

R.   The Latin word "littera", which means "letter".

EXERCISE 4-5

Problem Notes:

In Problems 21 through 30, the variables stand for physical quantities.

21. Weight = (Density)(Volume)
22. Force = (Mass)(Acceleration)
23. Circumference = (2 pi)(radius), for a circle
24. Area = (pi)(radius)^2, for a circle
25. Volume = $\left(\dfrac{4}{3}\right)$(pi)(radius)^3, for a sphere
26. Volume = (Length)(Width)(Height), for a block
27. rate = (distance)/(time)
28. Volume = (pi)(radius)^2(height), for a cylinder
29. Area = $\left(\dfrac{1}{2}\right)$(base)(height), for a triangle
30. Pressure = (constant)(Temperature)/(Volume), for a gas

Problems 31 and 32 combine all the techniques of this section.

For Problems 1 through 20, solve the literal equation for x.

1. $5x + t = 17$ $x = \frac{17 - t}{5}$
2. $7x - k = 8$ $x = \frac{8 + k}{7}$
3. $4 - 2x = g$ $x = \frac{4 - g}{2}$
4. $15 + 3x = u$ $x = \frac{u - 15}{3}$
5. $a + 6x = c$ $x = \frac{c - a}{6}$
6. $b - 7x = n$ $x = \frac{b - n}{7}$
7. $ax - b = k$ $x = \frac{k + b}{a}$
8. $hx + j = r$ $x = \frac{r - j}{h}$
9. $2x = 4a + 2b$ $x = 2a + b$
10. $3x = 12c + 6d$ $x = 4c + 2d$
11. $x + 3v = 9v$ $x = 6v$
12. $x - 7f = f$ $x = 8f$
13. $pcx = 2p$ $x = \frac{2}{c}$
14. $0.25ax = 3ab$ $x = 12b$
15. $\dfrac{ax}{6} = 2b$ $x = \dfrac{12b}{a}$
16. $\dfrac{mx}{r} = 4r$ $x = \dfrac{4r^2}{m}$
17. $\dfrac{21w}{x} = 3$ $x = 7w$
18. $\dfrac{pc}{x} = \dfrac{c}{p}$ $x = p^2$
19. $16(x - a) = 4(2a - x)$ $x = \dfrac{6a}{5}$
20. $13(x + 2g) - 3(4x + 5g) = 0$ $x = -11g$

For Problems 21 through 30, evaluate the formula for the given values of the literal constants.

21. $W = DV$, $D = 7$ and $V = 4$ $W = 28$
22. $F = MA$, $M = 100$ and $A = 9.8$ $F = 980$
23. $C = 2pr$, $p = 3.14$, $r = 20$ $C = 125.6$
24. $A = pr^2$, $p = 3.14$, $r = 20$ $A = 1256$
25. $V = \left(\dfrac{3}{4}\right)pr^3$, $p = 3.14$, $r = 2$ $V = 18.84$
26. $V = LWH$, $L = 5$, $W = 3$, $H = 2$ $V = 30$
27. $r = \dfrac{d}{t}$, $d = 500$ and $t = 20$ $r = 25$
28. $V = pr^2h$, $p = 3.14$, $r = 4$, $h = 7$ $V = 351.68$
29. $A = 0.5bh$, $b = 22$, $h = 3$ $A = 33$
30. $P = \dfrac{5000T}{V}$, $T = 300$, $V = 20$ $P = 75,000$

31. *Force, Mass, and Acceleration Problem*   If you pull or push an object with a certain force, the object can accelerate (go faster). Newton's second law of motion says that

$$F = MA,$$

where F stands for force, M stands for mass, and A stands for acceleration.

a. What force is required to give a 3 kilogram mass an acceleration of 5 meters per second^2? (The units of force in the metric system are Newtons.) Do you evaluate a formula or solve an equation?

b. Solve $F = MA$ for A in terms of F and M.

c. If a force of 200 Newtons acts on a mass of 30 kilograms, what will the acceleration be?

32. *Spike Heel Problem*   The pressure exerted on the floor by a person's shoe heel depends on the weight of the person and the width of the heel. The formula is

$$P = \frac{1.2W}{H^2},$$

where P is pressure in pounds per square inch, W is weight in pounds, and H is heel width in inches.

a. How much pressure does a 270 pound wrestler exert on the floor if his heel is 3 inches wide?

b. How much pressure does a 120-pound model exert on the floor if she is wearing a spike heel $\frac{1}{4}$ inch wide? Surprising?!

c. Suppose that the floor in an airplane can stand pressures up to 40 pounds per square inch. What is the heaviest a person wearing a 3-inch heel could be without exceeding this pressure?

31. a. 15 Newtons; evaluate
     b. $A = \dfrac{F}{M}$
     c. 6.67 m/s^2

32. a. 36 lb/in.^{2}
     b. 2304 lb/in.^{2}
     c. $W = 300$ lbs

4-6   PROBLEMS THAT INVOLVE MORE THAN ONE EXPRESSION

Suppose that Butch Err starts peeling potatoes. Four minutes later his sister Janet joins him, and both peel potatoes. There are several variable quantities in this situation.

The number of minutes Butch has been peeling.

The number of minutes Janet has been peeling.

The number of potatoes Butch has peeled.

The number of potatoes Janet has peeled.

The total number of potatoes that have been peeled.

Time: 4 days

Chalkboard Examples:

Day 1:

Wages Problem—Lee King earns $5 per hour. Let x be the number of hours Lee has been working.
a. Write an expression for the number of dollars he has earned.
b. Lee's brother, Nosmo, starts working 3 hours after Lee, and both work together. In terms of x, how long has Nosmo been working?
c. Nosmo earns $7 per hour. In terms of x, how many dollars has Nosmo earned?
d. What total number of dollars have they earned when Lee has been working for 8 hours?
e. Write an equation that says each has earned the *same* amount. Then solve it to find out how long Lee has been working when their amounts are the same.

Solutions:

a. x = no. of hours for Lee
   $5x$ = no. of dollars Lee has earned

b. $x - 3$ = no. of hours for Nosmo
   Note: Students may have difficulty with this expression. If so, ask, "If Lee has worked for 5 hours, how long has Nosmo been working?" They will usually be able to answer 2. Then ask, "How did you get it?" After a couple of examples like this, students can usually respond correctly to, "If Lee has been working x hours, how long has Nosmo been working?"
c. $7(x - 3)$ = no. of dollars for Nosmo
d. $5x + 7(x - 3)$
    $= 5(8) + 7(8 - 3)$
    $= 75$
   They make $75.
e. $5x = 7(x - 3)$
   $5x = 7x - 21$
   $-2x = -21$
   $x = 10.5$
   After $10\frac{1}{2}$ hours.
   Note: Nosmo King ("no smoking") was a radio comedian in England after World II.

If you are given some information about how fast each one peels and you pick a variable to represent one of the variable quantities, you can write expressions for the other quantities. In this section you will work problems in which there is more than one expression involving the variable.

Objective :
Be able to solve problems in which there are two or more variable expressions.

Cover the answers as you work the examples. Uncover the answer to one part to make sure you are right before going on to the next part.

EXAMPLE 1

Potato Peeling Problem   Butch starts peeling potatoes at the rate of 3 potatoes per minute. Four minutes later Janet joins him and peels at the rate of 5 potatoes per minute. Butch continues at 3 per minute.

a.   Define a variable for the number of minutes Butch has been peeling.

b.   Write expressions for:
   i.   the number of minutes Janet has been peeling;
   ii.   the number of potatoes Butch has peeled;
   iii.   the number of potatoes Janet has peeled;
   iv.   the total number of potatoes that have been peeled.

c.   Write an equation stating that they have peeled a total of 36 potatoes. Then solve the equation to find out how long Butch has been peeling when 36 have been peeled.

d.   How many of the 36 potatoes did each one peel?

– – – – –   – – – – –

a.   Let x = the number of minutes Butch has been peeling. (See Note 1.)

– – – – –   – – – – –

b. i. $\underline{x - 4}$ = number of minutes Janet has been peeling. (See Note 2.)

    ii. $\underline{3x}$ = number of potatoes Butch has peeled. (See Note 3.)

    iii. $\underline{5(x - 4)}$ = number of potatoes Janet has peeled. (See Note 4.)

    iv. $\underline{3x + 5(x - 4)}$ = total number of potatoes.

– – – – –   – – – – –

	Think These Reasons

c.

$$3x + 5(x - 4) = 36$$ Set total number of potatoes equal to 36.

$$3x + 5x - 20 = 36$$ Distribute the 5.

$$8x - 20 = 36$$ Combine like terms.

$$8x = 56$$ Add 20 to each member.

$$x = 7$$ Divide each member by 8.

__Butch peeled for 7 min.__   Answer the question.

- - - - -   - - - - -

d.   *Butch*:   *Janet*:

   3(7)   5(7 − 4)   Substitute 7 for x in the appropriate

   = 21   = 5(3)   expressions and evaluate.

                = 15

__Butch peeled 21 potatoes.__   Answer the question. (See Note 5.)
__Janet peeled 15 potatoes.__

Notes:

1. You should *always* write a definition of the variable, even if it is given in the problem. This way you will not forget which of the variable quantities it stands for.
2. Since Janet starts 4 minutes *after* Butch, she has been peeling for 4 *fewer* minutes. So her time is 4 *less* than x.
3. Three potatoes per minute for x minutes gives $3x$ potatoes.
4. Multiply Janet's rate, 5, by *her* time, $(x - 4)$.
5. You can check your answers by seeing that 21 and 15 have a sum of 36, the total number of potatoes peeled.

Some problems involve distances. For these problems, it is helpful to draw a diagram showing the distances. You can mark the expressions representing the distances on the diagram, much as you did in Section 1.2. Here is an example.

EXAMPLE 2

Worm and Snail Problem   A worm starts at the oak tree and moves away, heading for the elm tree at a constant rate of 13 meters per hour (m/h). At the same time, a snail starts at the elm tree and moves toward the oak tree at a constant rate of 17 m/h. The two trees are 100 m apart. Let x be the number of hours the two creatures have been creeping.

Day 2:

Calvin and Phoebe Problem—Calvin Butterball and Phoebe Small live in houses that are 1000 yards apart. Calvin starts from home on his bicycle at 3.4 yards per second and rides toward Phoebe's. At the same time, Phoebe starts from her house at 4.1 yards per second and rides toward Calvin's.

a. How far is Calvin from his house after x seconds?
b. How far is Phoebe from *Calvin's* house after x seconds?
c. After 3 minutes, who is closer to Calvin's house?
d. When are they the same distance from Calvin's house?

Solutions:

a. x = no. of seconds each has been riding
   $3.4x$ = no. of yards Calvin is from home
b. $1000 - 4.1x$ = no. of yards Phoebe is from Calvin's
c. $3.4x$ $1000 - 4.1x$
    $= 3.4(180)$ $= 1000 - 4.1(180)$
    $= 612$ $= 262$
   Phoebe is closer (by 350 yards).
d. $3.4x = 1000 - 4.1x$
   $7.5x = 1000$
   $x = 133.33$
   After $133\frac{1}{3}$ seconds.

Assignments:

Day 1: 1, 3, 5 or 2, 4, 6
Day 2: 7, 9, 11 or 8, 10, 12
Day 3: 13, 15, 17 or 14, 16, 18
Day 4: Prepare for test, using Exercise 4–7. If you choose, you can assign two problems the first night, three the second, and four the third. Problems 19–22 may be used for extra practice.

a. Draw a diagram showing the two trees 100 m apart and the worm and
    snail somewhere between the trees. Draw arrows marking each
    creature's distance from the *oak* tree.
b. Write the definition of x. Then write an expression for each one's dis-
    tance from the oak tree.
c. Who is closer to the oak tree after 2 hours? How much closer?
d. Who is closer to the oak tree after 4 hours? How much closer?
e. When do they pass each other?
f. How far are they from the oak tree when they pass each other?

– – – – –   – – – – –

a.   (See Note 1.)

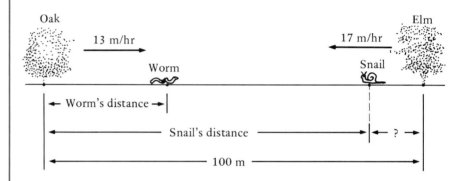

b. x = number of hours they have been going.

            $13x$ = number of meters worm is from
                    oak tree.   (See Note 2.)

        $100 - 17x$ = number of meters snail is from
                    oak tree.   (See Note 3.)

– – – – –   – – – – –

c. *Worm:*   *Snail:*

        $13x$ $100 - 17x$

    $= 13(2)$ $= 100 - 17(2)$

    $= 26$ $= 66$

    Worm is closer by 40 m.

– – – – –   – – – – –

d. *Worm:*   *Snail:*

        $13x$ $100 - 17x$

    $= 13(4)$ $= 100 - 17(4)$

    $= 52$ $= 32$

    Snail is closer by 20 m.

Think These Reasons

e. $13x = 100 - 17x$ Let the two distances be *equal*. (See Note 4.)

$30x = 100$ Add $17x$ to each member.

$x = 3\frac{1}{3}$ Divide each member by 30.

$3\frac{1}{3}$ hours   Answer the question.

- - - - -   - - - - -

f.   *Worm:*   or   *Snail:*

$13x$ $100 - 17x$

$= 13\left(3\frac{1}{3}\right)$ $= 100 - 17\left(3\frac{1}{3}\right)$

$= 13\left(\dfrac{10}{3}\right)$ $= 100 - \dfrac{170}{3}$

$= \dfrac{130}{3}$ $= 100 - 56\frac{2}{3}$

$= 43\frac{1}{3}$ $= 43\frac{1}{3}$

$43\frac{1}{3}$ meters $43\frac{1}{3}$ meters   (See Note 5.)

Notes:

1.   Show enough information in the diagram to show clearly which distance is which.
2.   13 is the rate and x is the time; distance $=$ rate $\times$ time.
3.   The snail has *gone* a distance of $17x$ m (rate $\times$ time). So its *position* is $100 - 17x$ meters from the oak tree.
4.   When they pass each other, each one is the *same* distance from the oak tree. So you let their distances equal each other.
5.   You can find either the worm's distance or the snail's distance, since both are equal. Finding *both* distances gives you a check on the correctness of your answer.

EXERCISE 4-6

Work the following problems. For those problems in which the answers are not integers, express the answers either as mixed numbers or as decimals, rounded to two decimal places.

Problem Notes:

The problems of this section have the same flavor as those in Chapters 1 and 2. The big difference here is that there are *two* expressions involving the variable. Sometimes these expressions are added together and set equal to a constant, and sometimes they are set equal to each other.

Problems 1–10 are value problems similar to Example 1. Problems 11–16 are distance, rate, time problems similar to Example 2. Problems 17 and 18 have parts whose answers are "no solution" or "all real numbers." Problem 21 is conceptually quite different from the other distance, rate, time problems of this section. It is a good problem algebraically but is somewhat impractical in the real world, because planes fly fixed distances rather than fixed lengths of time. In Problem 22 it is necessary for students to distinguish between the total length of fence material (a constant 100 meters) and the overall length of the pens (a variable quantity).

2. a. x = no. of min. for Moe.
   $x - 15$ = no. of min. for Fran.

   c. $9x + 16(x - 15) = 760$
   40 min

3. a. x = no. of days.
   $100 - 3x$ = Phil's no. of dollars.
   $20 + 5x$ = Ernest's no. of dollars.

   d. $\begin{array}{ll} 100 - 3x & 20 + 5x \\ = 100 - 3(10) & = 20 + 5(10) \\ = 70 & = 70 \end{array}$
   ⎵ same ⎵

4. a. x = no. of weeks.
   $100 + 5x$ = Les's no. of dollars.
   $300 - 10x$ = Lotta's no of dollars.

1. *Coal Shoveling Problem* Doug Upp can shovel coal at the rate of 16 tons per day. His brother, Sid, can shovel 10 tons per day.
   a. Define a variable for the number of days Doug has been shoveling. Then write an expression for the number of tons Doug has shoveled. x = no. of days, $16x$ = Doug's no. of tons.
   b. Three days later Sid joins Doug, and both shovel together. Write an expression for the number of *days* Sid has been shoveling in terms of the variable in part (a). Then write an expression for the number of *tons* Sid has shoveled. $x - 3$, $10(x - 3)$
   c. Write an equation stating that the total number of tons Doug and Sid have shoveled is 100. Then solve the equation to find out how many days Doug dug when they have shoveled this much coal.   5 days
   d. How much of the 100 tons did Sid shovel?   20 tons

2. *Dishwashing Problem* Moe Tell starts washing dishes at the Greasy Spoon Cafe. Fifteen minutes later Fran Tick joins Moe, and both wash until all the dishes are done.
   a. Define a variable for the number of minutes Moe has been washing dishes. Then write an expression in terms of that variable for the number of minutes Fran has been washing.
   b. Moe washes 9 dishes per minute and Fran washes 16 dishes per minute. Write expressions representing the number of dishes Moe has washed and the number of dishes Fran has washed. $9x$, $16(x - 15)$
   c. Write an equation stating that the total number of dishes washed is 760. Then solve it to find out how long Moe worked.
   d. How many dishes did each one wash?   Moe: 360   Fran: 400 dishes

3. *Money Problem* Phil T. Rich has $100 and spends $3.00 of it per day. Ernest Worker has only $20 but is adding to it at the rate of $5.00 per day. Let x be the number of days that have passed.
   a. Write the definition of x. Then write two expressions, one representing how much Phil has after x days and the other representing how much Ernest has after x days.
   b. Who has more money, and how much more, after:
      i.   1 week;   Phil has $24 more.   ii.   2 weeks?   Ernest has $32 more.
   c. After how many days will each have the *same* amount of money? Write and solve an equation to find this number of days.   After 10 days.
   d. Show that each actually *does* have the same amount of money after the number of days you calculated in part (c).

4. *Another Money Problem* Les Moore now has $100 and adds to it at $5 per week. Lotta Spences now has $300, but she is spending $10 of it per week. Let x be the number of weeks that have passed.
   a. Write the definition of x. Then write expressions for the numbers of dollars each have after x weeks.

b. Write an equation stating that each has the same number of dollars. Solve it to find out when they have this number of dollars. $13\frac{1}{3}$ weeks

c. How many dollars will this be? $166.67

4. b. $100 + 5x = 300 - 10x$

5. *Temperature Problem*   The temperature in Scorpion Gulch is 38°C and is dropping at the rate of 1.7 degrees per hour. The temperature at Conn Junction is 25°C and is going up at 2.1 degrees per hour.

a. Write expressions representing the temperature at each place after *x* hours.

b. Write an equation stating that both places are at the same temperature. Solve it to find out *when* they are at the same temperature.   After about 3.42 hours

c. What is the temperature when both are the same? About 32.18 degrees

5. a. x = no. of hours.
   $38 - 1.7x$ = no. of degrees in S. G.
   $25 + 2.1x$ = no. of degrees in C. J.

   b. $38 - 1.7x = 25 + 2.1x$

6. *Weight Change Problem*   Fred weighs 187 pounds but is on a diet that makes him lose 1.7 pounds per week. Joe weighs only 93 pounds but is on a diet that makes him gain 0.9 pounds per week.

a. Write an expression representing Fred's weight after *x* weeks and another expression representing Joe's weight after *x* weeks.

b. What is each one's weight after:
   i. 10 weeks; Fred 170 lb, Joe 102 lb   ii. one year? Fred 98.6 lb, Joe 139.8 lb

c. After how many weeks will each be the *same* weight? Show your work.   After about 36.15 weeks

6. a. x = no. of weeks
   $187 - 1.7x$ = Fred's no. of lb.
   $93 + 0.9x$ = Joe's no. of lb.

7. *Equation-Solving Problem*   Kay Oss can solve equations at the rate of 26 per hour. Her boy friend, Dan D. Lyons, can solve them at 20 per hour. When they start their homework assignments, Kay has already solved 3 equations in study hall, and Dan has already solved 8.

a. Define a variable for the number of hours they have been working.

b. How many equations has each solved after 20 minutes? Kay $11\frac{2}{3}$, Dan $14\frac{2}{3}$

c. How long will it take until each has solved the *same* number? How many equations is this? $\frac{5}{6}$ hour (50 minutes)

d. There are 27 equations to be solved all together. Who finishes first? Show your work.

7. a. Let x = no. of hours worked.
   $3 + 26x$ = Kay's no. of equations.
   $8 + 20x$ = Dan's no. of equations.

   d. *Kay* finishes first. After $24\frac{2}{3}$ equations they are tied, and Kay works faster than Dan.

8. *Waitress and Cook Problem*   The waitress at the Greasy Spoon Cafe makes wages of $32 per day and the cook makes $50 per day. In addition, they divide the tips received in such a way that the waitress gets 70% of the tip money and the cook gets 30% of it. ("70% of . . ." means "0.7 times . . . .") Let *x* be the number of dollar tips in a day.

a. Write an expression representing the total amount of money (wages plus tips) the waitress makes and the total amount the cook makes a day.

b. How much does each make if there are:
   i. $20 in tips; Waitress $46, cook $56   ii. $100 in tips?
   Waitress $102, cook $80

8. a. x = no. of dollars in tips.
   $32 + 0.7x$ = no. of dollars for waitress
   $50 + 0.3x$ = no. of dollars for cook.

c.   What amount of tip money makes each person get the *same* total number of dollars per day? $45

9.   *Plumber Problem*   Nick O'Teen, the plumber, charges $30 per hour. His brother, Gil, the plumber's helper, charges $20 per hour. Nick starts working on a job. Four hours later, Gil joins him and both work until the job is finished.
a.   If Nick has been working for x hours, how long has Gil been working? $x - 4$ hours
b.   Write expressions for the number of dollars Nick has earned and for the number of dollars Gil has earned after x hours. $30x$, $20(x - 4)$
c.   The total bill for the job is $470. Write an equation stating this fact, and solve it to find out how long Nick worked.   11 hours
d.   How much of the $470 does each one get?   Nick $330, Gil $140

10.   *Bathtub Problem*   Suppose that you turn on the hot water, which flows at 8.7 liters per minute into the bathtub. Two minutes later you also turn on the cold water, which flows at 13.2 liters per minute. Let x be the number of minutes since you turned on the *cold* water.
a.   Write expressions in terms of x for the number of minutes the hot water has been running, the number of liters the hot faucet has delivered, and the number of liters the cold faucet has delivered.
b.   Write an equation stating that the hot and cold faucets have delivered the *same* number of liters. Solve the equation to find out when this happens.   About 3.87 min
c.   The tub holds 100 liters. Will it have overflowed by the time the hot and cold faucets have delivered the same amounts? Justify your answer.   Tub overflows. 102 liters flows in 3.87 min., or 3.77 min. for 100 l.

11.   *Truck and Patrol Car Problem*   A truck passes a highway patrol station going 70 kilometers per hour (km/h). When the truck is 10 kilometers past the station, a patrol car starts after it, going 100 km/h. Let t be the number of hours the patrol car has been going.
a.   Write the definition of t. Then write two expressions, one representing the patrol car's distance from the station and the other representing the truck's distance from the station after t hours.

b. If they continue at the same speeds, who will be farther from
the station, and how many kilometers farther, after:
    i.   10 minutes; Truck is 5 km farther. ii.   30 minutes? Patrol car is 5 km farther.
c. At what time t does the patrol car reach the truck? $\frac{1}{3}$ hour or 20 min.
d. Show that the two distances really *are* the same at the time you
calculated in part (c).   Both are $33\frac{1}{3}$ km.

12. *Cougar and Fawn Problem* A cougar spots a fawn 132 meters
away. The cougar starts toward the fawn at a speed of 18 meters per
second (m/sec). At the same instant, the fawn starts running away at
11 m/sec. Let x be the number of seconds they have been running.
a. Write the definition of x. Then write expressions for the
cougar's and fawn's distances from the *cougar's* starting point
after x seconds.
b. How far is the cougar from the fawn after 8 seconds?   76 m apart
c. Write an equation stating that the distance between the cougar
and the fawn (fawn's distance minus cougar's distance) equals
60 meters. Then solve the equation to find out *when* they are 60
meters apart.   About 10.29 sec
d. The cougar has enough energy to run for a total of 17 seconds.
Will it catch the fawn before it runs out of energy? Justify your
answer.   Cougar misses by 13 meters *or* cougar needs $1\frac{6}{7}$ more seconds

12. **a.** x = no. of seconds.
$18x$ = cougar's no. of meters.
$132 + 11x$ = fawn's no. of meters.

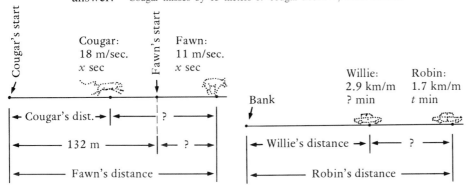

13. *Pursuit Problem* Robin Banks robs a bank and takes off in his get-
away car at 1.7 kilometers per minute (km/m). 5 minutes later
Willie Katchup leaves the bank and chases Robin at 2.9 km/m. Let t
be the number of minutes Robin has been driving.
a. Write the definition of t. Then write an expression representing
Robin's distance from the bank in terms of t.
b. In terms of t, how long has Willie been driving? Write an expression representing Willie's distance from the bank in terms
of t.
c. When Willie catches up with Robin, their distances from the
bank are *equal*. Write an equation stating this fact and solve it
to find out *when* Willie Katchup will catch up with Robin
Banks.   About 12.08 min after Robin starts.
d. *Where* does Willie catch Robin?   About 20.54 km from bank.

13. **a.** t = Robin's no. of minutes.
$1.7t$ = Robin's no. of km.

b. $t - 5$ = Willie's no. of minutes.
$2.9(t - 5)$ = Willie's no. of km.

14. a. x = no. of days for Crew A.
$9x$ = no. of meters A has dug.

   b. $x - 2$ = no. of days for Crew B.
   $12(x - 2)$ = no. of meters for B.

14. *Tunnel Problem* Ornery and Sly Company has a contract to dig a tunnel through Bald Mountain. Crew A starts at the west end and digs at 9 meters per day. Let x be the number of days Crew A has been digging.
   a. Write an expression for the number of meters Crew A has dug after x days.
   b. Crew B starts at the east end two days after Crew A and digs at 12 meters per day. In terms of x, how many days has Crew B been digging? How many meters have they dug in this number of days?
   c. After how many days will both crews have dug the *same* number of meters?   8 days
   d. The total length of the tunnel is to be 2000 meters. Write an equation stating this fact. Then solve the equation to find out how many days it takes to dig the tunnel from the time Crew A starts.   About 96.38 days

15. a.

   b. x = Lois's no. of hours.
   $50x$ = Lois's no. of km.
   c. $x - 3$ = Superman's no. of hours.
   $300(x - 3)$ = Superman's no. of km.
   d. $50x = 300(x - 3)$

15. *Lois and Superman Problem* Lois Lane leaves Metropolis driving 50 km/h. Three hours later Superman leaves Metropolis to catch her, flying 300 km/h.
   a. Draw a diagram showing Lois's distance from Metropolis, Superman's distance from Metropolis, and the distance between them.
   b. Let x be the number of hours Lois has been driving. In terms of x, how far has she gone?
   c. In terms of x, how many hours has Superman been flying? How *far* has he flown in this number of hours?
   d. Write an equation involving x that is true when Superman catches up with Lois.
   e. When does Superman catch up with Lois? How far are they from Metropolis then?   After 3.6 hours; 180 km

16. *Rescue Problem* Phoebe Small is swimming in the ocean, 187 meters out from the beach. She screams for help and starts swimming for the beach at a speed of 0.7 meters per second (m/sec). Fifteen seconds later Calvin Butterball starts toward her in a rowboat, going 1.6 m/sec.

a. Draw a diagram showing the beach where Calvin starts and the point 187 m away where Phoebe starts. Show Calvin and Phoebe somewhere in between.

b. Let x be the number of seconds since Phoebe screamed. Write expressions for the distance she has gone and for her distance from the beach.

c. Write expressions for the number of seconds Calvin has been rowing and for his distance from the beach.

d. How far apart will they be 33 seconds after Phoebe screamed?   135.1 m apart

e. Phoebe has enough strength to swim for 1 min 40 sec. Will Calvin reach her before she runs out of strength? Justify your answer.

17. **Car and Bus Problem**   A bus is 13 kilometers from town, going away at 80 kilometers per hour (km/h). At the same moment a car leaves town going the same direction as the bus, at the same speed.

a. Draw a diagram showing town, the bus's starting point (13 kilometers from town), and the bus and car in appropriate places. Show the bus's distance from town and the car's distance from town.

b. Let x be the number of hours the car and bus have been going. Write expressions for each vehicle's distance from town.

c. After how long will the bus's distance from town be twice the car's distance?   9.75 min

d. After how long will the car's distance from town be 90% of the bus's distance? ("90% of . . ." means "0.9 times . . . .")   1 hr 17.75 min

e. Write an equation stating that both are the same distance from town. Then show that the equation has *no* solutions. Why is this result reasonable?

18. **Age Problem**   K. Paso is now 13 years old. Her father, L. Paso, is now 31.

a. Write expressions for each person's age x years from now.

b. Write an equation stating that L. is twice as old as K. Then solve it to find out *when* L. is twice as old.   5 years from now.

c. When is L. *three* times as old as K.?   4 years ago

d. Write an equation stating that L. is *exactly* as old as K. When will this be true?   They are *never* the same age.

e. Write an equation stating that K.'s age is 18 years less than L.'s age. When will this be true?   They are *always* 18 years apart.

f. When will the sum of their ages be:
   i. 85;   20.5 years from now
   ii. 36?   4 years ago

19. **Magazine Sales Problem**   The student council of a high school arranges with a publisher to sell subscriptions to its magazines. The school will keep 40% of the subscription money and give the other 60% to the publisher. ("40% of . . ." means "0.4 times . . . .") As

16. a.

b. x = no. of sec. since Phoebe screamed.
$0.7x$ = no. of m Phoebe has gone.
$187 - 0.7x$ = Phoebe's no. of m from B.

c. $x - 15$ = Calvin's no. of sec
$1.6(x - 15)$ = Calvin's no. of m from B.

e. $187 - 0.7x$ $1.6(x - 15)$
$= 187 - 0.7(100)$ $= 1.6(100 - 15)$
$= 117$ $= 136$
He makes it because he is 19 m further from the beach than she is when time = 100 sec.
                        or
$187 - 0.7x = 1.6(x - 15)$
$187 - 0.7x = 1.6x - 24$
$211 = 2.3x$
$91.74 = x$
He makes it because it takes him less than 100 seconds to reach her.

17. a.

b. x = no. of hours.
$80x$ = car's no. of km.
$13 + 80x$ = bus's no. of km.

e. $80x = 13 + 80x$
$0 = 13$ No solution!
This is reasonable. Since each is going the same speed, the car never catches up.

18. a. x = no. of years from now.
$13 + x$ = K's age.
$31 + x$ = L's age.

19. **a.** x = no. of dollars for subscriptions sold.
$0.6x - 100$ = publisher's no. of dollars.
$0.4x + 100$ = school's no. of dollars.

an added incentive, the publisher will pay the school an additional $100, regardless of how many subscriptions are sold. Let x be the total number of dollars worth of subscriptions sold.

a. Write an expression for the number of dollars the publisher makes and another expression for the number of dollars the school makes. Remember—if no magazines are sold, the school makes $100 and the publisher makes −$100.

b. For what amount of sales does the publisher "break even"? That is, when does the publisher make $0? $166.67

c. How much does the school make when the publisher breaks even? $166.67

d. For what amount of sales do the school and the publisher make the *same* amount of money? $1000

20. **a.** See diagram.
b. x = no. of hours at 900 km/h.
$3 - x$ = no. of hours at 700 km/h.
$700(3 - x)$ = no. of km at 700.
$900x$ = no. of km at 900 km/h.

```
|←——— 900x ———→|←— 700(3 – x) —→|
●————————————————●————————————————●
Start                          End
```

20. *Airplane Engine Shutdown Problem*   A Fly-by-Night Airlines plane starts off on a trip with all engines running. It flies at 900 kilometers per hour (km/h). Then after it has been flying for x hours, the pilot shuts down one engine to conserve fuel. The speed is reduced to 700 km/h. The plane flies for a total of 3 hours.

a. Draw a diagram showing the starting and ending points for the trip. Somewhere between, mark the point at which the engine was shut down. Show the distance flown at 900 km/h and the distance flown at 700 km/h.

b. Write an expression for the time flown at 700 km/h, for the distance flown at 700 km/h, and for the distance flown at 900 km/h.

c. If the plane flies 1.3 hours before shutting down one engine, how far does it fly all together in 3 hours?   2360 km

d. How long should the pilot fly before shutting down the engine in order to go a total distance of 2352 kilometers in 3 hours?   1.26 h.

e. How long should the pilot fly before shutting down the engine in order to go a total distance of 2970 kilometers in 3 hours?   Not possible. It would take 4.35 hours.

21. **a.** t = no of min. since missile was detected.
$2800 - 300t$ = km from tracking station.

21. *Missile Problem*   A missile tracking station in the Pacific Ocean detects a ballistic missile coming straight toward it at 300 kilometers per minute from a test site in the continental United States.

a. Let t be the number of minutes since the missile was detected. At time $t = 0$, the missile was 2800 kilometers from the tracking station. Write an expression in terms of t for the missile's distance from the station.

b. Where is the missile:
  i. 6 minutes after it is detected;   1000 km from tracking station
  ii. 4 minutes *before* it is detected?   4000 km from tracking station

c. $431(t - 7)$ = int's no. of km.

c. At time $t = 7$, the tracking station fires an interceptor directly toward the oncoming missile. The interceptor travels at 431 kilometers per minute. Write an expression for the interceptor's distance from the tracking station at time *t*. Think carefully about how many minutes the interceptor has been traveling!

    d.   Write an equation that is true when the interceptor *meets* the missile. At what value of *t* will they meet? How far from the tracking station will they be? 7.96 min after detection; 412.72 km from tracking station

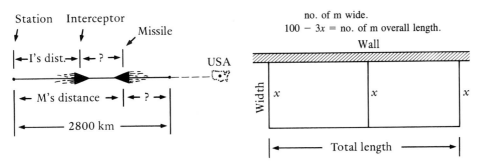

22.   *Stock Pens Problem* Two stock pens are to be built next to each other, with one side of each being against an existing wall (see the figure). The width (perpendicular to the wall) is *x* meters. The total amount of fence material to be used is 100 meters.

    a.   Write an expression for the total length, indicated in the diagram. $100 - 3x$

    b.   What overall length will the pens be if they are 10 meters wide? 70 m

    c.   How wide will the pens be if they are 30 meters long overall? $23\frac{1}{3}$ m

    d.   How wide will the pens be if the width is one-third the overall length? $16\frac{2}{3}$ m

4-7 | CHAPTER REVIEW AND TEST

In this chapter you learned how to solve equations like

$$3(x + 5) = 2x + 7,$$

in which the variable appears in more than one place. By using the distributive properties, adding appropriate numbers to each member, and combining like terms, you learned how to transform these equations to more familiar forms and solve them. Finally, you learned how to solve problems in which there was more than one expression involving the variable.

The Chapter Test below is fairly long. You should put yourself under pressure and see how much of it you can work in one, continuous session the length of a normal classroom test. Don't dawdle! Make yourself concentrate the whole time just as though you were actually taking a test!!

Time: 1 day

Test Ideas:

Your test can consist exclusively of word problems, if you like, because these problems include all the equation-solving techniques of the chapter. The most effective problems are ones you make up yourself, using local situations familiar to your students. An all-word-problem test thwarts students who rationalize, "They will only be a part of the test, and I can get enough points just solving equations to pass."

Assignment:

Following the test, study Section 5–1 and work Exercise 5–1, all twelve problems.

CHAPTER TEST

Problem Notes:

Problems 1–16 involve the equation-solving techniques that should be the content of your first test. The word-problems test should have about four problems like Problems 17, 18, and 19.

1.	$x = 15$	**2.**	$x = 9$
3.	$t = 0$	**4.**	$-4.86 \approx x$
5.	$r = -4.5$	**6.**	$x = -20$
7.	$x = 6$	**8.**	No solution
9.	Identity	**10.**	$x = -12$
11.	$x \approx 8.29$	**12.**	$x = -9$
13.	$x \approx 3.84$	**14.**	$d \approx 0.31$

Checks:

1.	$165 = 165$	**2.**	$49 = 49$
3.	$14 = 14$	**4.**	$31 = 31$
5.	$5 = 5$		
6.	$-140 = -140$		
7.	$45 = 45$	**8.**	none
9.	none	**10.**	$-37 = -37$
11.	$74.57\ldots = 74.57\ldots$		
12.	$-62.8 = -62.8$		
13.	$5.34\ldots = 5.34\ldots$		
14.	$3.66\ldots = 3.66\ldots$		

For Problems 1 through 15, solve the equation and check your answer. Round off approximate answers to two decimal places.

1. $3x + 8x = 165$

2. $7x + 4 - 2x = 49$

3. $4(t + 5) - 3(t + 2) = 14$

4. $31 = 5 - 2(3x + 4) - x$

5. $5(r + 4) - (r - 3) = 5$

6. $7x = 3x - 80$

7. $5(2x - 3) = 6x + 9$

8. $2(4c - 7) = 8c + 14$

9. $6x + 33 + 5x = 11(x + 3)$

10. $5 + 3(x - 2) = x + x - 13$

11. $9x = 2x + 58$

12. $7.4x + 3.8 = 5.9x - 9.7$

13. $7(2.3 - 0.4x) = x + 1.5$

14. $5.3 - 5.3d = 2.8 + 2.8d$

15. Juan Moore solves the equation

$$3(2x + 7) = 5x + 21 + x$$

and gets $x = 4$ for an answer.
a. Substitute 4 for x and show that it *is* a solution. $45 = 45$
b. Is 4 the *only* solution? Explain.   No. Every number is a solution.

16. Solve for x: $3x + 12y = 57$ $x = 19 - 4y$

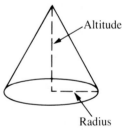

Altitude

Radius

17. The volume of a cone is given by

$$V = \left(\frac{1}{3}\right)pr^2h,$$

where V is the volume, p is about 3.14, r is the radius of the cone's base, and h is the cone's altitude (see sketch). Find out how many cubic centimeters a conical drinking cup will hold if its radius is 4 cm and its altitude is 10 cm. $V \approx 167.47$ cm³

18. a. $x = $ no. of hours for assistant.
      $x - 2 = $ no. of hours for master.
   b. $50x = $ assistant's no. of bricks.
      $80(x - 2) = $ master's no. of bricks.

18. *Bricklaying Problem*   A bricklayer's assistant starts building a wall, laying 50 bricks per hour. Two hours later the master bricklayer joins the assistant, and both lay bricks. The master bricklayer lays 80 bricks per hour.
   a. Let x be the number of hours since the assistant started laying bricks. In terms of x, how many hours has the master been laying bricks?
   b. Write expressions for the number of bricks the assistant has laid and the number of bricks the master has laid.

c. Write an equation stating that the assistant and the master have laid the *same* number of bricks. How long has each one worked when they have laid the same number? $5\frac{1}{3}$ h, $3\frac{1}{3}$h

d. They must lay a total of 1000 bricks. Will they finish before the assistant has worked 8 hours? Justify your answer.   No. They take 8.92 hr or they lay only 880 bricks.

19. *Marathon Problem*   Mary Thon starts at a point 26 miles from school and runs toward school at 6 miles per hour (mph). Randy Miles starts from school 1.3 hours later and runs toward Mary at 8 mph.

19. a.

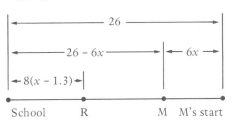

School   R   M M's start

a. Draw a diagram showing the school and Mary's starting point 26 miles apart. Show Mary and Randy somewhere in between. Mark each person's distance from school.

b. Let x be the number of hours Mary has been running. Write expressions for the distance she has run and for her distance from school.

b. x = Mary's number of hours.
   $6x$ = no. of miles she has run.
   $26 - 6x$ = her no. of mi from school.

c. In terms of x, how many hours has Randy been running? How far is he from school?

c. $x - 1.3$ = Randy's no. of hours.
   $8(x - 1.3)$ = his no. of mi.

d. How long has Mary been running when she and Randy meet?   Mary has run for 2.6 h.

e. How far from school do they meet?   10.4 mi from school

20. *Ceramic Sales Problem*   Clay Potts owns a ceramics store. His brother, Jack, works for him, earning wages of $50 per day plus 10% of the profits. All Clay gets is the other 90% of the profits. ("90% of . . ." means "0.9 times . . . .")

20a. x = no. of dollars profit.
   $50 + 0.1x$ = Jack's no. of dollars.
   $0.9x$ = Clay's no. of dollars.
   Note: The $50 Clay gets is taken out of *gross* sales, and thus is *not* part of the profit.

c. Clay makes $30 more.

a. Let x be the number of dollars profit the store makes in a day. Write expressions for the total number of dollars Jack gets (wages plus profits) and for the total number of dollars Clay gets.

b. On Monday the store makes a profit of only $30. How much does each one make?   Jack $53, Clay $27

c. Business is better on Tuesday, and the store makes a profit of $100. Who makes more, Clay or Jack? How much more?

d. What number of dollars profit must the store make in a day for each one to get the *same* amount of money?
   Profit must be $62.50.

5

Some Operations with Polynomials and Radicals

In the first four chapters, you learned how to solve various kinds of equations. In this chapter and the next, you will learn ways to solve equations in which the variable is squared. Expressions that appear in these equations are called polynomials. *This chapter concentrates on operations with polynomials. In the next chapter you will learn the actual procedures for solving such* quadratic equations.

Expression:
$x^2 + 5x + 2$
A polynomial

Expression:
$\sqrt{1776}$
A radical

Equation:
$x^2 + 5x + 2 = 0$
A quadratic equation

5-1	INTRODUCTION TO POLYNOMIALS

Time: $\frac{1}{2}$ day, with Section 5–2

This section is meant for you to read and understand on your own. You should be able to do this and work the problems without help from your teacher.

The expressions below are polynomials.

$$3x^2 + 5x - 7$$

$$8x^4 - 11x + 2x^5 - x^2$$

$$5x^7 + 9x^4 - 3x^2 + 8$$

The polynomial $5x^7 + 9x^4 - 3x^2 + 8$ is arranged in *descending powers of x*, because the exponents of x in each term go *down* in value,

$$7, \quad 4, \quad 2, \quad 0 \text{ (no variable)},$$

as you go from left to right. The polynomial below is arranged in *ascending powers of y*.

$$9y - 7y^3 + y^5$$

As you go from term to term, the exponents go *up* in value: 1, 3, 5.

A polynomial is considered to be simpler if it is arranged in either ascending or descending powers of the variable.

Objective :

Given a polynomial with several terms, arrange it in ascending or descending powers of the variable.

In order to accomplish this objective, all you need to do is commute terms so that the exponents either increase or decrease from term to term.

Chalkboard Examples:

See Section 5–2 for examples for both sections.

Assignment:

All ten problems already should have been assigned following the Chapter 4 test in preparation for your first class on Chapter 5. See assignments, Section 4–7.

Cover the answers as you work these examples.

EXAMPLE 1

Arrange in descending powers of z: $5z - 6z^3 + 4z^2 - 11$.

– – – – –   – – – –

| | ***Think These Reasons*** |

$$5z - 6z^3 + 4z^2 - 11$$ Write the given expression.

$$= -6z^3 + 4z^2 + 5z - 11$$ Commute terms so that the value of the exponents of z *decrease*: 3, 2, 1, no variable. (Remember that the $-$ sign goes along with the term it precedes.)

EXAMPLE 2

Arrange in ascending powers of x: $4x^6 - 7x - 5x^3 + x^2$.

– – – – –   – – – –

$$4x^6 - 7x - 5x^3 + x^2$$ Write the given expression.

$$= -7x + x^2 - 5x^3 + 4x^6$$ Commute terms so that the exponents of x *increase*: 1, 2, 3, 6. Note that x is equivalent to x^1.

Now, work the problems below to make sure you have the right idea. There are also some problems to renew your skills from previous chapters.

Problem Notes:

Problems 1–5 involve the new concept of this section. The main thing for students to remember is that the $-$ sign goes along with the term it is in front of. This is because subtraction does *not* commute and must be changed to adding the opposite. Some students may have difficulty realizing that the constant is the lowest power of the variable. So it comes last for descending powers and first for ascending powers.

EXERCISE 5-1

You should work *all* these problems, not just the odds or just the evens.

For Problems 1 through 5, commute terms so that the polynomial is in
a.   descending powers of the variable,
b.   ascending powers of the variable.

1. **a.** $5x^2 + 3x + 4$ **b.** $4 + 3x + 5x^2$
2. **a.** $4x^2 - 3x + 6$ **b.** $6 - 3x + 4x^2$
3. **a.** $x^5 + x^3 + x^2 + 9$
  b. $9 + x^2 + x^3 + x^5$
4. **a.** $-x^5 + x^4 + x + 1$
  b. $1 + x + x^4 - x^5$
5. **a.** $2x^5 + 5x^4 - 9x^3 + x^2 + 8x$
  b. $8x + x^2 - 9x^3 + 5x^4 + 2x^5$

1. $3x + 5x^2 + 4$ 2. $6 + 4x^2 - 3x$

3. $x^3 + x^2 + x^5 + 9$ 4. $x^4 - x^5 + x + 1$

5. $8x + 2x^5 - 9x^3 + 5x^4 + x^2$

Problems 6 through 12 reinforce concepts you have learned in earlier sections.

6. Solve and check: $3x + 9 = -21$. $x = -10; -21 = -21$

7. Simplify $5x - 7 + 3x$. $8x - 7$

8. Solve and check: $8x - 12 = 4x$. $x = 3; 12 = 12$

9. Simplify $5(x + 4) - 3(2x - 7)$. $-x + 41$

10. Solve and check: $2(4x - 3) = 5(2x - 12)$. $x = 27; 210 = 210$

11. Evaluate $4x - 7(3x + 2)$ if x is -5. 71

12. Solve and check: $2.7x = 4(3.1x - 7.6)$. $x \approx 3.13; 8.46... = 8.46...$

Problems 6–12 review concepts from previous chapters and constitute distributed homework practice.

5-2 | NAMES OF POLYNOMIALS

In the last section you learned that an expression like

$$3x^2 + 5x - 7$$

is called a polynomial. The only operations that appear in a polynomial are *addition, subtraction,* and *multiplication*.

DEFINITION

> **POLYNOMIAL**
> A **polynomial** is an expression that has no operations other than addition, subtraction, and multiplication by or of the variable(s).

Notes:

1. Expressions such as

$$\frac{x - 2}{3x + 4} \quad \text{or} \quad |x - 5|,$$

   which have *division* by a variable or the *absolute value* of a variable, are *not* polynomials.

2. Powers of variables, such as x^3, *are* permitted in polynomials because they imply *multiplication*: $x \cdot x \cdot x$.

3. Single terms like $2x$, $5y^2$, x, or even just a constant such as 7 are also called polynomials.

As a result of this definition, polynomials always consist of one or more terms, each of which looks something like the expression shown at the top of the next page.

Time: $\frac{1}{2}$ day, with Section 5–1

Chalkboard Examples:

Definition:

Polynomials	Not Polynomials
$5x^7 + 9x^2 - 3x + 4$	$\dfrac{5}{x - 6}$
$8x^2 - 4x + 11$	
$x + 3$	$\lvert 5x - 7 \rvert$
x	
6	

Conclusion: Polynomials have only addition, subtraction, and multiplication and not other operations such as division (by a variable) or absolute value (of a variable).

Names:

Polynomial	Degree	Degree name	Polynomial name
$5x + 8$	First	Linear	Linear binomial
$x^2 - 4x + 1$	Second	Quadratic	Quadratic trinomial
$7x^3$	Third	Cubic	Cubic monomial

This list was picked, as was the one in the book, because none of the polynomials has a degree equal to the number of terms. In this way the students are forced to distinguish between the two concepts.

Coefficients:

$$5x^3 - x^2 + 4x - 9$$

The coefficients are 5, -1, 4, and -9. Make sure that students know the x^2 term *does* have a coefficient, and it is -1.

Assignment:

1–57 odd (Some may be done orally) and 58–61 (The even-numbered problems will be assigned in later exercises as part of the distributed homework practice.)

Coefficient variable   Exponent

If the polynomial is just a power of the variable, then the coefficient is equal to 1.

x^4 equals $1 \cdot x^4$.
──── The coefficient is 1.

If the variable appears without an exponent, then the exponent is 1.

$3x$ equals $3x^1$.
──── The exponent is 1.

Just as $1 \cdot x$ equals x, x^1 also equals x. An expression is considered to be simpler when written with x rather than with $1x$ or x^1.

If there is no variable in a term, then that term is called the **constant** term.

$4x^2 + 2x + 5$ ← 5 is the constant term.

If there is a $-$ sign in front of a term, as in $x^2 - 3x$, the coefficient is considered to be *negative*.

$x^2 - 3x$ equals $x^2 + (-3)x$.
──── The coefficient is -3.

$x^5 - x^2$ equals $x^5 + (-1)x^2$.
──── The coefficient is -1.

Polynomials with one, two, or three terms are given special names.

Number of Terms	Example	Name
One	$8x$	Monomial
Two	$13x - 4$	Binomial
Three	$5x^2 - 9x + 11$	Trinomial

As you can see, all these names end with *-nomial*. This suffix comes from the Latin word *nomens*, which means *name*. So binomial means, literally, *two names*. The prefix *poly-* means *many*, although the word polynomial can be used for any number of terms, including one, two, or three.

Polynomials with only one variable are also named according to the highest power of that variable that appears in the expression. This number is called the *degree* of the polynomial. For example,

$$5x^3 + 13x^2$$

is of *third* degree, because x^3 is the highest power of x.

DEFINITION

DEGREE
The **degree** of a polynomial with one variable is the exponent of the highest power of that variable.

First, second, and third degree polynomials have special names.

Degree	Example	Name
First	$17x - 4$	**Linear**
Second	$9x^2 - 2x + 11$	**Quadratic**
Third	x^3	**Cubic**

These words come from the fact that lines, squares (*quadrangles*), and cubes have 1, 2, and 3 dimensions, respectively.

By putting together the names for degree and number of terms, you can name various polynomials. For instance, $x^2 + 5x + 2$ is a *quadratic trinomial*, because it is of *second* degree and has *three* terms.

Objective :
Given an expression, tell whether or not it is a polynomial. If it is, tell the coefficient of each term, and name the polynomial by degree and by number of terms.

Cover the answers as you work these examples.

EXAMPLE 1

Tell whether or not the expression is a polynomial. If it is, tell *why*. If it is not, tell why *not*.

a. $5x^3 - 4x + 1$

– – – – –   – – – – –

Think These Reasons

Polynomial   No operations other than $+, -, \times$

b. $3x$

– – – – –   – – – – –

    Polynomial   No operations other than $+, -, \times$

c. $\dfrac{3}{x}$

- - - - -   - - - - -

    <u>Not a polynomial</u>   Division by a variable

d. $|x + 3|$

- - - - -   - - - - -

    <u>Not a polynomial</u>   Absolute value of a variable

EXAMPLE 2

Give the coefficient of each term in $5x^4 - 7x^3 + x^2 - x + 8$.

- - - - -   - - - - -

    <u>5; -7; 1; -1; 8</u>   Read the explanation above.

EXAMPLE 3

Name each polynomial according to degree and number of terms.

a. $13x - 7$

- - - - -   - - - - -

    <u>Linear binomial</u>   First degree, two terms

b. $5x^3$

- - - - -   - - - - -

    <u>Cubic monomial</u>   Third degree, one term

c. $6x^2 + 11x - 8$

- - - - -   - - - - -

    <u>Quadratic trinomial</u>   Second degree, three terms

d. $5x^4 + x^7$

- - - - -   - - - - -

    <u>Seventh-degree binomial</u>   Two terms (No special name for seventh degree)

e. $x^3 + x^2 + x + 1$

- - - - -   - - - - -

    <u>Cubic polynomial with four terms</u>   Third degree (No special name for four terms)

EXERCISE 5-2

If your teacher prefers, part or all of this exercise may be done orally instead of in writing.

For Problems 1 though 12, tell whether or not the expression is a polynomial. If so, tell why. If not, tell why not.

1. $x^3 + 4x$ 2. $x^4 - 5x$ 3. $x^3 + \dfrac{4}{x}$ 4. $x^4 - \dfrac{5}{x}$

5. y^5 6. z^6 7. x 8. 5

9. 3 10. $|x - 7|$ 11. $|x + 4|$ 12. $2x$

For Problems 13 through 20, give the coefficient of each term.

13. $3x^5 + 2x^3 - 4x + 7$ 14. $5x^4 - 3x^2 + 6x - 9$

15. $z^3 - 5z^2 + 2z$ 16. $y^5 + 4y^2 - 3y$

17. $4x^2 + x$ ₄, ₁   18. $3z^2 + z$ ₃, ₁

17. $4x^2 + x$ 4, 1   18. $3z^2 + z$ 3, 1

19. $x^3 - x + 5$ 1, -1, 5   20. $c^4 - c^2 + 3$ 1, -1, 3

For Problems 21 through 36, name the polynomial by degree and by number of terms.

21. $x^2 + 3x + 4$ 22. $x^3 - 7$

23. $5x^3$ 24. $5x^2 - 8x + 17$

25. $x^2 - 7$ 26. x^2

27. x 28. $4x + 5$

29. x^5 30. $2431x$

31. $8x^4 + 7x^3$ 32. $19x^6 - 4x + 7$

33. $2x^3 + 5x^2 + 11x - 1$ 34. $x^7 - x^5 + x^3 - x + 9$

35. $5x + 2$ 36. $8 - 7x - 6x^2$

For Problems 37 through 46, give an example of the polynomial described.

37. Linear binomial   38. Quadratic binomial

39. Quadratic trinomial   40. Linear monomial

41. Cubic trinomial   42. Cubic binomial

43. Quadratic monomial   44. Fourth-degree trinomial

45. Sixth-degree binomial   46. Cubic polynomial with four terms

1. Polynomial.
   No operations besides $+$, $-$, $\times$
2. Polynomial.
   No operations besides $+$, $-$, $\times$
3. Not polynomial. Division by a variable
4. Not polynomial. Division by a variable
5. Polynomial.
   No operations besides $+$, $-$, $\times$
6. Polynomial.
   No operations besides $+$, $-$, $\times$
7. Polynomial.
   No operations besides $+$, $-$, $\times$
8. Polynomial. No operations besides $+$, $-$,
   $\times$ (no operations *at all*!)
9. Polynomial.
   No operations besides $+$, $-$, $\times$
10. Not polynomial. Absolute value of a
    variable
11. Not polynomial. Absolute value of a
    variable
12. Polynomial.
    No operations besides $+$, $-$, $\times$
13. 3, 2, -4, 7   14. 5, -3, 6, -9
15. 1, -5, 2   16. 1, 4, -3
21. Quadratic trinomial
22. Cubic binomial
23. Cubic monomial
24. Quadratic trinomial
25. Quadratic binomial
26. Quadratic monomial
27. Linear monomial
28. Linear binomial
29. 5th-degree monomial
30. Linear monomial
31. 4th-degree binomial
32. 6th-degree trinomial
33. Cubic, 4 terms
34. 7th degree, 5 terms
35. Linear binomial
36. Quadratic trinomial
Examples:
37. $x + 1$ 38. $x^2 + 1$
39. $x^2 + x + 1$ 40. x
41. $x^3 + x^2 + 1$ 42. $x^3 + 1$
43. x^2 44. $x^4 + x + 1$
45. $x^6 + 1$ 46. $x^3 + x^2 + x + 1$

47. $7x^2 + 5x + 2$ **48.** $3x^2 + 18x + 6$
49. $-x^7 + x^5 + x^3 + 11$
50. $x^4 - x^3 - x^2 + 4x$
51. $x^4 + 2x^3 - x - 3$
52. $5x^7 + x^5 - 5x - 2$
53. $x^5 + 3x^4 - 9x^3 + x^2 + 7x$
54. $2x^4 - 5x^3 + x^2 + x + 3$
55. $-x^5 + 4^5$ (Note: 4^5 is a *constant*, not a power of x!)
56. $x^6 + 3^8$ (Note: 3^8 is a *constant*, not a power of x!)
57. $x = 5$. Denominator would be 0.

Problem Notes:

Problem 56, $3^8 + x^6$, is a trap! It is designed to make sure students know that it is the exponent of the *variable* that matters.

Problems 58–61 review previous techniques and constitute distributed homework practice.

For Problems 47 through 56, commute terms so that the polynomial is in descending powers of x. (See Section 5-1 for examples.)

47. $5x + 7x^2 + 2$ **48.** $6 + 3x^2 + 18x$

49. $x^5 + x^3 - x^7 + 11$ **50.** $4x + x^4 - x^2 - x^3$

51. $2x^3 + x^4 - 3 - x$ **52.** $5x^7 - 2 + x^5 - 5x$

53. $7x + x^5 - 9x^3 + 3x^4 + x^2$ **54.** $x + 3 + x^2 - 5x^3 + 2x^4$

55. $4^5 - x^5$ **56.** $3^8 + x^6$

57. The expression $\frac{7}{x-5}$ is *not* a polynomial, since it involves division by an expression containing a variable. For what value of x is the expression *not* equal to a real number? Explain.

Problems 58 through 61 review concepts and techniques from previous sections.

58. Simplify $9(x + 7) - 8x$. $x + 63$

59. Evaluate $14 - 2(4x + 7)$ if x is -3.   24

60. Solve and check: $5(x + 3) = 7(x - 4)$. $x = 21.5$, $122.5 = 122.5$

61. *Lawn Mowing Problem*   Moe Delaune, who can mow the lawn at a rate of 10 square meters per minute, mows for x minutes. Dru Upp, who can mow at 12 square meters per minute, joins Moe 7 minutes after he started, and both mow the lawn together.
a. Write expressions in terms of x for the numbers of square meters each has mowed.   Moe: $10x$; Dru: $12(x - 7)$
b. How long has Moe been mowing:
i. when they have mowed a total of 202 square meters;   13 min.
ii. when they have mowed the *same* number of square meters?   42 min.

Time: 1 or 2 days

Chalkboard Examples:

Multiply:
1. $(x + 4)(x + 6)$ Ans.: $x^2 + 10x + 24$
2. $(x + 9)(x - 3)$ Ans.: $x^2 + 6x - 27$
3. $(x - 2)(x + 8)$ Ans.: $x^2 + 6x - 16$
4. $(x - 5)(x - 7)$ Ans.: $x^2 - 12x + 35$
5. $(3x + 1)(x - 6)$ Ans.: $3x^2 - 17x - 6$
6. $(x - 5)^2$ Ans.: $x^2 - 10x + 25$
   [Write as $(x - 5)(x - 5)$.]

You know how to use the distributive properties to multiply a constant by a binomial. For example,

$$4(x + 5)$$
$$= 4 \cdot x + 4 \cdot 5$$
$$= 4x + 20.$$

Suppose that instead of 4 times $x + 5$, you have another *binomial* times $(x + 5)$, such as

$$(x + 3)(x + 5).$$

You can still distribute $(x + 3)$ the same way you did 4. Both expressions simply stand for numbers! You get

Distribute!

$$(x + 3)(x + 5)$$

$$= (x + 3) \cdot x + (x + 3) \cdot 5.$$

This can be simplified by distributing x and 5, getting

$$x^2 + 3x + 5x + 15.$$

Combining like terms gives

$$x^2 + 8x + 15.$$

If you look at the next-to-the-last step, above,

$$(x + 3)(x + 5) = x^2 + 3x + 5x + 15,$$

you should see that each term in $x + 5$ is multiplied by each term in $(x + 3)$. This fact gives a *quick* way to multiply two binomials.

1. Multiply each term by x.

$$(x + 3)(x + 5) = x^2 + 5x \ldots$$

2. Multiply each term by 3.

$$(x + 3)(x + 5) = x^2 + 5x + 3x + 15$$

3. Combine like terms.

$$(x + 3)(x + 5) = x^2 + 8x + 15$$

With practice, you can combine the like terms mentally and write only the question and the answer, like this:

$$(x + 3)(x + 5) = \underline{x^2 + 8x + 15}.$$

TECHNIQUE

> **MULTIPLYING TWO BINOMIALS**
>
> 1. Multiply each term of one binomial by each term of the other.
> 2. Combine the like terms.

Objective:
Be able to multiply two binomials *quickly,* by writing only the question and the answer, if possible.

The Oral Practice problems for this section are particularly useful for conveying the technique for calculating the middle term. Have all students spend a few minutes and work all problems. Then call on some students to tell their answers.

Assignments:

Day 1: 1–39 odd or 2–40 even and selected problems from 61 through 70

Day 2: Split assignment:
Those who understood: selected problems from 41 to 64
Those who need more practice: 2–40 even or 1–39 odd

Note: The acronym FOIL is deliberately avoided since it masks the idea of "multiplying each term of one binomial by each term of the other."

Cover the answers as you work these examples.

EXAMPLE 1

Multiply $(x + 7)(x + 2)$.
- - - - -   - - - - -

	Think These Reasons
$(x + 7)(x + 2)$	Write the given expression.
$= x^2 + 2x + 7x + 14$	Multiply each term in $(x + 2)$ by each term in $(x + 7)$.
$= \underline{\underline{x^2 + 9x + 14}}$	Combine like terms.

EXAMPLE 2

Multiply $(x + 5)(x + 8)$.
- - - - -   - - - - -

$(x + 5)(x + 8)$	Write the given expression.
$= \underline{\underline{x^2 + 13x + 40}}$	The middle term is $8x + 5x$. (Try doing this in your head if you are brave!)

EXAMPLE 3

Multiply $(x - 3)(x + 8)$.
- - - - -   - - - - -

$(x - 3)(x + 8)$	Write the given expression.
$= x^2 + 8x - 3x - 24$	$-3(x)$ is $-3x$ and $-3(8)$ is -24.
$= \underline{\underline{x^2 + 5x - 24}}$	Combine like terms.

EXAMPLE 4

Multiply $(x + 2)(x - 10)$.
- - - - -   - - - - -

$(x + 2)(x - 10)$	Write the given expression.
$= x^2 - 10x + 2x - 20$	$x(-10)$ is $-10x$ and $2(-10)$ is -20.
$= \underline{\underline{x^2 - 8x - 20}}$	Combine like terms (in your head, if possible).

EXAMPLE 5

Multiply $(x - 7)(x - 9)$.

$- - - - -$ $- - - - -$

$(x - 7)(x - 9)$ Write the given expression.

$= x^2 - 9x - 7x + 63$ $(-7)(-9)$ is $+63$.

$= \underline{x^2 - 16x + 63}$ Combine like terms (in your head, if possible).

EXAMPLE 6

Multiply $(3x - 5)(4x + 1)$.

$- - - - -$ $- - - - -$

$(3x - 5)(4x + 1)$ Write the given expression.

$= 12x^2 + 3x - 20x - 5$ The first term is $(3x)(4x)$, or $12x^2$.

$= \underline{12x^2 - 17x - 5}$ Combine like terms.

EXAMPLE 7

Simplify $(x - 3)^2$.

$- - - - -$ $- - - - -$

$(x - 3)^2$ Write the given expression.

$= (x - 3)(x - 3)$ Definition of squaring

$= \underline{x^2 - 6x + 9}$ Multiply, and combine like terms.

It is possible to check your answers to this kind of problem by substituting a simple value of x into both the original expression and into the answer. In Example 4, for instance, let $x = 3$.

$$(x + 2)(x - 10) \qquad\qquad x^2 - 8x - 20$$

$$= (5)(-7) \qquad\qquad\qquad = 9 - 24 - 20$$

$$= -35 \qquad \longleftarrow \text{Same!} \longrightarrow \qquad = -35$$

If you get the same answer for both, you can be reasonably sure the expressions are equivalent.

ORAL PRACTICE

Give the middle term if these binomials are multiplied.

EXAMPLES

Answers

i. $(x + 3)(x + 7)$ i. $10x$
ii. $(x - 4)(2x + 5)$ ii. $-3x$
iii. $(3x - 4)(2x + 5)$ iii. $7x$
iv. $(x - 8)(x + 8)$ iv. 0

A. $(x + 2)(x + 5)$ $7x$ B. $(x - 3)(x - 4)$ $-7x$

C. $(x + 7)(x - 4)$ $3x$ D. $(x + 3)(x - 8)$ $-5x$

E. $(x - 1)(x + 6)$ $5x$ F. $(x - 10)(x + 10)$ 0

G. $(3x + 2)(x + 4)$ $14x$ H. $(x + 5)(2x - 3)$ $7x$

I. $(3x - 5)(x - 2)$ $-11x$ J. $(2x + 5)(3x + 4)$ $23x$

K. $(4x - 1)(3x - 2)$ $-11x$ L. $(5x - 2)(3x + 2)$ $4x$

EXERCISE 5-3

For Problems 1 through 40, multiply the binomials. If possible, write down only the given expression and the answer, combining the middle terms in your head. It is advisable for you to check your answers.

Problem Notes:

Problems 35–40 are intended to reinforce the definition of squaring. Have the students write out the factors as $(x + 6)(x + 6)$, then multiply.

1. $(x + 4)(x + 3)$ $x^2 + 7x + 12$ 2. $(x + 7)(x + 9)$ $x^2 + 16x + 63$

3. $(x + 8)(x - 5)$ $x^2 + 3x - 40$ 4. $(x + 6)(x - 2)$ $x^2 + 4x - 12$

5. $(x + 2)(x - 7)$ $x^2 - 5x - 14$ 6. $(x + 3)(x - 9)$ $x^2 - 6x - 27$

7. $(r - 4)(r + 7)$ $r^2 + 3r - 28$ 8. $(b - 3)(b + 8)$ $b^2 + 5b - 24$

9. $(s - 6)(s + 1)$ $s^2 - 5s - 6$ 10. $(t - 5)(t + 2)$ $t^2 - 3t - 10$

11. $(x - 8)(x - 4)$ $x^2 - 12x + 32$ 12. $(x - 7)(x - 6)$ $x^2 - 13x + 42$

13. $(x - 1)(x - 2)$ $x^2 - 3x + 2$ 14. $(x - 5)(x - 8)$ $x^2 - 13x + 40$

15. $(2x + 3)(x + 4)$ $2x^2 + 11x + 12$ 16. $(4x + 5)(x + 2)$ $4x^2 + 13x + 10$

17. $(3x + 1)(x - 2)$ $3x^2 - 5x - 2$ 18. $(2x + 1)(x - 4)$ $2x^2 - 7x - 4$

19. $(x - 5)(2x - 1)$ $2x^2 - 11x + 5$ 20. $(x - 3)(3x - 2)$ $3x^2 - 11x + 6$

21. $(x + 4)(3x + 5)$ $3x^2 + 17x + 20$ 22. $(x + 5)(2x + 6)$ $2x^2 + 16x + 30$

23. $(2x - 3)(4x + 3)$ $8x^2 - 6x - 9$ 24. $(3x - 5)(2x + 3)$ $6x^2 - x - 15$

25. $(5x + 4)(2x - 7)$ $10x^2 - 27x - 28$ 26. $(7x + 5)(2x - 4)$ $14x^2 - 18x - 20$

27. $(4x + 3)(4x + 3)$ $16x^2 + 24x + 9$ 28. $(5x + 2)(5x + 2)$ $25x^2 + 20x + 4$

29. $(4x + 3)(4x - 3)$ $16x^2 - 9$ 30. $(5x + 2)(5x - 2)$ $25x^2 - 4$

31. $(2x - 7)(2x - 7)$ $4x^2 - 28x + 49$ 32. $(3x - 7)(3x - 7)$ $9x^2 - 42x + 49$

33. $(2x - 7)(2x + 7)$ $4x^2 - 49$ 34. $(3x - 7)(3x + 7)$ $9x^2 - 49$

35. $(x + 6)^2$ $x^2 + 12x + 36$ 36. $(x + 8)^2$ $x^2 + 16x^2 + 64$

37. $(x - 9)^2$ $x^2 - 18x + 81$ 38. $(x - 4)^2$ $x^2 - 8x + 16$

39. $(3x + 5)^2$ $9x^2 + 30x + 25$ 40. $(4x - 5)^2$ $16x^2 - 40x + 25$

For Problems 41 through 50 a binomial is multiplied by a trinomial. Find the product by multiplying each term in the trinomial by each term in the binomial and combining the like terms.

EXAMPLE

$(x + 3)(x^2 - 5x + 7)$

$= x^3 - 5x^2 + 7x + 3x^2 - 15x + 21$

$= \underline{\underline{x^3 - 2x^2 - 8x + 21}}$

41. $(x + 2)(x^2 + 3x + 5)$ 42. $(x + 3)(x^2 + 2x + 6)$

43. $(x - 3)(x^2 + 4x + 2)$ 44. $(x - 2)(x^2 + 5x + 3)$

45. $(x + 5)(x^2 - 2x + 3)$ 46. $(x + 4)(x^2 - 3x + 5)$

47. $(x - 6)(x^2 - 4x - 5)$ 48. $(x - 5)(x^2 - 4x - 6)$

49. $(2x + 3)(3x^2 - 4x + 5)$ 50. $(3x - 2)(2x^2 + 5x - 4)$

For Problems 51 through 60 you are to multiply *three* binomials. You can do this by associating and multiplying two of them first.

EXAMPLE

$(x + 5)(x + 2)(x - 6)$

$= (x + 5)(x^2 - 4x - 12)$

$= x^3 - 4x^2 - 12x + 5x^2 - 20x - 60$

$= \underline{\underline{x^3 + x^2 - 32x - 60}}$

51. $(x + 2)(x + 3)(x + 4)$ 52. $(x + 5)(x + 4)(x + 3)$

53. $(x - 5)(x + 2)(x + 1)$ 54. $(x - 2)(x + 6)(x + 1)$

55. $(x + 6)(x - 3)(x - 5)$ 56. $(x + 4)(x - 2)(x - 6)$

57. $(x - 1)(x + 2)(x - 7)$ 58. $(x - 1)(x + 3)(x - 5)$

59. $(x - 2)(x - 6)(x - 4)$ 60. $(x - 3)(x - 7)(x - 2)$

Problems 41–50 involve multiplying binomials by trinomials. The words "Distribute the x through the second factor . . ." are helpful.

41. $x^3 + 5x^2 + 11x + 10$
42. $x^3 + 5x^2 + 12x + 18$
43. $x^3 + x^2 - 10x - 6$
44. $x^3 + 3x^2 - 7x - 6$
45. $x^3 + 3x^2 - 7x + 15$
46. $x^3 + x^2 - 7x + 20$
47. $x^3 - 10x^2 + 19x + 30$
48. $x^3 - 9x^2 + 14x + 30$
49. $6x^3 + x^2 - 2x + 15$
50. $6x^3 + 11x^2 - 22x + 8$

Problems 51–60 reduce to problems like 41–50 after the first multiplication is done. It is advisable for students to associate the second and third factors first so that the second multiplication will be by a binomial, as in the earlier problems.
Problems 61–65 review concepts earlier in this chapter.
Problems 66–70 review concepts from previous chapters.

51. $x^3 + 9x^2 + 26x + 24$
52. $x^3 + 12x^2 + 47x + 60$
53. $x^3 - 2x^2 - 13x - 10$
54. $x^3 + 5x^2 - 8x - 12$
55. $x^3 - 2x^2 - 33x + 90$
56. $x^3 - 4x^2 - 20x + 48$
57. $x^3 - 6x^2 - 9x + 14$
58. $x^3 - 3x^2 - 13x + 15$
59. $x^3 - 12x^2 + 44x - 48$
60. $x^3 - 12x^2 + 41x - 42$

Problems 61 through 70 review skills previously learned.

61. $-8x^5 - 3x^2 + 7x + 4$

61. Arrange in descending powers of x: $7x - 3x^2 + 4 - 8x^5$.

62. a. 5th degree binomial
  b. Cubic polynomial with 4 terms
  c. Linear binomial

62. Name by degree and by number of terms:
  a. $6x^5 + 11$;   **b.** $x^3 + 9x^2 - 3x + 14$;   **c.** $9 - 3x$.

63. $3x$, e.g.

63. Write an example of a linear monomial.

64. $x^2 + 5x - 2$, e.g.

64. Write an example of a quadratic trinomial.

65. a. Polynomial   **b.** Polynomial
  c. Not polynomial—division by a variable
  d. Polynomial

65. Tell whether or not these are polynomials. If so, tell *why*. If not, tell why *not*.

66. $x \approx 1.11$; $4.42\ldots = 4.42\ldots$

  a. $x^5 + 2$ **b.** $\dfrac{1}{5}x - 7$ **c.** $\dfrac{5}{x} - 8$ **d.** $x^3 - 5x + 1$

67. $19x - 32$ **68.** 8

66. Solve and check: $4x = 3(7 - 5x)$. Round off the answer to two decimal places.

69. -25

67. Simplify $3x - 8(4 - 2x)$.

68. Evaluate this absolute value expression $|38 - 2x|$ if $x = 23$.

69. Evaluate $-x^2$ if x is 5.

70. a. x = no. of min.
      $200 - 3x$ = no. of ft. left.

70. *Ice Worm Problem*   An ice worm lives at the South Pole in a hole that is 200 feet below the surface of the ice. The worm decides to come out and see what the weather is like, so it starts slithering up at 3 feet per minute.
  a. Define a variable for the number of minutes it has been slithering, then write an expression for how far it has left to go to reach the surface.
  b. How far from the surface will it be after 17 minutes?   149 ft
  c. How long does it take the worm to get to a point 30 feet from the surface? $56\frac{2}{3}$ min

For Problems 71 and 72, multiply the binomials the "long" way, by distributing twice, as shown at the beginning of this section.

71. $(3x - 5)(2x + 4)$ $6x^2 + 2x - 20$ 72. $(4x - 3)(2x + 5)$ $8x^2 + 14x - 15$

73. Check the answer to Problem 71 by substituting 3 for x in both the original expression and in your answer.   40 = 40 (same!)

In Problems 73 and 74 students are often amazed to find that evaluating both forms of the polynomial gives the *same* answer. You can capitalize on this amazement by pointing out that this is the reason the "=" sign is used between steps. The expression still stands for the same number. You have just changed its *form* ("transform") by doing the multiplying.

74. Check the answer to Problem 72 by substituting 3 for x in both the original expression and in your answer.   99 = 99 (same!)

5-4 | FACTORING QUADRATIC TRINOMIALS

In the last section you learned how to multiply two binomials together. For example,

$$(x + 3)(x + 5) = x^2 + 8x + 15.$$

In this section you learn how to *reverse* the process. You will start with a quadratic trinomial, such as $x^2 + 8x + 15$, and transform it into *factored form*, $(x + 3)(x + 5)$. The process is called *factoring* the polynomial.

DEFINITION

FACTORING A POLYNOMIAL
To factor a polynomial means to transform it to a *product* of two or more factors.

Objective:
Given a quadratic trinomial with the x^2-coefficient equal to 1, factor it into a product of linear binomials (if possible).

The way to factor $x^2 + 8x + 15$ is to recall where the 8 and the 15 came from in the multiplication process. The 8 is 3 *plus* 5. The 15 is 3 *times* 5. See the following diagram.

$$\text{Sum, } 3 + 5$$
$$(x + 3)(x + 5) = x^2 + 8x + 15$$
$$\text{Product, } 3 \cdot 5$$

To find the factors of $x^2 + 8x + 15$, you write

$$(x \qquad)(x \qquad).$$

Then you look for two *factors* of 15 whose *sum* is 8. The factors of 15 are

$$1, 15;$$
$$3, 5.$$

The 3 and 5 have a sum equal to 8. So you put the 3 and 8 in the spaces inside each pair of parentheses. The entire problem would look like this:

$$x^2 + 8x + 15$$
$$= (x + 3)(x + 5).$$

Cover the answers as you work these examples.

EXAMPLE 1

Factor $x^2 + 7x + 10$.

Time: 3 days, including test or quiz

Chalkboard Examples:

Day 1:
Factor:
1. $x^2 + 11x + 28$ Ans.: $(x + 4)(x + 7)$
2. $x^2 + 8x + 12$ Ans.: $(x + 2)(x + 6)$
3. $x^2 - 11x + 30$ Ans.: $(x - 5)(x - 6)$
4. $x^2 - 17x + 30$ Ans.: $(x - 2)(x - 15)$
5. $x^2 - 20x + 30$ Ans.: Prime.
   (No factors of 30 add up to -20.)

Day 2:

Have students put homework problems on the board.
   The Oral Practice problems in this section help students realize that getting the correct middle term is the key to success in factoring. It is best to have all students spend a few minutes working all problems, then call on individuals to tell the answer.

Assignments:

Day 1: 1–17 odd or 2–18 even, and 41–50
   (all) for review

Day 2: 19–39 odd or 20–40 even, and 51–56
   (all) for review

Day 3: After test or quiz, study Section 5–5,
   work the examples, and work Exercise
   5–5, Problems 1, 3, and 5 or 2, 4, and
   6.

– – – – –   – – – – –

	Think These Reasons

$x^2 + 7x + 10$

Write the given expression.

$= (x + 2)(x + 5)$

10 equals $2 \cdot 5$, and $2 + 5$ is 7. The factors can appear in either order, $(x + 2)(x + 5)$ or $(x + 5)(x + 2)$, since multiplication is a commutative operation.

EXAMPLE 2

Factor $x^2 + 9x + 20$.

– – – – –   – – – – –

$x^2 + 9x + 20$

Write the given expression.

$= (x + 4)(x + 5)$

The factors of 20 are
   1, 20;
   2, 10;
   4, 5.
The sum of 4 and 5 is 9.

EXAMPLE 3

Factor $x^2 + 12x + 20$.

– – – – –   – – – – –

	Think These Reasons

$x^2 + 12x + 20$

$= (x + 2)(x + 10)$

See Example 2. The sum of 2 and 10 is 12.

EXAMPLE 4

Factor $x^2 + 21x + 20$.

– – – – –   – – – – –

$x^2 + 21x + 20$

$= (x + 1)(x + 20)$

See Example 2. The sum of 1 and 20 is 21.

EXAMPLE 5

Factor $x^2 - 12x + 20$.

– – – – –   – – – – –

$x^2 - 12x + 20$

Write the given expression.

$= (x - 2)(x - 10)$

$-12x$ is *negative*. So you need two factors of 20 whose sum is -12. They are -2 and -10.

EXAMPLE 6

Factor $x^2 + 15x + 20$.

– – – – –   – – – – –

$x^2 + 15x + 20$ Write the given expression.

Prime

$1 + 20 = 21$
$2 + 10 = 12$ ⟵   Skips 15!
$4 + 5 = 9$

DEFINITION

> **PRIME POLYNOMIAL**
> A **prime polynomial** is a polynomial whose only factors are 1 and the polynomial itself.

ORAL PRACTICE

For each trinomial, give two factors of the constant term whose sum equals the coefficient of the linear term.

EXAMPLES

Answers

i. $x^2 + 9x + 20$ i.   4 and 5
ii. $c^2 - 7c + 6$ ii. -1 and -6

A. $x^2 + 5x + 6$ 3 and 2   B. $x^2 + 6x + 5$ 5 and 1
C. $t^2 + 8t + 15$ 5 and 3   D. $y^2 - 6y + 8$ -2 and -4
E. $x^2 - 5x + 4$ -1 and -4 F. $b^2 - 8b + 12$ -2 and -6
G. $z^2 + 11z + 10$ 10 and 1   H. $x^2 - 7x + 10$ -5 and -2
I. $x^2 + 7x + 12$ 4 and 3   J. $x^2 + 5x + 8$ None
K. $x^2 - 8x + 7$ -1 and -7 L. $x^2 - 9x + 12$ None

EXERCISE 5-4

Factor the following quadratic trinomials or write that they are prime. It is advisable for you to check your answers mentally by multiplying the factors together.

1. $x^2 + 7x + 6$ $(x + 1)(x + 6)$ 2. $x^2 + 11x + 10$ $(x + 1)(x + 10)$

Problem Notes:

Students should always check the answer by multiplying. The reason is not so much to make sure they have the right answer but rather to make sure they understand the *concept* of what factoring really means.

In Problems 39, 1001 factors into (7) (11) (13), a product of consecutive primes. In Problem 40, 2001 factors into (3) (23) (29).

3. $x^2 + 6x + 5$ $(x + 1)(x + 5)$ 4. $x^2 + 8x + 7$ $(x + 1)(x + 7)$

5. $x^2 - 26x + 25$ $(x - 1)(x - 25)$ 6. $x^2 - 17x + 16$ $(x - 1)(x - 16)$

7. $r^2 - 8r + 12$ $(r - 2)(r - 6)$ 8. $s^2 - 7s + 12$ $(s - 3)(s - 4)$

9. $z^2 + 5z + 6$ $(z + 2)(z + 3)$ 10. $y^2 + 6y + 8$ $(y + 2)(y + 4)$

11. $x^2 + 6x + 9$ $(x + 3)(x + 3)$ 12. $x^2 + 4x + 4$ $(x + 2)(x + 2)$

13. $x^2 + 10x + 9$ $(x + 1)(x + 9)$ 14. $x^2 + 5x + 4$ $(x + 1)(x + 4)$

15. $x^2 - 10x + 21$ $(x - 3)(x - 7)$ 16. $x^2 - 15x + 26$ $(x - 2)(x - 13)$

17. $a^2 - 13a + 40$ $(a - 5)(a - 8)$ 18. $c^2 - 16c + 15$ $(c - 1)(c - 15)$

19. $x^2 + 16x + 48$ $(x + 4)(x + 12)$ 20. $x^2 + 19x + 60$ $(x + 4)(x + 15)$

21. $x^2 + 14x + 48$ $(x + 6)(x + 8)$ 22. $x^2 + 16x + 60$ $(x + 6)(x + 10)$

23. $x^2 - 19x + 48$ $(x - 3)(x - 16)$ 24. $x^2 - 17x + 60$ $(x - 5)(x - 12)$

25. $x^2 - 20x + 48$ Prime   26. $x^2 - 23x + 60$ $(x - 3)(x - 20)$

27. $x^2 - 26x + 48$ $(x - 2)(x - 24)$ 28. $x^2 - 30x + 60$ Prime

29. $m^2 + 11m + 18$ $(m + 2)(m + 9)$ 30. $h^2 + 11h + 24$ $(h + 3)(h + 8)$

31. $x^2 - 52x + 100$ $(x - 2)(x - 50)$ 32. $x^2 - 43x + 120$ $(x - 3)(x - 40)$

33. $x^2 + 45x + 120$ Prime   34. $x^2 + 39x + 140$ $(x + 4)(x + 35)$

35. $b^2 + 25b + 150$ $(b + 10)(b + 15)$ 36. $z^2 + 30z + 160$ Prime

37. $y^2 - 37y + 300$ $(y - 12)(y - 25)$ 38. $u^2 + 77u + 360$ $(u + 5)(u + 72)$

39. $x^2 - 90x + 1001$ $(x - 13)(x - 77)$ 40. $x^2 - 98x + 2001$ $(x - 29)(x - 69)$

For Problems 41 through 50, multiply the binomials.

41. $(x + 4)(3x + 5)$ $3x^2 + 17x + 20$ 42. $(2x - 3)(4x + 3)$ $8x^2 - 6x - 9$

43. $(5x + 4)(2x - 7)$ $10x^2 - 27x - 28$ 44. $(4x + 3)(4x + 3)$ $16x^2 + 24x + 9$

45. $(2x - 7)(2x - 7)$ $4x^2 - 28x + 49$ 46. $(4x + 3)(4x - 3)$ $16x^2 - 9$

47. $(2x - 7)(2x + 7)$ $4x^2 - 49$ 48. $(x + 6)^2$ $x^2 + 12x + 36$

49. $(x - 9)^2$ $x^2 - 18x + 81$ 50. $(3x + 5)^2$ $9x^2 + 30x + 25$

51. Solve and check: $5(x - 7) = x - 3$. $x = 8; 5 = 5$

52. Evaluate $x^2 + 8$ if $x = 9$.   89

53. Simplify $4x - (7 - 9x)$. $13x - 7$

54. Write an example of a sixth-degree binomial. $x^6 + 1$, e.g.

55. Arrange in descending powers of x: $x^2 - 2x^3 + 11 - 5x$. $-2x^3 + x^2 - 5x + 11$

56. *Tutoring Problem*   Let x be the number of minutes Mally Factor has been working algebra problems. Her tutor, Val Ewing, joins her when Mally has been working for 20 minutes. Val charges $.30 per

minute for tutoring services. Write an expression in terms of x for the number of dollars Val charges Mally. $0.30(x - 20)$

5-5 | FACTORING QUADRATIC TRINOMIALS—THIRD TERM NEGATIVE

Time: 1 day

In the last section, you factored trinomials such as

$$x^2 + 8x + 15 = (x + 3)(x + 5).$$

Perhaps you noticed that, although the middle term was sometimes positive and sometimes negative, the last term was always *positive*. If the last term is *negative,* the two binomials will have *opposite* signs. For example, multiplying

$$(x - 4)(x + 7)$$

gives

$$x^2 + 3x - 28.$$

In this section, you will factor quadratic trinomials in which the last term is negative.

Objective:
Be able to factor quadratic trinomials such as $x^2 + 3x - 28$, in which the constant term is *negative*.

The procedure is exactly the same as in the last section. This time you want two factors of -28 that add up to $+3$. Writing the factors of -28 shows which pair to pick.

Factors	Sum
$-1, 28$	27
$-2, 14$	12
$-4, 7$	3 ⟵ That's it!

So $x^2 + 3x - 28$ factors as follows:

$$x^2 + 3x - 28$$
$$= \underline{\underline{(x - 4)(x + 7)}}.$$

The answer can be checked by multiplying the binomials back together again.

$(x - 4)(x + 7)$	Write the answer.
$= x^2 + 7x - 4x - 28$	Multiply each term in one factor by each term in the other.
$= x^2 + 3x - 28$ ✔	Combine like terms.

Chalkboard Examples:

Factor:
1. $x^2 - 8x + 12$ Ans. $(x - 2)(x - 6)$
   (a refresher)
2. $x^2 + 2x - 15$ Ans. $(x - 3)(x + 5)$
   (teacher)
3. $x^2 + 8x - 20$ Ans.: $(x - 2)(x + 10)$
   (students)
4. $x^2 - 2x - 24$ Ans.: $(x + 4)(x - 6)$
5. $x^2 - x - 12$ Ans.: $(x + 3)(x - 4)$
   (x-coefficient $= -1$)
6. $x^2 + 6x - 10$ Ans.: Prime
   (No factors of -10 add up to 6.)
7. $x^2 - 5x + 6$ Ans.: $(x - 2)(x - 3)$
   (Don't forget how to do old problems!)

These examples provide a good way to make sure students have the right idea before they do problems on their own. Be sure they follow the instructions and cover the answers at the dotted lines while they are working the problems. You should circulate among the students as they work the examples to make sure they are following the instructions.

Assignment:

7–45 odd or 8–46 even (Problems 47–49 are optional.)

Cover the answers as you work these examples.

EXAMPLE 1

Factor $x^2 + 3x - 10$.

- - - - -   - - - - -

	Think These Reasons

$x^2 + 3x - 10$ Write the given expression.

$= (x - 2)(x + 5)$ The factors of -10 are:
$-1, 10$ (Sum $= 9$. Not right.)
$-2, 5$ (Sum $= 3$. That's it!)

EXAMPLE 2

Factor $x^2 - 3x - 10$.

- - - - -   - - - - -

$x^2 - 3x - 10$ Write the given expression.

$= (x + 2)(x - 5)$ $-3x$ is *negative*. So the two factors of -10 must be $+2$ and -5.

EXAMPLE 3

Factor $x^2 + x - 20$.

- - - - -   - - - - -

$x^2 + x - 20$ Write the given expression.

$= (x - 4)(x + 5)$

Factors of -20	*Sum*
$-1, 20$	19
$-2, 10$	8
$-4, \ 5$	1 ⟵—— That's it!

(You must realize that the coefficient of the middle term, x, is 1.)

EXAMPLE 4

Factor $x^2 - 8x - 20$.

- - - - -   - - - - -

$x^2 - 8x - 20$ Write the given expression.

$= (x + 2)(x - 10)$ See the factors of -20 in Example 3. This time the *larger* one must be negative since the sum is -8.

EXAMPLE 5

Factor $x^2 - 9x - 20$.

- - - - -   - - - - -

$x^2 - 9x - 20$ Write the given expression.

Prime

$$1 + (-20) = -19$$
$$2 + (-10) = -8$$
$$5 + (-5) = -1$$

Skips -9.

Therefore, *no* factors of -20 have a sum of -9.

ORAL PRACTICE

For each trinomial, give two factors of the constant term whose sum equals the coefficient of the linear term.

EXAMPLES

Answers

i. $x^2 + 2x - 15$ i. -3 and 5
ii. $p^2 - 4p - 12$ ii. 2 and -6

A. $x^2 + 2x - 3$ -1 and 3 B. $x^2 + 4x - 5$ -1 and 5

C. $z^2 + 9z - 10$ -1 and 10 D. $y^2 - 3y - 10$ 2 and -5

E. $x^2 - 3x - 4$ 1 and -4 F. $v^2 - 2v - 15$ 3 and -5

G. $x^2 + x - 6$ -2 and 3 H. $x^2 + x - 12$ -3 and 4

I. $u^2 - u - 20$ 4 and -5 J. $x^2 + 4x - 6$ None

K. $x^2 - 5x - 14$ 2 and -7 L. $x^2 - 5x + 6$ -2 and -3

EXERCISE 5-5

For Problems 1 through 40, factor the trinomial or state that it is prime. Check your answers by multiplication.

1. $x^2 + 3x - 10$ $(x - 2)(x + 5)$ 2. $x^2 + 4x - 12$ $(x - 2)(x + 6)$

3. $x^2 + 2x - 8$ $(x - 2)(x + 4)$ 4. $x^2 + 3x - 4$ $(x - 1)(x + 4)$

5. $x^2 + 8x - 9$ $(x - 1)(x + 9)$ 6. $x^2 + 9x - 10$ $(x - 1)(x + 10)$

7. $r^2 - 4r - 12$ $(r + 2)(r - 6)$ 8. $s^2 - 2s - 15$ $(s + 3)(s - 5)$

9. $a^2 - a - 30$ $(a + 5)(a - 6)$ 10. $b^2 - b - 20$ $(b + 4)(b - 5)$

11. $x^2 + x - 20$ $(x - 4)(x + 5)$ 12. $x^2 + x - 6$ $(x - 2)(x + 3)$

13. $x^2 - 5x - 50$ $(x + 5)(x - 10)$ 14. $x^2 - 7x - 30$ $(x + 3)(x - 10)$

15. $x^2 - 23x - 50$ $(x + 2)(x - 25)$ 16. $x^2 - 13x - 30$ $(x + 2)(x - 15)$

17. $x^2 - 20x - 50$ Prime   18. $x^2 - 12x - 30$ Prime

19. $u^2 - 71u - 72$ $(u + 1)(u - 72)$ 20. $t^2 - 8t - 48$ $(t + 4)(t - 12)$

Problem Notes:

In Problems 9–12 and elsewhere, the linear coefficient does not appear. If students realize that $a^2 - a - 30$ means $a^2 - 1a - 30$, then they will have no difficulty.

Problems 13–26 have groups of problems with the same constant term and differing middle terms. These problems are intended to show the students that the trinomial may be factorable for some values of the middle coefficient but not for others.

Problems 27–40 have some constant terms *positive*, as in the previous section. Problems 29–36 are interesting because the polynomial will factor regardless of the combination of signs that appear. A discussion of such trinomials is given by Bert Miller in the December 1980 issue of *Mathematics Teacher*, page 649.

Problem 49 shows a systematic way to generate all factorable quadratic trinomials with a given constant term and 1 for the x^2 coefficient. You may use this technique to write your own problems. A more direct way to get factorable trinomials is simply to multiply together two linear binomials.

21. $u^2 + 20u - 72$ Prime   22. $t^2 + 2t - 48$ $(t - 6)(t + 8)$

23. $u^2 - 14u - 72$ $(u + 4)(u - 18)$ 24. $t^2 + 16t - 48$ Prime

25. $u^2 + u - 72$ $(u - 8)(u + 9)$ 26. $t^2 - 13t - 48$ $(t + 3)(t - 16)$

27. $x^2 - 13x + 42$ $(x - 6)(x - 7)$ Surprise!   28. $x^2 - 17x + 42$ $(x - 3)(x - 14)$ Surprise!

29. $x^2 + 5x - 6$ $(x - 1)(x + 6)$ 30. $x^2 + 13x - 30$ $(x - 2)(x + 15)$

31. $x^2 - 5x + 6$ $(x - 2)(x - 3)$ 32. $x^2 - 13x + 30$ $(x - 3)(x - 10)$

33. $x^2 + 26x + 120$ $(x + 6)(x + 20)$ 34. $x^2 - 17x + 60$ $(x - 5)(x - 12)$

35. $x^2 + 26x - 120$ $(x - 4)(x + 30)$ 36. $x^2 - 17x - 60$ $(x + 3)(x - 20)$

37. $x^2 - 21x + 98$ $(x - 7)(x - 14)$ 38. $x^2 + 24x + 63$ $(x + 3)(x + 21)$

39. $x^2 + 14x - 51$ $(x - 3)(x + 17)$ 40. $x^2 - 9x - 52$ $(x + 4)(x - 13)$

For Problems 41 through 46, multiply the binomials.

41. $(x + 2)(x - 7)$ $x^2 - 5x - 14$ 42. $(x - 3)(x - 8)$ $x^2 - 11x + 24$

43. $(x - 2)(4x + 3)$ $4x^2 - 5x - 6$ 44. $(3x - 4)(x + 5)$ $3x^2 + 11x - 20$

45. $(3x + 8)(7x + 4)$ $21x^2 + 68x + 32$ 46. $(5x + 3)(2x - 1)$ $10x^2 + x - 3$

47. Kay Paso and Holly Peña factor a trinomial as follows:
Kay: $x^2 + 6x - 40 = (x + 10)(x - 4)$;
Holly: $x^2 + 6x - 40 = (x - 10)(x + 4)$.
Who is right? Explain.   Kay

48. Calvin Butterball and Phoebe Small factor a trinomial as follows:
Calvin: $x^2 - 11x - 42 = (x - 14)(x + 3)$;
Phoebe: $x^2 - 11x - 42 = (x + 3)(x - 14)$.
Who is right? Explain.   Both

49. Here is one way to make up factoring problems. For example, if the last term is to be -12, you can write the factors as shown on the next page.

Factors	Sum
$-1, 12$	11
$-2, 6$	4
$-3, 4$	1
$-4, 3$	-1
$-6, 2$	-4
$-12, 1$	-11

The possible trinomials are:

$$x^2 + 11x - 12 \qquad x^2 + 4x - 12 \qquad x^2 + x - 12$$

$$x^2 - 11x - 12 \qquad x^2 - 4x - 12 \qquad x^2 - x - 12.$$

Write all factorable quadratic trinomials whose first term is x^2 and whose last term is:

a. -6;   b. -8;   c. 10;   d. 18;   e. 25.

49. a.
Factors	Sum	Trinomials
$-1 + 6$	$+5$	$x^2 + 5x - 6$
$-2 + 3$	$+1$	$x^2 + x - 6$
$-3 + 2$	-1	$x^2 - x - 6$
$-6 + 1$	-5	$x^2 - 5x - 6$

b.
Factors	Sum	Trinomials
$-1 + 8$	7	$x^2 + 7x - 8$
$-2 + 4$	2	$x^2 + 2x - 8$
$-4 + 2$	-2	$x^2 - 2x - 8$
$-8 + 1$	-7	$x^2 - 7x - 8$

c.
Factors	Sum	Trinomials
$1 + 10$	11	$x^2 + 11x + 10$
$2 + 5$	7	$x^2 + 7x + 10$
$-2 + (-5)$	-7	$x^2 - 7x + 10$
$-1 + (-10)$	-11	$x^2 - 11x + 10$

d.
Factors	Sum	Trinomials
$1 + 18$	19	$x^2 + 19x + 18$
$2 + 9$	11	$x^2 + 11x + 18$
$3 + 6$	9	$x^2 + 9x + 18$
$-3 + (-6)$	-9	$x^2 - 9x + 18$
$-2 + (-9)$	-11	$x^2 - 11x + 18$
$-1 + (-18)$	-19	$x^2 - 19x + 18$

e.
Factors	Sum	Trinomials
$1 + 25$	26	$x^2 + 26x + 25$
$5 + 5$	10	$x^2 + 10x + 25$
$-5 + (-5)$	-10	$x^2 - 10x + 25$
$-1 + (-25)$	-26	$x^2 - 26x + 25$

5-6 | FACTORING QUADRATIC TRINOMIALS— FIRST COEFFICIENT NOT 1

Time: 2 days

Chalkboard Examples:

Factor:
1. $2x^2 + 15x + 7$ Ans.: $(2x + 1)(x + 7)$
2. $3x^2 + 5x + 2$ Ans.: $(3x + 2)(x + 1)$
3. $5x^2 - 9x - 2$ Ans.: $(5x + 1)(x - 2)$
4. $3x^2 + 7x - 6$ Ans.: $(3x - 2)(x + 3)$
    (Two possibilities for second terms: 2, 3 or 1, 6.)
5. $4b^2 - 8b + 3$ Ans.: $(2b - 1)(2b - 3)$
    (Two possibilities for b-coefficient: 2, 2 or 4, 1.)

Assignments:

Day 1: 1–19 odd and 31, 33, 35

Day 2: 2–30 even (Problems 37–40 are optional.)
    (Fewer can be assigned at a time if students get weary.)

In the factoring problems of the last two sections, the trinomials always looked like

$$x^2 - 6x + 8 \quad \text{or} \quad x^2 + 5x - 6.$$

The x^2-term always had a coefficient of 1 (although you did not *write* the 1). In this section you will learn how to factor quadratic trinomials like

$$3x^2 - 11x - 4,$$

in which the x^2-term has a coefficient *other* than 1. This coefficient is often called the **leading coefficient.**

Objective :
Be able to factor quadratic trinomials in which the coefficient of the squared term is not equal to 1.

The procedure that you used for trinomials like $x^2 + 5x - 6$ no longer works for trinomials like $3x^2 - 11x - 4$. So you simply search for two binomials whose product is $3x^2 - 11x - 4$. Start by writing the given expression and two empty pairs of parentheses.

$$3x^2 - 11x - 4$$
$$= (\quad)(\quad)$$

You know that the first terms in the two factors must be $3x$ and x, so that you will get $3x^2$ when you multiply them together. You can fill in these terms.

$$3x^2 - 11x - 4$$
$$= (3x \quad)(x \quad)$$

The second terms must be one of the pairs

$$-2 \quad \text{and} \quad 2 \qquad 2 \quad \text{and} \quad -2$$
$$-1 \quad \text{and} \quad 4 \qquad 4 \quad \text{and} \quad -1$$
$$1 \quad \text{and} \quad -4 \qquad -4 \quad \text{and} \quad 1$$

so that their product will be -4. One way to find the right pair is to multiply the binomials and see which one gives the right middle term, $-11x$.

$$(3x + 2)(x - 2) \rightarrow -6x + 2x \rightarrow -4x \qquad \text{No}$$

$$(3x + 4)(x - 1) \rightarrow -3x + 4x \rightarrow +x \qquad \text{No}$$

$$(3x - 1)(x + 4) \rightarrow +12x - x \rightarrow +11x \qquad \text{Right number, wrong sign}$$

$$(3x + 1)(x - 4) \rightarrow -12x + x \rightarrow -11x \qquad \text{That's it!}$$

All of this trial-and-error work can be done on scratch paper or in your head. When you find the right factors, you simply write the final answer on your paper.

$$3x^2 - 11x - 4$$
$$= \underline{\underline{(3x + 1)(x - 4)}}$$

Cover the answers as you work these examples.

EXAMPLE 1

Factor $2x^2 + 7x + 5$.

$-\ -\ -\ -\ -$ $-\ -\ -\ -\ -$

| | **Think These Reasons** |

$$2x^2 + 7x + 5 \qquad \text{Write the given expression.}$$
$$= \underline{\underline{(2x + 5)(x + 1)}} \qquad \text{Middle term is } 2x + 5x = 7x.$$

EXAMPLE 2

Factor $2x^2 + 11x + 5$.

$-\ -\ -\ -\ -$ $-\ -\ -\ -\ -$

$$2x^2 + 11x + 5 \qquad \text{Write the given expression.}$$
$$= \underline{\underline{(2x + 1)(x + 5)}} \qquad \text{Middle term is } 10x + x = 11x.$$

EXAMPLE 3

Factor $3a^2 + 5a - 2$.

$-\ -\ -\ -\ -$ $-\ -\ -\ -\ -$

$$3a^2 + 5a - 2 \qquad \text{Write the given expression.}$$
$$= \underline{\underline{(3a - 1)(a + 2)}} \qquad \text{Middle term is } 6a - a = 5a.$$

EXAMPLE 4

Factor $3x^2 - x - 2$.

$-\ -\ -\ -\ -$ $-\ -\ -\ -\ -$

$$3x^2 - x - 2 \qquad \text{Write the given expression.}$$
$$= \underline{\underline{(3x + 2)(x - 1)}} \qquad \text{Middle term is } -3x + 2x = -x.$$

EXAMPLE 5

Factor $4x^2 - 7x - 2$.

- - - - -   - - - - -

$$4x^2 - 7x - 2 \qquad \text{Write the given expression.}$$

$$= \underline{(4x + 1)(x - 2)} \qquad \text{Middle term is } -8x + x = -7x.$$

ORAL PRACTICE

Tell what the middle term will be when the following factors are multiplied together.

EXAMPLE

	Answer
$(3x - 5)(2x + 7)$	$11x$

A. $(4x + 3)(2x + 5)$ $26x$ B. $(6x + 1)(2x + 5)$ $32x$

C. $(5x + 3)(3x + 4)$ $29x$ D. $(2x - 7)(3x - 4)$ $-29x$

E. $(2x - 3)(2x - 3)$ $-12x$ F. $(2x - 3)(3x - 2)$ $-13x$

G. $(3x - 5)(2x + 4)$ $2x$ H. $(4x - 2)(6x + 1)$ $-8x$

I. $(5x + 7)(2x - 3)$ $-x$ J. $(x - 10)(2x - 3)$ $-23x$

K. $(x + 3)(5x - 3)$ $12x$ L. $(5x + 3)(5x - 3)$ 0

EXERCISE 5-6

For Problems 1–30, factor the trinomial.

1. $5x^2 + 8x + 3$ $(x + 1)(5x + 3)$ 2. $7x^2 + 9x + 2$ $(x + 1)(7x + 2)$

3. $2x^2 + 5x + 2$ $(x + 2)(2x + 1)$ 4. $3x^2 + 10x + 3$ $(x + 3)(3x + 1)$

5. $2y^2 + 7y + 3$ $(y + 3)(2y + 1)$ 6. $3z^2 + 7z + 2$ $(z + 2)(3z + 1)$

7. $2x^2 + 9x + 4$ $(x + 4)(2x + 1)$ 8. $3x^2 + 13x + 4$ $(x + 4)(3x + 1)$

9. $3x^2 - 16x + 5$ $(x - 5)(3x - 1)$ 10. $2x^2 - 11x + 5$ $(x - 5)(2x - 1)$

11. $3x^2 - 5x + 2$ $(x - 1)(3x - 2)$ 12. $2x^2 - 5x + 3$ $(2x - 3)(x - 1)$

13. $3p^2 - 8p + 4$ $(p - 2)(3p - 2)$ 14. $3b^2 - 11b + 6$ $(b - 3)(3b - 2)$

Problem Notes:

Students sometimes get the misconception from the previous two sections that you just find two factors of the constant term whose sum equals the middle coefficient. That pattern breaks down when the x^2-coefficient is not 1, and students must go back to the basic idea of multiplication.

The first twenty problems have squared coefficients that are primes, so students have only one way of writing the first terms in the factors. The next ten problems have composite numbers for the squared coefficients.

Problem 37 is meant to show students that the two factors in the answer may be commuted to either order.

Problem 38 is meant to show that students can get the right middle term but still have the wrong answer. It is necessary to do the entire multiplication problem to check the answer.

Problem 39 has quadratic trinomials masked in clever disguises to see if students realize that expressions stand for *numbers*. Parts (d) and (g) are differences of two squares, the topic of the next section.

15. $3x^2 - 8x - 3$ $(x - 3)(3x + 1)$ 16. $2x^2 - 3x - 2$ $(x - 2)(2x + 1)$

17. $3v^2 + v - 2$ $(v + 1)(3v - 2)$ 18. $5w^2 + 2w - 3$ $(w + 1)(5w - 3)$

19. $5x^2 - 8x - 4$ $(x - 2)(5x + 2)$ 20. $3x^2 + 4x - 4$ $(x + 2)(3x - 2)$

21. $4x^2 + 8x + 3$ $(2x + 3)(2x + 1)$ 22. $4x^2 + 12x + 5$ $(2x + 5)(2x + 1)$

23. $4x^2 + 7x + 3$ $(x + 1)(4x + 3)$ 24. $4x^2 + 9x + 5$ $(4x + 5)(x + 1)$

25. $4u^2 + 8u - 5$ $(2u + 5)(2u - 1)$ 26. $4m^2 + 4m - 3$ $(2m + 3)(2m - 1)$

27. $4x^2 + x - 5$ $(4x + 5)(x - 1)$ 28. $4x^2 + x - 3$ $(x + 1)(4x - 3)$

29. $6x^2 + 17x + 12$ $(2x + 3)(3x + 4)$ 30. $10x^2 + 19x + 6$ $(2x + 3)(5x + 2)$

For Problems 31 through 36, multiply the binomials.

31. $(x + 7)(x - 4)$ $x^2 + 3x - 28$ 32. $(x - 9)(x + 2)$ $x^2 - 7x - 18$

33. $(3x - 5)(x + 8)$ $3x^2 + 19x - 40$ 34. $(x + 3)(7x + 8)$ $7x^2 + 29x + 24$

35. $(2x - 1)(7x - 4)$ $14x^2 - 15x + 4$ 36. $(4x + 5)(6x - 7)$ $24x^2 + 2x - 35$

37. Faye Doubt and her brother Peter factor a trinomial as follows:
Faye: $3x^2 - 2x - 8 = (3x + 4)(x - 2)$;
Peter: $3x^2 - 2x - 8 = (x - 2)(3x + 4)$.
Who is right? Explain.   Both. Factors can be commuted.

38. Polly Nomial and Clara Fye factor a trinomial as follows:
Polly: $12x^2 + 7x - 12 = (3x + 4)(4x - 3)$;
Clara: $12x^2 + 7x - 12 = (x + 4)(x + 3)$.
Who is right? Explain.   Polly. Clara gets only middle term right.

39. Factor the following. This may require some cleverness!
a. $6 + 5x + x^2$ $(3 + x)(2 + x)$ b. $1 + 5x + 6x^2$ $(1 + 3x)(1 + 2x)$
c. $x^2 + 10x + 25$ $(x + 5)(x + 5)$ d. $x^2 - 25$ $(x + 5)(x - 5)$
e. $25x^2 + 10x + 1$ $(5x + 1)(5x + 1)$ f. $4x^2 - 12x + 9$ $(2x - 3)(2x - 3)$
g. $4x^2 - 9$ $(2x + 3)(2x - 3)$
h. $(a + b)^2 + 7(a + b) + 6$ $(a + b + 1)(a + b + 6)$
i. $(r - s)^2 + 3(r - s) + 2$ $(r - s + 1)(r - s + 2)$
j. $(\text{number})^2 - 3(\text{number}) - 10$ $(\text{number} + 2)(\text{number} - 5)$

Problem 40 shows what happens when both terms of the binomials contain a variable. Parts (a) through (e) and parts (f) through (j) form equivalent sets of problems. These problems are deliberately left out of the mainstream at this point, because the objective is to get students to the Quadratic Formula as quickly as possible.

40. *Binomials with Two Variables*   If you multiply two binomials such as
$$(x + 3y)(x + 2y)$$
you get
$$x^2 + 5xy + 6y^2.$$

So if you factor $x^2 + 5xy + 6y^2$, the factors are binomials with *two* variables, $(x + 3y)(x + 2y)$. Otherwise, factoring $x^2 + 5xy + 6y^2$ is just like factoring $x^2 + 5x + 6$. Factor the following.
a. $x^2 + 11xy + 10y^2$ $(x + y)(x + 10y)$ f. $x^2 + 7xy + 6y^2$ $(x + y)(x + 6y)$
b. $x^2 + 3xy - 4y^2$ $(x - y)(x + 4y)$ g. $x^2 + 2xy - 8y^2$ $(x - 2y)(x + 4y)$
c. $a^2 - 7ab - 30b^2$ $(a + 3b)(a - 10b)$ h. $a^2 - 5ab - 50b^2$ $(a + 5b)(a - 10b)$
d. $2x^2 - 11xy + 5y^2$ $(2x - y)(x - 5y)$ i. $3x^2 - 16xy + 5y^2$ $(3x - y)(x - 5y)$
e. $3c^2 + 4cd - 4d^2$ $(3c - 2d)(c + 2d)$ j. $5c^2 - 8cd - 4d^2$ $(5c + 2d)(c - 2d)$

5-7 | FACTORING A DIFFERENCE OF TWO SQUARES

In Section 5-5 you factored quadratic trinomials such as

$$x^2 + 5x - 36$$

by asking, "What two factors of -36 have a sum of 5?" The answer is 9 and -4. So you wrote

$$x^2 + 5x - 36 = (x + 9)(x - 4).$$

Suppose that you must factor $x^2 - 36$. The same reasoning can be used. Since there is no x-term, its coefficient must be *zero*. So you ask, "What two factors of -36 have a sum of 0?" The answer is 6 and -6. Thus you can write

$$x^2 - 36 = (x + 6)(x - 6).$$

Two binomials like $x + 6$ and $x - 6$, which are the same except for the sign between them, are called *conjugate binomials*.

DEFINITION

> **CONJUGATE BINOMIALS**
> **Conjugate binomials** are binomials that are the same except for the sign between the terms.
>
> (For example, $3x + 5$ and $3x - 5$ are conjugate binomials.)

Whenever you multiply two conjugate binomials together, the middle term is zero (it "drops out"). For instance,

$$(x + 6)(x - 6) = x^2 - 6x + 6x - 36 = x^2 - 36.$$

The first and last terms of the answer are both squares of other numbers, and the sign between them is $-$. Therefore, $x^2 - 36$ is called a *difference of two squares*.

CONCLUSION

> **DIFFERENCE OF TWO SQUARES**
> The factors of a **difference of two squares** are conjugate binomials.
>
> For instance, $a^2 - b^2 = (a + b)(a - b)$.

Time: 2 days, including test or quiz

Chalkboard Examples:

Factor:
1. $x^2 + 5x - 36$ (for review)
   Ans.: $(x + 9)(x - 4)$
   (Find two factors of -36 whose sum is $+5$.)
2. $x^2 - 36$ Ans.: $(x + 6)(x - 6)$
   (Find two factors of -36 whose sum is zero.)
3. $x^2 - 25$ Ans.: $(x + 5)(x - 5)$
   (Conclusion: Both terms must be squares. The sign must be $-$.)
4. $c^2 - 81$ Ans.: $(c + 9)(c - 9)$
5. $x^2 - 18$ Ans.: Prime
6. $4x^2 - 4x - 15$ (for review)
   Ans: $(2x + 3)(2x - 5)$
7. $4x^2 - 49$ Ans.: $(2x + 7)(2x - 7)$
8. $36y^2 - 1$ Ans.: $(6y + 1)(6y - 1)$
9. $x^2 + 25$ Ans.: Prime
   (The sign must be $-$.)

Assignments:

Day 1: 1–39 odd or 2–40 even

Day 2: Following test or quiz, Exercise 5-7, #41–61 odd or 42–62 even, or Study 5–8; Work #5–8, 1–9 odd

Beware! A *sum* of two squares does *not* factor. For instance, to factor

$$x^2 + 36,$$

you would need two factors of $+36$ whose sum is 0. Since they would have to be opposites of each other, their product could not possibly equal $+36$. Thus $x^2 + 36$ is *prime*.

Objective:

Be able to factor a difference of two squares as a product of conjugate binomials.

To accomplish this objective, you should recognize certain numbers that are perfect squares. if you do not already know these, take some time to memorize them. The following problems will be easier if you do.

$$0 = 0^2 \qquad 1 = 1^2 \qquad 4 = 2^2 \qquad 9 = 3^2 \qquad 16 = 4^2 \qquad 25 = 5^2$$
$$36 = 6^2 \qquad 49 = 7^2 \qquad 64 = 8^2 \qquad 81 = 9^2 \qquad 100 = 10^2$$

Cover the answers as you work these examples.

EXAMPLE 1

Factor $x^2 - 9$.

– – – – –   – – – – –

| | *Think These Reasons* |

$$x^2 - 9$$ Write the given expression.

$$= \underline{\underline{(x + 3)(x - 3)}}$$ $9 = 3^2$

EXAMPLE 2

Factor $r^2 - 49$.

– – – – –   – – – – –

$$r^2 - 49$$ Write the given expression.

$$= \underline{\underline{(r + 7)(r - 7)}}$$ $49 = 7^2$

EXAMPLE 3

Factor $4x^2 - 25$.

- - - - -   - - - - -

$4x^2 - 25$ Write the given expression.

$= \underline{\underline{(2x + 5)(2x - 5)}}$ $4x^2 = (2x)^2$ and $25 = 5^2$

EXAMPLE 4

Factor $81b^2 - 1$.

- - - - -   - - - - -

$81b^2 - 1$ Write the given expression.

$= \underline{\underline{(9b + 1)(9b - 1)}}$ $81b^2 = (9b)^2$ and $1 = 1^2$

EXAMPLE 5

Factor $x^2 - 12$.

- - - - -   - - - - -

$x^2 - 12$ Write the given expression.

$\underline{\underline{\text{Prime}}}$ 12 is *not* a perfect square.

EXAMPLE 6

Factor $x^2 + 16$.

- - - - -   - - - - -

$x^2 + 16$ Write the given expression.

$\underline{\underline{\text{Prime}}}$ $x^2 + 16$ is a *sum* of two squares, not a difference.

ORAL PRACTICE

Tell whether or not the binomial is a difference of two squares. If it is, give its factors. If it is not, tell *why* not.

EXAMPLES

		Answers	
i.	$x^2 - 9$	i.	Yes; $(x + 3)(x - 3)$.
ii.	$a^3 - 16$	ii.	No; a^3 is not a perfect square.
iii.	$x^2 + 25$	iii.	No; it is a *sum* of two squares.

A. $x^2 - 4$ Yes; $(x + 2)(x - 2)$.   B. $x^2 - 9$ Yes; $(x + 3)(x - 3)$.

C. $x^2 - 16$ Yes; $(x + 4)(x - 4)$.   D. $x^2 + 25$ No; it is a *sum* of two squares.

E. $a^2 - 36$ Yes; $(a + 6)(a - 6)$.   F. $36 - x^2$ Yes; $(6 + x)(6 - x)$.

G. $b^2 - 49$ Yes; $(b + 7)(b - 7)$.   H. $x^2 - 1$ Yes; $(x + 1)(x - 1)$.

I. $x^2 - 10$ No; 10 is *not* square.   J. $u^2 - 100$ Yes; $(u + 10)(u - 10)$.

K. $81 - z^2$ Yes; $(9 + z)(9 - z)$.   L. $9x^2 - 4$ Yes; $(3x + 2)(3x - 2)$.

EXERCISE 5-7

For Problems 1 through 40, factor the polynomial or state that it is prime.

Problem Notes:

Problems 1–30 are ordinary problems such as in the examples.

1. $x^2 - 16$ $(x + 4)(x - 4)$ 2. $x^2 - 4$ $(x + 2)(x - 2)$

3. $x^2 - 64$ $(x + 8)(x - 8)$ 4. $x^2 - 25$ $(x + 5)(x - 5)$

5. $a^2 - 4$ $(a + 2)(a - 2)$ 6. $a^2 - 64$ $(a + 8)(a - 8)$

7. $c^2 - 9$ $(c + 3)(c - 3)$ 8. $d^2 - 49$ $(d + 7)(d - 7)$

9. $x^2 - 1$ $(x + 1)(x - 1)$ 10. $p^2 - 1$ $(p + 1)(p - 1)$

11. $4x^2 - 25$ $(2x + 5)(2x - 5)$ 12. $4x^2 - 9$ $(2x + 3)(2x - 3)$

13. $9x^2 - 49$ $(3x + 7)(3x - 7)$ 14. $9x^2 - 16$ $(3x + 4)(3x - 4)$

15. $25a^2 - 36$ $(5a + 6)(5a - 6)$ 16. $25j^2 - 81$ $(5j + 9)(5j - 9)$

17. $81r^2 - 4$ $(9r + 2)(9r - 2)$ 18. $49x^2 - 36$ $(7x + 6)(7x - 6)$

19. $9x^2 - 100$ $(3x + 10)(3x - 10)$ 20. $100x^2 - 9$ $(10x + 3)(10x - 3)$

21. $4 - 25x^2$ $(2 + 5x)(2 - 5x)$ 22. $16 - 9x^2$ $(4 + 3x)(4 - 3x)$

23. $100 - 9x^2$ $(10 + 3x)(10 - 3x)$ 24. $64 - 25x^2$ $(8 + 5x)(8 - 5x)$

25. $15 - x^2$ Prime   26. $32 - x^2$ Prime

27. $1 - p^2$ $(1 + p)(1 - p)$ 28. $k^2 - 1$ $(k + 1)(k - 1)$

29. $x^2 + 16$ Prime   30. $36 + x^2$ Prime

In Problems 31 through 40, a variable appears in *both* terms. Factor these binomials.

Problems 31–40 are slightly more difficult because they have a variable in each term.

31. $4x^2 - 9y^2$ $(2x + 3y)(2x - 3y)$ 32. $9x^2 - 4y^2$ $(3x + 2y)(3x - 2y)$

33. $25x^2 - 81y^2$ $(5x + 9y)(5x - 9y)$ 34. $25x^2 - 36y^2$ $(5x + 6y)(5x - 6y)$

35. $x^2 - 49y^2$ $(x + 7y)(x - 7y)$ 36. $x^2 - 81y^2$ $(x + 9y)(x - 9y)$

37. $36a^2 - b^2$ $(6a + b)(6a - b)$ 38. $49r^2 - p^2$ $(7r + p)(7r - p)$

39. $c^2 - d^2$ $(c + d)(c - d)$ 40. $h^2 - m^2$ $(h + m)(h - m)$

Problems 41–50 are good for reinforcing the concept that an expression, no matter how complicated it looks, just stands for a *number*!

Problems 51–62 review concepts from earlier in the text.

For Problems 41 through 50 you must recognize that an expression, no matter how complicated it looks, just stands for a *number*. Factor these.

41. $(a + b)^2 - 4$ 42. $(x + y)^2 - 36$

43. $9x^2 - (c + d)^2$

44. $25x^2 - (m + c)^2$

45. $81 - 64(xy)^2$

46. $16(xy)^2 - 49$

47. $(x + 3)^2 - (x + 5)^2$

48. $(x - 4)^2 - (x - 6)^2$

49. $25(\text{number})^2 - 1$

50. $1 - 4(\text{number})^2$

Problems 51 through 62 review techniques from previous sections.

51. Multiply $(3x - 7)(4x + 2)$.

52. Multiply $(5x - 1)(4x - 7)$.

53. Factor $x^2 + 13x - 30$.

54. Factor $x^2 - 17x + 60$.

55. Factor $x^2 + 13x + 30$.

56. Factor $x^2 - 17x - 60$.

57. Solve and check $22 = 3x - 17$.

58. Solve and check $21 = 3(x - 17)$.

59. Simplify $34 - 5x + 7$.

60. Simplify $18x - 5 - 2x$.

61. Evaluate $(x - 7)(13 - 2x)$ if x is 9.

62. Evaluate $x^2 - 5x + 7$ if x is -3.

41. $(a + b + 2)(a + b - 2)$
42. $(x + y + 6)(x + y - 6)$
43. $(3x + c + d)(3x - c - d)$
44. $(5x + m + c)(5x - m - c)$
45. $(9 + 8xy)(9 - 8xy)$
46. $(4xy + 7)(4xy - 7)$
47. $-4(x + 4)$ 48. $4(x - 5)$
49. $(5\text{ number} + 1)(5\text{ number} - 1)$
50. $(1 + 2\text{ number})(1 - 2\text{ number})$
51. $12x^2 - 22x - 14$
52. $20x^2 - 39x + 7$ 53. $(x - 2)(x + 15)$
54. $(x - 5)(x - 12)$ 55. $(x + 3)(x + 10)$
         56. $(x + 3)(x - 20)$
57. $13 = x; 22 = 22$ 58. $24 = x; 21 = 21$
59. $41 - 5x$ 60. $16x - 5$
61. -10 62. 31

5-8 | SQUARING A BINOMIAL

The expression $(x - 5)^2$ is the square of a binomial. Because $(x - 5)^2$ means $(x - 5)(x - 5)$, squaring a binomial involves the same process as multiplying two binomials together.

$$(x - 5)^2$$
$$= (x - 5)(x - 5)$$
$$= x^2 - 10x + 25$$

In this section you will practice squaring binomials. While doing so, you should look for a pattern that will allow you to square a binomial in *one* step, in your head!

Objective:
Learn a pattern for squaring a binomial in one step.

Cover the answers as you work these examples.

EXAMPLE 1

| Do the squaring: $(x + 3)^2$.

Time: 1 day

Chalkboard Examples:

Square by writing as two bionomials and multiplying.

1. $(x + 5)^2$ 2. $(x - 6)^2$
   $= (x + 5)(x + 5)$ $= (x - 6)(x - 6)$
   $= x^2 + 10x + 25$ $= x^2 - 12x + 36$
3. $(3x + 7)^2$ 4. $(5x - 4)^2$
   $= (3x + 7)(3x + 7)$ $= (5x - 4)(5x - 4)$
   $= 9x^2 + 42x + 49$ $= 25x^2 - 40x + 16$

After all four Examples are on the board, erase the middle lines $(3x + 7)(3x + 7)$ and $(5x - 4)(5x - 4)$ in Examples 3 and 4. Then ask the students how they could go directly from the question to the answer. Most will be able to see the pattern.

Square using the pattern:
5. $(7x + 6)^2$ Ans.: $49x^2 + 84x + 36$
6. $(x - 10)^2$ Ans.: $x^2 - 20x + 100$
7. $(4x + 1)^2$ Ans.: $16x^2 + 8x + 1$

Assignment:

If problems 1–9 odd previously assigned:
  11–59 odd or 12–60 even
If problems 1–9 odd not previously assigned:
  1–39 and 51–59 odd or 2–40 and 52–60 even

- - - - -   - - - - -

$(x + 3)^2$ Write the given expression.

$= (x + 3)(x + 3)$ Definition of squaring.

$= \underline{\underline{x^2 + 6x + 9}}$ Middle term is $3x + 3x$.

EXAMPLE 2

Do the squaring: $(y - 7)^2$.

- - - - -   - - - - -

$(y - 7)^2$ Write the given expression.

$= (y - 7)(y - 7)$ Definition of squaring.

$= \underline{\underline{y^2 - 14y + 49}}$ Middle term is $-7y - 7y$.

EXAMPLE 3

Do the squaring: $(3x + 5)^2$.

- - - - -   - - - - -

$(3x + 5)^2$ Write the given expression.

$= (3x + 5)(3x + 5)$ Definition of squaring.

$= \underline{\underline{9x^2 + 30x + 25}}$ First term is $(3x)^2$, or $9x^2$.
                                             Middle term is $15x + 15x$.

In Example 3, the middle term is $30x$. This term comes from adding *two* terms, $15x + 15x$. The term $15x$ can be found easily from the original binomial, $3x + 5$. You just multiply the two terms together! This pattern can be used to get the middle term in *one* step.

$$(3x + 5)^2 \qquad = \qquad 9x^2 + 30x + 25$$
$$(3x)(5) = 15x; \qquad 2(15x) = 30x$$

The first and last terms in the answer are just the *squares* of the two terms in the binomial.

$$(3x)^2 = 9x^2$$
$$(3x + 5)^2 \quad = \quad 9x^2 + 30x + 25$$
$$5^2 = 25$$

CONCLUSION

> **BINOMIAL SQUARE PATTERN**
> To square a binomial quickly, you:
>
> 1.   Square the first term.
> 2.   Add *twice* the *product* of the two terms.
> 3.   Add the square of the last term.

In the next examples you will practice using this shortcut.

EXAMPLE 4

Square using the pattern: $(x + 9)^2$.

- - - - -   - - - - -

| $\boxed{\textit{Think These Reasons}}$ |

$(x + 9)^2$ Write the given expression.

$= x^2 + 18x + 81$ Middle term is $2(x)(9)$.

EXAMPLE 5

Square using the pattern: $(x - 5)^2$.

- - - - -   - - - - -

$(x - 5)^2$ Write the given expression.

$= x^2 - 10x + 25$ Middle term is $2(x)(-5)$.
                                     Last term is $(-5)^2$.

EXAMPLE 6

Square using the pattern: $(7x - 3)^2$.

$(7x - 3)^2$ Write the given expression.

$= 49x^2 - 42x + 9$ First term is $(7x)^2$.
                                     Middle term is $2(7x)(-3)$.

ORAL PRACTICE

Tell what the middle term will be when the squaring is done.

A. $(x + 5)^2$ $10x$ B. $(p + 7)^2$ $14p$ C. $(x - 11)^2$ $-22x$

D. $(h - 3)^2$ $-6h$ E. $(3x + 7)^2$ $42x$ F. $(5x - 4)^2$ $-40x$

G. $(6b - 7)^2$ $-84b$ H. $(9c + 1)^2$ $18c$ I. $(10 + x)^2$ $20x$

J. $(7 - x)^2$ $-14x$ K. $(2x - 3y)^2$ $-12xy$ L. $(a + b)^2$ $2ab$

EXERCISE 5-8

Problem Notes:

Problems 1–10 reinforce the definition of squaring and show that these problems are just special cases of a product of two binomials. If students skip these exercises, they are likely to learn squaring of a binomial as a mechanical process with little or no idea of what they are really doing.

  Problems 11–40 give students practice with squaring the quick way once they understand what they are doing. Problems 35–38 are special cases in which the coefficients are 1 or 2. They are deliberately sequenced near the end of the problem set so that students will learn the process with somewhat larger, relatively prime coefficients first.

  Problems 41–50 form an optional continuation of problems in previous sections where the binomial has two different variables.
  Problems 51–60 review techniques from previous sections. Do not skip these problems!
  Problems 61 and 62 illustrate two common mistakes: leaving out the middle term and getting a negative answer for the square of a negative number.
  Problem 63 illustrates that $(x - 3)^2$ and $(3 - x)^2$ are equivalent. The reason is because the two binomials are *opposites* of each other, and you get the same answer when you square two numbers that are opposites.
  Problem 64 shows geometrically the meaning of the middle term in $(a + b)^2$.
  Problems 65 and 66 extend the students' knowledge to cubing a binomial and squaring a trinomial. These problems are suitable for use by the better students if more time is needed for the weaker students to master previous concepts. For Problem 65, some teachers like to show also the pattern

For Problems 1 through 10, write the binomial square as a product of two binomials, then multiply the binomials.

1. $(x + 9)^2$ $x^2 + 18x + 81$

2. $(x + 7)^2$ $x^2 + 14x + 49$

3. $(x - 10)^2$ $x^2 - 20x + 100$

4. $(x - 3)^2$ $x^2 - 6x + 9$

5. $(5x + 6)^2$ $25x^2 + 60x + 36$

6. $(3x + 4)^2$ $9x^2 + 24x + 16$

7. $(4x - 7)^2$ $16x^2 - 56x + 49$

8. $(8x - 3)^2$ $64x^2 - 48x + 9$

9. $(6 - x)^2$ $36 - 12x + x^2$

10. $(9 - x)^2$ $81 - 18x + x^2$

For Problems 11 through 50, square the binomial in *one* step, writing just the given expression and the answer.

11. $(x + 8)^2$ $x^2 + 16x + 64$

12. $(x + 6)^2$ $x^2 + 12x + 36$

13. $(x + 3)^2$ $x^2 + 6x + 9$

14. $(x + 5)^2$ $x^2 + 10x + 25$

15. $(h - 6)^2$ $h^2 - 12h + 36$

16. $(n - 4)^2$ $n^2 - 8n + 16$

17. $(x + 12)^2$ $x^2 + 24x + 144$

18. $(x + 10)^2$ $x^2 + 20x + 100$

19. $(k - 7)^2$ $k^2 - 14k + 49$

20. $(p - 8)^2$ $p^2 - 16p + 64$

21. $(4x + 3)^2$ $16x^2 + 24x + 9$

22. $(5x + 4)^2$ $25x^2 + 40x + 16$

23. $(5x - 2)^2$ $25x^2 - 20x + 4$

24. $(3x - 5)^2$ $9x^2 - 30x + 25$

25. $(7x - 1)^2$ $49x^2 - 14x + 1$

26. $(9x - 1)^2$ $81x^2 - 18x + 1$

27. $(6x + 7)^2$ $36x^2 + 84x + 49$

28. $(5x + 8)^2$ $25x^2 + 80x + 64$

29. $(3c - 7)^2$ $9c^2 - 42c + 49$

30. $(6d - 3)^2$ $36d^2 - 36d + 9$

31. $(5 + x)^2$ $25 + 10x + x^2$

32. $(11 + x)^2$ $121 + 22x + x^2$

33. $(9 - 4x)^2$ $81 - 72x + 16x^2$

34. $(3 - 10x)^2$ $9 - 60x + 100x^2$

35. $(t + 1)^2$ $t^2 + 2t + 1$

36. $(v - 1)^2$ $v^2 - 2v + 1$

37. $(x - 2)^2$ $x^2 - 4x + 4$

38. $(x + 2)^2$ $x^2 + 4x + 4$

39. $(9a - 7)^2$ $81a^2 - 126a + 49$

40. $(8b - 9)^2$ $64b^2 - 144b + 81$

In Problems 41 through 50, there is a variable in both terms. If you understand what you have been doing, these problems should be straightforward.

41. $(x + 4y)^2$ $x^2 + 8xy + 16y^2$

42. $(x + 3y)^2$ $x^2 + 6xy + 9y^2$

43. $(5a - b)^2$ $25a^2 - 10ab + b^2$

44. $(3c - d)^2$ $9c^2 - 6cd + d^2$

45. $(2y + 5z)^2$ $4y^2 + 20xy + 25z^2$

46. $(6a + 2h)^2$ $36a^2 + 24ah + 4h^2$

47. $(a + b)^2$ $a^2 + 2ab + b^2$

48. $(x + y)^2$ $x^2 + 2xy + y^2$

49. $(a - b)^2$ $a^2 - 2ab + b^2$

50. $(x - y)^2$ $x^2 - 2xy + y^2$

Problems 51 through 60 review techniques from previous sections.

51. Factor $x^2 + 8x + 15$.

52. Factor $x^2 - 3x - 28$.

53. Factor $5w^2 + 2w - 3$.

54. Factor $7k^2 + 9k + 2$.

55. Factor $d^2 - 49$.

56. Factor $a^2 - 64$.

57. Factor $100x^2 - 9$.

58. Factor $49x^2 - 36$.

59. Multiply $(x + 3)(4x - 7)$.

60. Multiply $(5x - 4)(x - 1)$.

61. Juana Ngo writes
$(x + 4)^2$
$= x^2 + 16.$
What mistakes did Juana make?

62. Bess Ting writes
$(x - 6)^2$
$= x^2 - 12x - 36.$
What mistakes did Bess make?

63. a. Do the squaring: $(x - 3)^2$. $x^2 - 6x + 9$
     b. Do the squaring: $(3 - x)^2$. $9 - 6x + x^2$
     c. Are the answers equivalent? Explain.   Yes. The terms can be commuted.

64. These questions refer to the diagram.
     a. What are the dimensions of the entire square? What is its area?
     b. What is the area of square 1?
     c. What is the area of square 2?
     d. What are the areas of rectangles 3 and 4?
     e. Show that the sum of the areas of 1, 2, 3, and 4 equals the area of the entire square found in part (a).

65. *Cube of a Binomial Problem*   There is a pattern for finding the *cube* of a binomial, such as $(x + y)^3$, in your head.
     a. Write $(x + y)^3$ as $(x + y)(x + y)(x + y)$.
     b. Associate and multiply the second and third factors.
     c. Multiply the first $(x + y)$ by the answer you got in part (b). To do this, multiply each term in one factor by each term in the other. Combine the like terms. Arrange in descending powers of x.
     d. Describe in words the patterns you observe in the answer to part (c).
     e. Use the pattern of part (c) to cube these binomials in one step.
         i. $(a + b)^3$ ii. $(r - s)^3$ iii. $(x + 2)^3$ iv. $(x - 5)^3$

$(a + b)^4 = a^4 + 4a^3b + 6a^2b^2 + 4ab^3 + b^4$

so that students will not come to the erroneous conclusion that the middle coefficients are always the same as the exponent.

51. $(x + 3)(x + 5)$
52. $(x + 4)(x - 7)$
53. $(5w - 3)(w + 1)$
54. $(7k + 2)(k + 1)$
55. $(d + 7)(d - 7)$
56. $(a + 8)(a - 8)$
57. $(10x + 3)(10x - 3)$
58. $(7x + 6)(7x - 6)$
59. $4x^2 + 5x - 21$
60. $5x^2 - 9x + 4$
61. Juana left out the middle term.
62. Bess thought $(-6)^2 = -36$.

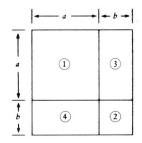

64. a. Square is $a + b$ by $a + b$.
        Area $= (a + b)(a + b) = a^2 + 2ab + b^2$.
     b. Square ①: Area $= a^2$
     c. Square ②: Area $= b^2$
     d. Areas of ③ and ④ are each ab.
     e. ① + ② + ③ + ④
        $= a^2 + b^2 + ab + ab$
        $= a^2 + 2ab + b^2$,
        which equals area in part (a).

65. a. $(x + y)^3 = (x + y)(x + y)(x + y)$
     b. $= (x + y)(x^2 + 2xy + y^2)$
     c. $= x^3 + 2x^2y + xy^2 + x^2y$
                 $+ 2xy^2 + y^3$
              $= x^3 + 3x^2y + 3xy^2 + y^3$
     d. The powers of x start at x^3 and *drop* 1 each term.
        The powers of y increase 1 each term.
        The coefficients are 1, 3, 3, 1.

     e. i. $a^3 + 3a^2b + 3ab^2 + b^3$
        ii. $r^3 - 3r^2s + 3rs^2 - r^3$
        iii. $x^3 + 6x^2 + 12x + 8$
        iv. $x^3 - 15x^2 + 75x - 125$

66. **a.** $(x + y + z)^2$
   $= (x + y + z)(x + y + z)$
   Definition of squaring
   b. and c.
   $= x^2 + xy + xz + xy + y^2 + yz$
   $+ xz + yz + z^2$

   d. $x^2 + y^2 + z^2 + 2xy + 2xz + 2yz$
   e. i. $a^2 + b^2 + c^2 + 2ab + 2ac$
   $+ 2bc$
   ii. $r^2 + 9s^2 + 25 + 6rs + 10r$
   $+ 30s$
   iii. $16x^2 + 25y^2 + 9z^2 + 40xy -$
   $24xz - 30yz$

66. *Square of a Trinomial Problem*   If you square a trinomial such as
$$(x + y + z)^2,$$
a pattern appears. To discover this pattern, do the following.
   a.   Write $(x + y + z)^2$ as $(x + y + z)(x + y + z)$. What fact allows you to do this?
   b.   Multiply the x in the first factor by each term in the second.

$$(x + y + z)(x + y + z) = \ldots$$

   c.   Do the same with the y and z in the first factor. You should now have *nine* terms in the answer.
   d.   Combine like terms. Commute all the *squared* terms to the left.
   e.   The pattern you should see in part (d) is
      (1)   Add the *squares* of each term.
      (2)   Add *twice* the *product* of each possible *pair* of terms.
      Use this pattern to square each trinomial.
         i. $(a + b + c)^2$ ii. $(r + 3s + 5)^2$ iii. $(4x + 5y - 3z)^2$

5-9 | FACTORING TRINOMIAL SQUARES

Time: 1 day

Chalkboard Examples:

Are these numbers perfect squares?
1. 196   Ans.: Yes $\sqrt{196} = 14$
2. 142,884 Ans.: Yes $\sqrt{142,884} = 378$
3. 3470   Ans.: No $\sqrt{3740} \approx 58.91$
4. −36 Ans.: No $\sqrt{-36}$ is not a real number. Once students are familiar with the square root key on the calculator, they are ready for factoring trinomial squares.

Factor, if it is a trinomial square.
1. $x^2 + 14x + 49$ Ans.: $(x + 7)^2$
2. $x^2 - 18x + 81$ Ans.: $(x - 9)^2$
3. $x^2 - 276x + 19,044$ Ans.: $(x - 138)^2$
4. $x^2 + 10x + 100$ Ans.: Not a trinomial square (The middle term is not 2(10).)
5. $x^2 + 10x + 20$ Ans.: Not a trinomial square (The constant term is not a perfect square.)

Assignment:

1–49 odd or 2–50 even

In the last section you learned a quick way to square a binomial. For instance,
$$(x - 5)^2 = x^2 - 10x + 25.$$
The answer, $x^2 - 10x + 25$, is called a **trinomial square.** Obviously, such a quadratic trinomial can be factored, as shown.
$$x^2 - 10x + 25$$
$$= (x - 5)(x - 5)$$
$$= (x - 5)^2$$
In this section you will learn how to go quickly from the first step to the last step, without writing the middle step.

Objective:
Given a quadratic trinomial such as $x^2 - 10x + 25$, tell whether or not it is a trinomial square and, if so, transform it in *one* step to the square of a binomial (such as $(x - 5)^2$).

In order for a quadratic trinomial to be a trinomial square, the first and last terms must each be perfect squares. You can use the *square root* key on a calculator, usually marked $\sqrt{x}$, to tell whether or not a large number is a perfect square. For instance, if you press

$$49 \quad \boxed{\sqrt{x}},$$

you should get 7 for the answer. Because $7^2 = 49$, 7 is called a *square root* of 49. The number -7 is also a square root of 49, because $(-7)^2 = 49$.

If you press

$$157 \quad \boxed{\sqrt{x}},$$

you get 12.52996409. Since the square root of 157 is not an *integer*, 157 is *not* a perfect square.

The symbol $\sqrt{n}$ stands only for the *positive* square root of n. The symbol $-\sqrt{n}$ stands for the negative square root of n. For example,

$$\sqrt{25} = 5 \quad \text{and} \quad -\sqrt{25} = -5.$$

However, the symbol $\sqrt{-25}$ does not stand for a real number at all! Since $5^2 = +25$ and $(-5)^2$ also equals $+25$, there is *no* real number you could square to get -25.

Cover the answers as you work these examples.

EXAMPLE 1

Decide whether or not the number is a perfect square by finding its square root on a calculator.

a.   169

– – – – –   – – – – –

    <u>Yes</u> $\sqrt{169} = 13$

b.   276,676

– – – – –   – – – – –

    <u>Yes</u> $\sqrt{276676} = 526$

c.   3250

– – – – –   – – – – –

    <u>No</u> $\sqrt{3250} \approx 57.00877125$

d. -64

– – – – –   – – – – –

    <u>No</u> $\sqrt{-64}$ is not a real number. You should get an error message if you put this into a calculator.

Here is a formal definition of square root.

DEFINITION

SQUARE ROOT
A **square root** of a number n is a number that gives n for the answer when it is squared.

That is, $\sqrt{n}$ is the non-negative number for which
$$(\sqrt{n})^2 = n.$$

With this background in mind, you are ready to accomplish the objective—identifying and factoring trinomial squares. The first thing to do is check the *constant* term.

$$x^2 - 10x + 25 \qquad \text{Is this a perfect square?}$$
Yes! $\sqrt{25}$ is 5.

If the answer had been no, you would need to go no further. The trinomial would not be a trinomial square. Since the answer is yes, $\sqrt{25} = 5$, you must check the *middle* term.

$$x^2 - 10x + 25$$
Is this *twice* $\sqrt{25}$?
Yes!

Again, if the answer had been no, the expression would not be a trinomial square. Since the answer is yes, you can now conclude that it *is* a trinomial square. You write

$$x^2 - 10x + 25$$
$$= (x - 5)^2 \qquad \textit{Think:} -5 \text{ is } \tfrac{1}{2} \text{ of } -10.$$

EXAMPLE 2

Tell whether or not each of the following is a trinomial square. If it is, then transform it into the square of a binomial. If it is not, tell *why* not.

a. $x^2 + 12x + 36$

- - - - -   - - - - -

	Think These Reasons
$x^2 + 12x + 36$	Write the given expression.
$= (x + 6)^2$	$\sqrt{36} = 6$ and $2(6) = 12$, the correct middle coefficient.

b. $x^2 - 20x + 100$

$- - - - -$ $- - - - -$

       $x^2 - 20x + 100$ Write the given expression.

  $= \underline{\underline{(x - 10)^2}}$ $\sqrt{100} = 10$, so -10 is also a square root of 100. $2(-10) = -20$, the correct middle coefficient.

c. $x^2 + 10x + 64$

$- - - - -$ $- - - - -$

  $= x^2 + 10x + 64$ Write the given expression.

  $\underline{\underline{\text{Not a trinomial square}}}$ $\sqrt{64} = 8$, but $2(8) = 16$, not 10

d. $x^2 - 8x + 15$

$- - - - -$ $- - - - -$

       $x^2 - 8x + 15$ Write the given expression.

  $\underline{\underline{\text{Not a trinomial square}}}$ 15 is not a perfect square.

ORAL PRACTICE

Give the following square roots from memory.

EXAMPLES

          Answers

i. $\sqrt{36}$ i. 6
ii. $-\sqrt{4}$ ii. -2
iii. $\sqrt{-25}$ iii. Not a real number

A. $\sqrt{49}$ 7   B. $\sqrt{25}$ 5   C. $\sqrt{81}$ 9

D. $-\sqrt{64}$ -8 E. $-\sqrt{16}$ -4 F. $\sqrt{-9}$ None

G. $-\sqrt{9}$ -3 H. $\sqrt{100}$ 10   I. $\sqrt{1}$ 1   J. $\sqrt{0}$ 0

Use a calculator to find out whether or not these are perfect squares. If so, give the square root.

EXAMPLES

        Answers
i.   169   i. Yes. Square root of 169 is 13.
ii. 180   ii. No. (Calculator shows 13.2164. . . .)

K.   729   27   L.   8836   94   M.   1369   37

N.   5041   71   O.   1024   32   P.   484   22

Q.   125   No   R.   128881   359   S.   242164   No

T.   149769   387   U.   29716   No   V.   41209   203

W.   9801   99   X.   5908   No   Y.   788544   888

EXERCISE 5-9

For Problems 1 through 40, either write the trinomial as a square of a binomial or tell why it is not a trinomial square.

Problem Notes:

Problems 1–20 can be done without a calculator.

Problems 21–40 require a calculator, if done as shown in the text. Students may discover the *reverse* process, which may also be used: "Take half of the middle coefficient and square it." The longer process is used in the text so that students will experience using the square root key on the calculator.

1. $x^2 + 6x + 9$ $(x + 3)^2$
2. $x^2 - 12x + 36$ $(x - 6)^2$
3. $x^2 - 10x + 25$ $(x - 5)^2$
4. $x^2 + 8x + 16$ $(x + 4)^2$
5. $x^2 + 16x + 64$ $(x + 8)^2$
6. $x^2 - 14x + 49$ $(x - 7)^2$
7. $x^2 - 4x + 4$ $(x - 2)^2$
8. $x^2 - 6x + 9$ $(x - 3)^2$
9. $x^2 - 2x + 1$ $(x - 1)^2$
10. $x^2 + 2x + 1$ $(x + 1)^2$
11. $x^2 - 8x + 20$ 20 is *not* a perfect square.
12. $x^2 - 10x + 25$ $(x - 5)^2$
13. $x^2 - 8x + 16$ $(x - 4)^2$
14. $x^2 - 10x + 36$ $10 \neq 2\sqrt{36}$
15. $x^2 - 8x - 16$ $\sqrt{-16}$ is *not* a real number.
16. $x^2 - 10x + 40$ 40 is *not* a perfect square.
17. $a^2 + 20a + 81$ $20 \neq 2\sqrt{81}$
18. $t^2 + 18t + 81$ $(t + 9)^2$
19. $a^2 + 20a + 100$ $(a + 10)^2$
20. $t^2 + 18t + 64$ $18 \neq 2\sqrt{64}$
21. $x^2 - 30x + 225$ $(x - 15)^2$
22. $x^2 + 50x + 625$ $(x + 25)^2$
23. $x^2 + 62x + 961$ $(x + 31)^2$
24. $x^2 + 102x + 2601$ $(x + 51)^2$
25. $x^2 - 94x + 2209$ $(x - 47)^2$
26. $x^2 - 74x + 1369$ $(x - 37)^2$
27. $x^2 + 178x + 7921$ $(x + 89)^2$
28. $x^2 + 198x + 9801$ $(x + 99)^2$
29. $x^2 - 148x + 5476$ $(x - 74)^2$
30. $x^2 - 66x + 4356$ Middle term $\neq 2 \times 66$
31. $x^2 + 68x + 4624$ Middle term $\neq 2 \times 68$
32. $x^2 + 70x + 1225$ $(x + 35)^2$
33. $x^2 - 222x + 12,321$ $(x - 111)^2$
34. $x^2 - 202x + 10,201$ $(x - 101)^2$
35. $x^2 + 20x + 400$ $20 \neq 2\sqrt{400}$
36. $x^2 - 30x + 900$ $30 \neq 2\sqrt{900}$
37. $x^2 - 200x + 10,000$ $(x - 100)^2$
38. $x^2 + 180x + 810$ 810 is *not* a perfect square.
39. $x^2 + 100x + 1000$ 1000 is *not* a perfect square.
40. $x^2 - 180x - 8100$ $\sqrt{-8100}$ is *not* a real number.

Problems 41 through 50 review techniques from previous sections.

Problems 41–50 keep alive old skills while students are learning new ones.

Problem 51 reinforces the concept of evalu-

41. Multiply $(3x - 2)(x + 4)$.
42. Multiply $(5x + 2)(x - 7)$.
43. Multiply $(4x + 3)^2$.
44. Multiply $(3x - 5)^2$.

45. Factor $3x^2 - 22x + 7$.

46. Factor $2x^2 + 7x + 5$.

47. Solve and check:
   $3(x + 2) = 5x - 19$.

48. Solve and check:
   $4(2 - x) = 6x - 18$.

49. Evaluate $|13 - 4x|$ if $x = 7$.

50. Evaluate $|5 - 7x|$ if $x = -2$.

51. Evaluate the trinomial square for the given value of x and thus show that it *is* a perfect square.
   a. $x^2 + 6x + 9$; $x = 4$ 7^2
   b. $x^2 - 10x + 25$; $x = 3$ 2^2
   c. $x^2 - 2x + 1$; $x = -5$ 6^2
   d. $9x^2 + 12x + 4$; $x = 2$ 8^2

52. The following trinomials have squared terms whose coefficients are not equal to 1. All but two of these are trinomial squares. For those that are trinomial squares, factor into the square of a binomial. Tell which two are *not* trinomial squares.
   a. $9x^2 + 24x + 16$ $(3x + 4)^2$
   b. $25x^2 - 70x + 49$ $(5x - 7)^2$
   c. $4x^2 + 10x + 25$ *Not* a trinomial square
   d. $4x^2 - 36x + 81$ $(2x - 9)^2$
   e. $9x^2 + 16x + 24$ *Not* a trinomial square
   f. $64x^2 - 16x + 1$ $(8x - 1)^2$
   g. $81x^2 - 36x + 4$ $(9x - 2)^2$
   h. $49x^2 + 42x + 9$ $(7x + 3)^2$

53. Explain each statement.
   a. 7 and -7 are *both* square roots of 49.
   b. $\sqrt{49}$ equals only 7, not -7.
   c. $-\sqrt{49}$ *is* a real number, but $\sqrt{-49}$ is *not* a real number.

54. Recall that the horizontal bar ("vinculum") over the top in $\sqrt{}$ expression means "Do what is underneath first." Answer these questions.
   a. Evaluate $\sqrt{5^2}$.   5
   b. Evaluate $\sqrt{(-5)^2}$.   5
   c. What do you discover about the two answers?

ating an expression by having students evaluate both the given expression and the factored one. By so doing, students also see what it means for two expressions to be *equivalent* and why the = sign is used between steps in the simplification of an expression.

Problem 52 may be used to show students trinomial squares with x^2-coefficient not equal to 1.

Problems 53 and 54 reinforce the concept that there is no real square root of a negative number and that the square root of a perfect square equals the absolute value of the number being squared.

41. $3x^2 + 10x - 8$
42. $5x^2 - 33x - 14$
43. $16x^2 + 24x + 9$
44. $9x^2 - 30x + 25$
45. $(3x - 1)(x - 7)$
46. $(2x + 5)(x + 1)$
47. $x = 12.5$; $43.5 = 43.5$
48. $x = 2.6$; $-2.4 = -2.4$
49. 15   50.   19

53. a. $7^2 = 49$ and $(-7)^2 = 49$. So 7 and -7 are both square roots of 49.
   b. $\sqrt{49} = 7$ because the symbol $\sqrt{}$ means the *positive* square root.
   c. $-\sqrt{49} = -7$, but $\sqrt{-49}$ is *not* a real number because no real number gives a *negative* answer when it is squared.

54. c. The two answers are the *same*. (In Chapter 6 students will learn that $\sqrt{n^2} = |n|$.)

5-10   RADICALS, IRRATIONAL NUMBERS, AND THE CLOSURE AXIOMS

In the last section you took square roots of numbers. An expression such as $\sqrt{49}$ is called a **radical**. The name comes from the Latin word *radix*, which means *root*. (The word *radish* has the same origin, since a radish is a root.)

You also learned that there is no real-number answer for the square root of a *negative* number. A radical such as $\sqrt{-9}$ does not represent a real number, because no real number squared gives a negative answer.

$$\sqrt{-9} \text{ is not } -3 \text{ because } (-3)^2 = +9.$$

$$\sqrt{-9} \text{ is not } +3 \text{ because } (+3)^2 = +9.$$

Time: 3 days

Chalkboard Examples:

Day 1:
Are these rational or irrational numbers?
1. $\sqrt{49}$ Ans.: 7   Rational
2. $\sqrt{913,936}$ Ans.: 956   Rational
3. $\sqrt{1390}$ Ans.: 37.28 . . .   Irrational
4. $-\sqrt{16}$ Ans.: -4 Rational
5. $\sqrt{-16}$ Ans.: Neither rational nor irrational

The following can be used as chalkboard examples to illustrate closure of various sets.

Closed or not closed? Give an example showing why or why not.

1. {positive numbers}, subtraction
   Ans.: Not closed. $3 - 7 = -4$ (not positive)

2. {positive numbers}, multiplication
   Ans.: Closed. $3 + 7 = 10$ (positive)

3. {positive numbers}, square root
   Ans.: Closed. $\sqrt{10} \approx 3.16$ (positive)

4. {rational numbers}, square root
   Ans.: Not closed. $\sqrt{10} \approx 3.16$ (not rational)

Note: For sets that are not closed, the example proves this fact. One counterexample constitutes a rigorous proof. However, for sets that are closed, the example merely illustrates what closure means. Students should realize that even thousands of examples do not prove closure of an infinite set of numbers.

Day 2:
Oral or chalkboard presentation by students of Problems 1–9 odd followed by 11–29 odd as oral practice

Day 3:
Review in preparation for test.

Assignments:

Day 1: 1–9 and 31–53 odd
Day 2: 2–20 and 46–54 even
Day 3: Study Exercise 5–11 in preparation for test.

So there is *no* real number equal to $\sqrt{-9}$.

Because of this fact, the set of real numbers is said to be *not closed* under the operation of taking the square root. The set of real numbers *is* closed under addition, subtraction, and multiplication. You *always* get a real number for an answer when you do these operations on real numbers.

Addition: $1\frac{1}{5} + 2\frac{3}{5} = 3\frac{4}{5}$ Real number

Subtraction: $3 - 7 = -4$ Real number

Multiplication: $(4.2)(3) = 12.6$ Real number

Other sets of numbers may or may not be closed under various operations. For instance, when you divide an integer by an integer, you do not always get an integer for the answer.

$$\frac{12}{4} = 3 \qquad \text{Integer}$$

$$\frac{13}{4} = 3\frac{1}{4} \qquad \textit{Not} \text{ an integer}$$

So the set of integers is *not* closed under division.

A fraction, such as $\frac{12}{4}$ or $\frac{13}{4}$, is called a **rational number.** The word *rational* is an adjective coming from the word *ratio,* which implies division. A ratio of two *integers* is a rational number.

DEFINITION

> **RATIONAL NUMBER**
> A **rational number** is a number that can be written as a ratio of two integers.

A radical such as $\sqrt{7}$ *cannot* be written as a ratio of two integers. The best you can do for such numbers is write them as nonending, nonrepeating decimals:

$$\sqrt{7} = 2.64575131.\ldots$$

It is to be hoped that you will continue studying mathematics long enough to find out *why* this is true. Such numbers are called *irrational numbers.*

DEFINITION

> **IRRATIONAL NUMBER**
> An **irrational number** is a real number that *cannot* be written as a ratio of two integers.

Since the square root of a rational number is not always a rational number, the set of rational numbers is *not* closed under the operation of taking the square root.

$$\sqrt{9} = 3 = \frac{3}{1} \qquad\qquad \text{Rational}$$

$$\sqrt{10} = 3.16227766. \ldots \qquad \text{Irrational}$$

The set of real numbers is closed under addition and multiplication. That is, when you add or multiply two real numbers, the answer is always a real number. These two facts are assumed to be true without proof—they are *axioms*.

CLOSURE AXIOMS

CLOSURE UNDER MULTIPLICATION
The set of real numbers is *closed under multiplication*.

That is, if x and y are any real numbers,
then xy is a unique real number.

CLOSURE UNDER ADDITION
The set of real numbers is *closed under addition*.

That is, if x and y are any real numbers,
then $x + y$ is a unique real number.

The word *unique* in these axioms means *only one*. For instance, $3 + 7$ *always* equals 10, never equals any other number besides 10.

In this section you are to learn the meaning of closure. You do this by finding out whether or not certain sets of numbers are closed under various operations.

Objective:
Given a set of numbers and an operation to be performed on these numbers, tell whether or not the set is closed under that operation.

Here is a formal definition of closure.

DEFINITION

CLOSURE

A given set of numbers is **closed** under an operation if there is just *one* answer, and that answer is *in* the given set whenever the operation is performed with numbers that are in that set.

That is,

(number in set)(operation)(number in set)
= (*unique* number *in* set)

Cover the answers as you work these examples.

EXAMPLE 1

Tell whether each set of numbers is closed under the given operation. If it is, give an example to show that you know what it means to be closed. If it is not, give an example that shows *why* not. (*Note*: The braces, {. . .}, mean *the set of*. . . or *the set containing* . . . .)

a. {integers}, subtraction

– – – – –   – – – – –

	Think These Reasons

Closed $5 - 7 = -2$, which is an integer.

b. {negative numbers}, multiplication

– – – – –   – – – – –

Not closed $(-3)(-2) = +6$, and $+6$ is *not* a negative number.

c. {rational numbers}, addition

– – – – –   – – – – –

Closed $\frac{2}{5} + \frac{1}{5} = \frac{3}{5}$, which is a rational number.

d. {0, 1}, addition

– – – – –   – – – – –

Not closed $1 + 1 = 2$, and 2 is *not* in the set.

e. {rational numbers}, square root

– – – – –   – – – – –

Not closed $\sqrt{10}$ is *not* a rational number.

Note: A counterexample is enough to prove that a set is *not* closed. However, an affirmative example is not enough to prove that it *is* closed. For instance, the set of integers is not closed under division, even though you sometimes do get an integer for an answer, such as $12 \div 6 = 2$.

EXAMPLE 2

Tell whether each radical represents a rational number, an irrational number, or neither.

a. $\sqrt{25}$

- - - - -   - - - - -

   <u>Rational</u>   25 is a perfect square.

b. $\sqrt{70}$

- - - - -   - - - - -

   <u>Irrational</u>   70 is *not* a perfect square.

c. $\sqrt{-36}$

- - - - -   - - - - -

   <u>Neither rational nor irrational</u>   Square roots of negative numbers
                                           are not real numbers.

d. $-\sqrt{36}$

- - - - -   - - - - -

   <u>Rational</u> $-\sqrt{36} = -6$ and $-6 = \dfrac{-6}{1}$,
                                           which is a ratio of two integers.

EXERCISE 5-10

For Problems 1 through 30, tell whether or not the set is closed under the given operation. Give an example to show why or why not.

1. {real numbers};   Closed
    multiplication $3 \times 4 = 12 \leftarrow$ real

2. {real numbers};   Closed
    addition $3 + 4 = 7 \leftarrow$ real

3. {negative numbers};   Closed
    addition $-3 + (-4) = -7 \leftarrow$ negative

4. {negative numbers};   Not closed
    subtraction $-2 - (-7) = 5 \leftarrow$ not negative

5. {positive integers};   Not closed
    division $2 \div 3 = \frac{2}{3} \leftarrow$ not an integer

6. {positive integers};   Closed
    multiplication $2 \times 3 = 6 \leftarrow$ positive integer

7. {positive numbers};   Closed
    division $2 \div 3 = \frac{2}{3} \leftarrow$ positive

8. {positive numbers};   Not closed
    subtraction $3 - 5 = -2 \leftarrow$ not positive

Problem Notes:

Problems 1–44 are suitable for oral practice.

Problems 45–54 both keep alive earlier skills and give students some problems they *can* do in case they do not understand closure the first time.

9. {negative integers}; Not closed 10. {negative integers}; Closed
multiplication $-3 \times (-2) = 6 \leftarrow$ not negative addition $-3 + (-2) = -5 \leftarrow$ negative integer

11. {real numbers}; Closed   12. {real numbers}; Not closed
subtraction $2 - 7 = -5 \leftarrow$ real   division $3 \div 0$ is not a real number.

13. {positive integers}; Closed   14. {positive integers}; Not closed
addition $2 + 5 = 7 \leftarrow$ positive integer   subtraction $3 - 5 = -2 \leftarrow$ not positive

15. {rational numbers}; Closed   16. {rational numbers}; Closed
multiplication $\frac{3}{5} \times \frac{1}{4} = \frac{3}{20} \leftarrow$ rational   addition $\frac{1}{5} + \frac{2}{5} = \frac{3}{5} \leftarrow$ rational

17. {integers}; Closed   18. {integers}; Closed
addition $3 + (-7) = -4 \leftarrow$ integer   multiplication $(3)(-7) = -21 \leftarrow$ integer

19. {0, 1}; Not closed   20. {0, 1}; Not closed
subtraction $0 - 1 = -1 \leftarrow$ not in set   division $1 \div 0$ is not in set.

21. {0, 1}; Closed   22. {0, 1}; Not closed
multiplication $(0)(1) = 0 \leftarrow$ in set   addition $1 + 1 = 2 \leftarrow$ not in set

23. {negative numbers}; Not closed 24. {positive numbers}; Closed
absolute value $|-3| = 3 \leftarrow$ not negative   absolute value $|5| = 5 \leftarrow$ positive

25. {positive integers}; Closed   26. {negative integers}; Not closed
raising to powers $2^3 = 8 \leftarrow$ positive integer square root $\sqrt{-9}$ is not a real number.

27. {real numbers}; Not closed   28. {rational numbers}; Not closed
square root $\sqrt{-9}$ is not a real number. square root $\sqrt{3} \leftarrow$ not rational

29. {0, 1}; Not closed   30. {perfect squares}; Not closed
square root 1 and -1 are both   square root $\sqrt{9} = 3 \leftarrow$ not a perfect square
square roots of 1.

For Problems 31 through 44, tell whether the radical represents a rational number, an irrational number, or neither.

31. $\sqrt{81}$ Rational   32. $\sqrt{64}$ Rational   33. $\sqrt{32}$ Irrational

34. $\sqrt{20}$ Irrational   35. $\sqrt{100}$ Rational   36. $\sqrt{9}$ Rational

37. $-\sqrt{49}$ Rational   38. $-\sqrt{36}$ Rational   39. $-\sqrt{60}$ Irrational

40. $-\sqrt{10}$ Irrational   41. $\sqrt{-16}$ Neither   42. $\sqrt{-4}$ Neither

43. $\sqrt{1}$ Rational   44. $\sqrt{0}$ Rational

Problems 45 through 54 review techniques from previous sections.

45. $8x^2 + 22x + 15$ 46. $30x^2 - 22x + 4$
47. $(2x + 3)(x - 4)$ 48. $(3x + 1)(x - 6)$
49. $(c - 9)^2$ 50. $(p + 6)^2$
51. $x = 5; 27 = 27$ 52. $x = -5; 30 = 30$

45. Multiply $(2x + 3)(4x + 5)$.   46. Multiply $(5x - 2)(6x - 2)$.

47. Factor $2x^2 - 5x - 12$.   48. Factor $3x^2 - 17x - 6$.

49. Write as a binomial squared: $c^2 - 18c + 81$.

50. Write as a binomial squared: $p^2 + 12p + 36$.

51. Solve and check: $3(x + 4) = 27$.

52. Solve and check: $4x + 50 = -6x$.

53.   Simplify $3(x + 4) - 27$.   54.   Simplify $4x + 50 - 6x$.

5-11 | CHAPTER REVIEW AND TEST

Time: 1 day

Test Ideas:

Your test should be largely on skills of multiplying and factoring polynomials, with a taste of irrational numbers and closure. If you have been assigning review problems that appear near the end of each section, students should be reasonably good at these skills. The chapter test in the text is longer than a normal classroom test.

In this chapter you have learned what a polynomial is. After learning their names, you concentrated on multiplying linear binomials and on the reverse process, factoring quadratic trinomials. As a special case, you learned how to *square* a binomial and to tell whether or not a quadratic trinomial *is* the square of a binomial. You also learned what a radical is and what it means for a set of numbers to be closed under an operation.

To make sure you know what this chapter is all about, skim through each section till you find the "Objective." Then *write it down*. The physical process of writing the words helps you remember it. If you don't understand what the objective means, turn to the exercise at the end of the section and look at some problems. Try to connect the words in the objective with what you are asked to do in the problems.

Before you try the Chapter Test on the following pages skim through the chapter again. This time, write a list of all words that "sound important." After you have finished the list, go back and think of a meaning or example for each word. If you are unsure of the meaning, look it up in the book or in your class notes.

After you have made the two lists above, doing the Chapter Test should be relatively straightforward. It may take you longer than a normal classroom test, though, if you work all of the problems.

Assignment:

Before the test, spend 5 minutes teaching students how to *read* the Quadratic Formula, as in Section 6–1. Do not attempt to explain its meaning yet. After the test, assign Exercise 6–1, Problem 1, which asks students to memorize the formula.

Problem Notes:

Problem 4 has polynomials in which the degree is different from the number of terms. This way, students who do not clearly distinguish between the two concepts cannot luck into the right answer.

CHAPTER TEST

1.   What is the difference in meaning in each case?
   a.   Expression that is a polynomial and one that is not
   b.   Trinomial and cubic
   c.   Second degree and two terms
   d.   The square of 9 and the square root of 9
   e. $-\sqrt{25}$ and $\sqrt{-25}$

2.   Write each of the following.
   a.   Definition of degree
   b.   Meaning of linear
   c.   Coefficients in $x^3 - 5x^2 + 4x - 11$
   d.   Example of a cubic monomial
   e.   Example of a quadratic trinomial

3.   a.   Arrange in descending powers of x:
        $7x - 2 + 3x^5 - 4x^2 + x^4$ $3x^5 + x^4 - 4x^2 + 7x - 2$

1.   a.   A polynomial has only $+$, $-$, $\times$.
        Other expressions can have $\sqrt{\text{variable}}$, $|\text{variable}|$, $\div$ by variable, etc.
     b.   "Trinomial" means 3 *terms*.
        "Cubic" means 3rd *degree*.
     c.   Second degree means, for example, x^2. Two terms means, for example, $x + 1$.
     d.   The square of 9 is 81.
        The square root of 9 is 3.
     e. $-\sqrt{25} = -5$
        $\sqrt{-25}$ is not a real number.

2.   a.   The degree of a polynomial with one variable is the exponent of the highest power of that variable.
     b.   "Linear" means "first degree."
     c.   Coefficients: 1, -5, 4, -11
     d.   Cubic monomial: eg., x^3
     e.   Quadratic trinomial: eg., $x^2 + x + 1$

Problem 6 has problems with polynomials involving factoring concepts from different sections. However, all problems are mixed together so that students must distinguish among the concepts based on the type of polynomial rather than on the section in which the problem appears.

b.   Arrange in ascending powers of x:
$x^3 - 3 - 5x + x^2$ $-3 - 5x + x^2 + x^3$

4.   Name the polynomials by degree and by number of terms.
a. $17x^3$ Cubic monomial   b. $13x + 5$ Linear binomial
c. $7x^2 - 3x + 11$ Quadratic trinomial

5.   Multiply.
a. $(x + 7)(x + 3)$ $x^2 + 10x + 21$ b. $(x - 2)(x - 11)$ $x^2 - 13x + 22$
c. $(y + 5)(y - 9)$ $y^2 - 4y - 45$ d. $(x - 6)(x + 1)$ $x^2 - 5x - 6$
e. $(3x + 4)(5x + 1)$ $15x^2 + 23x + 4$ f. $(2z + 7)(3z - 4)$ $6z^2 + 13z - 28$
g. $(4x - 5)(6x - 2)$ $24x^2 - 38x + 10$ h. $(9m - 7)(2m + 3)$ $18m^2 + 13m - 21$
i. $(x - 8)(x + 8)$ $x^2 - 64$ j. $(4x + 10)(4x - 10)$ $16x^2 - 100$
k. $(x + 3)(x + 3)$ $x^2 + 6x + 9$ l. $(6x - 5)(6x - 5)$ $36x^2 - 60x + 25$

6.   Factor each expression or state that it is prime.
a. $x^2 + 6x + 8$ $(x + 2)(x + 4)$ b. $x^2 - 11x + 30$ $(x - 5)(x - 6)$
c. $a^2 + 2a - 3$ $(a - 1)(a + 3)$ d. $v^2 - 5v - 14$ $(v + 2)(v - 7)$
e. $x^2 + 13x + 40$ $(x + 5)(x + 8)$ f. $x^2 - 14x + 40$ $(x - 4)(x - 10)$
g. $x^2 - 22x - 40$ Prime   h. $x^2 - 23x - 50$ $(x + 2)(x - 25)$
i. $3x^2 + 16x + 5$ $(3x + 1)(x + 5)$ j. $2x^2 + 5x - 7$ $(2x + 7)(x - 1)$
k. $5w^2 - 9w - 2$ $(5w + 1)(w - 2)$ l. $3x^2 - 5x + 2$ $(3x - 2)(x - 1)$
m. $x^2 - 16$ $(x + 4)(x - 4)$ n. $25x^2 - 36$ $(5x + 6)(5x - 6)$
o. $x^2 + 49$ Prime

7.   Do the squaring.
a. $(x + 8)^2$ $x^2 + 16x + 64$ b. $(x - 7)^2$ $x^2 - 14x + 49$
c. $(2x + 5)^2$ $4x^2 + 20x + 25$ d. $(3a - 4)^2$ $9a^2 - 24a + 16$
e. $(7 - 3x)^2$ $49 - 42x + 9x^2$ f. $(r + s)^2$ $r^2 + 2rs + s^2$

8.   Transform to the square of a binomial, or tell why it is *not* a trinomial square.
a. $x^2 + 18x + 81$ $(x + 9)^2$ b. $x^2 - 48x + 576$ $(x - 24)^2$
c. $x^2 + 142x - 5041$ Not. $\sqrt{-5041}$ is not a real number.   d. $x^2 - 210x + 11{,}025$ $(x - 105)^2$
e. $x^2 - 174x + 7570$ Not. 7570 is not a square.   f. $a^2 + 2ab + b^2$ $(a + b)^2$

9.   Tell whether or not the set is closed under the given operation. If it is not, give an example that shows *why* not.
a.   {positive integers}; subtraction   Not closed. $5 - 7 = -2 \leftarrow$ not positive
b.   {integers}; division   Not closed. $3 \div 5 = \frac{3}{5} \leftarrow$ not an integer
c. $\{-1, 0, 1\}$; multiplication   Closed. $(-1)(1) = -1 \leftarrow$ in set
d.   {real numbers}; square root   Not closed. $\sqrt{-5} \leftarrow$ not real

10.   Tell whether the following are rational numbers, irrational numbers, or neither.
a. $\sqrt{100}$ Rational   b. $\sqrt{80}$ Irrational
c. $-\sqrt{49}$ Rational   d. $\sqrt{-1}$ Neither

6

Quadratic Equations

In the last chapter you learned that quadratic *means second degree. In this chapter you will learn how to solve* quadratic equations, *in which the variable is squared. Reducing such an equation to one without squares of variables requires taking the* square root *of each member. Once you have learned how to solve quadratic equations, you can use the techniques for such things as predicting the height of a football several seconds after it is kicked*

Variable:

t Number of seconds since football was kicked

Expression:

$25t - 5t^2$ Number of meters it is above the ground

Equation:

$25t - 5t^2 = 20$ Says that the ball is 20 meters up

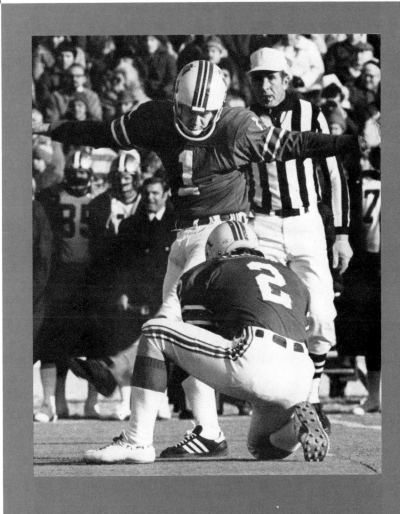

6-1	INTRODUCTION TO THE QUADRATIC FORMULA

Time: 0 days (include with Section 6–2)

Chalkboard Examples:

Spend 5 minutes writing the formula on the board and teaching the students how to *say* it. After this they should be willing to memorize it for homework. There seems to be a certain amount of prestige in being able to say such a mouthful of mathematics, even though students may not yet realize what it means. Don't expect them to read it cold and memorize it. And don't skip this section! The entire chapter is written as the unravelling of a mystery in which students are led to solve equations whose solutions look more and more like the Quadratic Formula.

The following equation is called the **Quadratic Formula**.

$$x = \frac{-b \pm \sqrt{b^2 - 4ac}}{2a}$$

It is read "*x* equals the opposite of *b*, plus or minus the square root of the quantity *b* squared minus 4*ac*, all divided by 2*a*." Later in this chapter you will learn for what the *a, b,* and *c* stand, for what the formula is used, and why the formula works. For the time being, you should just learn to say it.

Objective :
Memorize the Quadratic Formula.

	EXERCISE 6-1

Assignment:

Assign Problem 1, preferably following your last test in Chapter 5. If it is too late to do this, assign it along with the first assignment in Section 6–2.

Problem Note:

Get the students to say the formula in unison. Although this may sound a bit babyish, it instills confidence. One does not have mastery over something until one can say the words!

1. Memorize the Quadratic Formula. You should be able to reproduce it from memory on a quiz. To assist you in doing this, you should learn to connect the *words* given above with various parts of the formula. Remember such things as the fact that the line of division starts below the − sign in front of *b* and goes all the way to the other side of the expression. However, it does *not* go under the = sign or the *x*.

$$x = \frac{-\ b \pm \sqrt{b^2 - 4ac}}{2a}$$

This line goes all the way to *here,* over the *c*.

Line of division starts *here,* under the − sign.

Line of division goes all the way to *here*.

6-2 | EVALUATING RADICAL EXPRESSIONS

Time: 1 day, with Section 6–1

Chalkboard Examples:

Evaluate the expression. Round to two decimal places.

1. $\sqrt{11 + 8}$ Ans.: 4.36 (Rounds up.)

2. $\sqrt{11} + \sqrt{8}$ Ans.: 6.15 (Rounds up.)
   [Answer is different from Number 1.]

3. $\sqrt{(9.2)(7.1)}$ Ans.: 8.08 (Rounds down.)

4. $\sqrt{9.2} \times \sqrt{7.1}$ Ans.: 8.08 (Rounds down.)
   [Answer is the same as Number 3.]

5. $\dfrac{-31 + \sqrt{92}}{6}$ Ans.: −3.57 (Rounds up.)

   [Looks like the Quadratic Formula.]

The first and second examples show that the operation *square root* does not distribute over addition. The third and fourth examples show that the square root *does* distribute over multiplication. These properties will be formalized in Chapter 12, but it never hurts to lay the groundwork early.

Assignment:

Exercise 6–2, #0 and 1–31 odd;
Exercise 5–10, #27, 29;
Exercise 5–9, #22, 24 (for review)

In the last chapter, you learned that square roots of numbers, such as $\sqrt{9}$, are called radicals. Various parts of a radical have special names.

$\sqrt{9}$ A *radical*

$\sqrt{}$ The *radical sign*

9   The *radicand*

$\overline{}$ A symbol of inclusion, called a vinculum

In this section you will learn how to use a calculator to evaluate expressions containing radicals.

Objective :
Given an expression containing a radical, evaluate the expression by calculator and round off the answer.

If you press 9 $\boxed{\sqrt{x}}$ on a calculator, you get 3 for the answer. However, $\sqrt{11}$ gives 3.316624790. From Section 5.10 you should recall that 3 is a *rational* number, because it can be written as $\frac{3}{1}$, a ratio of two integers. But $\sqrt{11}$ is an irrational number. The value 3.316624790. . . is the first part of a nonending, nonrepeating decimal. For most problems in this book, you will round decimals like this to two decimal places. So you would say

$$\sqrt{11} \approx 3.32.$$

If the radical is part of a more complicated expression, you do all the calculator work *first*. You round off only the final answer. Otherwise your answer would not be as accurate. For the expression

$$\frac{5 + \sqrt{11}}{7},$$

you would press

5 $\boxed{+}$ 11 $\boxed{\sqrt{x}}$ $\boxed{=}$ $\boxed{\div}$ 7 $\boxed{=}$

The answer is 1.1880893. . . , which rounds to 1.19. You must press $\boxed{=}$ *before* dividing if your calculator multiplies and divides before it adds and subtracts. Otherwise, only the $\sqrt{11}$ would be divided by 7.

Evaluating expressions by calculator is a skill that must be learned and practiced. If you press the buttons in the wrong order, you will probably get a wrong answer! Practice by working the following examples before you attempt Exercise 6-2. Cover the answers as you work the examples.

EXAMPLE 1

Evaluate $\sqrt{5 + 7}$. Round your answer to two decimal places.

– – – – –   – – – – –

	Think These Reasons
$\sqrt{5 + 7}$	Write the given expression.
$= \sqrt{12}$	Do the operations under the bar *first*.
$\approx \underline{3.46}$	Press 12, $\boxed{\sqrt{x}}$. Then round.

EXAMPLE 2

Evaluate $\sqrt{5} + \sqrt{7}$. Round your answer to two decimal places.

– – – – –   – – – – –

$\sqrt{5} + \sqrt{7}$	Write the given expression.
$\approx \underline{4.88}$	Press 5, $\boxed{\sqrt{x}}$, $\boxed{+}$, 7, $\boxed{\sqrt{x}}$, $\boxed{=}$. (See the instruction manual for your calculator if it uses a different order of operations, such as reverse Polish.)

From the answers to Examples 1 and 2, you can see that $\sqrt{5 + 7}$ does *not* equal $\sqrt{5} + \sqrt{7}$.

EXAMPLE 3

Evaluate $\sqrt{(3.6)(5.7)}$. Round your answer to two decimal places.

– – – – –   – – – – –

$\sqrt{(3.6)(5.7)}$	Write the given expression.
$\approx \underline{4.53}$	Press 3.6, $\boxed{\times}$, 5.7, $\boxed{=}$, $\boxed{\sqrt{x}}$. (Try doing the whole computation on the calculator without writing down intermediate steps. Write just the given expression and the answer.)

EXAMPLE 4

– – – – –   – – – – –

Evaluate $\sqrt{3.6} \times \sqrt{5.7}$. Round your answer to two decimal places.

$\sqrt{3.6} \times \sqrt{5.7}$	Write the given expression.

$\approx \underline{4.53}$ Press 3.6, $\boxed{\sqrt{x}}$, $\boxed{\times}$, 5.7, $\boxed{\sqrt{x}}$, $\boxed{=}$.

From the answers to Examples 3 and 4, you can see that $\sqrt{(3.6)(5.7)}$ *is* equal to $\sqrt{3.6} \times \sqrt{5.7}$.

EXAMPLE 5

Evaluate $\dfrac{-70 + \sqrt{384}}{12}$. Round your answer to two decimal places.

- - - - -   - - - - -

$\dfrac{-70 + \sqrt{384}}{12}$ Write the given expression.

$\approx \underline{-4.20}$ Press 70, $\boxed{+/-}$ to enter -70. Then press $\boxed{+}$,
          384, $\boxed{\sqrt{x}}$, $\boxed{=}$, $\boxed{\div}$, 12, $\boxed{=}$.
          (The calculator should read -4.2003402. The final
          0 in -4.20 *is* significant. If you had written only
          -4.2, the number could have been something like
          -4.23 or -4.18.)

ORAL PRACTICE

Evaluate the following radicals by calculator. Tell whether the answer is a rational number or an irrational number. Round irrational numbers to two decimal places.

EXAMPLES

          Answers
  i. $\sqrt{37}$ i.   6.08, irrational
  ii. $\sqrt{49}$ ii. 7, rational

A. $\sqrt{17}$ 4.12, irr.   B. $\sqrt{60}$ 7.75, irr.   C. $\sqrt{121}$ 11, rat.

D. $\sqrt{2}$ 1.41, irr.   E. $\sqrt{25}$ 5, rat.   F. $-\sqrt{13}$ -3.61, irr.

G. $-\sqrt{289}$ -17, rat.   H. $\sqrt{-9}$ No value   I. $\sqrt{56169}$ 237, rat.

J. $\sqrt{265435}$ 515.20, irr.   K. $\sqrt{5.29}$ 2.3, rat.   L. $\sqrt{22.09}$ 4.7, rat.

M. $\sqrt{42.73}$ 6.54, irr.   N. $-\sqrt{1.44}$ -1.2, rat.   O. $-\sqrt{50.51}$ -7.11, irr.

Problem Notes:

In this section students learn for the first time how to do some really significant computations on the calculator. They should work toward being able to do the whole computation without writing down and reentering various intermediate steps. If no calculators are available, it is possible for you to teach your students how to use the Table of Square Roots in the back of the book. Use of the table is discouraged, however. The resulting long-hand computations are so tedious that students may develop a negative attitude toward your course.

Problems 21–32 present expressions that appear in parts of the Quadratic Formula. Problems 31 and 32 are examples of the entire formula.

Problems 33–36 present certain distributive properties that either do or do not exist and the fact that the square root of a perfect square is the absolute value of the number being squared.

Problem 37 is easy. All the students must realize is that perfect squares never end in 7, so the radical is an irrational number.

EXERCISE 6-2

0. Write the Quadratic Formula. If you cannot do this from memory, go back to Section 6-1 and look it up.

For Problems 1 through 32, evaluate the expression. Round off irrational answers to two decimal places.

1. $\sqrt{(7)(9)}$ 7.94
2. $\sqrt{(11)(25)}$ 16.58
3. $\sqrt{7 + 9}$ 4
4. $\sqrt{11 + 25}$ 6
5. $\sqrt{7} + \sqrt{9}$ 5.65
6. $\sqrt{11} + \sqrt{25}$ 8.32
7. $7 + \sqrt{9}$ 10
8. $11 + \sqrt{25}$ 16
9. $7\sqrt{9}$ 21
10. $11\sqrt{25}$ 55
11. $\sqrt{\dfrac{7}{9}}$ 0.88
12. $\sqrt{\dfrac{11}{25}}$ 0.66
13. $\sqrt{7 - 9}$ No value
14. $\sqrt{11 - 25}$ No value
15. $8\sqrt{17 - 3}$ 29.93
16. $6\sqrt{19 - 5}$ 22.45
17. $\sqrt{(9.2)(7.5)}$ 8.31
18. $\sqrt{(6.7)(8.9)}$ 7.72
19. $\sqrt{4.2} \times \sqrt{3.5}$ 3.83
20. $\sqrt{3.7} \times \sqrt{9.8}$ 6.02
21. $3 + \sqrt{9 - 5}$ 5
22. $5 - \sqrt{25 - 8}$ 0.88
23. $-10 + \sqrt{67}$ -1.81
24. $-6 + \sqrt{23}$ -1.20
25. $\dfrac{5 - \sqrt{257}}{4}$ -2.76
26. $\dfrac{7 - \sqrt{423}}{8}$ -1.70
27. $\dfrac{-6 - \sqrt{21}}{2}$ -5.29
28. $\dfrac{-9 - \sqrt{39}}{2}$ -7.62
29. $-8 + \sqrt{64 - 4(3)(2)}$ -1.68
30. $-3 + \sqrt{9 + 4(5)(7)}$ 9.21
31. $\dfrac{17 - \sqrt{289 - 4(3)(5)}}{6}$ 0.31
32. $\dfrac{13 - \sqrt{169 - 4(5)(6)}}{10}$ 0.6

33. Demonstrate that the operation $\sqrt{}$ (taking the positive square root) *distributes* over multiplication by evaluating the two expressions and showing that they are equal.
    a. $\sqrt{4 \times 9}$ and $\sqrt{4} \times \sqrt{9}$
    b. $\sqrt{3 \times 7}$ and $\sqrt{3} \times \sqrt{7}$
    c. $\sqrt{12 \times 75}$ and $\sqrt{12} \times \sqrt{75}$
    d. $\sqrt{2.9 \times 7.3}$ and $\sqrt{2.9} \times \sqrt{7.3}$

33. a. $\sqrt{4 \times 9} = \sqrt{36} = 6$
        $\sqrt{4} \times \sqrt{9} = 2 \times 3 = 6$ Same
     b. $\sqrt{3 \times 7} = \sqrt{21} \approx 4.5825756$
        $\sqrt{3} \times \sqrt{7} \approx 1.732 \ldots$
        $\times 2.645 \ldots \approx 4.5825756$ Same
     c. $\sqrt{12 \times 75} = \sqrt{900} = 30$
        $\sqrt{12} \times \sqrt{75} \approx 3.464 \ldots$
        $\times 8.660 \ldots \approx 30$ Same
     d. $\sqrt{2.9 \times 7.3} = \sqrt{21.17}$
        ≈ 4.6010868
        $\sqrt{2.9} \times \sqrt{7.3} \approx 1.702 \ldots$
        $\times 2.701 \ldots \approx 4.6010868$ Same

34. Demonstrate that the operation $\sqrt{}$ (taking the positive square root) distributes over *division* by evaluating the two expressions and showing that they are equal.

    a. $\sqrt{\dfrac{100}{4}}$ and $\dfrac{\sqrt{100}}{\sqrt{4}}$ b. $\sqrt{\dfrac{37}{2}}$ and $\dfrac{\sqrt{37}}{\sqrt{2}}$

    c. $\sqrt{\dfrac{75}{3}}$ and $\dfrac{\sqrt{75}}{\sqrt{3}}$ d. $\sqrt{\dfrac{3.7}{8.5}}$ and $\dfrac{\sqrt{3.5}}{\sqrt{8.5}}$

35. Demonstrate that the operation $\sqrt{}$ does *not* distribute over addition or subtraction by showing:
    a. $\sqrt{25 + 36}$ does *not* equal $\sqrt{25} + \sqrt{36}$;
    b. $\sqrt{100 - 49}$ does *not* equal $\sqrt{100} - \sqrt{49}$.

36. Evaluate the following.
    a. $\sqrt{(-5)^2}$ 5   b. $\sqrt{(-7)^2}$ 7   c. $\sqrt{(-9)^2}$ 9
    d. $\sqrt{6^2}$ 6   e. $\sqrt{11^2}$ 11   f. $\sqrt{(-123)^2}$ 123
    g. Explain why $\sqrt{n^2}$ equals $|n|$, the *absolute value of n*, and not *n*.

37. Phoebe Small must tell whether $\sqrt{289{,}329{,}955{,}237}$ is a rational number or an irrational number. Her calculator will not help, because it will not take 12-digit numbers. She is smart, though, and quickly reaches the right answer. Which is it? How did she tell?

6-3 | EQUATIONS CONTAINING ABSOLUTE VALUES

In Section 2-2 you learned that the absolute value of a number is the distance between that number and the origin on a number line.

$$|-5| = 5 \qquad\qquad |3| = 3$$

You are now ready to learn a formal definition of absolute value.

If the number inside the absolute value sign is *positive*, such as $|3|$, then its absolute value is just the number itself:

$$|3| = 3.$$

If the number inside the absolute value sign is *negative*, you take its *opposite*.

If you choose to have your students do the harder equations in Problems 25–36, the following examples can be used.
Find the solution set.
6. $|x| - 7 = 13$ Ans.: $S = \{20, -20\}$
7. $5 - |x - 4| = 2$ Ans.: $S = \{7, 1\}$
   [Don't lose the $-$ sign in front of the absolute value!]

Assignments:

One day on section:
Exercise 6–3, 0 and 1–23 odd or 2–24 even

Two days on section:
Day 1: Exercise 6–3, #0 and 1–13 odd;
   Exercise 6–2, #22, 24, 26 (for review)
Day 2: Those who got it: Exercise 6–3,
   #15–35 odd or 16–36 even
   Those who didn't: Exercise 6–3,
   #2–24 even

$$|-5| = 5 \qquad 5 \text{ is the } opposite \text{ of } -5.$$

If the number inside the absolute value sign is 0, it does not matter *which* you do, because 0 and -0 are the same number:

$$|0| = 0.$$

DEFINITION

ABSOLUTE VALUE
The **absolute value** of a number is the number itself or the opposite of the number, whichever is *positive* (or zero).

That is,

$$|n| = n, \qquad \text{if } n \text{ is positive (or 0)};$$
$$|n| = -n, \qquad \text{if } n \text{ is negative.}$$

Note that $-n$ means the *opposite* of n. It does *not* necessarily stand for a negative number. For instance, the opposite of -9, written $-(-9)$, is 9. And 9 is a positive number.

A positive number, such as 7, has two different numbers with this as their absolute value.

$$|-7| = 7 \qquad |7| = 7$$

So if a *variable* appears inside the absolute value sign, as in

$$|x| = 7,$$

there are two possible values for x.

$$x = 7 \quad \text{or} \quad x = -7$$

Both of these values of x have 7 as their absolute value. So the equation $|x| = 7$ has *two* solutions, 7 and -7.

Since equations can have more than one solution, the solutions can be written in a *set*. For $|x| = 7$, the **solution set** is

$$S = \{7, -7\}.$$

The letter S stands for "solution set." As mentioned in Section 5-10, the braces, { }, are used as set symbols. The symbols $\{7, -7\}$ are read "The set containing 7 and -7." From now on, *solving an equation* will mean writing the solution set.

AGREEMENT

> **SOLVING AN EQUATION**
> **Solving an equation** means writing its solution set.

Objective:
Given an equation involving the absolute value of a variable expression, find its solution set.

Cover the answers as you solve the following equations.

EXAMPLE 1

Find the solution set of $|x| = 15$.

- - - - -   - - - - -

	Think These Reasons

$|x| = 15$ — Write the given equation.

$x = 15$ or $x = -15$ — $|15|$ and $|-15|$ both equal 15.

$\therefore S = \{15, -15\}$ — Write the solution set.

EXAMPLE 2

Find the solution set of $|5x - 7| = 62$.

- - - - -   - - - - -

$|5x - 7| = 62$ — Write the given equation.

$5x - 7 = 62$ or $5x - 7 = -62$ — The number in the absolute value sign must be 62 or -62.

$5x = 69$ or $5x = -55$ — Add 7 to each member of both equations.

$x = 13.8$ or $x = -11$ — Divide each member of both equations by 5.

$\therefore S = \{13.8, -11\}$ — Write the solution set.

Note: There is a more compact way to write the transformed equation. The $\pm$ sign means plus or minus, or positive or negative. You saw this sign in the Quadratic Formula in Section 6-1. So you could write the following.

$\lvert 5x - 7 \rvert = 62$	Write the given equation.
$5x - 7 = \pm 62$	Use the $\pm$ sign.
$5x = 7 \pm 62$	Add 7 to each member.
$x = \dfrac{7 \pm 62}{5}$	Divide each member by 5.
$x = \dfrac{69}{5}$ or $\dfrac{-55}{5}$	$7 + 62 = 69; \quad 7 - 62 = -55$
$x = 13.8$ or -11	Do the division.
$\therefore S = \{13.8,\, -11\}$	Write the solution set.

Note: The step $x = \dfrac{7 \pm 62}{5}$ looks a little bit like the Quadratic Formula!

EXAMPLE 3

Find the solution set of $\lvert x + 5 \rvert = -7$.

$- \ - \ - \ - \ -$ $\qquad\qquad\qquad\qquad\qquad$ $- \ - \ - \ - \ -$

There are *no* solutions. Absolute values of numbers are always positive or zero. So the solution set has *no* numbers in it. It is called the **empty set.** There are two ways of writing the empty set:

$$S = \emptyset \quad \text{or} \quad S = \{\ \}.$$

In both cases you read "S equals the empty set" or "S equals the null set."

EXAMPLE 4

Find the solution set of $42 - \lvert x + 3 \rvert = 15$.

$- \ - \ - \ - \ -$ $\qquad\qquad\qquad\qquad\qquad$ $- \ - \ - \ - \ -$

$42 - \lvert x + 3 \rvert = 15$	Write the given equation.
$-\lvert x + 3 \rvert = -27$	Subtract 42 from each member.
$\lvert x + 3 \rvert = 27$	Multiply each member by -1. (From here on, the problem is just like those above.)
$x + 3 = \pm 27$	The number in the absolute value sign must be 27 or -27.
$x = -3 \pm 27$	Add -3 to each member.
$x = 24$ or -30	Do the arithmetic.
$\therefore S = \{24,\, -30\}$	Write the solution set.

ORAL PRACTICE

For Problems A through F give the result after the first step in solving the equation.

EXAMPLE

Answer

$|x - 7| = 13$ $x - 7 = \pm 13$

A. $|x - 3| = 7$ $x - 3 = \pm 7$ B. $|x + 4| = 2$ $x + 4 = \pm 2$

C. $|3x - 8| = 5$ $3x - 8 = \pm 5$ D. $|4x + 3| = 9$ $4x + 3 = \pm 9$

E. $|7 - 5x| = 4$ $7 - 5x = \pm 4$ F. $|x + 5| = -6$ No solution

Tell the solution set of the equation.

EXAMPLE

Answer

$x = 4 \pm 7$ $S = \{11, -3\}$

G. $x = 10 \pm 3$ $S = \{13, 7\}$ H. $x = 4 \pm 6$ $S = \{10, -2\}$

I. $x = -2 \pm 8$ $S = \{6, -10\}$ J. $x = -7 \pm 3$ $S = \{-4, -10\}$

K. $x = \dfrac{5 \pm 9}{2}$ $S = \{7, -2\}$ L. $x = \dfrac{8 \pm 7}{5}$ $S = \{3, 0.2\}$

Give the first step in solving the equation.

EXAMPLE

Answer

$|x + 3| - 7 = 15$ Add 7 to each member.

M. $|x + 4| - 6 = 5$ N. $|x + 3| + 7 = 22$

O. $|3x - 5| - 8 = 2$ P. $6 - |x + 4| = 1$

M. Add 6 to each member.
N. Subtract 7 from each member.
O. Add 8 to each member.
P. Subtract 6 from each member.

EXERCISE 6-3

0. Write the Quadratic Formula. If you cannot do this from memory, look it up in Section 6-1.

$$x = \frac{-b \pm \sqrt{b^2 - 4ac}}{2a}$$

Problem Notes:

Problems 1–24 are bread-and-butter problems that students must know how to work in order to understand the later derivation of the Quadratic Formula.

For Problems 1 through 24, find the solution set of the equation.

1. $|x| = 15$ $S = \{15, -15\}$
2. $|x| = 29$ $S = \{29, -29\}$
3. $|x| = 132$ $S = \{132, -132\}$
4. $|x| = 540$ $S = \{540, -540\}$
5. $|x - 2| = 7$ $S = \{9, -5\}$
6. $|x - 5| = 13$ $S = \{18, -8\}$
7. $|x + 3| = 19$ $S = \{16, -22\}$
8. $|x + 7| = 15$ $S = \{8, -22\}$
9. $|x - 4| = -8$ $S = \emptyset$
10. $|x + 3| = -5$ $S = \emptyset$
11. $|5 - x| = 31$ $S = \{-26, 36\}$
12. $|4 - x| = 19$ $S = \{-15, 23\}$
13. $|2x - 5| = 29$ $S = \{17, -12\}$
14. $|2x - 7| = 43$ $S = \{25, -18\}$
15. $|4x + 7| = 45$ $S = \{9.5, -13\}$
16. $|4x + 19| = 7$ $S = \{-3, -6.5\}$
17. $|5x - 33| = 22$ $S = \{11, 2.2\}$
18. $|5x - 11| = 29$ $S = \{8, -3.6\}$
19. $|7 - 10x| = 38$ $S = \{-3.1, 4.5\}$
20. $|18 - 10x| = 173$ $S = \{-15.5, 19.1\}$
21. $|3 + 4x| = -19$ $S = \emptyset$
22. $|3 + 8x| = -1$ $S = \emptyset$
23. $|x - 8| = 0$ $S = \{8\}$
24. $|x - 13| = 0$ $S = \{13\}$

For Problems 25 through 36, solve the equation. You may need to do a preliminary transformation before removing the absolute value signs.

Problems 25–36 are intended to challenge the better students.

25. $S = \{30, -30\}$ 26. $S = \{37, -37\}$
27. $S = \{24, -24\}$ 28. $S = \{14, -14\}$
29. $S = \{9.5, -12.5\}$ 30. $S = \{12, -17\}$
31. $S = \{10, -8\}$ 32. $S = \{7, -1\}$
33. $S = \{3, 6\}$ 34. $S = \{2, 1.2\}$
35. $S = \{x : x \geq 0\}$ 36. $S = \{x : x \leq 0\}$

25. $|x| - 9 = 21$
26. $|x| - 4 = 33$
27. $38 - |x| = 14$
28. $95 - |x| = 81$
29. $|2x + 3| - 5 = 17$
30. $|2x + 5| - 7 = 22$
31. $4 - |x - 1| = -5$
32. $5 - |x - 3| = 1$
*33. $|3x - 12| = x$
*34. $|4x - 6| = x$
*35. $|x| = x$
*36. $|x| = -x$

*These are tough. You must be very clever to solve them! You should remember *all parts* of the definition of absolute value.

Problem 37 keeps before the students the connection between what they are doing and the Quadratic Formula that they have memorized but probably do not yet comprehend.

Problem 38 again gets at the idea that the square root of a perfect square is the absolute value of the number being squared.

37. You solve an equation like

$$|7x + 3| = 5 \qquad x = \frac{-3 \pm 5}{7}$$

by transforming it to simpler forms. At one step in the process the equation looks a bit like the Quadratic Formula. Show this step.

38. Evaluate the following radicals. Remember, $\sqrt{n}$ stands for the *positive* square root of n. Then answer part (e).

    a. $\sqrt{(-6)^2}$ 6
    b. $\sqrt{(-5)^2}$ 5
    c. $\sqrt{7^2}$ 7
    d. $\sqrt{8^2}$ 8
    e. $\sqrt{n^2}$ is *positive*, whether n is positive or negative. Explain why $\sqrt{n^2}$ can be written as $|n|$. $\sqrt{n^2}$ equals n, if n is positive; or $-n$, if n is negative. This is the definition of $|n|$. Therefore, $\sqrt{n^2} = |n|$.

6-4 | EQUATIONS WITH SQUARES

Time: 1 or 2 days

Chalkboard Examples:

Solve. Round to two decimal places, if necessary.
1. $(x + 6)^2 = 100$ Ans.: $S = \{4, -16\}$
2. $(0.7x - 4.2)^2 = 43.9$
   Ans.: $S = \{15.47, -3.47\}$
3. $(3x + 5)^2 = -49$ Ans.: $S = \emptyset$
   [There is no real square root of -49.]

In the last section you solved equations such as

$$|x - 3| = 5.$$

In this section you will solve equations such as

$$(x - 3)^2 = 25.$$

The second equation can be transformed to the first one by taking the *square root* of each member. The fact that you can do this is called the square root property of equality.

Assignments:

One day on section:
Exercise 6–4, #0 and 1–35 odd or 2–36 even
   (This is a long assignment. Perhaps start it in class.)

Two days on section:
Day 1: Exercise 6–4, #0 and 1–29 odd
Day 2: Exercise 6–4, #12–40 even;
        Exercise 6–2, #28, 30;
        Exercise 5–9, #26, 28 (for review)

SQUARE ROOT PROPERTY OF EQUALITY
If two positive numbers are equal, then their positive square roots are equal.

That is, if $a = b$, then $\sqrt{a} = \sqrt{b}$.

Objective:
Be able to solve equations like $(x - 3)^2 = 25$, in which the square of a binomial equals a constant.

To see why the transformation can be done, you need to realize two things about the radical sign. Suppose you must evaluate

$$\sqrt{(-7)^2}.$$

First, the vinculum means to do what is underneath *first,* so you write

$$\sqrt{49},$$

because $(-7)^2$ equals $+49$. Second, $\sqrt{}$ means to take the *positive* square root, so you write

$$7.$$

The number you started with was -7. The answer is $+7$, which is the *absolute value* of -7, written $|-7|$. So

$$\sqrt{(-7)^2} = |-7| = 7.$$

This conclusion is summarized below.

SQUARE ROOT OF A PERFECT SQUARE

$$\sqrt{(\text{number})^2} = |\text{number}|$$

Using this conclusion you can solve equations like $(x - 3)^2 = 25$. Cover the answers as you work the examples on the next page.

EXAMPLE 1

Solve $(x - 3)^2 = 25$.

- - - - -

	Think These Reasons
$(x - 3)^2 = 25$	Write the given equation.
$\sqrt{(x - 3)^2} = \sqrt{25}$	Take the positive square root of each member.
$|x - 3| = 5$	$\sqrt{(\text{number})^2} = |\text{number}|$, and $\sqrt{25} = 5$. (From here on this is just like the problems of Section 6-3. You have transformed a new problem into an old problem.)
$x - 3 = \pm 5$	Definition of absolute value
$x = 3 \pm 5$	Add 3 to each member.
$x = 8 \quad \text{or} \quad -2$	Do the arithmetic.
$S = \{8, -2\}$	Write the solution set.

Note: Recall that solving now means writing the solution set.

EXAMPLE 2

Solve $(0.3x + 1.9)^2 = 28.7$.

- - - - -

$(0.3x + 1.9)^2 = 28.7$	Write the given equation.
$\sqrt{(0.3x + 1.9)^2} = \sqrt{28.7}$	Take the square root of each member.

$$|0.3x + 1.9| = \sqrt{28.7} \qquad\qquad \sqrt{n^2} = |n|$$

$$0.3x + 1.9 = \pm\sqrt{28.7} \qquad\qquad \text{Definition of absolute value}$$

$$0.3x = -1.9 \pm \sqrt{28.7} \qquad\qquad \text{Add } -1.9 \text{ to each member.}$$

$$x = \frac{-1.9 \pm \sqrt{28.7}}{0.3} \qquad\qquad \text{Divide each member by 0.3.}$$

$$x \approx 11.52 \quad\text{or}\quad -24.19 \qquad\qquad \text{Do the arithmetic.}$$

$$S = \{11.52, -24.19\} \qquad\qquad \text{Write the solution set.}$$

Because there are a lot of chances for error, it is advisable to check your answers. The best way is to store the answer in the calculator's memory *without* rounding off. The check of 11.52 . . . would look like this:

Check: $(0.3(11.52\ldots) + 1.9)^2 \overset{?}{=} 28.7$ Substitute 11.52 . . . for x.

$$28.7 = 28.7 \quad \text{✔}$$ Answer checks. (The calculator may show an answer slightly different from 28.7.)

Note: Recall the Quadratic Formula from Section 6-1 and notice that

$$x = \frac{-1.9 \pm \sqrt{28.7}}{0.3}$$

in the solution of Example 2 looks very much like

$$x = \frac{-b \pm \sqrt{b^2 - 4ac}}{2a}.$$

EXAMPLE 3

Solve $(2x + 7)^2 = -64$.

$$(2x + 7)^2 = -64 \qquad\qquad \text{Write the given equation.}$$

$$\sqrt{(2x + 7)^2} = \sqrt{-64} \qquad\qquad \text{Take the square root of each member.}$$

$$S = \emptyset \qquad\qquad$$ Since $\sqrt{-64}$ is *not* a real number, there are *no* real values of x that satisfy the equation. Therefore, the solution set is the *empty* set. You could tell that this is so before you take the square root. No real number squared could equal -64.

ORAL PRACTICE

Give the result after the first step in solving the equation.

EXAMPLES

Answers

i. $(x + 5)^2 = 81$ i. $|x + 5| = 9$

ii. $(x - 7)^2 = 34$ ii. $|x - 7| = \sqrt{34}$

A. $(x + 4)^2 = 36$ $|x + 4| = 6$ B. $(x - 3)^2 = 64$ $|x - 3| = 8$

C. $(x + 2)^2 = 100$ $|x + 2| = 10$ D. $(x - 6)^2 = 49$ $|x - 6| = 7$

E. $(x + 8)^2 = 21$ $|x + 8| = \sqrt{21}$ F. $(x - 1)^2 = 79$ $|x - 1| = \sqrt{79}$

G. $(x + 7)^2 = 38.2$ $|x + 7| = \sqrt{38.2}$ H. $(x - 6.2)^2 = 9.71$ $|x - 6.2| = \sqrt{9.71}$

I. $(3x - 9)^2 = 16$ $|3x - 9| = 4$ J. $(0.6x + 2.3)^2 = 1.7$ $|0.6x+2.3|=\sqrt{1.7}$

K. $(x + 10)^2 = -9$ No solution   L. $(x - 1)^2 = 0$ $|x - 1| = 0$

Problem Notes:

Problems 1–30 are like the examples. Students should check as shown in the text, storing the answer without round-off and recalling it for substitution. Students seem more willing to check answers with untidy decimals because they do not have the false feedback that the answer came out even and thus might be right.

Problems 31–40 are a review of absolute value equations. In spite of the fact that the equations of this section reduce to absolute value equations after the first step, students sometimes compartmentalize their knowledge and forget how to solve the equation when it *starts off* with an absolute value. The most common error is taking the square root of each member. Problems 31, 32, 37, and 38 deliberately have perfect squares as their right members to tempt the fuzzy thinkers into this mistake.

Problem 41 addresses the theoretical concept of the square root of a perfect square.

1. $S = \{12, -2\}$ **2.** $S = \{11, -5\}$
3. $S = \{7, -13\}$ **4.** $S = \{4, -14\}$
5. $S = \{6.60, -10.60\}$
6. $S = \{2.75, -16.75\}$
7. $S = \{14.24, 1.76\}$
8. $S = \{9.28, -5.28\}$
9. $S = \{16.28, -2.28\}$
10. $S = \{9.57, -7.57\}$
11. $S = \{2, -7\}$ **12.** $S = \{-1, -6\}$
13. $S = \{5.12, 2.21\}$
14. $S = \{3.06, 1.27\}$
15. $S = \{-2.31, -3.29\}$
16. $S = \{-1.27, -2.33\}$
17. $S = \{\frac{2}{3}\}$ **18.** $S = \{3\}$
19. $S = \{9.74, 2.26\}$ **20.** S
         $= \{16.24, 3.76\}$
21. $S = \{-1.40, -6.80\}$
22. $S = \{-3.09, -9.31\}$
23. $S = \{1.85, -0.85\}$
24. $S = \{3.15, -1.28\}$
25. $S = \{20.68, -57.18\}$
26. $S = \{1.44, -18.01\}$ **27.** $S = \{16, 0\}$
28. $S = \emptyset$ **29.** $S = \emptyset$
30. $S = \{10, 0\}$

EXERCISE 6-4

0.   Write the Quadratic Formula. If you cannot do this from memory, go back and look in Section 6-1. $x = \dfrac{-b \pm \sqrt{b^2 - 4ac}}{2a}$

For Problems 1 through 30, find the solution set of the equation. Round off irrational answers to two decimal places.

1. $(x - 5)^2 = 49$ 2. $(x - 3)^2 = 64$

3. $(x + 3)^2 = 100$ 4. $(x + 5)^2 = 81$

5. $(x + 2)^2 = 74$ 6. $(x + 7)^2 = 95$

7. $(x - 8)^2 = 39$ 8. $(x - 2)^2 = 53$

9. $(x - 7)^2 = 86.2$ 10. $(x - 1)^2 = 73.5$

11. $(2x + 5)^2 = 81$ 12. $(2x + 7)^2 = 25$

13. $(3x - 11)^2 = 19$ 14. $(6x - 13)^2 = 29$

15. $(5x + 14)^2 = 6$ 16. $(5x + 9)^2 = 7$

17. $(3x - 2)^2 = 0$ 18. $(4x - 12)^2 = 0$

19. $(6 - x)^2 = 14$ 20. $(10 - x)^2 = 39$

21. $(x + 4.1)^2 = 7.3$ 22. $(x + 6.2)^2 = 9.7$

23. $(7x - 3.5)^2 = 88.9$ 24. $(3x - 2.8)^2 = 44.2$

25. $(0.4x + 7.3)^2 = 242.5$ 26. $(0.7x + 5.8)^2 = 46.31$

27. $(x - 8)^2 = 64$ 28. $(x + 9)^2 = -36$

29. $(x + 2)^2 = -25$ 30. $(x - 5)^2 = 25$

For Problems 31 through 40, solve the equation as you did in Section 6-3.

31. $|x + 4| = 25$ 32. $|x + 3| = 81$

33. $|x - 6| = 7$ 34. $|x - 8| = 10$

35. $|2x + 5| = 21$ 36. $|3x + 6| = 30$

37. $|5 - 4x| = 49$ 38. $|9 - 5x| = 64$

39. $|x + 2| = -1$ 40. $|x + 7| = 0$

41. Explain why $\sqrt{(x - 3)^2}$ must be written $|x - 3|$, not $x - 3$.

31. $S = \{21, -29\}$ **32.** $S = \{78, -84\}$
33. $S = \{13, -1\}$ **34.** $S = \{18, -2\}$
35. $S = \{8, -13\}$ **36.** $S = \{8, -12\}$
37. $S = \{-11, 13.5\}$
38. $S = \{-11, 14.6\}$
39. $S = \emptyset$ **40.** $S = \{-7\}$
41. $\sqrt{(x - 3)^2}$ means the *positive* square root. Since $x - 3$ can be a *negative* number, the answer must be $|x - 3|$.

6-5   EQUATIONS WITH TRINOMIAL SQUARES

Time: 2 days, including quiz

Chalkboard Examples:

One chalkboard example is probably enough before you start students working the examples on their own. Another example can be presented if students will be solving equations with decimals the first day. The following are reasonable examples.

Solve. Round to two decimal places, if necessary.

1. $x^2 - 14x + 49 = 33$
   Ans.: $S = \{12.74, 1.26\}$
2. $x^2 + 11x + 30.25 = 4.3$
   Ans.: $S = \{-3.43, -7.57\}$

Assignments:

One day on section:
Exercise 6–5, 0 and 1–39 odd

Two days on section:
Day 1: Exercise 6–5, #0; 1–19 odd; and 31–39 odd

Day 2: Exercise 6–5, #12–40 even

This chapter is about solving quadratic equations. In some special cases, such as

$$x^2 - 10x + 25 = 70,$$

the left member may be a *trinomial square*. From Section 5-9 you should recall how to transform $x^2 - 10x + 25$ into the square of a binomial.

$$\text{Is this } 2 \times \sqrt{25}? \qquad \text{If so, make this } \tfrac{1}{2}(-10).$$

$$x^2 - 10x + 25 = (x - 5)^2$$

Thus the equation above can be written

$$(x - 5)^2 = 70.$$

From here, on, it is an *old* problem.

	Think These Reasons
$\sqrt{(x - 5)^2} = \sqrt{70}$	Take the square root of each member.
$|x - 5| = \sqrt{70}$	$\sqrt{n^2} = |n|$
$x - 5 = \pm\sqrt{70}$	Definition of absolute value
$x = 5 \pm \sqrt{70}$	Add 5 to each member.
$x \approx 13.37 \text{ or } -3.37$	Do the arithmetic.
$\therefore S = \{13.37, -3.37\}$	Write the solution set.

Objective:

Be able to solve quadratic equations in which the left member is a trinomial square.

Cover the answers as you work the examples below.

EXAMPLE 1

Solve $x^2 + 6x + 9 = 113$.

– – – – –   – – – – –

	Think These Reasons

$x^2 + 6x + 9 = 113$	Write the given equation.
$(x + 3)^2 = 113$	Half of 6 is 3, and 3^2 is 9. So the left member is a trinomial square.
$\sqrt{(x + 3)^2} = \sqrt{113}$	Take the square root of each member.
$\lvert x + 3 \rvert = \sqrt{113}$	$\sqrt{(\text{number})^2} = \lvert \text{number} \rvert$
$x + 3 = \pm\sqrt{113}$	Definition of absolute value
$x = -3 \pm \sqrt{113}$	Add -3 to each member.
$S = \{7.63, -13.63\}$	Do the arithmetic and write the solution set.

Note: It is best *not* to use a calculator until you get to the step $x = \ldots$. Then you write the answers in the solution set as you find them on the calculator. You can also *check* the answers before you clear the calculator. Just store the answer—for instance, $-13.63 \ldots$— in memory and recall it as needed in the check.

Check:

$(-13.63 \ldots)^2 + 6(-13.63 \ldots) + 9 \overset{?}{=} 113$ Substitute $-13.63 \ldots$ for x.

$113 = 113$ ✔   Evaluate the expression. (The calculator may show a number slightly different from 113.)

EXAMPLE 2

Solve $x^2 - 7.4x + 13.69 = 8.3$.

– – – – –   – – – – –

$x^2 - 7.4x + 13.69 = 8.3$ Write the given equation.

$(x - 3.7)^2 = 8.3$ $\frac{1}{2}(-7.4)$ is -3.7, and $(-3.7)^2$ is 13.69. So the left member *is* a trinomial square.

$\sqrt{(x - 3.7)^2} = \sqrt{8.3}$ Take the square root of each member.

$|x - 3.7| = \sqrt{8.3}$ Square root of a perfect square

$x - 3.7 = \pm\sqrt{8.3}$ Definition of absolute value

$x = 3.7 \pm \sqrt{8.3}$ Add 3.7 to each member.

$S = \{6.58, 0.82\}$ Do the arithmetic and write the solution set.

Check (of 6.58):

$(6.58 \ldots)^2 - 7.4(6.58 \ldots) + 13.69 \stackrel{?}{=} 8.3$ Substitute $6.58 \ldots$ for x.

$8.3 = 8.3$ ✔   Answer checks. (Your calculator may show a slightly different value.)

ORAL PRACTICE

Give the result after the first step in solving the equation.

EXAMPLE

Answer

$x^2 - 10x + 25 = 41$ $(x - 5)^2 = 41$

A. $x^2 - 6x + 9 = 13$

B. $x^2 + 8x + 16 = 7$

C. $x^2 - 2x + 1 = 11$

D. $x^2 + 12x + 36 = 22$

E. $x^2 + 4x + 4 = 51$

F. $x^2 - 14x + 49 = 0$

G. $x^2 + 5x + 6.25 = 17$

H. $x^2 - 7x + 12.25 = 9.5$

I. $x^2 - 3.8x + 3.61 = 2.4$

J. $x^2 + 7.6x + 14.44 = 2$

A. $(x - 3)^2 = 13$ B. $(x + 4)^2 = 7$
C. $(x - 1)^2 = 11$ D. $(x + 6)^2 = 22$
E. $(x + 2)^2 = 51$ F. $(x - 7)^2 = 0$
G. $(x + 2.5)^2 = 17$ H. $(x - 3.5)^2 = 9.5$
I. $(x - 1.9)^2 = 2.4$ J. $(x + 3.8)^2 = 2$

EXERCISE 6-5

Problem Notes:

Problems 1–20 have x-coefficients that are even integers, so factoring into perfect squares involves no decimals. Problems 21–30 have x-coefficients that are not even integers, so the numbers are a little more untidy.

Problems 31–40 review techniques from earlier sections. It is important to assign these so that students do not forget old techniques while learning new ones. Students must decide whether or not to take the square root of each member based on the form of the *expression* in the left member and not on whether the constant on the right is a perfect square.

Problems 41–48 may be assigned to give your students a review of fractions in the context of solving quadratic equations. Don't bog down on these problems, though.

0. Write the Quadratic Formula. If you cannot do this from memory, reread Section 6-1.

For Problems 1 through 30, solve the equation by writing the left member as the square of a binomial. Write any irrational solutions as decimals, correct to two decimal places.

1. $x^2 + 6x + 9 = 16$
2. $x^2 - 10x + 25 = 81$
3. $x^2 - 4x + 4 = 25$
4. $x^2 + 6x + 9 = 49$
5. $x^2 + 2x + 1 = 42$
6. $x^2 + 4x + 4 = 73$
7. $x^2 - 18x + 81 = 2001$
8. $x^2 - 16x + 64 = 1776$
9. $x^2 + 8x + 16 = 98.6$
10. $x^2 - 14x + 49 = 74.3$
11. $x^2 - 12x + 36 = 29$
12. $x^2 - 2x + 1 = 57$
13. $x^2 - 20x + 100 = 8.6$
14. $x^2 + 18x + 81 = 20.3$
15. $x^2 - 6x + 9 = -4$
16. $x^2 - 8x + 16 = 0$
17. $x^2 + 14x + 49 = 49$
18. $x^2 + 12x + 36 = -25$
19. $x^2 + 10x + 25 = 0$
20. $x^2 + 20x + 100 = 100$
21. $x^2 + 5x + 6.25 = 49$
22. $x^2 + 3x + 2.25 = 81$
23. $x^2 - 7x + 12.25 = 9$
24. $x^2 - 5x + 6.25 = 36$
25. $x^2 - 9x + 20.25 = 73$
26. $x^2 - 13x + 42.25 = 19$
27. $x^2 + 2.6x + 1.69 = 5.7$
28. $x^2 - 8.6x + 18.49 = 7.1$
29. $x^2 - 1.4x + 0.49 = 0.35$
30. $x^2 + 1.8x + 0.81 = 0.47$

For Problems 31 through 40, solve the equation as you did in Section 6-3 or 6-4.

31. $|x - 5| = 36$
32. $|x - 11| = 81$
33. $|x + 300| = 2000$
34. $|x + 0.03| = 0.08$
35. $|5x - 1| = 14$
36. $|10x - 6| = 93$
37. $(x + 7)^2 = 100$
38. $(x + 4)^2 = 25$
39. $(x - 0.3)^2 = 0.49$
40. $(x - 20)^2 = 900$

For Problems 41 through 48, use the fact that "taking the positive square root" distributes over division. (See Problem 34, Section 6-2.) For example,

Answers

1. $S = \{1, -7\}$
2. $S = \{14, -4\}$
3. $S = \{7, -3\}$
4. $S = \{4, -10\}$
5. $S = \{5.48, -7.48\}$
6. $S = \{6.54, -10.54\}$
7. $S = \{53.73, -35.73\}$
8. $S = \{50.14, -34.14\}$
9. $S = \{5.93, -13.93\}$
10. $S = \{15.62, -1.62\}$
11. $S = \{11.39, 0.61\}$
12. $S = \{8.55, -6.55\}$
13. $S = \{12.93, 7.07\}$
14. $S = \{-4.49, -13.51\}$
15. $S = \emptyset$
16. $S = \{4\}$
17. $S = \{0, -14\}$
18. $S = \emptyset$
19. $S = \{-5\}$
20. $S = \{0, -20\}$
21. $S = \{4.5, -9.5\}$
22. $S = \{7.5, -10.5\}$
23. $S = \{6.5, 0.5\}$
24. $S = \{8.5, -3.5\}$
25. $S = \{13.04, -4.04\}$
26. $S = \{10.86, 2.14\}$
27. $S = \{1.09, -3.69\}$
28. $S = \{6.96, 1.64\}$
29. $S = \{1.29, 0.11\}$
30. $S = \{-0.21, -1.59\}$
31. $S = \{41, -31\}$
32. $S = \{92, -70\}$
33. $S = \{1700, -2300\}$
34. $S = \{0.05, -0.11\}$
35. $S = \{3, -2.6\}$
36. $S = \{9.9, -8.7\}$
37. $S = \{3, -17\}$
38. $S = \{1, -9\}$
39. $S = \{1, -0.4\}$
40. $S = \{50, -10\}$

$$\sqrt{\frac{36}{49}} = \frac{\sqrt{36}}{\sqrt{49}} = \frac{6}{7}.$$

41. $x^2 + \frac{2}{3}x + \frac{1}{9} = \frac{4}{9}$

42. $x^2 + \frac{2}{9}x + \frac{1}{81} = \frac{64}{81}$

43. $x^2 - \frac{6}{5}x + \frac{9}{25} = \frac{81}{25}$

44. $x^2 - \frac{8}{5}x + \frac{16}{25} = \frac{9}{25}$

45. $x^2 + \frac{7}{3}x + \frac{49}{36} = \frac{25}{36}$

46. $x^2 + \frac{5}{3}x + \frac{25}{36} = \frac{1}{36}$

47. $x^2 - \frac{5}{4}x + \frac{25}{64} = \frac{121}{64}$

48. $x^2 - \frac{3}{4}x + \frac{9}{64} = \frac{121}{64}$

41. $S = \left\{\frac{1}{3}, -1\right\}$

42. $S = \left\{\frac{7}{9}, -1\right\}$

43. $S = \left\{\frac{12}{5}, -\frac{6}{5}\right\}$

44. $S = \left\{\frac{7}{5}, \frac{1}{5}\right\}$

45. $S = \left\{-2, -\frac{1}{3}\right\}$

46. $S = \left\{-\frac{2}{3}, -1\right\}$

47. $S = \left\{2, -\frac{3}{4}\right\}$

48. $S = \left\{\frac{7}{4}, -1\right\}$

49. In the equation $x^2 + 10x + 13 = 47$, the left member is *not* a trinomial square since 13, the constant term, is not a perfect square.

    a. What would the constant term have to be in order for the left member to be a trinomial square?

    b. Add a number to each member of the equation to *make* the left member a trinomial square.

    c. Solve the equation.
$$x^2 + 10x + 25 = 59$$
$$(x + 5)^2 = 59$$
$$x = -5 \pm \sqrt{59}$$
$$S = \{2.68, -12.68\}$$

Problem 49 introduces the concept of completing the square in the next section.

49. a. $x^2 + 10x + 13 = 47$
    Constant term would have to be
    $[\frac{1}{2}(10)]^2 = 5^2 = 25$.
   b. So *add* 12 to each member.
    $x^2 + 10x + 13 + 12 = 47 + 12$

6-6 | COMPLETING THE SQUARE

You already know how to square a binomial. For example,

$(x + 5)^2$

$= (x + 5)(x + 5)$ Definition of squaring

$= x^2 + 5x + 5x + 25$ Multiply each term of one binomial by each term of the other.

$= x^2 + 10x + 25$ Combine like terms.

Recall that the quick way to do this is as follows:

1. *Square* the first term of $(x + 5)$.
$$(x + 5)^2 = x^2 \ldots$$

2. Add *twice* the *product* of the two terms in $(x + 5)$.
$$(x + 5)^2 = x^2 + 10x \ldots$$

3. Add the square of the *last* term in $(x + 5)$.
$$(x + 5)^2 = x^2 + 10x + 25.$$

Time: Combine with Section 6–7, or spend 1 day

Chalkboard Examples:

This section is intended to give students practice in reading on their own; therefore, chalkboard exercises are inappropriate. See Section 6–7 for follow-up chalkboard exercises.

Assignment:

Combined with Section 6–7:
Use Problems 11–30 as oral practice.

1 day on this section:
Exercise 6–6, #1–29 odd or 2–30 even and 31;
Exercise 6–5, #10;
Exercise 6–4, #10;
Exercise 6–3, #8 (for review)

To make sure you can do this, work the example below, covering the answer till you have finished each part.

EXAMPLE 1

Do the squaring.

a. $(x + 7)^2$

$-\ -\ -\ -\ -$ $-\ -\ -\ -\ -$

	Think These Reasons

$(x + 7)^2$ Write the given expression.

$= \underline{x^2 + 14x + 49}$ $14x$ is $2(x)(7)$ and 49 is 7^2.

b. $(x - 9)^2$

$-\ -\ -\ -\ -$ $-\ -\ -\ -\ -$

$(x - 9)^2$ Write the given expression.

$= \underline{x^2 - 18x + 81}$ $-18x$ is $2(x)(-9)$ and 81 is $(-9)^2$. Do not forget the $-$ sign.

If you know this pattern, you can *reverse* the process and find the constant term needed to make a trinomial a trinomial square. For instance, what number could you add to

$$x^2 + 6x$$

to make it a trinomial square? The thought process goes like this.

1. Write $x^2 + 6x$ and *part* of a binomial squared. Leave a blank space in the binomial.
$$x^2 + 6x$$
$$(x\ \ \ \ \ )^2$$

2. Fill in the number in the binomial.
$$x^2 + 6\ x$$
$$(x + 3)^2$$
$$\text{3 is } \tfrac{1}{2}(6).$$

3. Fill in the number in the trinomial.
$$x^2 + 6x + 9$$
$$\text{9 is } 3^2.$$
$$(x + 3)^2$$

The process of adding 9 to $x^2 + 6x$ is called *completing the square*. Once you see the pattern, it is easy to do in your head. The technique is given below.

TECHNIQUE

COMPLETING THE SQUARE
If the x^2-coefficient equals 1 (as in $x^2 + 6x$),
then to **complete the square** you do the following:

1.   Take *half* the coefficient of x.
     ($\frac{1}{2}$ of 6, in this case)

2.   Square it.
     ($3^2 = 9$, in this case)

3.   Add the result.
     ($x^2 + 6x + 9$, in this case)

Objective :
Be able to add a constant to a quadratic binomial, such as $x^2 + 6x$, to make the result a trinomial square.

EXAMPLE 2

Complete each square.

a. $x^2 + 8x + \cdots$

- - - - -   - - - - -

   $\underline{x^2 + 8x + 16}$ $\frac{1}{2}$ of 8 is 4, and 4^2 is 16. (Do *not* write an = sign, since the expression given does not *equal* the answer.)

b. $x^2 - 10x + \cdots$

- - - - -   - - - - -

   $\underline{x^2 - 10x + 25}$ $\frac{1}{2}$ of (-10) is -5, and $(-5)^2$ is 25.

c. $x^2 + 7x + \cdots$

- - - - -   - - - - -

   $\underline{x^2 + 7x + 12.25}$ $\frac{1}{2}$ of 7 is 3.5, and 3.5^2 is 12.25.

d. $x^2 - 2.7x + \cdots$

- - - - -   - - - - -

   $\underline{x^2 - 2.7x + 1.8225}$ $\frac{1}{2}$ of -2.7 is -1.35, and $(-1.35)^2$ is 1.8225.

EXERCISE 6-6

0. State the Quadratic Formula. $x = \dfrac{-b \pm \sqrt{b^2 - 4ac}}{2a}$

Problem Notes:

Problems 1–30 may be used as oral practice.

   Problems 11–30 go very quickly (5 minutes) once students get the idea. It is therefore appropriate to assign work from previous sections, as prescribed above, to serve as distributed practice.

   Problem 31 allows students to apply their knowledge to a new situation; namely, to discovering how to solve equations by completing the square, as they will do in the next section. This problem goes very well with most students. Many even figure out a shortcut by adding 8 to each member, getting 25 for the constant term, without first subtracting 17 from each member.

For Problems 1 through 10, square the binomial in *one* step.

1. $(x + 6)^2$ $x^2 + 12x + 36$

2. $(x + 8)^2$ $x^2 + 16x + 64$

3. $(x - 5)^2$ $x^2 - 10x + 25$

4. $(x - 3)^2$ $x^2 - 6x + 9$

5. $(x + 9)^2$ $x^2 + 18x + 81$

6. $(x + 4)^2$ $x^2 + 8x + 16$

7. $(x - 2)^2$ $x^2 - 4x + 4$

8. $(x - 1)^2$ $x^2 - 2x + 1$

9. $(x + 1)^2$ $x^2 + 2x + 1$

10. $(x + 2)^2$ $x^2 + 4x + 4$

For Problems 11 through 30, copy the expression and add a constant to complete the square.

11. $x^2 + 10x + \cdots$ 25

12. $x^2 + 20x + \cdots$ 100

13. $x^2 - 6x + \cdots$ 9

14. $x^2 - 12x + \cdots$ 36

15. $x^2 + 24x + \cdots$ 144

16. $x^2 + 14x + \cdots$ 49

17. $x^2 - 50x + \cdots$ 625

18. $x^2 - 100x + \cdots$ 2500

19. $x^2 - 2x + \cdots$ 1

20. $x^2 - 4x + \cdots$ 4

21. $x^2 + 5x + \cdots$ 6.25

22. $x^2 + 3x + \cdots$ 2.25

23. $x^2 - 13x + \cdots$ 42.25

24. $x^2 - 15x + \cdots$ 56.25

25. $x^2 - 3.8x + \cdots$ 3.61

26. $x^2 - 2.6x + \cdots$ 1.69

27. $x^2 + 5.1x + \cdots$ 6.5025

28. $x^2 + 3.7x + \cdots$ 3.4225

29. $x^2 + 0.3x + \cdots$ 0.0225

30. $x^2 + 0.7x + \cdots$ 0.1225

31. The equation $x^2 + 10x + 17 = 21$ cannot be solved by the method of Section 6-5 since the left member is not a trinomial square. Now that you know how to *complete* the square, you should be able to figure out a way to solve this equation. First, subtract 17 from each member. Then, figure out what number to add to $x^2 + 10x$ to complete the square. Add this number to *each* member of the equation. Then solve it the way you learned in Section 6-5. $S = \{0.39, -10.39\}$

6-7 | SOLVING QUADRATIC EQUATIONS BY
COMPLETING THE SQUARE

Time: 3 or 4 days, including test

Chalkboard Examples:

First day:
Solve by completing the square.
$x^2 + 12x - 17 = 0$ Ans.: $x = -6 \pm \sqrt{53}$
$S = \{1.28, -13.28\}$
Second or third day:
Solve by completing the square.
$3x^2 - 21x + 15 = 0$ Ans.: $x = 3.5 \pm \sqrt{7.25}$
$S = \{6.19, 0.81\}$

Once you understand the process of completing the square, you can use the technique to solve quadratic equations such as

$$x^2 - 10x + 7 = 0.$$

If the left member were a trinomial square, you could solve the equation as in Section 5-5. Therefore, you *make* it a trinomial square by completing the square.

Objective :
Be able to solve quadratic equations such as $x^2 - 10x + 7 = 0$ by completing the square and adding the same number to the other member.

Assignments:

Day 1: 0 and 1–19 odd or 2–20 even
Day 2: 21–39 odd or 22–40 even
Day 3: 41–59 odd or 42–60 even
Day 4: Following test, assign 61 and 62.
For stronger students it may be possible to spend fewer days by assigning about ten equations per assignment but skipping some of the more repetitive problems.

Cover the answers as you work these examples.

EXAMPLE 1

Solve $x^2 - 10x + 7 = 0$ by completing the square.

— — — — —   — — — — —

Think These Reasons

$x^2 - 10x + 7 = 0$	Write the given equation.
$x^2 - 10x \quad\quad = -7$	Add -7 to each member, leaving a space in which to complete the square.
$x^2 - 10x + 25 = -7 + 25$	Add 25 to each member of the equation to complete the square on the left.
$(x - 5)^2 = 18$	Write the left member as a square. -5 is *half* of -10. Do the arithmetic on the right.

From here on, the problem is just like those in Section 6-4.

— — — — —   — — — — —

$\sqrt{(x - 5)^2} = \sqrt{18}$	Take the square root of each member.
$\lvert x - 5 \rvert = \sqrt{18}$	$\sqrt{(\text{number})^2} = \lvert \text{number} \rvert$
$x - 5 = \pm\sqrt{18}$	Definition of absolute value

$$x = 5 \pm \sqrt{18} \qquad \text{Add 5 to each member.}$$

$$S = \{9.24, 0.76\} \qquad \text{Do the arithmetic and write the solution set.}$$

Checking the answer may give a small surprise.

$$(9.24 \ldots)^2 - 10(9.24 \ldots) + 7 \overset{?}{=} 0$$

$$0 = 0 \quad ✔$$

The number on the left will probably be close to, but not equal to, zero. On a scientific calculator, it may look something like 2-08. This is how the calculator shows 2×10^{-8}, which equals 0.00000002. You will learn about this kind of number when you study scientific notation in Section 9-6.

The preceding method for completing the square does not work if the x^2-coefficient is not equal to 1. To solve an equation like

$$5x^2 + 13x + 8 = 0,$$

you simply divide each member by 5, getting

$$\frac{5x^2 + 13x + 8}{5} = \frac{0}{5}.$$

On the left, division distributes over addition. On the right, $\frac{0}{5}$ is 0. So the equation becomes

$$x^2 + 2.6x + 1.6 = 0.$$

From here on you would solve the equation as in Example 1.

EXAMPLE 2

Solve $4x^2 + 12x - 7 = 0$ by completing the square.

– – – – –   – – – – –

$4x^2 + 12x - 7 = 0$	Write the given equation.
$x^2 + 3x - 1.75 = 0$	Divide each member by 4.
$x^2 + 3x \qquad = 1.75$	Add 1.75 to each member.
$x^2 + 3x + 2.25 = 1.75 + 2.25$	Complete the square.

– – – – –   – – – – –

$(x + 1.5)^2 = 4$	Write the left member as a square. Do the arithmetic on the right.
$x + 1.5 = \pm 2$	Take the square root of each member.
$x = -1.5 \pm 2$	Add -1.5 to each member.
$S = \{0.5, -3.5\}$	Write the solution set.

Check (of −3.5):

$$4(-3.5)^2 + 12(-3.5) - 7 \overset{?}{=} 0 \qquad \text{Substitute } x = -3.5.$$

$$0 = 0 \ \text{✔} \qquad \text{Check is } \textit{exact}.$$

ORAL PRACTICE

For Problems A through L on the next page, give the number that must be added to complete the square.

EXAMPLES

	Problem	*Answers*	
i.	$x^2 - 12x + \cdots$	i.	36
ii.	$x^2 + 7x + \cdots$	ii.	12.25

A. $x^2 + 14x + \cdots$ 49   B. $x^2 - 10x + \cdots$ 25

C. $x^2 + 6x + \cdots$ 9   D. $x^2 - 20x + \cdots$ 100

E. $x^2 - 5x + \cdots$ 6.25   F. $x^2 + 3x + \cdots$ 2.25

G. $x^2 - 7x + \cdots$ 12.25   H. $x^2 + 9x + \cdots$ 20.25

I. $x^2 + 2x + \cdots$ 1   J. $x^2 + x + \cdots$ 0.25

K. $x^2 + 2.2x + \cdots$ 1.21   L. $x^2 - 3.2x + \cdots$ 2.56

EXERCISE 6-7

0. Write the Quadratic Formula. $x = \dfrac{-b \pm \sqrt{b^2 - 4ac}}{2a}$

For Problems 1 through 50, solve the equation by completing the square. Write any irrational answers as decimals, correct to two decimal places.

1. $x^2 + 6x + 4 = 0$ 2. $x^2 + 8x + 3 = 0$

3. $x^2 - 8x + 3 = 0$ 4. $x^2 + 10x + 21 = 0$

5. $x^2 - 16x - 17 = 0$ 6. $x^2 - 12x - 34 = 0$

7. $x^2 + 14x - 43 = 0$ 8. $x^2 - 4x - 77 = 0$

9. $x^2 - 10x + 21 = 0$ 10. $x^2 + 16x + 20 = 0$

(Problems 11 through 20 have decimals in the equation or other surprises!)

11. $x^2 + 20x - 19.8 = 0$ 12. $x^2 + 10x - 8.7 = 0$

13. $x^2 - 2x - 33.4 = 0$ 14. $x^2 - 6x - 21.9 = 0$

Problem Notes:

Problems 15 and 16 have empty solution sets.
  Problems 17 and 18 have left members that are already trinomial squares.
  Problems 19 and 20 have 0 for the constant term.

1. $S = \{-0.76, -5.24\}$
2. $S = \{-0.39, -7.61\}$
3. $S = \{7.61, 0.39\}$ 4. $S = \{-3, -7\}$
5. $S = \{17, -1\}$
6. $S = \{14.37, -2.37\}$
7. $S = \{2.59, -16.59\}$ 8. $S = \{11, -7\}$
9. $S = \{7, 3\}$
10. $S = \{-1.37, -14.63\}$
11. $S = \{0.95, -20.95\}$
12. $S = \{0.81, -10.81\}$
13. $S = \{6.87, -4.87\}$
14. $S = \{8.56, -2.56\}$

15. $S = \emptyset$ **16.** $S = \{10\}$
17. $S = \{6\}$ **18.** $S = \emptyset$
19. $S = \{0, -18\}$ **20.** $S = \{14, 0\}$

15. $x^2 + 4x + 15 = 0$ 16. $x^2 - 20x + 100 = 0$

17. $x^2 - 12x + 36 = 0$ 18. $x^2 + 2x + 9 = 0$

19. $x^2 + 18x = 0$ 20. $x^2 - 14x = 0$

(In Problems 21 through 30, the x-coefficient is not an even integer.)

21. $S = \{-0.70, -4.30\}$
22. $S = \{-0.30, -6.70\}$
23. $S = \{7.53, -0.53\}$
24. $S = \{6.27, -1.27\}$
25. $S = \{6.22, -3.22\}$ **26.** $S = \{11, -2\}$
27. $S = \{6, 5\}$ **28.** $S = \{2.62, 0.38\}$
29. $S = \{1.28, -4.68\}$
30. $S = \{1.24, -4.04\}$

21. $x^2 + 5x + 3 = 0$ 22. $x^2 + 7x + 2 = 0$

23. $x^2 - 7x - 4 = 0$ 24. $x^2 - 5x - 8 = 0$

25. $x^2 - 3x - 20 = 0$ 26. $x^2 - 9x - 22 = 0$

27. $x^2 - 11x + 30 = 0$ 28. $x^2 - 3x + 1 = 0$

29. $x^2 + 3.4x - 6 = 0$ 30. $x^2 + 2.8x - 5 = 0$

(Problems 31 through 40 require other transformations before you complete the square.)

31. $S = \{8, -2\}$ **32.** $S = \{2, -10\}$
33. $S = \{-1, -7\}$ **34.** $S = \{11, 3\}$
35. $S = \{1.3, 0.5\}$
36. $S = \{-1.2, -1.4\}$
37. $S = \{0.2, -10\}$ **38.** $S = \{5.4, -10\}$
39. $S = \{1.19, -4.19\}$ **40.** $S = \{4.65, 0.44\}$
41. $S = \{3.37, 1.63\}$ **42.** $S = \{5.90, 1.10\}$
43. $S = \{-0.76, -1.84\}$
44. $S = \{-1.15, -3.65\}$
45. $S = \{5.72, -26.22\}$ **46.** $S = \{0.5, -19\}$
47. $S = \{6.5, -1.5\}$
48. $S = \{1.16, -6.66\}$
49. $S = \emptyset$ **50.** $S = \emptyset$

31. $x^2 - 6x + 13 = 29$ 32. $x^2 + 8x + 7 = 27$

33. $x^2 = -8x - 7$ 34. $x^2 = 14x - 33$

35. $x^2 + 0.65 = 1.8x$ 36. $x^2 + 1.68 = -2.6x$

37. $9.8x = 2 - x^2$ 38. $4.6x = 54 - x^2$

39. $x^2 + 5x = 2x + 5$ 40. $x^2 - x = 4x - 2$

41. $2x^2 - 10x + 11 = 0$ 42. $2x^2 - 14x + 13 = 0$

43. $5x^2 + 13x + 7 = 0$ 44. $5x^2 + 24x + 21 = 0$

45. $0.2x^2 + 4.1x - 30 = 0$ 46. $0.2x^2 + 3.7x - 1.9 = 0$

47. $-4x^2 + 20x + 39 = 0$ 48. $-4x^2 - 22x + 31 = 0$

49. $5x^2 - 13x + 12 = 0$ 50. $5x^2 + 8x + 9 = 0$

Problems 51–60 are important to remind students how to solve equations with absolute value or squares of binomials. Even though these are intermediate steps in solving by completing the square, students sometimes get lost when asked to start in the middle of a problem. Problems 59 and 60 are deliberate traps for students who are working with their brains turned off. These are just *linear* equations!

For Problems 51 through 60, solve the equation. These are like equations you have solved before this section. *Think* carefully about what you are doing!

51. $|x - 5| = 64$ $S = \{69, -59\}$ 52. $|x + 7| = 9$ $S = \{2, -16\}$

53. $|3x + 21| = 9$ $S = \{-4, -10\}$ 54. $|5x - 34| = 49$ $S = \{16.6, -3\}$

55. $(x - 6)^2 = 100$ $S = \{16, -4\}$ 56. $(x + 8)^2 = 4$ $S = \{-6, -10\}$

57. $(x + 4.7)^2 = 81$ $S = \{4.3, -13.7\}$ 58. $(x - 2.3)^2 = 36$ $S = \{8.3, -3.7\}$

59. $(x - 7) = 25$ $S = \{32\}$ 60. $(x + 13) = 1$ $S = \{-12\}$

61. a., b., c. See Additional Answers.

61. The words *completing the square* can be illustrated by area. For instance, the diagram shows a square with side x, flanked by two rect-

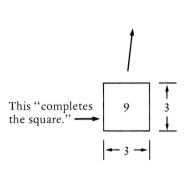

This "completes the square." ⟶

Problem 61 shows a geometrical meaning for the words *completing the square*.

Problem 62 shows that there are other ways to complete the square. This technique is used in second-year algebra for factoring expressions like $x^4 + 4$.

angles of dimension 3 by x. The total area is $x^2 + 3x + 3x$, or $x^2 + 6x$. As you can see, adding a 3-by-3 square (area 9) "completes" the big square! Draw pictures showing completing the square for the following expressions.

a. $x^2 + 10x$ b. $x^2 + 18x$ c. $x^2 - 12x$ (Be clever!)

62.   It is possible to complete the square by adding a *middle* term. For instance, if $x^2 + 9$ were to be made into a trinomial square, the middle term would have to be $6x$. What would the middle term have to be to make these expressions trinomial squares?

a. $x^2 + \cdots + 16$ $_{8x}$ b. $x^2 + \cdots + 100$ $_{20x}$ c. $x^2 - \cdots + 81$ $_{18x}$
d. $x^2 - \cdots + 49$ $_{14x}$ e. $x^2 + \cdots + 53$ $_{2\sqrt{53}x}$

6-8 | THE QUADRATIC FORMULA

You have learned what the Quadratic Formula *is*:

$$x = \frac{-b \pm \sqrt{b^2 - 4ac}}{2a}.$$

Now you are ready to learn:

1.   what it *means*;
2.   *why* it works.

After you have this knowledge, you will be able to:

3.   *use* the formula to solve quadratic equations.

There is a pattern in the solution of a quadratic equation that shows up if you do *not* simplify as you go along. For instance, to solve

$$5x^2 + 13x + 7 = 0,$$

Time: 3 days

Chalkboard Examples:

Day 1:
To *derive* the formula:
$3x^2 + 11x + 5 = 0$
Ans.:
$x = \dfrac{-11 \pm \sqrt{121 - 4(3)(5)}}{6}$ or

$x = \dfrac{-11 \pm \sqrt{61}}{6}$

To *use* the formula:
$5x^2 + 17x + 7 = 0$
Ans.:
$x = \dfrac{-17 \pm \sqrt{149}}{10} \approx -0.48$ or -2.92

Use examples in which coefficients are relatively prime integers so students can distinguish among them and the 2 and 4 from the formula. Have students work at least one example before they leave.

Subsequent days: Homework problems on board.

you first divide each member by 5, getting

$$x^2 + \frac{13}{5}x + \frac{7}{5} = 0.$$

The fractions $\frac{13}{5}$ and $\frac{7}{5}$ are deliberately left in that form. Clearing space to complete the square gives

$$x^2 + \frac{13}{5}x = -\frac{7}{5}. \qquad \text{Add } -\frac{7}{5} \text{ to each member.}$$

Half *of* $\frac{13}{5}$ means $\frac{1}{2} \cdot \frac{13}{5}$, which equals $\frac{13}{10}$. Since $\frac{13}{10}$ squared is $\frac{169}{100}$, you get

$$x^2 + \frac{13}{5}x + \frac{169}{100} = \frac{169}{100} - \frac{7}{5}. \qquad \text{Add } \frac{169}{100} \text{ to each member.}$$

The two fractions on the right can be added by finding a common denominator, as you have before. To find a common denominator, divide 5 into 100, getting 20, and then multiply $\frac{7}{5}$ by 1 in the form $\frac{20}{20}$.

$$x^2 + \frac{13}{5}x + \frac{169}{100} = \frac{169}{100} - \frac{20}{20} \cdot \frac{7}{5}$$

Writing the left member as a square and adding on the right gives

$$\left(x + \frac{13}{10}\right)^2 = \frac{169 - 20(7)}{100}.$$

Taking the square root of each member gives

$$x + \frac{13}{10} = \pm\sqrt{\frac{169 - 20(7)}{100}}.$$

The square root of a fraction equals the square root of the numerator divided by the square root of the denominator. For instance, $\sqrt{25/16} = \sqrt{25}/\sqrt{16}$, as you can check by doing the arithmetic. So the equation can be written

$$x + \frac{13}{10} = \pm\frac{\sqrt{169 - 20(7)}}{10}.$$

The denominator is 10, since $\sqrt{100} = 10$. The numerator is left as a radical. Its radicand is not a perfect square, as you can see by doing the arithmetic; you get $\sqrt{29}$.

Adding $-\frac{13}{10}$ to each member gives

$$x = -\frac{13}{10} \pm \frac{\sqrt{169 - 20(7)}}{10}.$$

Since these fractions have the same denominator, you can add and subtract their numerators, getting

$$x = \frac{-13 \pm \sqrt{169 - 20(7)}}{10}.$$

This looks very much like the Quadratic Formula! Comparing this with the original equation,

$$5x^2 + 13x + 7 = 0,$$

you can see 13 and 7 in the answer. The 169 is 13^2. The 5 also shows up after a bit of searching: 20 is 4(5) and 10 is 2(5). So the solutions can be written

$$x = \frac{-13 \pm \sqrt{13^2 - 4(5)(7)}}{2(5)}.$$

If the equation had been $ax^2 + bx + c = 0$, the answer would be the Quadratic Formula! The a, b, and c are the three coefficients in the quadratic equation. If you know the formula, you can write the solutions for *any* quadratic equation, without having to complete the square.

QUADRATIC FORMULA
If $ax^2 + bx + c = 0$, and $a \neq 0$ then

$$x = \frac{-b \pm \sqrt{b^2 - 4ac}}{2a}.$$

The restriction "a does not equal 0" is needed for two reasons. If a were 0, the equation would not be quadratic and you would not need the Quadratic Formula. Also, if a were 0 you could not *use* the formula because it would lead to division by 0.

Objective :
Be able to solve a given quadratic equation using the Quadratic Formula.

Cover the answers as you work these examples.

EXAMPLE 1

Solve by the Quadratic Formula: $5x^2 + 12x + 3 = 0$.

- - - - -   - - - - -

	Think These Reasons

$5x^2 + 12x + 3 = 0$ — Write the given equation.

$x = \dfrac{-12 \pm \sqrt{144 - 4(5)(3)}}{2(5)}$ — Use the Quadratic Formula; $a = 5$, $b = 12$, $c = 3$.

$S = \{-0.28, -2.12\}$ — Write the solution set. The radical is $\sqrt{84}$, which is approximately 9.16515390.

EXAMPLE 2

Solve by the Quadratic Formula: $3x^2 - 5x - 9 = 0$.

— — — — —   — — — — —

$3x^2 - 5x - 9 = 0$	Write the given equation.
$x = \dfrac{5 \pm \sqrt{25 - 4(3)(-9)}}{2(3)}$	Use the Quadratic Formula; $a = 3,\ b = -5,\ c = -9$.
$\underline{\underline{S = \{2.76, -1.09\}}}$	Write the solution set. The radical is $\sqrt{133}$, which is approximately 11.53256259.

EXAMPLE 3

Solve by the Quadratic Formula: $5x^2 + 13x - 6 = 0$.

— — — — —   — — — — —

$5x^2 + 13x - 6 = 0$	Write the given equation.
$x = \dfrac{-13 \pm \sqrt{169 - 4(5)(-6)}}{2(5)}$	Use the Quadratic Formula; $a = 5,\ b = 13,\ c = -6$.
$\underline{\underline{S = \{0.4, -3\}}}$	Write the solution set. The radical is $\sqrt{289}$, which is *exactly* 17. So the solutions are *rational* numbers. (This happens whenever $b^2 - 4ac$ is a *perfect square*.)

EXAMPLE 4

Solve by the Quadratic Formula: $7x^2 - 3x + 6 = 0$.

— — — — —   — — — — —

	Think These Reasons
$7x^2 - 3x + 6 = 0$	Write the given equation.
$x = \dfrac{3 \pm \sqrt{9 - 4(7)(6)}}{2(7)}$	Use the Quadratic Formula; $a = 7,\ b = -3,\ c = 6$.
$\underline{\underline{S = \emptyset}}$	The radical is $\sqrt{-159}$, which is *not* a real number! (This happens whenever $b^2 - 4ac$ is *negative*.)

EXAMPLE 5

Solve by the Quadratic Formula: $(3x + 4)(x - 5) = 17$.

— — — — —   — — — — —

$(3x + 4)(x - 5) = 17$	Write the given equation.
$3x^2 - 11x - 20 = 17$	Multiply the binomials.

$3x^2 - 11x - 37 = 0$ Make the left member zero, since the Quadratic Formula begins: "If $ax^2 + bx + c = 0$. . ."

$$x = \frac{11 \pm \sqrt{121 - 4(3)(-37)}}{2(3)}$$ Use the Quadratic Formula; $a = 3$, $b = -11$, $c = -37$.

$S = \{5.79, -2.13\}$ The radical is $\sqrt{565}$, which is approximately 23.769629.

ORAL PRACTICE

Give the values of a, b, and c to use in the Quadratic Formula.

EXAMPLE

Answer

$8x^2 - 9x + 1 = 0$ $a = 8$, $b = -9$, $c = 1$

A. $3x^2 + 5x + 7 = 0$ 3, 5, 7   B. $2x^2 + 6x - 9 = 0$ 2, 6, -9

C. $4x^2 - 3x - 8 = 0$ 4, -3, -8   D. $-5x^2 - 4x + 1 = 0$ -5, -4, 1

E. $x^2 + 10x - 1 = 0$ 1, 10, -1   F. $6x^2 + x + 12 = 0$ 6, 1, 12

G. $7x^2 - x + 5 = 0$ 7, -1, 5   H. $-x^2 + x - 3 = 0$ -1, 1, -3

I. $3x^2 + 7x = 0$ 3, 7, 0   J. $4x^2 + 9 = 0$ 4, 0, 9

K. $3x + 5 + 4x^2 = 0$ 4, 3, 5   L. $2 - x^2 + 3x = 0$ -1, 3, 2

EXERCISE 6-8

For Problems 1 through 20, solve the equation using the Quadratic Formula. Write irrational solutions as decimals, correct to two decimal places. Check each answer by storing it in the calculator's memory. Then evaluate the expression(s) in the equation using the stored value.

1. $3x^2 + 14x + 15 = 0$

2. $7x^2 + 10x + 3 = 0$

3. $7x^2 - 20x + 9 = 0$

4. $3x^2 - 24x + 17 = 0$

5. $9x^2 + 5x - 8 = 0$

6. $6x^2 + 7x - 9 = 0$

7. $-5x^2 - 18x + 79 = 0$

8. $-8x^2 + 5x + 21 = 0$

9. $5x^2 - 13x + 12 = 0$

10. $5x^2 - 13x - 6 = 0$

11. $6x^2 - 17x - 3 = 0$

12. $6x^2 + 9x + 10 = 0$

Problem Notes:

Problems 1–20 involve straightforward substitution into the Quadratic Formula.

Problems 21–30 have one of the three coefficients a, b, or c equal to 0. In 29 and 30 where $a = 0$, the equations are *linear*, and the Quadratic Formula cannot be used!

1. $S = \{-1\frac{2}{3}, -3\}$ 2. $S = \{-\frac{3}{7}, -1\}$

3. $S = \{2.30, 0.56\}$ 4. $S = \{7.21, 0.79\}$

5. $S = \{0.71, -1.26\}$

6. $S = \{0.77, -1.94\}$

7. $S = \{-6.16, 2.56\}$

8. $S = \{-1.34, 1.96\}$

9. $S = \emptyset$ 10. $S = \{3, -0.4\}$

11. $S = \{3, -\frac{1}{6}\}$ 12. $S = \emptyset$

13. $S = \{-0.32, -21.68\}$
14. $S = \{-0.93, -2.82\}$ 15. $S = \{7, -3\}$
16. $S = \{35, -1.5\}$
17. $S = \{1.52, -8.52\}$ 18. $S = \{5.45, 0.55\}$
19. $S = \{-1.62, 0.62\}$
20. $S = \{-0.62, 1.62\}$

13. $0.5x^2 + 11x + 3.5 = 0$
14. $0.8x^2 + 3x + 2.1 = 0$

15. $0.2x^2 - 0.8x - 4.2 = 0$
16. $0.2x^2 - 6.7x - 10.5 = 0$

17. $x^2 + 7x - 13 = 0$
18. $x^2 - 6x + 3 = 0$

19. $-x^2 - x + 1 = 0$
20. $-x^2 + x + 1 = 0$

For Problems 21 through 30, solve the equation as above. Note that one term is missing.

EXAMPLES

  i. $3x^2 + 7 = 0$ can be written $3x^2 + 0x + 7 = 0$;
       so $a = 3$, $b = 0$, and $c = 7$.
  ii. $8x^2 - 5x = 0$ can be written $8x^2 - 5x + 0 = 0$;
       so $a = 8$, $b = -5$, and $c = 0$.

21. $S = \{1.34, -1.34\}$
22. $S = \{1.73, -1.73\}$
23. $S = \emptyset$ 24. $S = \emptyset$
25. $S = \{0, -1\frac{2}{3}\}$ 26. $S = \{0, -1.4\}$
27. $S = \{1, 0\}$ 28. $S = \{0, -1\}$
29. $S = \{2.5\}$ 30. $S = \{5.5\}$

21. $5x^2 - 9 = 0$
22. $6x^2 - 18 = 0$

23. $6x^2 + 7 = 0$
24. $3x^2 + 8 = 0$

25. $3x^2 + 5x = 0$
26. $5x^2 + 7x = 0$

27. $x^2 - x = 0$
28. $x^2 + x = 0$

29. $4x - 10 = 0$ (Be clever!)   30. $2x - 11 = 0$ (Be clever!)

For Problems 31–50, it is important for students to recognize that a, b, and c are the coefficients of the x^2, x, and constant terms, respectively. They are *not* the first, second, and third numbers appearing in the equation.

31. $S = \{-\frac{2}{3}, -1\}$ 32. $S = \{-0.5, -3\}$
33. $S = \{0.29, -0.69\}$
34. $S = \{0.24, -0.84\}$
35. $S = \{4.54, -1.54\}$
36. $S = \{5.70, -0.70\}$ 37. $S = \{5, -6\}$
38. $S = \{5, -7\}$ 39. $S = \{-1, -7\}$
40. $S = \{0.52, -9.52\}$
41. $S = \{2.41, -5.41\}$ 42. $S = \{5.82, -4.82\}$
43. $S = \{2, -3.83\}$ 44. $S = \{1, -2.25\}$
45. $S = \emptyset$ 46. $S = \emptyset$
47. $S = \{-0.32, 0.62\}$ 48. $S = \{-1.2, 0.5\}$
49. $S = \{-6\}$ 50. $S = \{4\}$

For Problems 31 through 50 solve the equation as above. You must first transform it to $ax^2 + bx + c = 0$ so that you can use the Quadratic Formula.

31. $3x^2 + 5x = -2$
32. $2x^2 + 7x = -3$

33. $3x^2 + 7x - 2 = 3x - 7x^2$
34. $x^2 + 4x - 1 = x - 4x^2$

35. $x(x - 3) = 7$
36. $x(x - 5) = 4$

37. $n(n + 1) = 30$
38. $z(z + 2) = 35$

39. $(x + 3)^2 + 2x = 2$
40. $(x + 5)^2 - x = 30$

41. $(x + 5)(x - 2) = 3$
42. $(x - 5)(x + 4) = 8$

43. $(3x - 2)(2x + 5) = 36$
44. $(4x - 1)(2x + 3) = 15$

45. $(x - 3)^2 + 25 = 0$
46. $(x + 5)^2 + 49 = 0$

47. $0.3(x - 5) = x^2 - 1.7$
48. $0.7(2 - x) = x^2 + 0.8$

49. $(x + 10)^2 + x = (x + 8)^2 + 6$

50. $(x - 7)^2 + 5x = (x + 3)^2 - 20$

For Problems 51 through 60, solve the equation using appropriate techniques from previous sections.

51. $|x + 2| = 2.3$ $S = \{0.3, -4.3\}$ 52. $|x - 5| = 7.1$ $S = \{12.1, -2.1\}$

53. $|5x - 28| = 49$ $S = \{15.4, -4.2\}$ 54. $|2x + 13| = 64$ $S = \{25.5, -38.5\}$

55. $(x + 7)^2 = 16$ $S = \{-3, -11\}$ 56. $(x - 3)^2 = 81$ $S = \{12, -6\}$

57. $x^2 + 2x - 15 = 0$ (Complete the square.) $S = \{3, -5\}$

58. $x^2 - 2x - 8 = 0$ (Complete the square.) $S = \{4, -2\}$

59. $x^2 - 5.4x + 7 = 0$ (Complete the square.) $S = \{3.24, 2.16\}$

60. $x^2 - 10.2x + 2 = 0$ (Complete the square.) $S = \{10, 0.2\}$

61. You have noticed that sometimes there are *no* real solutions to certain quadratic equations. This happens when the number under the radical sign is *negative*. From the Quadratic Formula, you know that this number is $b^2 - 4ac$. Without actually solving the following equations, find the value of $b^2 - 4ac$ and use the result to tell whether or not the equation has real-number solutions.
   a. $3x^2 + 2x + 5 = 0$ $-56 \rightarrow$ *No solutions*
   b. $x^2 + 7x - 3 = 0$ $61 \rightarrow$ *Has solutions*
   c. $5x^2 + x - 20 = 0$ $401 \rightarrow$ *Has solutions*
   d. $2x^2 - 3x + 7 = 0$ $-47 \rightarrow$ *No solutions*

62. ***General Proof of Quadratic Formula***   Starting with the equation $ax^2 + bx + c = 0$, derive the Quadratic Formula by completing the square.

Problems 51–60 review techniques of previous sections. Problems 53 and 54 force students to realize that they do not always take the square root of each member.

Problem 61 introduces the concept of the discriminant, which is the subject of Section 6–10.

62. $ax^2 + bx + c = 0$

$$x^2 + \frac{b}{a}x + \frac{b^2}{4a^2} = \frac{b^2}{4a^2} - \frac{c}{a}$$

$$\left(x + \frac{b}{2a}\right)^2 = \frac{b^2 - 4ac}{4a^2}$$

$$\left|x + \frac{b}{2a}\right| = \frac{\sqrt{b^2 - 4ac}}{2a}$$

$$x = \frac{b}{2a} \pm \frac{\sqrt{b^2 - 4ac}}{2a}$$

$$x = \frac{-b \pm \sqrt{b^2 - 4ac}}{2a}$$

6-9 | VERTICAL MOTION PROBLEMS

You recall from Section 2-8 that distance equals rate multiplied by time—that is,

$$d = rt,$$

This formula works if the rate, r, is *constant*. When something is thrown upward into the air, the rate *varies*. The rate gets slower and slower as the object goes up, then becomes negative as it comes back down again. In physics you will learn that instead of d equaling rt, it is given approximately by

$$d = rt - 5t^2,$$

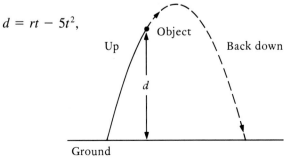

Up   Object   Back down

d

Ground

Time: 2 days

Chalkboard Examples:

Bow and Arrow Problem—Ann Archer shoots an arrow into the air with an initial upward velocity of 60 meters per second.
a. Write an equation relating d and t.

b. How high is the arrow after 4 seconds?
c. When will it be 75 meters high?
d. When will it be 200 meters high?
e. When will it come back to the ground?
(It helps to have a tennis ball to throw up in the air to illustrate why something must be *subtracted* from rt to give the correct distance.)

Solutions:

a. $d = 60t - 5t^2$
b. $60t - 5t^2$
    $= 60(4) - 5(4^2)$
    $= 160$
    160 meters

c. $75 = 60t - 5t^2$
$t^2 - 12t + 15 = 0$
$t = \dfrac{12 \pm \sqrt{84}}{2}$
$t \approx 10.58$ or 1.42
After 1.42 sec (going up) and after 10.58 sec (coming down)

d. $200 = 60t - 5t^2$
$t^2 - 12t + 40 = 0$
$t = \dfrac{12 \pm \sqrt{-16}}{2}$
The arrow never reaches 200 m.

e. $0 = 60t - 5t^2$
$t^2 - 12t = 0$
$t = \dfrac{12 \pm \sqrt{144}}{2}$
$t = 12$ or 0
After 12 sec.

Assignments:

Day 1: Exercise 6-9, #1, 3, 5 or 2, 4, 6
Day 2: Exercise 6-9, #7, 9, 11 or 8, 10, 12

where t is the number of seconds since the object was thrown upward, d is its distance in meters above where it was thrown, and r is the rate when it was first thrown (the *initial upward velocity*) in meters per second.

Since the variable t is squared, this formula is a quadratic equation. In this section you use the formula to solve problems involving vertical motion.

Objective :

For a known value of r, find d when t is given, or find t when d is given.

Put paper at the dotted lines. Uncover to the next dotted lines after you have worked that part of the example.

EXAMPLE

A ball is thrown upward with an initial velocity of 35 meters per second (m/sec).

a.   Write an equation relating d and t.

b.   How high is the ball after 3 sec?

c.   After how many seconds will it be 50 m high?

d.   When will it be 57 m high?

e.   When will it be 70 m high?

f.   When will the ball be back to the ground?

- - - - -   - - - - -

	Think These Reasons

a. $d = 35t - 5t^2$ Substitute 35 for r in $d = rt - 5t^2$.

- - - - -   - - - - -

b. $d = 35(3) - 5(3)^2$ Substitute 3 for t.

$d = 60$ Do the arithmetic.

<u>60 meters</u>   Write the answer.

- - - - -   - - - - -

c. $50 = 35t - 5t^2$ Substitute 50 for d.

$5t^2 - 35t + 50 = 0$ Make the right member equal zero.

$t^2 - 7t + 10 = 0$ Divide each member by 5.

$t = \dfrac{7 \pm \sqrt{49 - 4(1)(10)}}{2(1)}$ Use the Quadratic Formula.

$$t = \frac{7 \pm 3}{2}$$ Arithmetic

$$t = 5 \quad \text{or} \quad 2$$ Arithmetic

After 2 seconds, and after 5 seconds   Answer the question. (At 2 seconds the ball is going up. At 5 seconds it is coming back down.)

– – – – –   – – – – –

d. $57 = 35t - 5t^2$ Substitute 57 for d.

$5t^2 - 35t + 57 = 0$ Make the right member equal zero.

$t^2 - 7t + 11.4 = 0$ Divide each member by 5.

$$t = \frac{7 \pm \sqrt{49 - 4(1)(11.4)}}{2(1)}$$ Use the Quadratic Formula.

$$t = \frac{7 \pm \sqrt{3.4}}{2}$$ Arithmetic

$$t \approx 4.42 \quad \text{or} \quad 2.58$$ Arithmetic

2.58 seconds (going up);   Answer the question.
4.42 seconds (coming down)   (Round off the answers, since they are approximate.)

– – – – –   – – – – –

e. $70 = 35t - 5t^2$ Substitute 70 for d.

$5t^2 - 35t + 70 = 0$ Make the right member equal zero.

$t^2 - 7t + 14 = 0$ Divide each member by 5.

$$t = \frac{7 \pm \sqrt{49 - 4(1)(14)}}{2(1)}$$ Use the Quadratic Formula.

$$t = \frac{7 \pm \sqrt{-7}}{2}$$ Arithmetic

Ball never reaches 70 m.   Answer the question. (Since $\sqrt{-7}$ is not a real number, there are *no* values of t at which the ball is 70 m high.)

– – – – –   – – – – –

f. $0 = 35t - 5t^2$ The ball is back on the ground when $d = 0$. So you substitute 0 for d.

$5t^2 - 35t = 0$ Subtract $35t$. Add $5t^2$.

$t^2 - 7t = 0$ Divide by 5.

$$t = \frac{7 \pm \sqrt{49 - 4(1)(0)}}{2(1)}$$ Use the Quadratic Formula.

$$t = \frac{7 \pm 7}{2}$$ Arithmetic; $\sqrt{49} = 7$

$$t = 7 \quad \text{or} \quad 0$$ Arithmetic

<u>After 7 seconds</u>   Answer the question. (The value 0 represents the time at which the ball was thrown.)

The Vertical Motion Formula is repeated below.

VERTICAL MOTION FORMULA

If an object is thrown into the air with an initial upward velocity of r meters per second then its distance, d meters, above its starting point at time t seconds after it was thrown is approximately

$$d = rt - 5t^2.$$

Problem Notes:

Problems 1–4 require the students to draw a diagram. The idea is to show the relative positions of the object in motion at various times and that there are two times at which the object reaches a given distance. In Section 14–5 students will learn that the diagram they are drawing is called a *parabola*. You can mention this term now, if you like.

ORAL PRACTICE

For Problems A through J, state an equation for distance above the starting point in terms of time if each object has the given initial upward velocity.

EXAMPLE

                    Answer
Spear, 30m/sec $d = 30t - 5t^2$

A.   Apple; 6 m/sec $d = 6t - 5t^2$ B.   Bullet, 700 m/sec $d = 700t - 5t^2$

C.   Cable; 3m/sec $d = 3t - 5t^2$ D.   Date, 7 m/sec $d = 7t - 5t^2$

E.   Eggplant; 2 m/sec $d = 2t - 5t^2$ F.   Flare, 100 m/sec $d = 100t - 5t^2$

G.   Gymnast; 13 m/sec $d = 13t - 5t^2$ H.   Horseshoe, 0.3 m/sec $d = 0.3t - 5t^2$

I.   Ice cube; 6.8 m/sec $d = 6.8 - 5t^2$ J.   Jumping bean, 0.04 m/sec $d = 0.04t - 5t^2$

EXERCISE 6-9

1. *Football Problem*   A football is kicked into the air with an initial up-
    ward velocity of 25 meters per second (m/sec).
    a.   Calculate its height after:
         i.   2 seconds;   30 m   ii.   3 seconds.   30 m
    b.   When will it be 20 meters above the ground?   At 1 sec and 4 sec
    c.   Copy the diagram. Show the answers to part (a) in relationship to
         the 20 meters of part (b).
    d.   When will the ball hit the ground?   After 5 sec

2. *Baton Problem*   A twirler throws a baton with an initial upward ve-
    locity of 20 meters per second (m/sec).
    a.   Calculate its height after 2 seconds.   20 m   At 1 sec
    b.   When will it be 15 meters above where it was thrown?   and at 3 sec
    c.   Copy the diagram. Show the answer to part (a) in relationship to
         the 15 meters of part (b).
    d.   When will the baton be back down at the twirler's level? After 4 sec

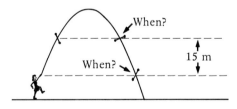

3. *Pop Fly Problem*   Milt Famey, the baseball player, hits a pop fly to
    the infield. It goes upward with an initial velocity of 30 m/sec.
    a.   What is its altitude after 2 seconds?   40 m
    b.   When is it 25 meters above where it was hit?   After 2 sec and
                                                        after 5 sec
    c.   When is it back down?   After 6 sec
    d.   The ball is at its highest halfway between the time it is hit
         ($t = 0$) and the time it gets back down. (See part (c).)
         i.   When is it at its highest?   3 sec
         ii. What is its highest distance?   45 m
    e.   Draw a diagram showing the positions of the ball in parts (a),
         (b), and (d).

4. *Cannonball Problem*   A cannonball is fired with an initial upward velocity of 100 m/sec.
   a.   Calculate its altitude after 3 seconds.   255 m
   b.   At what time(s) will it be 480 meters high?   After 8 sec and after 12 sec
   c.   When does it return to the ground?   After 20 sec
   d.   The cannonball reaches its highest point halfway between the time it was fired ($t = 0$) and the time it hits the ground.
       i.   When is it at its highest?   10 sec
       ii.   How high is it at its highest?   500 m
   e.   Draw a diagram showing the positions of the cannonball in parts (a), (b), and (d).

4. e.

Problems 5 on may have negative values of distance, meaning the object is *below* its starting point. It is important for your students to realize that negative numbers can have a very real meaning in the real world.

5. *Snoopy's Dogfight Problem*   Snoopy is flying in his Sopwith Camel. He fires at the Red Baron. The bullet has an initial upward velocity of 120 m/sec.
   a.   The Red Baron is 400 meters above Snoopy. When will the bullet first reach his altitude?   4 sec
   b.   The bullet misses on the way up. When could it hit the Red Baron on its way back down?   20 sec
   c.   If the bullet also misses the Red Baron on its way down, when will it be back at the level of Snoopy's Sopwith Camel?   24 sec
   d.   If it misses Snoopy on the way down, when will it hit the ground, 900 meters *below* where it was fired?   30 sec

6. *Rock off the Cliff Problem*   Suppose that you throw a rock into the air from the top of a cliff. The initial upward velocity is 15 m/sec.
   a.   How high will the rock be above the cliff top after 2 seconds?   10 m
   b.   Where will it be after 4 seconds? Think!   20 m *below* the top
   c.   When will it again be at the same level you threw it?   3 sec
   d.   When will it hit the water, 50 meters *below* where you threw it?   5 sec

7. *Clown's Cannon Problem*   At the circus, Art Tillery is fired into the air from a cannon on a platform. His initial upward velocity is 7 m/sec.
   a.   How high is he above the firing point after 0.6 sec? 2.4 m
   b.   When will he be 2 m above his firing point? After 0.4 sec and after 1 sec
   c.   When will he be back at the level of the cannon? After 1.4 sec
   d.   When will he land in the tank of water, 20 m *below* his firing point? After 2.82 sec

8. *Coyote and Roadrunner Problem*   Wile E. Coyote is standing on a springboard atop a high cliff. Roadrunner drops a boulder on the other end of the springboard, sending Wile up with an initial velocity of 45 m/sec.
   a.   How high will Wile be after 4 seconds?   100 m
   b.   At what *other* time will he be at the same altitude as in part (a)? After 5 sec
   c.   At 4 seconds, was Wile going *up* or *down?* Explain.   Going up. It was *later* at that altitude going down.
   d.   When does he again reach the level of the springboard? After 9 sec
   e.   On the way down, Wile misses the cliff! At what time does he land in the river, 120 meters *below* the top of the cliff? After 11.15 sec

9. *Chuck's Rock Problem*   Chuck throws a rock with an initial upward velocity of 12 m/sec.
   a.   How high is it after 0.7 sec?   5.95 m
   b.   When will it be 7.2 meters up? After 1.2 sec
   c.   At the time in part (b), is it going *up* or *down?* Explain.   9. c. Neither up nor down. It had reached its high point, since there was only *one* value of *t*.
   d.   When does the rock get back to ground level?   After 2.4 sec
   e.   On the way back down, the rock goes straight down a well, splashing at the bottom 4 seconds after it was thrown. How deep is the well?   32 m deep

10. *Ski Jump Problem*   As Al Pine jumps off the end of the ski jump, he has an initial upward velocity of 13 m/sec.
    a.   How high will he be 2 seconds after he jumps?   6 m
    b.   At what *other* time is he as high as in part (a)? After 0.6 sec

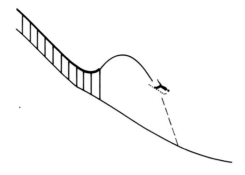

c.   At 2 seconds, was Al going *up* or going *down*?
     Explain.   Going down. *Earlier* he was at that height going up.
d.   When is he again at the level of the end of the ski
     jump?   After 2.6 sec
e.   Al spends a total of 5.2 seconds in the air. How far below the
     end of the ski jump does he land?   67.6 m below

11. *Basketball Problem*   A basketball player shoots a long shot. The
     ball has an initial upward velocity of 6 m/sec. When it is released,
     the ball is at the same level as the basket.
     a.   After 0.3 seconds, how high is the ball above the basket?   1.35 m
     b.   The basket is 3 meters above the gym floor. After 0.3 seconds,
          how high is the ball above the gym floor?   4.35 m
     c.   Assuming that the aim is good, when will the ball go in the bas-
          ket?   1.2 sec
     d.   The ball is at its highest halfway between the time it is thrown
          and the time it goes in the basket. What time is this? How high
          is the ball above the gym floor?   0.6 sec, 4.8 m

12. *Volleyball Problem*   In an underhanded volleyball serve, the ball leaves the server's hand 1 m above the floor. Suppose that its initial upward velocity is 7 m/sec.
   a.   How high above the *floor* will it be after 0.3 seconds?   2.65 m
   b.   If nobody else touches it, when will it be:
       i.   back to the level where it was served;   1.4 sec
       ii. down on the floor?   1.53 sec
   c.   The ball reaches its highest level halfway between the time it is served and the time it is back at the same level. What time is this? How high is it above the floor then?   0.7 sec, 3.45 m

13. *Golf Problem*   A golf ball is hit high into the air with an initial upward velocity of 33 m/sec.
   a.   How high is it after 3 seconds? 54 m
   b.   When will it be 29 meters above the ground?   5.56 sec or 1.04 sec
   c.   Substitute 60 for *d* and try to solve for *t*. What does this tell you about when the ball will be 60 m up?   Ball is *never* 60 m high!
   d.   Draw a diagram that illustrates your answer to part (c).

13. d.

Never reaches 60 m

14. *Naval Gunnery Problem*   Big guns on naval ships must fire projectiles many kilometers. To do this, the projectile must also go high into the air. Suppose that the initial upward velocity of a projectile is 300 m/sec.
   a.   How high will the projectile be 20 seconds after it is fired? 4000 m
   b.   When will it reach 1 kilometer above where it was fired?   56.46 sec or 3.54 sec
   c.   Will it ever be 5000 meters above where it was fired? Explain.   It never reaches 5000 m. Equation has no solution.
   d.   How long does it take to reach the target, which is at the same level as the projectile was fired?   60 sec

Target

15. *Moon Jumping Problem*   An astronaut on the earth practices jumping to the ground from a spaceship resting 3 meters above the ground. The initial upward velocity of the jump is 4 m/sec.
   a.   When will the astronaut be back at the same level as the jump?   0.8 sec
   b.   At what time is the highest point reached? How high above the ground is that?   0.4 sec., 3.8 m

Problems 15, 16, and 17 involve the vertical motion equation with a t^2-coefficient other than 5. Problems 15 and 16 apply on the moon, where weaker gravity makes the coefficient about -0.8. Problem 17 uses the more accurate value -4.893.

c.   When does the astronaut reach the ground?   1.27 sec

3 m

d.   When the astronaut is on the moon, gravity is much weaker. The equation there is

$$d = rt - 0.8t^2.$$

Suppose the initial velocity of the jump is still 4 m/sec.
   i.   When will the astronaut be back at the same level as the jump?   5 sec
   ii.   How high above the moon's surface does the astronaut go?   5 m
   iii.   When does the astronaut land on the moon's surface?   5.66 sec

16.   *Sports on the Moon Problem*   Since gravity is much weaker on the moon, an object thrown upward from its surface reaches an altitude *d* given by

$$d = rt - 0.8t^2.$$

a.   Find the time it takes for each of the following to return to the level from which they started.
   i.   A high jumper, $r = 7$ m/sec.   8.75 sec
   ii.   A baseball, $r = 30$ m/sec.   37.5 sec
   iii.   A golf ball, $r = 33$ m/sec.   41.25 sec
   iv.   An arrow, $r = 50$ m/sec.   62.5 sec
b.   Each of the above will be at its maximum altitude halfway between the time it starts and the time it gets back down. Find the maximum altitude for each object in part (a).   i.   15.31 m
ii.   281.25 m   iii.   340.31 m   iv.   781.25 m

17.   *Rhoda's Motorcycle Problem*   Rhoda Davidson prepares to jump her motorcycle from one ramp to another. Since precise calculations are essential to her safe landing, she uses the equation

$$d = rt - 4.893t^2,$$

in which 5 is replaced by the more precise value 4.893, which is the value at her latitude, 20 degrees.

Up ramp   Down ramp

a.   If she takes off with an upward initial velocity of
     $r = 13.7$ m/sec:
     i.   when will she land on the down ramp;   2.80 sec
     ii. what is the highest she goes above the *ground* (see
          figure)?   11.59 m
b.   If her time of flight is to be precisely 3.7 seconds:
     i.   what must her initial upward velocity be;   18.10 m/sec
     ii. what is the highest she goes above the ground?   18.75 m
c.   If her initial upward velocity is $r = 11$ m/sec, will she ever be 9
     meters above the ground (7 m above the top of the ramp)? Jus-
     tify your answer.   She'll *never* be 9 m off the ground. No times at which dist. is 9

18. *Diving Board Problem*   Suppose that you spring into the air from
     the 3-meter diving board. You hit the water, 3 meters *below* the
     board, at 1.6 seconds from the time you sprang.
     a.   What was your initial upward velocity, r?   6.125 m/sec
     b.   When do you pass the board on your way back down?   1.225 sec
     c.   How high above the board did you go?   1.88 m
     d.   If you spring from the 1-meter board with the same initial up-
          ward velocity as in part (a), when will you hit the water?   1.37 sec
     e.   If another diver *steps* off the 10-meter platform (initial velocity
          is $r = 0$) at the same time as you *spring* from the 3-meter
          board, as in part (a), who reaches the water sooner? How *much*
          sooner?   Other diver, 0.186 sec sooner

6-10 | THE DISCRIMINANT

Time: 2 days, or 0 days

If you solve the equation

$$x^2 + 7x - 3 = 0$$

using the Quadratic Formula, you get

$$x = \frac{-7 \pm \sqrt{49 - 4(1)(-3)}}{2(1)}$$

$$= \frac{-7 \pm \sqrt{61}}{2}$$

$$\approx 0.41 \quad \text{or} \quad -7.41.$$

Chalkboard Examples:

Day 1:
Evaluate the discriminant and describe the
solutions.
1. $5x^2 + 8x + 11 = 0$
    Ans.: $b^2 - 4ac = -156$
    No real solutions
2. $6x^2 - 10x + 2 = 0$
    Ans.: $b^2 - 4ac = 52$
    Real, irrational solutions
3. $15x^2 + 7x - 2 = 0$
    Ans.: $b^2 - 4ac = 169 = 13^2$
    Real, rational solutions

Day 2:

Fire Hose Problem—Water comes out of a fire hose with a velocity of 23 meters per second. If the hose is aimed straight up, will the water reach:

a. the fifth story, 25 meters up;
b. the sixth story, 30 meters up?

Justify your answers.

Solutions:

a. $25 = 23t - 5t^2$
   $5t^2 - 23t + 25 = 0$
   $b^2 - 4ac = 29 > 0$
   Water will reach the fifth story.
b. $30 = 23t - 5t^2$
   $5t^2 - 23t + 30 = 0$
   $b^2 - 4ac = -71 < 0$
   Water will not reach the sixth story.

Assignments:

Day 1: Exercise 6–10, #1–19 odd or 2–20 even;
       Exercise 6–9, one previously unassigned problem for review
Day 2: Exercise 6–10, #21–39 odd or 22–40 even

However, solving the equation

$$2x^2 - 3x + 7 = 0$$

gives

$$x = \frac{3 \pm \sqrt{9 - 4(2)(7)}}{2(2)}$$

$$= \frac{3 \pm \sqrt{-47}}{4}.$$

There are *no* real solutions, because $\sqrt{-47}$ is *not* a real number.

The expression $b^2 - 4ac$ under the radical sign in the Quadratic Formula is called the *discriminant*. By looking at the value of this expression, you can discriminate between quadratic equations that *have* solutions and those that *do not*. You can also tell whether real solutions will be *rational* numbers or *irrational* numbers.

DEFINITION

> **DISCRIMINANT**
> The expression $b^2 - 4ac$, which appears in
> $$x = \frac{-b \pm \sqrt{b^2 - 4ac}}{2a},$$
> is called the **discriminant.**

Objective :
Given a quadratic equation, use the discriminant to tell whether or not the equation has real solutions and, if so, whether they are rational numbers or irrational numbers.

Cover the answers as you work this example.

EXAMPLE

For each equation, evaluate the discriminant and use it to tell what kind of solutions the equation has.

a. $3x^2 + 5x + 7 = 0$

- - - - -   - - - - -

Think These Reasons

$\quad b^2 - 4ac$ Write the discriminant.

$= 25 - 4(3)(7)$ Substitute for a, b, and c.

$= \underline{-59}$ Do the arithmetic.

<u>No real solutions</u> $\sqrt{-59}$ is not a real number because -59 is *negative*.

Note: the radical sign is *not* part of the discriminant!

b. $5x^2 + 3x - 2 = 0$

- - - - -   - - - - -

$\quad b^2 - 4ac$ Write the discriminant.

$= 9 - 4(5)(-2)$ Substitute for a, b, and c ($c = -2$).

$= \underline{49}$ Do the arithmetic.

<u>Real solutions,</u> $\sqrt{49}$ is a real number because 49 is *positive*.

<u>Rational numbers</u> $\sqrt{49}$ is a rational number because 49 is a *perfect square*.

c. $x^2 - 6x + 3 = 0$

- - - - -   - - - - -

$\quad b^2 - 4ac$ Write the discriminant.

$= 36 - 4(1)(3)$ Substitute for a, b, and c ($a = 1$).

$= \underline{\underline{24}}$ Do the arithmetic.

<u>Real solutions,</u> $\sqrt{24}$ is a real number because 24 is *positive*.

<u>Irrational numbers</u> $\sqrt{24}$ is an irrational number because 24 is *not* a perfect square.

From the above examples, you can see that the nature of the solutions of a quadratic equation can be found from the value of the discriminant. A positive discriminant means there *are* solutions. A negative discriminant means there are *no* solutions. A perfect square discriminant means the solutions are *rational* numbers.

CONCLUSION

SOLUTIONS OF A QUADRATIC EQUATION
1. If $b^2 - 4ac$ is *negative,* such as -25, there are no real solutions, because $\sqrt{-25}$ is *not* a real number.
2. If $b^2 - 4ac$ is *positive* or *zero,* such as 29, 81, or 0, there are real solutions, because $\sqrt{29}$, $\sqrt{81}$, and $\sqrt{0}$ are real numbers.
3. If $b^2 - 4ac$ is a *perfect square,* such as 49, the solutions are *rational* numbers, because $\sqrt{49}$ is 7, a rational number.

ORAL PRACTICE

Assume that the following numbers are discriminants of quadratic equations. Tell whether or not the equation has real solutions. If so, tell whether those solutions are rational numbers or irrational numbers.

EXAMPLES

Answers
i. 23   i. Real solutions, irrational numbers
ii. 36   ii. Real solutions, rational numbers
iii. -9 iii. No real solutions

A. 37 Real sol., irr. nos   B. 49 Real sol., rat. nos

C. 100 Real sol., rat. nos   D. -25 No real sol.

E. 56 Real sol., irr. nos   F. -10 No real sol.

G. 81 Real sol., rat. nos   H. 12 Real sol., irr. nos

I. -16 No real sol.   J. -3 No real sol.

K. 1 Real sol., rat. nos   L. 0 Real sol., rat. nos (just *one* distinct sol.)

Problem Notes:

Problems 1–20 involve straightforward substitution into and interpretation of the discriminant.

Problems 21–34 require preliminary transformations before a, b, and c can be determined reliably.

Problems 35–40 are yes-or-no questions that can be answered by first finding the discriminant.

EXERCISE 6-10

For Problems 1 through 20, evaluate and write the discriminant. Then use the answer to tell whether or not the equation has real solutions, and, if so, whether they are rational numbers or irrational numbers.

1. $3x^2 + 10x + 2 = 0$ D = 76 Irrat.   2. $5x^2 + 10x + 2 = 0$ D = 60 Irrat.

3. $7x^2 + 8x + 5 = 0$ 4. $2x^2 + 6x - 5 = 0$

5. $5x^2 + 6x - 7 = 0$ 6. $2x^2 + 6x + 5 = 0$

7. $6x^2 - 5x - 21 = 0$ 8. $9x^2 - 42x + 49 = 0$

9. $4x^2 + 20x + 25 = 0$ 10. $9x^2 - 85x + 49 = 0$

11. $x^2 + 3x - 5 = 0$ 12. $x^2 + 5x - 14 = 0$

13. $3x^2 - x + 2 = 0$ 14. $x^2 + 5x + 14 = 0$

15. $x^2 - x - 6 = 0$ 16. $x^2 - x - 30 = 0$

17. $x^2 + x + 1 = 0$ 18. $x^2 + x - 3 = 0$

19. $x^2 + x - 1 = 0$ 20. $x^2 + x + 3 = 0$

3. D $= -76$ None   4. D $= 76$ Irrat.
5. D $= 176$ Irrat.   6. D $= -4$ None
7. D $= 529 = 23^2$ Rat. 8. D $= 0 = 0^2$ Rat.
9. D $= 0 = 0^2$ Rat.   10. D $= 5461$ Irrat.
11. D $= 29$ Irrat.
12. D $= 81 = 9^2$ Rat.
13. D $= -23$ None   14. D $= -31$ None
15. D $= 25 = 5^2$ Rat.
16. D $= 121 = 11^2$ Rat.
17. D $= -3$ None   18. D $= 13$ Irrat.
19. D $= 5$ Irrat.   20. D $= -11$ None
21. D $= 109$ Irrat.
22. D $= 361 = 19^2$ Rat.
23. D $= 49 = 7^2$ Rat.   24. D $= 57$ Irrat.
25. D $= 289 = 17^2$ Rat. 26. D $= -311$ None
27. D $= -31$ None
28. D $= 529 = 23^2$ Rat.
29. D $= 8.97$ Irrat.
30. D $= 57.76 = 7.6^2$ Rat.
31. D $= 2.39^2$ Rat.
32. D $= -5.76$ None
33. D $= 0$ Rat.   34. D $= 1.65$ Rat.

For Problems 21 through 34, first transform the equation to the form $ax^2 + bx + c = 0$, making the right member equal zero. Then use the discriminant to tell the nature of the solutions, as in Problems 1 through 20.

21. $3x^2 + 11x + 6 = 5$ 22. $10x^2 + 11x + 4 = 10$

23. $x^2 - 5x - 10 = -2x$ 24. $x^2 - 2x - 8 = 3x$

25. $13x + 6x^2 - 5 = 0$ 26. $5x + 12x^2 + 7 = 0$

27. $2x^2 - 6x = x - 10$ 28. $12x^2 - 20x = 5 - 3x$

29. $0.6x^2 + 2.1x = 1.9$ 30. $0.6x^2 + 6.4x = 7$

31. $2.86 + 1.51x = 0.3x^2$ 32. $1 = 0.8x - 1.6x^2$

33. $x^2 = 1.8x - 0.81$ 34. $0.7x^2 = -1.3 + 2.3x$

For Problems 35 through 40, recall that when an object is thrown into the air, its vertical distance, d, above where it was thrown is given by

$$d = rt - 5t^2,$$

where d is in meters, r is the initial upward velocity in meters per second, and t is the time in seconds since it was thrown. To find out whether d ever equals a certain given value, substitute that value for d. Transform the equation so that the right member is zero. Then use the discriminant to find out whether or not there are any real values of t satisfying the equation.

35. *Antiaircraft Problem*   A target plane flies at 2100 meters. An anti-aircraft gun fires a projectile with an initial upward velocity of 200 m/sec. Will the projectile ever reach the altitude of the target plane? Justify your answer.   D $= -2000$ Never reaches!

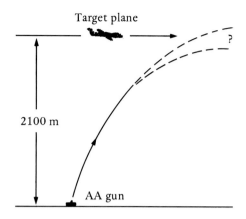

36. *Flea Jump Problem*   A flea on the floor wishes to jump up on a dog's back, 0.9 meters above. The flea can jump with an initial velocity of 4.3 meters per second. Can the flea jump as high as the dog's back? Justify your answer. $D = 0.7^2$ *Makes* it!

37. *Basketball Dunking Problem*   In order to dunk a basketball, Jim Shortz must jump 1.2 meters above the floor. He can jump up with an initial velocity of 5.1 m/sec. Can Jim dunk the ball? Justify your answer. $D = 2.01$ *Can* dunk!

38. *Ball over the House Problem*   Sally Forth and Stan Back stand on opposite sides of a house. They plan to throw a ball back and forth over the house. Stan can throw the ball with an initial upward velocity of 16 m/sec, and Sally can throw it with an initial upward velocity of 15 m/sec. The house is 10 meters high. Will they be able to play the game? Justify your answer. $D = 56$ (Stan); $D = 25$ (Sally) They *can* both get it over.

39. *Escape by Knight Problem*   Sir Mount is trapped in Dracula's castle. To escape, he must jump up 1.7 meters so that his hands will reach the top of the wall. Sir Mount is a good athlete and can jump with an initial upward velocity of 5.8 m/sec. Will he be able to reach the top of the wall? Justify your answer. $D = -0.36$ *Can't* make it!

40.   *Rescue Problem*   A rescue party approaches a mountain climber stranded on a ledge 15 meters above. The rescuers can throw a rope upward with an initial velocity of 16 m/sec. Will they be able to reach the stranded climber with the rope? Justify your answer.

D = −44 Can't reach

6-11 | CHAPTER REVIEW AND TEST

This chapter ties together almost everything you have learned in algebra so far. In order to solve quadratic equations, you had to complete the square, factor trinomial squares, find square roots, solve absolute value equations, and write solution sets. You learned that quadratic expressions such as $13t - 5t^2$ can represent things in the real world such as distance above the ground. You evaluated such expressions for given values of t and solved for t if you knew the value of the expression.

To get the most benefit from the Chapter Test, you should put yourself under pressure and try to finish as much as possible in the time of a normal classroom test.

CHAPTER TEST

1.   What is the difference in each case?
  a. $\sqrt{-36}$ and $|-36|$
  b.   Radical and radicand
  c.   Quadratic equation and Quadratic Formula
  d.   When $d = rt$ applies and when $d = rt - 5t^2$ applies
  e.   Quadratic equation with a positive discriminant and one with a negative discriminant

2.   Write each of the following.
  a.   The Quadratic Formula
  b.   A radical that is a rational number
  c.   What $\sqrt{n^2}$ equals
  d.   The coefficient in the expression x^2
  e.   The number to add to $x^2 + 7x$ to complete the square   12.25

3.   Evaluate the following radicals by calculator. Tell whether each represents a *rational* number, an *irrational* number, or *neither*.
  a. $\sqrt{85}$ $\sqrt{85} = 9.22$ Irrational
  b. $-\sqrt{15,129}$ $-\sqrt{15,129} = -123$ Rational
  c. $\sqrt{-1369}$ Not a real number
  d. $\sqrt{817.96}$ $\sqrt{817.96} = 28.6$ Rational

Time: 1 day

Test Ideas:

This chapter summarizes most of what the students have learned so far in Algebra I. If you have assigned distributed practice problems on absolute value equations and completing the square as you have gone along, the students should be well prepared for the test. If this is the end of a grading period, you can combine this test with the cumulative exam of the next section.

Assignment:

Following the test, assign selected problems from the Cumulative Review, Section 6–12.

Problem Notes:

Problem 1c asks students to distinguish between "quadratic equation" and "Quadratic Formula." Often they slip into the bad habit of saying, "I used the quadratic equation" when what they really mean is that they used the Quadratic Formula.

In Problem 4, make sure students know they are to solve the equations *without* using the Quadratic Formula.

1.   a. $\sqrt{-36}$ is not a real number.
  $|-36|$ equals 36.
  b. A radical is an expression such as $\sqrt{6}$. A radicand is the number under the radical sign, such as 6 in $\sqrt{6}$.
  c. $ax^2 + bx + c = 0$ is a quadratic equation.
  $x = \dfrac{-b \pm \sqrt{b^2 - 4ac}}{2a}$ is the Quadratic Formula.
  d. $d = rt$ applies when the rate is *constant*.
  $d = rt - 5t^2$ applies for objects in *vertical* motion (rate varies).
  e. If the discriminant is positive, the equation has solutions.
  If the discriminant is negative, the equation does *not* have solutions.

2. a. If $ax^2 + bx + c = 0$, then
$x = \dfrac{-b \pm \sqrt{b^2 - 4ac}}{2a}$.

b. e.g., $\sqrt{9}$, which equals 3, is a rational number.

c. $\sqrt{n^2} = |n|$

d. x^2 has 1 for its coefficient.

4. f. $S = \emptyset$ (Absolute values cannot equal negative numbers.)

7. a. $S = \{1.84, -23.34\}$
b. $S = \{0.45, 0\}$
c. $S = \{6.05, -0.39\}$
d. $S = \{-5\}$

9. d.

20 m
13.2 m
10 m

4. Solve *without* using the Quadratic Formula.
   a. $(x + 6)^2 = 81$ $S = \{3, -15\}$ b. $(0.3x - 2.7)^2 = 17.8$ $S = \{23.06, -5.06\}$
   c. $x^2 + 10x + 25 = 9$ $S = \{-2, -8\}$ d. $x^2 - 4x + 4 = -9$ $S = \emptyset$
   e. $|5x - 7| = 49$ $S = \{11.2, -8.4\}$ f. $|3x + 2| = -25$ $S = \emptyset$

5. What number can be added to complete the square?
   a. $x^2 + 12x$ 36   b. $x^2 - 5x$ 6.25   c. $x^2 + 2.6x$ 1.69

6. For the equation $5x^2 + 7x - 3 = 0$
   a. Solve using the Quadratic Formula. $S = \{0.34, -1.74\}$
   b. Solve by first dividing each member by 5 and then completing the square. $S = \{0.34, -1.74\}$
   c. Show that both solution sets are the same.   They're the *same!*

7. Solve.
   a. $0.2x^2 + 4.3x - 8.6 = 0$ b. $11x^2 - 5x = 0$
   c. $(3x - 2)(x - 5) = 17$ d. $(x + 6)^2 - 5x = x^2 + 1$

8. Find the discriminant. Use it to tell whether or not the equation has real-number solutions and, if so, whether they are rational or irrational numbers.
   a. $5x^2 - 3x - 7 = 0$ 149 Irr.   b. $x^2 + 6x + 10 = 0$ -4 None
   c. $3x^2 + 10x - 8 = 0$ 196 Rat.

9. *Soccer Problem*   A soccer player kicks the ball, giving it an initial upward velocity of 17 meters per second.
   a. How high will it be after 1.2 seconds?   13.2 m
   b. When will it be 10 meters above the ground?   2.64 sec, 0.76 sec
   c. Use the discriminant to show that it will *never* be 20 m high.   D = -111 Never that high
   d. Draw a sketch showing the results of parts (a), (b), and (c).

Time: 1 to 4 days, including exam

6-12 | CUMULATIVE REVIEW, CHAPTERS 1 THROUGH 6

In the first part of this book you learned to evaluate expressions and to solve equations. Along the way you learned such words as *commute, associate,* and *distribute,* which describe ways you can transform an expression without actually evaluating it. You also learned some things that can be done to each member of an equation, such as adding the same number or reversing the two members. Some of these properties are called *axioms.* Others can be proved using the axioms. You should know the names listed below and what they mean.

**AXIOMS FOR ADDITION AND MULTIPLICATION
OF REAL NUMBERS**

1. Commutative axiom for addition
2. Commutative axiom for multiplication
3. Associative axiom for addition
4. Associative axiom for multiplication
5. Distributive axiom for multiplication over addition
6. Closure under addition
7. Closure under multiplication
8. Additive identity
9. Multiplicative identity
10. Additive inverses
11. Multiplicative inverses

The axioms for equality are as follows:

AXIOMS OF EQUALITY

1. Transitive axiom
2. Symmetric axiom
3. Reflexive axiom

Some properties that can be proved from the axioms are as follows:

MULTIPLICATION PROPERTY OF −1
For any real number x, $-1 \cdot x = -x$.

MULTIPLICATION PROPERTY OF 0
For any real number x, $0 \cdot x = 0$.

OTHER DISTRIBUTIVE PROPERTIES
(See Section 3-3.)

ADDITION PROPERTY OF EQUALITY
For real numbers x, y, and z, if $x = y$, then $x + z = y + z$. (That is, you can add the same number to each member of an equation.)

MULTIPLICATION PROPERTY OF EQUALITY
For real numbers x, y, and z, if $x = y$, then $xz = yz$. (That is, you can multiply each member of an equation by the same number.)

These axioms and properties can be used to accomplish the three major things done in algebra.

THREE MAJOR THINGS DONE IN ALGEBRA

- Write an expression representing something in the real world.
- Find the value of the expression when you know what x equals.
- Find the value of x when you know what the expression equals.

As you review, you should make a list of words you have learned, such as

> commute
> equation
> solve
> linear
> evaluate
> factor
> .
> .
> .

For each item on your list you should try to tell which of the three major things applies. For instance, "combining like terms" makes expressions easier to *evaluate* and makes equations easier to *solve*.

After you have done the reviewing, try working the following exercise. This should be roughly equivalent to a 2-hour semester exam. You may want to try working on it several days before your own semester exam so that you will have time to learn things you have forgotten.

EXERCISE 6-12

1. Name the three major things one does in algebra.

2. Write a definition of each of the following.
   a. Variable
   b. Power
   c. Rational number
   d. Subtraction
   e. Commute
   f. Axiom
   g. Negative number
   h. Integer
   i. Quadratic
   j. Discriminant

---

*Answer column (left margin):*

1. a. Write an expression representing something in the real world.
   b. Find the value of the expression when you know what x equals.
   c. Find the value of x when you know what the expression equals.
2. a. A variable is a letter that represents a number.
   b. A power is a number such as 2^3 that has a base and an exponent.
   c. A number that can be written as a ratio of two integers
   d. Subtracting a number means adding its opposite, $x - y = x + (-y)$.
   e. To switch positions
   f. A property that is assumed to be true without proof
   g. A number that is less than zero
   h. A positive, negative, zero "whole" number, ... $-3, -2, -1, 0, 1, 2, 3, \ldots$
   i. Second degree
   j. $b^2 - 4ac$ if $ax^2 + bx + c = 0$

3. What is the difference in each case?
   a. Equation and expression   b. Real number and integer
   c. Term and factor   d. Trinomial and cubic expression
   e. Coefficient and exponent

4. Write a statement of the following properties or axioms.
   a. Multiplication property of -1
   b. Distributive axiom
   c. Associative axiom for multiplication
   d. Closure axiom for addition
   e. Additive identity axiom
   f. Multiplicative inverse axiom
   g. Addition property of equality
   h. Multiplication property of zero
   i. Reflexive axiom of equality
   j. Square root property of equality

5. Tell what axiom was used.
   a. $x + (y + z) = (x + y) + z$ b. $x(y + z) = xy + xz$
   c. $x(y + z) = x(z + y)$ d. If $6 = x$, then $x = 6$.
   e. If $6 = x$ and $x = y$, then $6 = y$.

6. Evaluate the following *constant* expressions:
   a. $4 + 2 \cdot 3 + 5$ $_{15}$ b. $(4 + 2) \cdot 3 + 5$ $_{23}$
   c. $4 + 2 \cdot (3 + 5)$ $_{20}$ d. $3 \cdot 2^5$ $_{96}$
   e. -3^4 $_{-81}$ f. $47 - 7(30 \div 5 \times 2)$ $_{-37}$

7. Write an expression representing each.
   a. The seventh power of x x^7 b. Seven times x $7x$
   c. Seven more than x $x + 7$ d. The sum of seven x's $7x$
   e. Seven less than twice x $2x - 7$
   f. The sum of the squares of seven and x $7^2 + x^2$
   g. The square of the sum of seven and x $(7 + x)^2$
   h. 128 as a power with 2 as its base 2^7
   i. A seventh-degree trinomial $x^7 + x + 1$, e.g.
   j. The length marked "?" $7 - x - y$ or $7 - (x + y)$

8. Transform the expression as indicated.
   a. Distribute: $4x(x^2 - 3x + 5)$ b. Multiply: $(3a - 2b)(a + 4b)$
   c. Multiply: $(4x + 7)(4x - 7)$ d. Square: $(x - 3.5)^2$
   e. Factor: $x^2 - 13x + 12$ f. Factor: $v^2 - 5v - 24$
   g. Factor: $x^2 + 10x + 25$ h. Factor: $b^2 - 1$
   i. Factor: $2x^2 - 9x - 5$
   j. Simplify: $3(x^2 - 2x - 1) - 4(x^2 - 3x + 2)$

3. a. An *equation* says that two expressions are equal.
   An *expression* just stands for a number.
   b. A *real number* is any number on the number line.
   An *integer* is just one of . . . -3, -2, -1, 0, 1, 2, 3, ...
   c. *Terms* are numbers that are added or subtracted.
   Factors are numbers that are multiplied.
   d. A *trinomial* has three terms.
   A *cubic* expression is third degree.
   e. *Coefficient* $\rightarrow 5x^3 \curvearrowleft$ *Exponent*.

4. a. For any real number x, $-1x = -x$.
   b. For any real numbers x, y, and z, $x(y + z) = xy + xz$.
   c. For any real numbers x, y, and z, $(xy)z = x(yz)$.
   d. For any real numbers x and y, $x + y$ is a unique real number.
   e. For any real number x, $x + 0 = x$.
   f. For any real number $x \neq 0$, there is a real number $\frac{1}{x}$ for which $x \cdot \left(\frac{1}{x}\right) = 1$.
   g. For real nos. x, y, and z, if $x = y$, then $x + z = y + z$.
   h. For any real number x, $x \cdot 0 = 0$.
   i. For any real number x, $x = x$.
   j. For any nonnegative numbers x and y, if $x = y$, then $\sqrt{x} = \sqrt{y}$.

5. a. Associative axiom for addition
   b. Distributive axiom for multiplication over addition
   c. Commutative axiom for addition
   d. Symmetric axiom of equality
   e. Transitive axiom for equality

8. a. $4x^3 - 12x^2 + 20x$
   b. $3a^2 + 10ab - 8b^2$
   c. $16x^2 - 49$
   d. $x^2 - 7x + 12.25$
   e. $(x - 1)(x - 12)$
   f. $(v + 3)(v - 8)$
   g. $(x + 5)^2$
   h. $(b + 1)(b - 1)$
   i. $(2x + 1)(x - 5)$
   j. $-x^2 + 6x - 11$

k. Simplify: $\dfrac{9x^2 - 15x + 21}{3}$ $3x^2 - 5x + 7$

l. Complete the square: $x^2 - 5x + \cdots$.   6.25

Problem Notes:

Problems 9–12 get at the heart of this course; namely, evaluating expressions and solving equations. The same type of thing is done in each problem. Only the kind of expression differs from problem to problem.

9. For the *linear* expression $3x + 17$:
   a. tell what the name *linear* means;   First degree
   b. evaluate the expression if x is -9; -10
   c. find x if the expression is equal to 52; $11\frac{2}{3}$
   d. find x if the expression is equal to $8x - 12$.   5.8

10. For the *absolute value* expression $|9 - 5x|$:
    a. evaluate it if x is 7;   26   b. evaluate it if x is 1;   4
    c. find x if the expression is equal to 31; $x = -4.4$ or $x = 8$
    d. find x if the expression is equal to -4.   No value

11. For the *quadratic* expression $5x^2 - 7x + 12$:
    a. evaluate it if x is -3;   78
    b. find x if the expression is equal to 18;   2 or -0.6
    c. find x if the expression is equal to 3;   No value of x
    d. find the discriminant of the original expression. -191

12. You have seen a few *radical* expressions. In this problem you will apply what you know to a new situation. For the expression $\sqrt{4x - 13}$:
    a. evaluate it if x is 8;   4.36   b. evaluate it if x is 2;   No value
    c. find x if the expression is 5. You can do this by setting the expression equal to 5, then solving the resulting equation by *squaring* each member.   9.5

In Problem 13 the earlier equations are intermediate steps in solving the last equation.

13. For parts (a) through (d), solve the equation *without* using the Quadratic Formula.
    a. $|x - 7| = 5$ $S = \{12, 2\}$ b. $(x - 7)^2 = 25$ $S = \{12, 2\}$
    c. $x^2 - 14x + 49 = 25$ $S = \{12, 2\}$ d. $x^2 - 14x + 24 = 0$ $S = \{12, 2\}$
    e. Explain how parts (a), (b), and (c) relate to part (d).

13. e. Each is a step in the following part.

14. *Age Problem*   Sarah Sota is 4 years older than her sister Minnie. Let x be Minnie's age.
    a. Write an expression for Sarah's age. $x + 4$
    b. How old is Sarah when Minnie is 17? Which of the three techniques of algebra is used here?   21 Evaluate.
    c. How old is Minnie when Sarah is 50? Which of the three techniques of algebra is used here?   46 Solve.
    d. How old are they when the sum of the squares of their ages is 208?   Minnie is 8, Sarah is 12.

15. *Eggs Problem*   A restaurant lets customers order any number of eggs for breakfast. They charge 65 cents per egg plus a one-time charge of 85 cents for cooking, service, and so on.
    a. Define a variable for the number of eggs ordered, and write an expression for the number of cents a customer must pay for this number of eggs. $x =$ no. of eggs. $65x + 85 =$ no of cents.

b.   How much must one pay for a dozen eggs? $8.65

c.   Juanita Lott has $5.40. How many eggs could she order for this amount?   7 eggs

16.   *Cross-Country Runners Problem*   Art and Bob are cross-country runners. Art starts running at 200 meters per minute. Three minutes later, Bob starts from the same point, going in the same direction at 215 meters per minute.

a.   Draw a diagram showing the starting point, Art, and Bob, with Art farther from the start than Bob.

b.   How far has Art gone in x minutes? Write this expression on your diagram from part (a).   200x

c.   How far has Bob gone when Art has been running for x minutes? Write this expression on your diagram from part (a).   215(x − 3)

d.   If they keep running at the same rates, will Bob have overtaken Art before x is 30? Justify your answer.

16a.
b.
c.

16.   **d.** No. At x = 30, Art is 6000 m from start. Bob is only 5805 m. or: Bob takes 43 sec. to catch up with Art.

17.   *Shotput Problem*   Ann Athlete throws the shot with an initial upward velocity of 7 meters per second.

a.   How high is it above where she threw it after 0.4 second?   2 m

b.   When will it hit the ground, 1.3 meters *below* where she threw it?   After 1.57 sec

18.   *Semester Average Problem*   Nita B. Topaz has an average of 75 for the semester so far, before her semester exam. She learns that her final grade will be 80% of this average, plus 20% of the semester exam grade. ("80% of . . ." means "0.8 times . . . .")

a.   Define a variable for Nita's exam grade. Then write an expression for her final grade. x = exam grade. 60 + 0.2x

b.   If Nita makes 90 on her exam, what will be her final grade?   78

c.   What does Nita need to make on the exam to have a final grade of 80?   She must make 100.

d.   If passing is 60 or above, could Nita possibly have a failing final grade? Explain.   She could *not* fail. Zero on exam gives 60 average.

Problem 18 is of great interest to students around exam time. You can vary the numbers to suit your school's grading system with regard to weight given the exam.

7

Evaluating Expressions by Computer

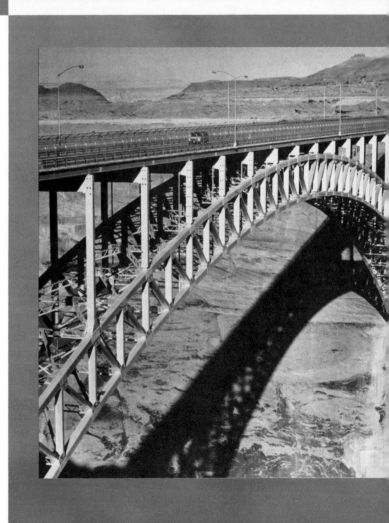

So far you have used two things to do computations, a calculator and your brain. The calculator is appropriate for difficult computations like taking square roots and doing hard division problems. The brain is quicker for easy computations like "3 times 7," or for problems that require only approximate answers. In this chapter you will learn a third way to do computations. The computer is appropriate when the same sequence of steps is to be done many *times, using different values of the variable. For instance, it can be used to find the length of each vertical column for a new bridge so that designers will know exactly how long to make them.*

Variable:

x Number of feet from end of bridge

Expression:

$0.000544x^2 - 0.571x + 161$

Length of vertical column that is x feet from end of bridge

7-1 | INTRODUCTION TO BASIC COMPUTER LANGUAGE

Computers can do only what they have been instructed to do. The instructions must be in a language that the computer understands. Once you learn this language, *you* can tell the computer what to do! In this section you will learn something about a computer language called BASIC. The following is called a *program* in BASIC:

```
10    LET X = 4
20    LET Y = 3 * X + 8
30    PRINT X, Y
40    LET X = X + 1
50    IF X = 7 THEN 70
60    GO TO 20
70    END
```

A **program** is a set of instructions for the computer to do. Each line has a number to the left. Unless it is told otherwise, the computer does each instruction in order, according to line number: 10, then 20, then 30, and so forth. Line 60 says GO TO 20. The computer goes *back* to line 20 and starts from there; 20, then 30, then 40, and so forth.

This program has two variables, X and Y. To see what the program does you should make a *list* of variables, as shown at the left. Leave plenty of space to record values of the variables.

X	
Y	

The first instruction says LET X = 4. So you record 4 for X in the list of variables, as shown.

X	4
Y	

The next instruction says LET Y = 3 * X + 8. The asterisk, *, is a *times* sign. It is used by the computer instead of · or ×, because these could be confused with decimal points or variables. The computer looks at the list,

Time: 1 day

Chalkboard Examples:

You may present the program at the beginning of the section and explain what it does, as in the text. Or you may take the opposite approach and pose a problem such as the following.

Write a computer program to evaluate the expression $21 - 4x$ for each integer value of x, starting at $x = 3$ and ending at $x = 6$.

Start by explaining how LET Y = $21 - 4 * X$ instructs the computer to evaluate the expression and store the answer as the value of Y. Then show how to start X at 3, increase it by 1, loop back to the LET statement, and print the answers. The program would be as follows.

10 LET X = 3		Memory:		
20 LET Y = $21 - 4 * X$	X	3 4 5 6		
30 PRINT X, Y	Y	9 5 1 −3		
40 IF X = 6 THEN 70	Output:			
50 LET X = X + 1	3	9		
60 GO TO 20	4	5		
70 END	5	1		
	6	−3		

After presentation, have students put the program on the computer(s) and verify that the output is as expected. Have them change line 40 to IF X = 20 THEN 70, so that the computer prints out many values.

Assignment:

Exercise 7–1, #1, 3, and 5 or 2, 4, and 6

finds that X is 4, multiplies 4 by 3, and adds 8. The result is 20. So you should record this for Y in the list of variables.

X	4
Y	20

The next instruction, PRINT X, Y, tells the computer to print the values of X and Y either on the screen or on paper. Since the computer keeps the list of variables inside its own memory, you must tell it to *print* whenever you want to know the values of the variables. Write the word *output* under the list of variables, and write 4 and 20 along this line.

X	4
Y	20

Output: 4   20

The instruction LET X = X + 1 tells the computer to take the present value of X (4), add 1 to it (getting 5), and record this as the *new* value of X. So you cross out the 4 in the variables list and put in 5.

X	~~4~~ 5
Y	20

Output: 4   20

The instruction IF X = 7 THEN 70 tells the computer to skip to line 70 if X equals 7. Since X is now 5, the computer does *not* skip. It simply goes on to the next instruction, 60, and does what that says to do.

The instruction GO TO 20 tells the computer to go *back* to line number 20 and start doing instructions from there. The computer will *repeat* lines 20, 30, and so on. When the computer again reaches line 50, the output and list of variables will be as shown.

X	~~4~~ ~~5~~ 6
Y	~~20~~ 23

Output: 4   20
          5   23

When the computer finally reaches line 50 with X equal to 7, it jumps to line 70, which contains the instruction END. The final variables list and output will look like this.

X	~~4~~ ~~5~~ ~~6~~ 7
Y	~~20~~ ~~23~~ 26

Output: 4   20
          5   23
          6   26

The process of reading a program step by step and doing what it says is called **tracing** the program. In this section you will learn how to trace BASIC programs.

Objective:

Be able to trace a BASIC program as the computer would, write the list of variables that would be in the computer's memory, write the output that the computer would print, and check your work by running the program on a computer.

In the following example, put a piece of paper so that only line 10 of the program is showing. Write a list of variables and a place for the output, as shown before. Then do what it says on lines 10, 20, 30, and so on, uncovering one line at a time. When you reach the END instruction, uncover the answer below the dotted lines. Be sure that both your variables list and output are exactly like those in the answer.

EXAMPLE

```
10    LET N = 2
20    LET A = 3 + 5 * N
30    PRINT N, A
40    IF N = 4 THEN 70
50    LET N = N + 1
60    GO TO 20
70    END
```

N	2̶ 3̶ 4
A	1̶3̶ 1̶8̶ 23

Output: 2   13
3   18
4   23

ORAL PRACTICE

Give the value of the BASIC expression.

EXAMPLES

		Answers	
i.	3 * 5	i.	15
ii.	5 - 2 * 3	ii.	- 1

A. 7 * 5   35   B. 9 * 8   72   C. 7 * 6 + 4   46

D. 5 * 2 + 6   16   E. 7 + 2 * 3   13   F. 6 + 4 * 5   26

G. 10 - 4 * 2   2   H. 13 - 4 * 2   5   I. 6 - 4 * 5   −14

J. 18 - 3 * 6   0

Tell what happens when the computer does the following. Assume that the memory is as shown at the left in each case.

X	7
Y	2

EXAMPLES

		Answers	
i.	LET X = 5	i.	Changes X from 7 to 5.
ii.	LET X = -2	ii.	Changes X from 7 to −2.
iii.	PRINT X	iii.	Prints 7 (the value of X).
iv.	GO TO 30	iv.	Does line 30 next.
v.	IF X = 7 THEN 100	v.	Goes to line 100 next, because X *does* equal 7.

K.   Changes Y from 2 to 3.
L.   Changes X from 7 to 10.
M.   Changes Y from 2 to 21.
N.   Changes Y from 2 to 11.
O.   Changes X from 7 to 10.
P.   Changes Y from 2 to 16.
Q.   Changes X from 7 to 16.
R.   Changes X from 7 to 8.
S.   Changes Y from 2 to 4.
T.   Does line 70 next.
U.   Does line 90 next.
V.   Does *not* go to line 100.
W.   Prints 7 2.
X.   Stops running the program.

K.	LET Y = 3	L.	LET X = 10
M.	LET Y = 3 * X	N.	LET Y = 4 + X
O.	LET X = 5 * Y	P.	LET Y = 30 - 2 * X
Q.	LET X = 6 + 5 * Y	R.	LET X = X + 1
S.	LET Y = Y + 2	T.	GO TO 70
U.	IF X = 7 THEN 90	V.	IF X = 8 THEN 100
W.	PRINT X , Y	X.	END

EXERCISE 7-1

Problem Notes:

The most important thing to insure is that students trace the program a line at a time, as the computer does. This is why an index card held at the line being worked on is an effective tactic. If they try to outsmart the program and fill in the memory by anticipating what the computer will do, they will come to grief on the more complicated problems that come later. They will also fail to gain appreciation for the fact that the computer follows instructions entirely without thinking.

See Additional Answers for answers to Problems 1–6.

For each of the following BASIC programs:

a. trace the program step by step, recording values of the variables in a list and showing the output that is printed;

b. type the program into a computer and run it. Make sure that your output in part (a) agrees with the output from the computer.

```
1.  10   LET K=3
    20   LET Z=100-7*K
    30   PRINT K , Z
    40   LET K=K+1
    50   IF K=7 THEN 70
    60   GO TO 20
    70   END
```

```
2.  10   LET D=5
    20   LET E=4*D+11
    30   PRINT D , E
    40   LET D=D+2
    50   IF D=13 THEN 70
    60   GO TO 20
    70   END
```

```
3.  10   LET P=2              4.  10   LET F=4
    20   LET C=P*P-5              20   LET B=100-F*F
    30   PRINT P, C               30   PRINT F, B
    40   LET P=P+1                40   LET F=F+1
    50   IF C<30 THEN 20          50   IF B>50 THEN 20
    60   END                      60   END
```

Note: The symbol < means *is less than,* and the symbol > means *is greater than.*

```
5.  10   LET A=-3             6.  10   LET X=5
    20   LET B=A*A                30   LET Y=X-7
    30   LET C=B-5                30   LET Z=Y*Y*Y
    40   PRINT A, C               40   PRINT X, Z
    50   IF A>0 THEN 80           50   LET X=X+1
    60   LET A=A+1                60   IF X < 9 THEN 20
    70   GO TO 20                 70   END
    80   END
```

7-2	EVALUATING EXPRESSIONS

In the last section you learned how to trace a computer program in BASIC. You go through it one line at a time, recording values in the list of variables and printing answers as output. In this section you will learn how to evaluate more complicated expressions.

A computer may be considered to have three major components.

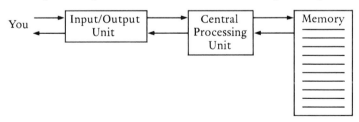

The **input/output unit** (the I/O unit) usually consists of a keyboard for putting information into the computer and a screen or printer for getting information out. The **central processing unit** (CPU) actually does the work the computer must do. The **memory** simply saves values of variables. It can be thought of as rows and rows of "mailboxes," each one capable of holding one number at a time. Each variable in a program has one memory location ("mailbox") assigned to it. If the central processing unit reads the instruction

```
LET X = 5
```

Time: 3 days

Chalkboard Examples:

First day:
Present homework problems to make sure students understand the steps. Overhead projector presentation is effective, with programs being uncovered a line at a time and memory and output being written in as you go. Then have students work the examples in Section 7–2. Conclude with Oral Practice. It is better to have students spend time consolidating their knowledge in class before they return to the computer.

Second day:
Do one homework problem at the board or on the overhead. Then have students work at the computer putting in and running assigned problems from Sections 7–1 and 7–2.

Third day:
Do one homework problem involving writing a program. Then have students work at the computer on assigned problems.

Assignments:

Day 1: Exercise 7–2, #1–9 odd (More can be assigned, depending on sophistication of the students and the number of computers available.)
Day 2: Exercise 7–2, #2–10 even, 11, 13
Day 3: Exercise 7–2, #15–19 odd or 16–20 even

it records 5 in the X-mailbox. If it later reads the instruction

```
LET X = 13.2
```

it tells the memory to "forget" the 5 and record 13.2 in the X-mailbox. If it then reads the instruction

```
PRINT X
```

it prints 13.2, the number *currently* in the X-mailbox. The computer does not remember that X was ever 5.

If the computer reads the instruction

```
INPUT X
```

it waits for you to type in a number. When you do, it stores this number as the value of X. Again, it forgets what X was before.

In this section you will play the role of the central processing unit. For a given program you will write a list of variables (called a **simulated computer memory**) and the output, as you did in the last section. By doing this, you will learn enough about BASIC to write some simple programs of your own.

Objectives:

a.   Given a BASIC program, trace it showing the simulated computer memory and the output, and check your answers by computer.

b.   Given a problem involving repeated evaluation of an expression, write and run a BASIC program.

All the algebraic operations can be done in BASIC. However, the symbols used are sometimes different, because the printer can write only along a line. Capital letters are used, as printers often have no lowercase letters.

The following are some operations in BASIC.

BASIC Symbol	Operation	Algebraic Symbol
A + B	Addition	$a + b$
A - B	Subtraction	$a - b$
A * B	Multiplication	$a \times b$, or ab
A / B	Division	$a \div b$, or $\dfrac{a}{b}$
A ^ B	Exponentiation	a^b
SQR(A)	Square root	$\sqrt{a}$
ABS(A)	Absolute value	$|a|$
INT(A)	Integer part	(The symbol [A] is sometimes used.)

Note: The operation INT(A) takes the *integer* part of the value of A and discards the decimal part. For instance, INT(34.79) = 34, INT(486.233) = 486, and INT(17) = 17.

The order of operations in BASIC is the same as in algebra.

1. Operations in parentheses are done *first*.

2. ^ is done next.

3. * and / are done next, from left to right.

4. + and − are done last, from left to right.

Once you learn these symbols, you can tell what a BASIC program does. For instance, if X is 6, the statement

```
LET Y = 3 + 4 * X - (X + 5) ^ 2
```

would be evaluated this way.

$$Y = 3 + 4 \times 6 - (6 + 5)^2 \qquad \text{Substitute 6 for X.}$$
$$= 3 + 4 \times 6 - 11^2 \qquad \text{Do what is in parentheses first.}$$
$$= 3 + 4 \times 6 - 121 \qquad \text{Raise to powers next.}$$
$$= 3 + 24 - 121 \qquad \text{Multiply and divide next.}$$
$$= -94 \qquad \text{Add and subtract last.}$$

The = sign in a LET statement is different from the = sign in algebra. It simply tells the computer where to put the answer. In this case, −94 would be stored in the computer's memory as the value of Y.

The = sign in an IF. . .THEN statement is the *same* as the = sign in algebra. There are also *inequality* signs, such as < and ≥, in algebra, about which you will learn more in Chapter 9. These signs are used to indicate that a number is either greater than or less than another. The signs in BASIC and in algebra are as follows:

BASIC	Meaning	Algebra
<	Is less than	<
>	Is greater than	>
< =	Is less than or equal to	≤
> =	Is greater than or equal to	≥
< >	Is not equal to	≠

In each of the following examples, put a piece of paper along the dotted lines to cover the answer. Read one line at a time, do what it says, and record the results in a simulated computer memory or as output. When you reach the END instruction, uncover the answer to be sure you are right.

EXAMPLE 1

Trace the program.

```
10    LET X = 7
20    LET Y = 23 - 14 / X + 3 * X ^ 2
30    PRINT X, Y
40    END
```

X	7
Y	168

Output: 7   168

Note: Some computers use the symbol $\emptyset$ to represent the number zero.

EXAMPLE 2

Trace the program. Put in 1 for X at line 10.

```
10    INPUT X
20    LET Y = ABS (3 * X - 7)
30    PRINT X, Y
40    LET X = X + 1
50    IF X < 5 THEN 20
60    END
```

X	1 2 3 4 5
Y	4 1 2 5

Output:

?10	
1	4
2	1
3	2
4	5

EXAMPLE 3

Trace the program. Put in 5 for X at line 10.

```
10    INPUT X
20    LET Y = 4 * X - 11
30    IF Y < 0 THEN 90
40    LET Z = SQR (Y)
50    LET N = INT (Z)
60    PRINT X, Z, N
70    LET X = X - 1
80    GO TO 20
90    END
```

X	5 4 3 2
Y	9 5 1 -3
Z	3 2.23607 1
N	3 2 1

Output:

?5		
5	3	3
4	2.23607	2
3	1	1

EXAMPLE 4

Write a BASIC program to evaluate $|x - 3| + \sqrt{x}$ for $x = 1, 2, 3,$ and 4. The computer should print each value of x and the corresponding value of the expression. Run the program on a computer.

Think These Reasons

```
10   LET X = 1
20   LET Y = ABS (X - 3) + SQR (X)
30   PRINT X, Y
40   LET X = X + 1
50   IF X < 5 THEN 20
         finished.
60   END
```

Start *x* at 1.
Calculate *y*.
Print the answers.
Increase *x* by 1.
Go back, if not

Stop.

Output: 1   3
            2   2.41421
            3   1.73205
            4   3

Note: There are several ways to write programs that give the correct output. If something is wrong, the program is said to have a **bug** in it. The term comes from the days when computers had hundreds of vacuum tubes in them. The heat from these tubes attracted (real!) bugs. Bodies of dead bugs sometimes caused the computer to malfunction. Nowadays, the process of correcting errors in a computer program is called **debugging** the program.

ORAL PRACTICE

Tell what happens when the computer does the following. Assume that the memory is as shown in each case.

X	5
Y	8

Problem Notes:

Each problem in the Oral Practice section refers back to the *original* memory, not to the memory as modified by the previous problems.

A.   Changes X from 5 to 13.
B.   Changes Y from 8 to 11.
C.   Changes Y from 8 to 13.
D.   Changes X from 5 to 2.
E.   Changes Y from 8 to 3.
F.   Changes X from 5 to 3.

EXAMPLES

Answers

```
  i.   LET X = 7
 ii.   LET Y = SQR(X + 11)
iii.   IF X < 9 THEN 40

 iv.   INPUT X
```

i.   Changes X from 5 to 7
ii.   Changes Y from 8 to 4
iii.   Does line 40 next, because X *is* less than 9
iv.   Lets you type in a new value of X

```
A.   LET X = 13              B.   LET Y = Y + 3

C.   LET Y = Y + X           D.   LET X = Y/4

E.   LET Y = 15/X            F.   LET X = SQR (Y + 1)
```

G. Changes X from 5 to 6.
H. Changes X from 5 to 4.
I. Changes Y from 8 to 25.
J. Changes Y from 8 to 5.
K. Does line 90 next.
L. Does line 10 next.
M. Does *not* go to line 100.
N. Does line 20 next.
O. Does *not* go to line 30.
P. Prints 8.
Q. Stores typed value as Y.
R. Stores typed value as X.

G. `LET X = ABS (2 - Y)`   H. `LET X = INT (4.9)`

I. `LET Y = X ^ 2`   J. `LET Y = SQR (X + 20)`

K. `IF X < 10 THEN 90`   L. `IF Y > 3 THEN 10`

M. `IF X < = 4 THEN 100`   N. `IF Y > = 8 THEN 20`

O. `IF X < > 5 THEN 30`   P. `PRINT Y`

Q. `INPUT Y`   R. `INPUT X`

If the computer's memory is as shown above, what BASIC statement would do the following?

EXAMPLES

Answers

i.   Change X to 11.   i.   `LET X = 11`
ii. Increase Y by 1.   ii. `LET Y = Y + 1`
iii. Do line 50 next, if Y
     is greater than or equal to 4.   iii. `IF Y > = 4 THEN 50`

S.   Change X to 13.   `LET X=13`   T.   Change Y to 100.   `LET Y=100`

U.   Increase X by 4.   `LET X=X+4`   V.   Increase Y by 3.   `LET Y=Y+3`

W.   Increase Y by X.   `LET Y=Y+X`   X.   Do line 40 next.   `GO TO 40`

Y.   Do line 60 next if X is less than 7.   `IF X<7 THEN 60`

Z.   Do line 70 next if Y is greater than 10.   `IF Y>10 THEN 70`

AA.   Do line 80 next if X is greater than or equal to 6.   `IF X>=6 THEN 80`

BB.   Do line 90 next if Y is less than or equal to 11.   `IF Y<=11 THEN 90`

CC.   Print the values of X and Y.   `PRINT X,Y`

DD.   Stop running the program.   `END`

EXERCISE 7-2

For Problems 1 through 10:

a.   trace the program, showing the simulated computer memory and the output;

b.   check your output by running the program on a computer.

See Additional Answers for answers to Problems 1–10.

1. Put in 3 for N at line 10.

```
10   INPUT N
20   LET X = -2
30   LET Y = X ^ 2
40   PRINT X,Y
50   LET X = X + 1
60   IF X < = N THEN 30
70   END
```

2. Put in 3 for K at line 10.

```
10   INPUT K
20   LET V = -2
30   LET E = V ^ 3
40   PRINT V,E
50   LET V = V + 1
60   IF V < = K THEN 30
70   END
```

3. Put in 16 for L at line 10.

```
10   INPUT L
20   LET Z = 2
30   LET A = SQR (2 * Z)
40   PRINT Z,A
50   LET Z = Z + 3
60   IF Z < L THEN 30
70   END
```

4. Put in 29 for H at line 10.

```
10   INPUT H
20   LET L = 1
30   LET R=L+SQR (L*8)
40   LET L = L + 7
50   PRINT L,R
60   IF L < H THEN 30
70   END
```

5. Put in 5 for U at line 10.

```
10   INPUT U
20   LET C = 1
30   LET N = 6
40   LET P = N+ABS(10-N)
50   PRINT C,N,P
60   LET N = N + 3
70   LET C = C + 1
80   IF C > U THEN 100
90   GO TO 40
100  END
```

6. Put in 6 for T at line 10.

```
10   INPUT T
20   LET K = 1
30   LET F = 7
40   LET J = F * ABS (5+F)
50   PRINT K,F,J
60   LET F = F - 4
70   LET K = K + 1
80   IF K > = T THEN 100
90   GO TO 40
100  END
```

7.
```
10   LET N = 7
20   LET F = N / 4
30   LET I = INT (F)
40   PRINT N,F,I
50   LET N = N + 1
60   IF N < = 13 THEN 20
70   END
```

8.
```
10   LET U = 17
20   LET R = U/5
30   LET A = INT(R)
40   PRINT U,R,A
50   LET U = U + 1
60   IF U < = 21 THEN 20
70   END
```

9.
```
10   LET C = 1
20   LET D = ABS(C - 3)
30   LET E = SQR(D + 1)
40   LET F = INT(E+0.5)
50   LET G = C ^ F
60   PRINT C,G
70   LET C = C + 2
80   IF C < = 10 THEN 20
90   END
```

10.
```
10   LET X = -5
20   LET Y = ABS(X)
30   LET Z = SQR(Y)
40   LET W = INT(Z)
50   LET V = Y ^ W
60   PRINT X,V
70   LET X = X + 4
80   IF X < 11 THEN 20
90   END
```

For Problems 11 through 20:

a. write a program to do the job indicated;

b. run the program on a computer.

An efficient way to grade Problems 11–20 is to have students store their completed programs on a single disk or other central memory device. They should store it under their names or group number. Then at your convenience you can grade all of their programs by recalling and running them, insuring that the output is correct. You can also have them submit printed output.

See Additional Answers for answers to Problems 11–20.

11. Print x and $\sqrt{x}$ for each integer value of x from 1 through 10.

12. Print x and x^2 for each integer value of x from 1 through 10.

13. Evaluate $x^2 - 2x + 6$ for each integer value of x from 1 through 10 and print the results.

14. Evaluate $x^2 - 8x + 1$ for each integer value of x from 1 through 10 and print the results.

15. Evaluate $|3x - 17|$ for each integer value of x from 1 through N, where N is a variable whose value you type in as the computer begins to run the program.

16. Evaluate $|30 - 5x|$ for each integer value of x from 1 through N, where N is a variable whose value you type in as the computer begins to run the program.

17. Evaluate the power 2^x for each integer value of x from 1 through N, where the value of N is input as the computer begins to run the program.

18. Evaluate the power 0.9^x for each integer value of x from 1 through N, where the value of N is input as the computer begins to run the program.

19. Evaluate $\sqrt{3x + 5}$ for each integer value of x from 1 through 10. At each step print the value of x, the value of the expression, and the *integer* part of the value of the expression.

20. Evaluate $\sqrt{98 - 7x}$ for integer values of x starting at $x = 0$. Calculate the value of the radicand, $98 - 7x$, first. The computer should stop when the radicand first becomes negative.

21. *Modifying Existing Programs*
For problems 11 through 14, simply retype line 20 with the new expression. For Problems 15 through 18, retype line 30.

21. *Modifying Existing Programs* The programs in Problems 11 through 14 are identical except for the step in which the value of the expression is calculated. The same is true for Problems 15 through 18. How could you write the new program *without* having to retype all of the steps that are the same?

7-3 | LOOPING AND STRING PRINTING

A program that goes back and repeats earlier steps is said to have a **loop** in it. For instance, there is a loop in this program.

```
       10   LET X = 3
       20   LET Y = SQR(X)
Loops  30   PRINT X,Y
back to 40  LET X = X + 1
line 20. 50  IF X < = 10 THEN 20
       60   END
```

There is a more efficient way in BASIC to make a computer do loops. The above program can be written this way.

```
       10   FOR X = 3 TO 10
       20   LET Y = SQR(X)
Loop   30   PRINT X,Y
       40   NEXT X
       50   END
```

The statement FOR X = 3 TO 10 tells the computer to start X at 3 and do the statements following. The statement NEXT X tells the computer to increase X by 1 (making it 4), go back to the FOR statement, and *repeat* the steps following. Each time the computer gets to the NEXT X statement, X is increased by 1 and the computer goes back to the FOR statement. When the computer increases *x* to 11, and finds that 11 is greater than 10, it stops looping and goes on with the next statement (END, in this case). The effect is the same as the first program, but the statements are more efficient.

The programs you have run so far have just printed numbers. You can make the computer print *messages,* too. The statement

```
    PRINT "HAVE A NICE DAY!"
```

will cause the computer to print the message

```
    HAVE A NICE DAY!
```

Such a message is called a **string,** because to the computer it is just a string of letters and symbols. Whatever string is enclosed in quotation marks will be printed by the computer. You can print a string that identifies which variable a number stands for.

```
    PRINT "X = "; X
```

If X happens to be 35, the computer will print

```
    X = 35
```

The semicolon is used instead of the comma to tell the computer to reduce the space between different things that are printed on the same line. Remember, in PRINT statements, if something appears in ". . ." marks, the string itself is printed. If something appears *without* quotation marks, the *value* of that variable is printed.

Objective:
Be able to trace and write BASIC programs containing FOR and NEXT statements and string-printing statements.

Time: 2 days

Chalkboard Examples:

First day:
Show the simulated memory and output:

10 FOR X = 4 TO 7	Memory:			
20 LET Y = 5 * X	X : 4 5 6 7 8			
30 PRINT "Y = "; Y	Y : 20 25 30 35			
40 NEXT X	Output:			
50 END	Y = 20			
	Y = 25			
	Y = 30			
	Y = 35			

Note that the FOR statement increases X to 8, then checks to see whether it is larger than 7. So 8 is the last value of X that appears in the simulated memory.

Second day:
Students should work at the computer, finishing programs from Section 7–2 and starting those from Section 7–3. The Oral Practice is effective *after* students have worked with FOR statements and string variables at the computer.

Assignments:

Day 1: Exercise 7–3, #1–9 odd or 2–10 even
Day 2: Select two or more problems from Exercise 7–3, 11–16

Cover the answers as you work these examples.

EXAMPLE 1

Trace the following program, showing the simulated computer memory and the output. Put in 5 for N at line 20.

```
10    PRINT "TYPE A VALUE OF N."
20    INPUT N
30    PRINT "  X", "  Y"
40    PRINT "___", "___"
50    FOR X = 1 TO N
60    LET Y = 7 - 3 * X
70    PRINT X,Y
80    NEXT X
90    END
```

- - - - -   - - - - -

N	5
X	1 2 3 4 5 6
Y	4 1 -2 -5 -8

Output: TYPE A VALUE OF N.
?5

X	Y
1	4
2	1
3	-2
4	-5
5	-8

EXAMPLE 2

Trace the following program as in Example 1. Note that STEP 2 in line 30 causes X to be increased by 2 each time instead of by 1.

```
10    PRINT "EXAMPLE 2"
20    LET S = 0
30    FOR X = 1 TO 9 STEP 2
40    LET S = S + X
50    PRINT X,S
60    NEXT X
70    PRINT "SUM EQUALS ";S
80    END
```

- - - - -   - - - - -

S	0 1 4 9 16 25
X	1 3 5 7 9 11

Output: EXAMPLE 2

1	1
3	4
5	9
7	16
9	25
SUM EQUALS 25	

EXAMPLE 3

Write a program to print values of the expression $3x^2 - 7x - 8$ for each integer value of x, starting at $x = 0$ and stopping when x reaches 10 or when the expression is larger than 100, whichever happens first. The computer should print the values of x and the expression, with headings as

in Example 1. Finally, the computer should print the message LAST
VALUE OF X WAS and the current value of *x*.

– – – – –   – – – – –

```
10    PRINT " X", " Y"
20    PRINT "---", "---"
30    FOR X = 0 TO 10
40    LET Y = 3 * X ^ 2 _ 7 * X _ 8
50    PRINT X,Y
60    IF Y > 100 THEN 80
70    NEXT X
80    PRINT "LAST VALUE OF X WAS ";X
90    END
```

Output:
```
          X      Y
          ---    ---
          0      -8
          1      -12
          2      -10
          3      -2
          4      12
          5      32
          6      58
          7      90
          8      128
          LAST VALUE OF X WAS 8
```

ORAL PRACTICE

Tell what happens when the computer does the following. Assume that the
memory is as shown in each case.

X	3
Y	7

EXAMPLES

Answers

i.   `FOR X = 1 TO 10`   i.   Starts X at 1. Stops when X is 10.
ii. `NEXT X`   ii. Increases X by 1. Goes back to
                               the FOR statement.
iii. `PRINT "X"`   iii. Prints the *letter* X.
iv. `PRINT X`   iv. Prints 3 (the *value* of X).

A. `FOR X = 2 TO 5`   B. `FOR Y = 8 TO 10`

C. `NEXT Y`   D. `FOR Y = 1 TO 5 STEP 2`

E. `PRINT "Y"`   F. `PRINT Y`

G. `PRINT X,Y`   H. `PRINT X;Y`

A.   Starts X at 2. Stops when X is over 5.
B.   Starts Y at 8. Stops when Y is over 10.
C.   Increases Y by 1. Goes back to FOR.
D.   Starts Y at 1. Increases by 2, stopping
     when Y is over 5.
E.   Prints Y.
F.   Prints 7.
G.   Prints 3 7.
H.   Prints 37.

I.   Prints X = 3.

J.   Prints IT WAS 7 DOLLARS.

K.   `PRINT X`
L.   `PRINT "X"`
M.   `PRINT "SQUARE ROOT"`
N.   `PRINT X;Y`
O.   `FOR X = 1 TO 6`
P.   `NEXT Y`
Q.   `IF Y < 10 THEN 30`
R.   `LET Y = SQR(X)`
S.   `LET X = Y ^ 3`
T.   `FOR X = 3 TO 11 STEP 2`
U.   `LET Y = ABS(-10)`
V.   `LET Y = INT(Y/X)`

I.   `PRINT "X = ";X`

J.   `PRINT "IT WAS ";Y;" DOLLARS."`

If the computer's memory is as shown above, what BASIC statement would do the following?

K.   Print the value of X.

L.   Print the letter X.

M.   Print the words SQUARE ROOT.

N.   Print the values of X and Y close together.

O.   Start X at 1 and stop when X gets to 6.

P.   Increase Y by 1 and go back to a FOR statement.

Q.   Do line 30 next if Y is less than 10.

R.   Make Y equal the square root of X.

S.   Make X equal Y cubed.

T.   Start X at 3, increase it by 2 each time, and stop when X is 11.

U.   Make Y equal the absolute value of -10.

V.   Divide Y by X and take the integer part of the answer.

EXERCISE 7-3

For Problems 1 through 8:

a.   trace the program, showing simulated memory and output;

b.   run the program on a computer.

See Additional Answers for answers to Problems 1–8.

Problem Notes:

Each problem in the Oral Practice refers back to the original memory and not to the memory as modified by previous problems.

Different students or groups of students can work different problems. This tactic allows you to assign easier problems to students less familiar with computing. It also helps avoid copying of programs. Debugged programs can be stored on a single disk or central storage facility for you to recall for grading.

```
1.  10   PRINT "PROB. 1"        2.  10   PRINT "PROB. 2"
    20   FOR X = 1 TO 5             20   FOR K = 4 TO 8
    30   LET Y = 3 + X * 5          30   LET E = 27 - 4 * K
    40   PRINT X,Y                  40   PRINT K,E
    50   NEXT X                     50   NEXT K
    60   PRINT "DONE!!"             60   PRINT "FINISHED!"
    70   END                       70   END
```

3.   Put in 5 for N at line 30.

```
    10    PRINT "PROB. 3"
    20    PRINT "WHAT IS N";
    30    INPUT N
    40    PRINT " V ",  " C"
```

```
50     PRINT "---", "---"
60     FOR V = 2 TO N
70     LET C = ABS ( - 3 * V + 8)
80     PRINT V,C
90     NEXT V
100    END
```

4. Put in 15 for L at line 30.

```
10     PRINT "PROB. 4"
20     PRINT "TYPE L-VALUE ";
30     INPUT L
40     PRINT " D ", "       S"
50     PRINT "---", "----------"
60     FOR D = 12 TO L
70     LET S = SQR (D - 5)
80     PRINT D,S
90     NEXT D
100    END
```

Note: The semicolon at the end of line 20 makes the computer *not* go on to the next line before printing again.

5.
```
10     PRINT "PROB. 5"
20     FOR X = 1 TO 10
30     LET Y = X ^ X
40     IF Y > 1000000 THEN 90
50     PRINT X,Y
60     NEXT X
70     PRINT "NEVER OVER A MILLION"
80     GO TO 110
90     PRINT "Y IS OVER A MILLION"
100    PRINT "WHEN X IS ";X
110    END
```

6.
```
10     PRINT "PROB. 6"
20     FOR X = 1 TO 10
30     LET Y = 3 ^ X
40     IF Y > 1000000 THEN 90
50     PRINT X,Y
60     NEXT X
70     PRINT "NEVER OVER A MILLION"
80     GO TO 110
90     PRINT "Y IS OVER A MILLION"
100    PRINT "WHEN X IS ";X
110    END
```

7. Put in 3 for N at line 30.

```
10   PRINT "PROB. 7"
20   PRINT "WHAT SIZE STEP";
```

```
30   INPUT N
40   FOR X = 0 TO 12 STEP N
50   LET Y = SQR (X)
60   LET Z = INT (Y + 0.5)
70   PRINT "X = ";X;"   Z = ";Z
80   NEXT X
90   END
```

8.
```
10    PRINT "PROB. 8"
20    FOR N = 3 TO 20 STEP 5
30    LET X = N / 2
40    LET Y = INT (X)
50    IF X < > Y THEN 80
60    PRINT N;" IS EVEN"
70    GO TO 90
80    PRINT N;" IS ODD"
90    NEXT N
100   END
```

For Problems 9 through 16:

a.   write a program to do the job indicated;

b.   run the program on a computer.

See Additional Answers for answers to Problems 9–16.

9. Print PROB. 9. Then print a table of squares of the integers, x^2, starting at $x = 1$ and ending at $x = 10$. The table should have the values of x and x^2, with the headings X and X^2.

10. Print PROB. 10. Then print a table of square roots of the integers, $\sqrt{x}$, starting at $x = 1$ and ending at $x = 10$. The table should have the values of x and $\sqrt{x}$, with the headings X and SQR(X).

11. Print PROB. 11. Then evaluate $x^3 - 5x$ for each integer value of x from 1 through 10. The computer should print values of x and the expression, with appropriate headings.

12. Print PROB. 12. Then evaluate 3^x for each integer value of x from 1 through 10. The computer should print the values of x and the expression, with appropriate headings.

13. Print PROB. 13. Then evaluate $|x^2 - 10x|$ for *even* values of x, starting at $x = 2$ and stopping when the expression first gets larger than 1000. Print values of x and the expression. End with the message LAST VALUE OF X WAS and the value of x.

14. Print PROB. 14. Then evaluate $\sqrt{7x - 15}$ for $x = 3, 5, 7, \ldots$. Print the value of x and the *integer* part of the value of the expression. The computer should stop when the expression first exceeds 10, and the computer should print ENDED WHEN X WAS and the value of x.

15. **Sum of the Numbers Problem** Write a program to find the *sum* of the numbers $2 + 5 + 8 + 11 + \cdots$. Start a variable S (for *sum*) at 0 and a variable X at 2. Then add X to S. Each following value of X is found by adding 3 to the previous value. Stop when S first gets larger than 100. Print the values of X and S at each step. Then print the final value of S with the message FINAL SUM IS.

16. **Bridge Problem** The photograph at the beginning of this chapter shows Glen Canyon Bridge near Page, Arizona. The length of the columns between the arch and the roadway are given by the expression

$$0.000544x^2 - 0.571x + 161$$

where x is the number of feet between that column and the leftmost column.

  a. Write a program that calculates and prints the length of each column. The first column is at $x = 0$, the last is at $x = 1050$, and the columns are 50 feet apart.

  b. Modify your program so that the computer also calculates and prints the *sum* of the lengths of the columns. Remember that there are columns on *both* sides of the bridge.

7-4	EVALUATING EXPRESSIONS WITH GIVEN DATA

In the last two sections you have learned how to make a computer evaluate expressions for *many* values of the variable. But the programs you have written so far have used regularly spaced values such as

$$1, 2, 3, 4, 5, \ldots ,$$

or

$$3, 5, 7, 9, 11, \ldots .$$

Suppose you had to evaluate $4x + 5$ for these values of x:

$$2, 7.3, 5.8, -11.$$

The way to do this in BASIC is to use READ and DATA statements. The program would look like this:

Second day:

Students should be working on assigned programs at the computer.

Third day:

Review the BASIC statements in Section 7–5. Students should be finishing assigned programs at the computer.

Assignments:

Day 1: Exercise 7–4, #1–11 odd or 2–12 even

Day 2: Work at least one program from Exercise 7–4, #11–17. Different students or groups can be assigned different problems.

Day 3: Exercise 7–5, #1–8 in preparation for test.

```
10   FOR C = 1 TO 4
20   READ X
30   DATA 2,7,3,5,8,-11
40   LET Y = 4 * X + 5
50   PRINT X,Y
60   NEXT C
70   END
```

Output:		
2	13	
7.3	34.2	
5.8	28.2	
-11	-39	

When the computer gets to the statement READ X in line 20, it looks for a DATA statement. The *first* number in the DATA statement becomes the value of X. So X equals 2. The next time through the loop, the computer takes the *second* number in the DATA statement, 7.3, and assigns this value to X. This process continues until either the computer finishes looping or until all the numbers in the DATA statement have been used.

If you look carefully at the above program, you will see that C never appears in the calculations! Its only purpose is to count the number of times the computer has gone through the loop. A variable used in this way is called a **counter.**

Objective:

Be able to write and trace BASIC programs with READ and DATA statements.

Cover the answers as you work these examples.

EXAMPLE 1

Trace the following program, showing the simulated computer memory and the output.

```
10   FOR C = 1 TO 3
20   READ X
30   DATA 4,7,9
40   LET Y = 30 - 5 * X
50   PRINT X,Y
60   NEXT C
70   END
```

C	1 2 3
X	4 7 9
Y	10 -5 -15

Output:		
4	10	
7	-5	
9	-15	

EXAMPLE 2

Trace the following program, as in Example 1.

```
10   FOR C = 1 TO 10
20   READ X
30   DATA 0,3,5,1,2,8
```

```
40   LET Y = 7 * X ^ 2
50   PRINT X,Y
60   IF Y > 100 THEN 80
70   NEXT C
80   END
- - - - -                                       - - - - -
```

C	1̶ 2̶ 3
X	0̶ 3̶ 5
Y	0̶ 6̶3̶ 175

Output:
```
0    0
3    63
5    175
```

Note: Line 60 causes the computer to *jump out* of the loop after 5 has been used for X. The other values in the DATA statement never get used!

EXAMPLE 3

Trace the following program, as in Example 1.

```
10    LET S = 0
20    FOR N = 0 TO 20
30    READ G
40    DATA 95,74,58,100,-1
50    IF G < 0 THEN 80
60    LET S = S + G
70    NEXT N
80    LET A = S / N
90    PRINT N;" GRADES"
100   PRINT "AVGE. = ";A
110   END
```

S	0̶ 9̶5̶ 1̶6̶9̶ 2̶2̶7̶ 327
N	0̶ 1̶ 2̶ 3̶ 4
G	9̶5̶ 7̶4̶ 5̶8̶ 1̶0̶0̶ -1
A	81.75

Output: 4 GRADES
          AVGE. = 81.75

Note: In this example, the "expression" being evaluated is the sum of the grades in the DATA statement. The purpose of the program is to find the averages of variable numbers of grades. The -1 at the end of the DATA statement is called a **flag.** Its only purpose is to signal the computer that all the grades have been read.

EXAMPLE 4

Write a BASIC program to evaluate $\sqrt{x - 3}$ for these values of x in this order:

$$7, 22, 2, 5, 11, 17.$$

Before the computer tries to take the square root, it should evaluate the radicand, $(x - 3)$. If it is *negative,* the computer should print the message X CANNOT BE and the value of x. Then it should stop.

		Think These Reasons
10	`FOR C = 1 TO 6`	There are 6 numbers to be used.
20	`READ X`	Get a value of x from the DATA statement.
30	`DATA 7,22,2,5,11,17`	These are the x's to use.
40	`IF X - 3 < 0 THEN 90`	Check $(x - 3)$ before taking the square root.
50	`LET Y = SQR (X - 3)`	Take the square root.
60	`PRINT X,Y`	Print the answers.
70	`NEXT C`	Go back through the loop.
80	`GO TO 100`	Skip line 90 if *all* x-values worked.
90	`PRINT "X CANNOT BE ";X`	Print the message.
100	`END`	Stop.

```
Output:  7       2
         22      4.35889894
         X CANNOT BE 2
```

EXERCISE 7-4

For Problems 1 through 10:

a.   trace the program, showing simulated memory and output;

b.   run the program on a computer.

See Additional Answers for answers to Problems 1–10.

```
1. 10   PRINT "PROBLEM 1"          2. 10   PRINT "PROBLEM 2"
   20   FOR C = 1 TO 4                20   FOR C = 1 TO 4
   30   READ X                        30   READ X
   40   DATA 7,15,20,30               40   DATA 2,8,6,4,1,9
   50   LET Y = 2 * X + 5             50   LET Y = 5 * X + 7
   60   PRINT X,Y                     60   PRINT X,Y
   70   NEXT C                        70   NEXT C
   80   END                          80   END
```

```
3. 10    PRINT "PROBLEM 3"        4. 10    PRINT "PROBLEM 4"
   20    FOR N = 1 TO 6             20    FOR N = 1 TO 6
   30    READ X                     30    READ X
   40    DATA 3,0,6,8,20,5,4        40    DATA 10,7,5,3,2,1
   50    LET Y = X ^ 2              50    LET Y = X ^ 3
   60    PRINT X,Y                  60    PRINT X,Y
   70    IF Y > 100 THEN 90         70    IF Y < 100 THEN 90
   80    NEXT N                     80    NEXT N
   90    PRINT N;" NUMBERS"         90    PRINT N;" NUMBERS"
   100   END                        100   END

5. 10    PRINT "PROBLEM 5"        6. 10    PRINT "PROBLEM 6"
   20    LET S = 0                  20    LET P = 1
   30    FOR C = 1 TO 4             30    FOR C = 1 TO 4
   40    READ X                     40    READ X
   50    DATA 85,63,99,90           50    DATA 2,3,5,7
   60    LET S = S + X              60    LET P = P * X
   70    PRINT X,S                  70    PRINT X,P
   80    NEXT C                     80    NEXT C
   90    END                        90    END

7. 10    PRINT "PROBLEM 7"        8. 10    PRINT "PROBLEM 8"
   20    LET P = 1                  20    LET S = 0
   30    FOR C = 1 TO 3             30    FOR C = 1 TO 3
   40    READ X                     40    READ X
   50    DATA 2,3,7,9,11            50    DATA 2,8,6,4,1,9
   60    LET Y = 5 - X              60    LET Y = 5 * X + 7
   70    PRINT X,Y                  70    PRINT X,Y
   80    LET P = P * Y              80    LET S = S + Y
   90    NEXT C                     90    NEXT C
   100   PRINT "PRODUCT=";P         100   PRINT "TOTAL = ";S
   110   END                        110   END

9. 10    PRINT "PROBLEM 9"       10. 10    PRINT "PROBLEM 10"
   20    LET S = 0                  20    LET S = 0
   30    LET C = 0                  30    FOR C = 0 TO 100
   40    FOR L = 1 TO 50            40    READ X
   50    READ N                     50    DATA 37,19,9,80,-1
   60    DATA 25,17,3,8,4,1,2,-1    60    IF X < 0 THEN 120
   70    IF N < 0 THEN 120          70    LET Y = SQR (X)
   80    LET C = C + 1              80    LET Z = INT (Y)
   90    LET S = S + N              90    LET S = S + Z
   100   PRINT N                    100   PRINT Y,Z
   110   NEXT L                     110   NEXT C
   120   PRINT "----"               120   PRINT
   130   PRINT S                    130   PRINT C;" NUMBERS,"
   140   PRINT C;" NUMBERS"         140   PRINT "SUM IS ";S
   150   END                        150   END
```

For Problems 11 through 16:

a.   write the BASIC program indicated;

b.   run your program on a computer.

See Additional Answers for answers to Problems 11–17.

11. Evaluate $3x + 5$ for these eight values of x: 27, 30, 41, 29, 6, 3, -8, and 0. Print each value of x and the corresponding value of the expression.

12. Evaluate $6 - 9x$ for these seven values of x: 4, 17, 8, -5, -20, 6, and 100. Print each value of x and the corresponding value of the expression.

Problem Notes:

Problem 13 can be used as the basis for a grade-averaging program. If the computer also counts the number of valid grades read, excluding the -1 flag at the end, the average will be the sum divided by this number of grades.

13. Write a program to find the sum of up to 100 numbers. The numbers will be in a DATA statement, such as

```
DATA 55,73,94,81,-1
```

The -1 is a flag signaling the end of the data and is *not* one of the numbers to be added. At each pass through the loop, the computer should print the number it has just read and the sum so far. After all numbers have been read, the computer should print the message SUM IS and the value of the sum.

14. Write a program to find the product of up to 10 numbers. The numbers will be read from a DATA statement, such as

```
DATA 3, 5.2, 7.4, 9.8, 4.7, -1
```

The -1 is a flag signaling the end of the data and is *not* one of the numbers to be multiplied. At each pass through the loop, the computer should print the number it has just read and the product so far. After all numbers have been read, the computer should print the message PRODUCT IS and the value of the product.

15. *Payroll Problem*   Calvin Butterball works part time for $6 per hour. Below are his hours for a particular week.

Day	Hours
1	2
2	1.5
3	0.75
4	2.25
5	1.8
6	3.6

Write a program that calculates and prints the number of dollars he earns each of these days, as well as the total for the week. The numbers of hours should be put in a DATA statement. There should be a message at the end saying TOTAL IS $, along with the value of that total.

16. *Baseball Batting Average Problem* Write a program to determine a player's batting average. The player's number of at-bats and number of hits for each game should be in a DATA statement. For each game, the computer should read and print the number of at-bats and the number of hits. It should also keep track of the *total* number of at-bats and the *total* number of hits, as well as the number of games. Use a negative number of at-bats as a flag to signal the end of the data. The average is computed by dividing the total number of hits by the total number of at-bats. The average is always reported as a three-place decimal, such as 0.279. To get the answer in this form, have the computer multiply the average by 1000, take the integer part of it, and divide the result by 1000. Test the program using

```
DATA 3,1,7,3,6,2,4,0,5,1,3,3,-1,-1
```

The first of each pair of numbers is the number of at-bats, and the second is the number of hits. For instance, in the first game, there were 3 at-bats and 1 hit. The pair -1, -1 flags the end of the data. If your program works right, it should give 0.357 for this sample set of data.

17. *Factorials Problem* The product of the first n positive integers,

$$1 \cdot 2 \cdot 3 \cdot \ldots \cdot n,$$

is called "n factorial." The symbol $n!$ is used for n factorial. For instance,

$$5! = 1 \cdot 2 \cdot 3 \cdot 4 \cdot 5$$

$$= 120.$$

Write a program to compute and print values of $n!$ The value of n should be input as the computer runs the program. The computer should start a variable P (for "product") at 1, then go into a loop that multiplies P by 1, then by 2, then by 3, and so on, up to n. The computer should print the value of P at each pass through the loop. At the end, if 5 has been input for n, the computer should print the answer like this:

$$5! = 120$$

Problem 17 will lead to numbers in scientific notation or to "overflow" if the factorials of large numbers are computed. This problem gives you a chance to introduce students to these concepts.

7-5   CHAPTER REVIEW AND TEST

Test Ideas:

The test shown is designed to measure with pencil and paper what the students have learned on the computer. Programs to be traced involve only three or four iterations, enough for students to show that they have the idea but not so many that the problem becomes tedious. A problem could be added in which students find and correct statements that contain errors. Use the errors your own students have made. It is possible for you to give a test in which each student demonstrates mastery of the subject at the computer. The decision on whether to use such a test should be based on the availability of sufficient computers and on time considerations.

Assignment:

Exercise 8–1, #1–9 odd or 2–10 even, or first section of next chapter if Chapter 7 has been done out of sequence.

In this chapter you have learned to use a computer to evaluate expressions. The computer is useful when the same expression must be evaluated repeatedly with different values of the variable.

The following is a list of BASIC features you should know by now. This list will be useful for future reference as you write programs later on. For review, you should cover the meanings on the right and try to tell in words what the statement or symbol on the left means. Then you should cover the left side and see if you can write the statement or symbol that is described on the right.

Summary of BASIC

Statement or Symbol	*Result*
1. *Input/Output*	
a. `INPUT X`	a. Waits for you to type a number at the keyboard as the program is running, then stores this number as the value of X.
b. `READ X`	b. Takes the next number from a DATA statement and stores this number as the value of X.
c. `DATA...`	c. Contains a list of data, separated by commas, to be used with a READ statement.
d. `PRINT X,Y`	d. Prints the current values of X and Y.
e. `PRINT X;Y`	e. Prints the values of X and Y close together.
f. `PRINT "X,Y"`	f. Prints the string X,Y.
2. *Computing Values*	
a. `LET X = ...`	a. Computes the value of the expression on the right of the $=$ sign and stores the answer as the value of the variable, X, on the left.
b. `+, -, *, /, ^`	b. Operators plus, minus, times, divided by, and raised to the power
c. `ABS(X)`	c. Finds the absolute value of X.
d. `SQR (X)`	d. Finds the square root of X.
e. `INT(X)`	e. Finds the integer part of X (the greatest integer less than or equal to X). For positive values of X, it simply "chops off" (truncates) the decimal part.

3. *Branching and Looping*

  a.   `GO TO 30`   a.   Unconditional branch. The next line run will be line 30.

  b.   `IF...THEN 30`   b.   Conditional branch. If the statement is true, the computer goes to line 30. Otherwise, it continues with the line below.

  c.   `<`   c.   Is less than
      `>`   Is greater than
      `< =`   Is less than or equal to
      `> =`   Is greater than or equal to
      `< >`   Is not equal to

  d.   `FOR...TO...STEP`   d.   Looping instruction. Starts looping with a given variable value, stops looping at a second value of that variable, and changes that variable by a given step at each pass through the loop.

  e.   `NEXT...`   e.   Signals the last instruction of a FOR loop

4. *Ending a Program*

  a.   `END`   a.   The last statement in any BASIC program

5. *System Commands*

  a.   `RUN`   a.   Tells the computer to start executing (running) the program.

  b.   `LIST`   b.   Tells the computer to print the statements in a program.

The following is a pencil-and-paper test of your knowledge of computing. If you are good at using the computer, you should easily be able to answer these questions.

CHAPTER TEST

T1. Name the three major components of a computer.

T2. a. Give the name of the process of finding and correcting errors in a program.
    b. How does one change a statement in a BASIC program?
    c. How does one insert a new statement between two others in a BASIC program?

CHAPTER TEST

T1. Input-output unit
Central processing unit
Memory

T2. **a.** Debugging
    b. Type a new statement with the *same* line number.
    c. Type a new statement with a line number *between* the other two.
    d. To leave room for possible additional statements between

T3. **a.** A *loop* is a part of the program that is run *repeatedly*.
    b. A *branch* is a point where the computer could go one of two ways, depending on conditions.
    c. A *flag* is a "dummy" piece of data inserted in a DATA statement to signal the end of the data.

d. A *counter* is a variable used to count the number of times the computer has run a given loop.

e. A string is a series of characters the computer prints as a message.

T4. a. PRINT A, B prints values *spaced apart*.
PRINT A; B prints values with *no* (or small) space between.

b. PRINT A, B prints the *values* of variables A and B.
PRINT "A, B" prints the *string* A,B.

T5. Computer—Repetitive calculations
Calculator—Difficult one-time calculations
Brain—Easy, approximate calculations

Problem Notes:

Problem 7 is a program that simulates the card game Blackjack.

T7.

S	0 5̶ 1̶4̶ 22
N	4
C	1̶ 2̶ 3
X	5̶ 9̶ 8

Output:
```
]RUN
SUM PROBLEM
?4
1   5
2   9
3   8
BUST WHEN C = 3
```

T8.
```
10 PRINT "QUADRATIC PROBLEM
20 FOR X = 0 TO 6
30 LET Y = 5 * X ^ 2 - 13 * X + 2
40 PRINT X,Y
50 NEXT X
60 END

]RUN
QUADRATIC PROBLEM
0    2
1   -6
2   -4
3    8
4   30
5   62
6  104
```

d. Why does one usually use lines numbered 10, 20, 30, . . . in a BASIC program instead of using 1, 2, 3, . . . ?

T3. Write the meanings of the following as they pertain to computing.
a. Loop   b. Branch   c. Flag   d. Counter   e. String

T4. What is the difference in the output for the following statements?
a. PRINT A,B   and   PRINT A;B
b. PRINT A,B   and   PRINT "A,B"

T5. A computer is one of three tools for doing computation. Name the other two, and tell the sorts of computations for which each of the three is most appropriate.

T6. If the current value of X is 5, find the value of each of these BASIC expressions.
a. 2 ^ X   32   b. X / 4   1.25
c. ABS(3 - 4 * X)   17   d. SQR(X ^ 3)   11.18
e. INT(10 + X / 3)   11

T7. Trace the following BASIC program, showing the simulated memory and the output. Put in 4 for N at line 30.
```
10     PRINT "SUM PROBLEM"
20     LET S = 0
30     INPUT N
40     FOR C = 1 TO N
50     READ X
60     DATA 5,9,8,2,11,-1
70     PRINT C,X
80     LET S = S + X
90     IF S > 21 THEN 130
100    NEXT C
110    PRINT "SUM = ";S
120    GO TO 140
130    PRINT "BUST WHEN C = ";C
140    END
```

T8. Write a BASIC program to evaluate the quadratic expression
$$5x^2 - 13x + 2$$
for each integer value of *x* from 0 through 6. The computer should begin by printing the string QUADRATIC PROBLEM. Then it should print each value of *x* and the corresponding value of the expression.

8

Expressions and Equations Containing Two Variables

In many situations from the real world there are two variable quantities. For instance, if x is the width of a rectangular field and y is its length, then an expression for its area is xy. The length of fence needed to enclose the field is equal to its perimeter, 2x + 2y. In this chapter you will do the normal things with such expressions, evaluate them, and solve equations containing them.

Variables:

x	Number of feet wide
y	Number of feet long

Expressions:

$2x + 2y$	Perimeter
xy	Area

| 8-1 | EVALUATING EXPRESSIONS CONTAINING TWO VARIABLES |

Time: $\frac{1}{2}$ day, with Section 8–2

Chalkboard Examples:

Evaluate $3x - 5y$ if:

a. $x = 6$ and $y = 11$;   Ans.: -37

b. $x = 12$ and $y = 2$;
    Ans.: 26 (different from (a))

c. $x = 17$ and $y = 5$.
    Ans.: 26 (same as (b))

Assignment:

Exercise 8–1, #1–9 odd or 2–10 even should have been assigned for students to work on their own prior to your first day on Chapter 8. If not, assign at least two of the problems in conjunction with Section 8–2.

This section is meant for you to read and work on your own, without help from your teacher. If you succeed, you will have gotten a good overview of the content of this chapter.

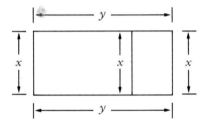

The diagram shows a rectangle x units by y units that is divided into two parts. If this were the plan for a cattle pen, the total of the lengths of the sides would be the length of fence needed to build the pen. This length would be

$$x + x + x + y + y,$$

or more simply

$$3x + 2y.$$

If x is 50 and y is 70, the total length would be

$$3(50) + 2(70)$$

$$= 150 + 140$$

$$= \underline{\underline{290.}}$$

If x is 70 and y is 50, the total length would be

$$3(70) + 2(50)$$

$$= 210 + 100$$

$$= \underline{\underline{310.}}$$

Obviously, it makes a difference which number you substitute for x and which you substitute for y! In this section you will evaluate expressions like this for various values of x and y.

Objective:

Given an expression with two variables, evaluate it for different values of the variables.

Cover the answers as you work the following examples.

EXAMPLE 1

For the expression $5x + 9y$:
a.   Evaluate it if $x = 3$ and $y = -2$.
b.   Find x if $y = 10$ and the expression equals 120.
c.   Find y if $x = -7$ and the expression equals 1.

	Think These Reasons

- - - - -   - - - - -

a. $5x + 9y$ Write the given expression.

   $= 5(3) + 9(-2)$ Substitute for x and y.

   $= -3$ Do the computation.

- - - - -   - - - - -

b. $5x + 9(10) = 120$ Set the expression equal to 120, and substitute 10 for y.

   $5x = 30$ Subtract 90 from each member.

   $x = 6$ Divide by 5.

- - - - -   - - - - -

c. $5(-7) + 9y = 1$ Set the expression equal to q, and substitute -7 for x.

   $9y = 36$ Add 35 to each member.

   $y = 4$ Divide by 9.

EXAMPLE 2

Evaluate $3x^2 - 5y^2$ if $x = -9$ and $y = 20$.

- - - - -   - - - - -

   $3x^2 - 5y^2$ Write the given expression.

$= 3(-9)^2 - 5(20)^2$ Substitute -9 for x and 20 for y.

$= 243 - 2000$ Do the computation.

$= -1757$ Do the computation.

EXERCISE 8-1

1. For the expression $8x + 5y$:
    a. Evaluate it if $x = 2$ and $y = 3$.
    b. Evaluate it if $x = 7$ and $y = -3$.
    c. Find x if the expression equals 61 and $y = -9$.
    d. Find y if the expression equals -50 and $x = 0$.

2. For the expression $6x + 10y$:
    a. Evaluate it if $x = 4$ and $y = 3$.
    b. Evaluate it if $x = -9$ and $y = 13$.
    c. Find x if the expression equals -38 and $y = -8$.
    d. Find y if the expression equals 12 and $x = 2$.

3. For the expression $10x - 7y$:
    a. Evaluate it if $x = 3$ and $y = 2$.
    b. Evaluate it if $x = 2$ and $y = 3$.
    c. Find x if the expression equals 67.7 and $y = -3.1$.
    d. Find y if the expression equals 86.9 and $x = -0.55$.

4. For the expression $-3.8x + 10y$:
    a. Evaluate it if $x = 3$ and $y = 7$.
    b. Evaluate it if $x = 7$ and $y = 3$.
    c. Find x if the expression equals -6 and $y = -2.5$.
    d. Find y if the expression equals 18.6 and $x = -0.3$.

5. Evaluate $7 - 3(x + 2y)$ if:
    a. $x = 9$ and $y = 7$;
    b. $x = 18$ and $y = -9$;
    c. $x = -4$ and $y = -11$.

6. Evaluate $8 - 5(4x - y)$ if:
    a. $x = 3$ and $y = 5$;
    b. $x = 2$ and $y = 8$;
    c. $x = -5$ and $y = 3$.

7. Evaluate $x^2 + 6y^2$ if:
    a. $x = 5$ and $y = 3$;
    b. $x = -7$ and $y = 10$;
    c. $x = 100$ and $y = -20$;
    d. $x = -8$ and $y = -1$.

8. Evaluate $4x^2 + y^2$ if:
    a. $x = 6$ and $y = 8$;
    b. $x = -3$ and $y = 30$;
    c. $x = 50$ and $y = -100$;
    d. $x = -6$ and $y = -12$.

1. a. 31   **b.** 41
c. 13.25   **d.** -10

2. a. 54   **b.** 76
c. 7   **d.** 0

3. a. 16   **b.** -1
c. 4.6   **d.** -13.2

4. a. 58.6   **b.** 3.4
c. -5 **d.** 1.746

5. a. -62 **b.** 7   **c.** 85
6. a. -27 **b.** 8   **c.** 123
7. a. 79   **b.** 649
c. 12,400   **d.** 70
8. a. 208   **b.** 936
c. 20,000   **d.** 288

8-2   THE CARTESIAN COORDINATE SYSTEM

Time: $\frac{1}{2}$ or $1\frac{1}{2}$ days, with Section 8–1

Chalkboard Examples:

Show the Cartesian coordinate system and
name the parts.

A number line is used to plot values of a variable. If an expression has
two variables, such as $3x + 2y$, it takes *two* number lines, one for x and
the other for y. The values $x = 4$ and $y = 7$ could be shown as follows.

The usual way to show both values in the same diagram is to cross the two number lines at their origins (see the graph). To plot a point, you start at the origin and move across 4 units in the *x*-direction. Then you move up 7 units in the *y*-direction. The point in the plane is called the **graph** of $x = 4$ and $y = 7$. The two number lines are called the **x-axis** and the **y-axis.**

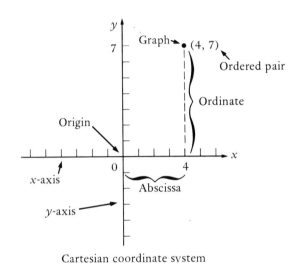

Cartesian coordinate system
(The Cartesian plane)

To shorten things, $x = 4$ and $y = 7$ is written $(4, 7)$. This symbol is called an **ordered pair** of numbers. The order in which the numbers occur tells which number goes with which variable. Unless you are told otherwise, the variables in an ordered pair come in alphabetical order, as in (x, y). People commonly use the idea of ordered pair for such things as time of day (three thirty), balls and strikes (a count of 3 and 2), and men's shirt sizes $(15\frac{1}{2}, 35)$.

The first number in an ordered pair is called the **abscissa.** The word comes from the same Latin root as the word *scissors*. This number tells you where to "cut off" as you run along the *x*-axis. The second number in an ordered pair is called the **ordinate.** This word comes from *order*. Together, the two numbers $(4, 7)$ are called the **coordinates** of a point in a plane.

The whole system—*x*-axis, *y*-axis, points in the plane—is called a **Cartesian coordinate system.** Cartesian is capitalized because it comes

Give the coordinates to one decimal place.

Give the coordinate to one decimal place.

Ans.: a. 1.7   b. 2.1   c. −3.8
Work the Oral Practice.

Assignments:

Day 1: Exercise 8–2, #1–11 odd or 2–12 even
Exercise 8–1, #1 and 3 or 2 and 4 (if not already done)

Day 2: (If necessary) Exercise 8–2, selected problems from 1–12 plus 13 and 15 or 14 and 16.

from the proper name René Descartes, a French mathematician who lived from 1596 to 1650.

A Cartesian coordinate system can be thought of as a piece of graph paper with two axes drawn on it. The axes divide the graph paper into four regions called **quadrants.** The quadrants are numbered counterclockwise, starting at the upper right (where both variables are positive), as shown in the figure.

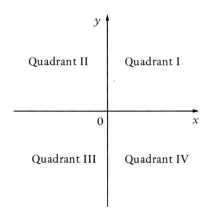

In this section you will plot graphs of ordered pairs and read coordinates of a given point.

Objective:
Given an ordered pair, plot its graph; or given a point in a Cartesian coordinate system, read its coordinates correct to the nearest 0.1 unit.

Cover the answer with paper until you have worked the example.

EXAMPLE 1

Plot $(2, 5)$ and $(-3, 1)$ in a Cartesian coordinate system.

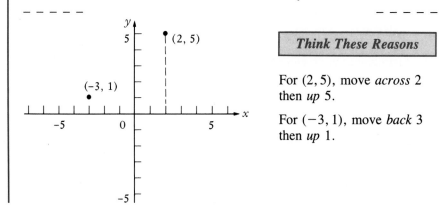

Think These Reasons

For $(2, 5)$, move *across* 2 then *up* 5.

For $(-3, 1)$, move *back* 3 then *up* 1.

Note: Be sure you label the *x*-axis and *y*-axis as shown, with arrow heads and the letters *x* and *y*. Also, show the **scale** on the two axes. For instance, you might put a number every 5 units, as shown above.

EXAMPLE 2

Write the coordinates of points *A* and *B*. Estimate noninteger coordinates to the nearest 0.1 unit.

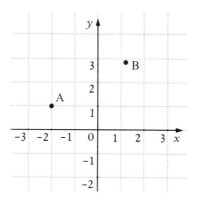

$\underline{A(-2, 1)}$ You move -2 in the *x*-direction, and then move up 1 in the *y*-direction to get to the point. So the ordered pair is $(-2, 1)$. The name of the point and the ordered pair are written together as $A(-2, 1)$.

$\underline{B(1.2, 2.9)}$ The abscissa is *between* 1 and 2. Since it is *less* than halfway, it is either $1.1, 1.2, 1.3$, or 1.4. Because the abscissa is not close to 1 or 1.5, rule out 1.1 and 1.4. So you pick either 1.2 or 1.3; in this case, 1.2 looks *best*. Your answer will be counted correct if it is within ± 0.1 of the "right" answer. So $1.1, 1.2$, or 1.3 would be acceptable values for *x*.

The ordinate is between 2 and 3. Since it is more than halfway, it is either $2.6, 2.7, 2.8$, or 2.9. Pick 2.9, because the point is so close to 3. Again, $2.8, 2.9$, or 3.0 would be acceptable since they are within ± 0.1 unit of the "right" answer.

ORAL PRACTICE

For A through T, give the coordinates of the point.

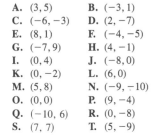

A. (3, 5)   B. (−3, 1)
C. (−6, −3)   D. (2, −7)
E. (8, 1)   F. (−4, −5)
G. (−7, 9)   H. (4, −1)
I. (0, 4)   J. (−8, 0)
K. (0, −2)   L. (6, 0)
M. (5, 8)   N. (−9, −10)
O. (0, 0)   P. (9, −4)
Q. (−10, 6)   R. (0, −8)
S. (7, 7)   T. (5, −9)

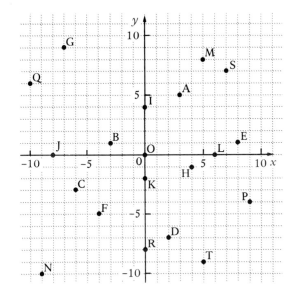

Note: U through DD can be checked by measurement. Spacing is 1 cm.
U. 4.5 V. 3.1 W. 2.6 X. 1.8 Y. 0.3
Z. −0.4 AA. −1.2 BB. −2.7 CC. −3.9
DD. −4.8

For U through DD, give the coordinate of the point correct to the nearest 0.1 unit.

Give the quadrant in which the following points are found.

EE. (5, 3) I   FF. (6, −2) IV

GG. (−7.2, 1) II   HH. (−3.4, −2.8) III

EXERCISE 8-2

For Problems 1 and 2, write the coordinates of each point as an ordered pair. All points have integer coordinates.

1. A (2, 5)   2. M (3, 1)
    B (−3, 2)   N (1, 5)
    C (−3, −2)   O (−2, −3)
    D (1, −5)   P (−3, 3)
    E (5, 0)   Q (2, −1)
    F (0, 3)   R (−4, −1)
    G (−3, 5)   S (0, −5)
    H (−5, 1)   T (−4, 5)
    I (−5, −4)   U (5, −3)
    J (−2, 0)   V (4, 0)

1.

2.
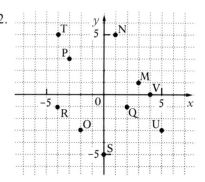

For Problems 3 and 4, draw a Cartesian coordinate system on graph paper. Then plot the points. Be sure to indicate which is which!

3. a. $(5, 2)$ 4. a. $(1, 3)$
    b. $(-3, 7)$ b. $(-2, 5)$
    c. $(4, -6)$ c. $(-4, -7)$
    d. $(-2, -1)$ d. $(3, -8)$
    e. $(0, 3)$ e. $(5, 0)$

5. Estimate the coordinates of points $A, B, C,$ and D, below, to the nearest 0.1 unit.

6. Estimate the coordinates of points $R, S, T,$ and U, below, to the nearest 0.1 unit.

3.

4.

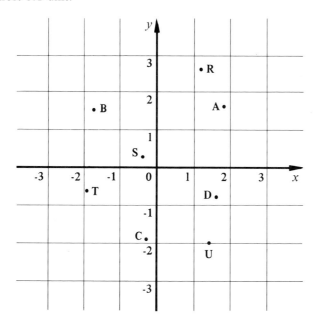

Problem Notes:

Problems 5 and 6 let students practice accurate reading of graphs for points that do not have integer coordinates. This skill is important. Students can become remarkably good at doing this, given a tolerance of ±0.1 unit. Do not let them use fractions or more than one decimal place.

Note: In Problems 5 and 6 the grid lines are 1 cm apart.
  5. A(1.8, 1.6) B(−1.7, 1.5) C(−0.3, −1.9)
         D(1.6, −0.8)
  6. R(1.2, 2.6) S(−0.4, 0.3) T(−1.9, −0.6)
         U(1.4, −2.0)

7. Plot points $A(7, 10)$ and $B(1, -2)$ on graph paper. Use a ruler to connect them with a straight line. Then write the coordinates of each point.
    a. The point midway between A and B (4, 4)
    b. The point $\frac{1}{3}$ of the way from A to B (5, 6)
    c. The point $\frac{2}{3}$ of the way from A to B (3, 2)
    d. The point where the line crosses the x-axis.   (2, 0)

8. Plot points $R(-2, 7)$ and $S(6, 3)$ on graph paper. Use a ruler to connect them with a straight line. Then write the coordinates of each point.
    a. The point midway between R and S (2, 5)
    b. The point $\frac{1}{4}$ of the way from R to S (0, 6)
    c. The point $\frac{3}{4}$ of the way from R to S (4, 4)
    d. The point where the graph crosses the y-axis.   (0, 6)

7.

8.

9.

10.

11.

12

Problems 15 and 16 anticipate plotting of linear graphs in the next section.

15.

16.

9. Connect points $A(-3, 1)$ and $B(5, 4)$ with a straight line. Connect points $C(1, 5)$ and $D(3, -1)$ with another straight line. Then estimate to the nearest 0.1 unit the coordinates of the point where the two lines intersect.   (1.7, 2.8)

10. Connect points $R(-2, 4)$ and $S(4, 1)$ with a straight line. Connect points $T(-1, -2)$ and $U(3, 4)$ with another straight line. Then estimate to the nearest 0.1 unit the coordinates of the point where the two lines intersect.   (1.7, 2.1)

11. Connect points $E(-4, -2)$ and $F(1, 1)$ with a straight line. Connect points $G(-3, 1)$ and $H(2, 4)$ with another straight line. What special relationship do the two lines have to each other?   The lines are *parallel.*

12. Connect points $P(-4, 1)$ and $J(2, 5)$ with a staight line. Connect points $U(-5, 5)$ and $W(-1, -1)$ with another straight line. What special relationship do the two lines have to each other?   The lines are *perpendicular.*

13. Write an example of an ordered pair with integer coordinates for each point described.
   a. In Quadrant I; abscissa is twice its ordinate.   (2, 1), (4, 2), . . .
   b. In Quadrant II; ordinate is 3 more than its abscissa.   (−1, 2), . . .
   c. In Quadrant III; ordinate is 5 times its abscissa.   (−1, −5), . . .
   d. In Quadrant IV; abscissa is 4 more than its ordinate.   (3, −1), . . .
   e. On the x-axis; negative abscissa   (−1, 0), (−2, 0), . . .

14. Write an example of an ordered pair with integer coordinates for each point described.
   a. In Quadrant I; ordinate is 3 times its abscissa.   (1, 3), (2,6), . . .
   b. In Quadrant II; abscissa is 5 less than its ordinate.   (−4, 1), . . .
   c. In Quadrant III; abscissa is 4 times its ordinate.   (−4, −1), . . .
   d. In Quadrant IV; ordinate is 6 less than its abscissa.   (1, −5), . . .
   e. On the y-axis; positive ordinate   (0, 1), (0, 2), . . .

15. Suppose that $3x + 5y = 60$.
   a. Substitute 10 for x in this equation. Then solve for y. Write the values of x and y as an ordered pair. Then repeat the procedure for $x = 15$ and for $x = -5$.
   b. Plot the three ordered pairs on a Cartesian coordinate system. If your work is correct, all three points should lie on a straight line.

16. Suppose that $5x - 2y = 30$.
   a. Substitute 4 for x in this equation. Then solve for y. Write the values of x and y as an ordered pair. Then repeat the procedure for $x = 8$ and for $x = -2$.
   b. Plot the three ordered pairs on a Cartesian coordinate system. If your work is correct, all three points should lie on a straight line.

8-3 | GRAPHS OF EQUATIONS CONTAINING TWO VARIABLES

Algebra is the study of expressions with variables. One thing you do with such expressions is to set them equal to some number and find the value of the variable. If the expression has *two* variables, there may be many values that satisfy the equation. For example,

$$2x + 5y = 30$$

is a true statement for ordered pairs $(0, 6)$, $(5, 4)$, and $(13, 0.8)$, as well as many others. For instance, for $(5, 4)$, $2(5) + 5(4)$ equals $10 + 20$, which *does* equal 30.

Such ordered pairs are called *solutions* of the equation.

DEFINITION

> **SOLUTION, EQUATION CONTAINING TWO VARIABLES**
> A **solution** of an equation with two variables is an ordered pair that makes the equation a *true* statement.

The set of *all* such ordered pairs is called the *solution set*.

Since the solution set contains so many ordered pairs, you usually draw a graph of it rather than trying to write the pairs. To plot the graph of an equation such as

$$2x + 5y = 30,$$

you must find some ordered pairs. One way is to pick a value of one variable, substitute it into the equation, then calculate the value of the other variable. For instance, choose $x = 7$.

$2(7) + 5y = 30$	Substitute 7 for x.
$14 + 5y = 30$	Do the computation.
$5y = 16$	Subtract 14 from each member.
$y = 3.2$	Divide each member by 5.

So one ordered pair would be $(7, 3.2)$.

An efficient way to calculate *many* ordered pairs is to get one variable by

Time: 2 days

Chalkboard Examples:

First day:
For $3x + 4y = 24$:
a. pick several values of x and calculate the corresponding values of y;
b. transform the equation so that y is in terms of x. Ans.: $y = -\frac{3}{4}x + 6$;
c. use the transformed equation to calculate more ordered pairs. (Use multiples of 4.) Plot these.

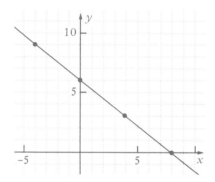

Students should now work the example to make sure they have the right idea.

Second day:
Homework problems on board, especially 9 and 11. Do Oral Practice.

Assignments:

Day 1: Exercise 8–2, #15 or 16 (if not previously done)
       Exercise 8–3, #1–11 odd
Day 2: Exercise 8–3, #10–20 even

itself on the left side and everything else on the right. Starting with
$2x + 5y = 30$ and isolating y, you would write the following.

$$2x + 5y = 30$$

$$5y = -2x + 30 \qquad \text{Add } -2x \text{ to each member.}$$

$$y = -\frac{2}{5}x + 6 \qquad \text{Divide each member by 5.}$$

In the last equation, y is said to be written *in terms of* x. This procedure is
the same as for solving the literal equations in Section 4-5. Finding values
of y is now the familiar process of evaluating an expression. For instance,

$$x = 10:$$

$$y = -\frac{2}{5}(10) + 6 = -4 + 6 = \underline{\underline{2}};$$

$$x = -5:$$

$$y = -\frac{2}{5}(-5) + 6 = 2 + 6 = \underline{\underline{8}}.$$

To keep track of all these values of x and y, it is convenient to make a
table of values. These values can then be plotted as ordered pairs, as
shown next.

x	y
0	6
5	4
10	2
15	0
−5	8
−10	10

Make a
table of values.

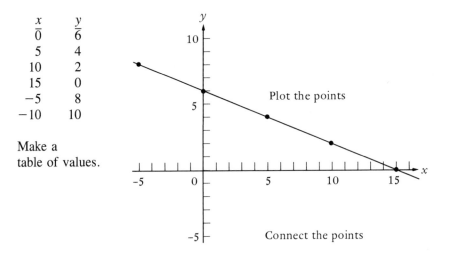

Plot the points

Connect the points

A pattern shows up when you plot the ordered pairs from this table. The
points are in a straight line! Later in this chapter you will learn why all
linear equations have straight-line graphs. To complete this graph, you can
simply connect the points. The second figure shows the finished graph.
Any point on this line represents an ordered pair in the solution set of this
equation.

Objective:

Given a linear equation with two variables (such as $2x + 5y = 30$), transform it so that y is written in terms of x. Then evaluate y for various values of x and use the resulting ordered pairs to plot the graph.

Cover the answers as you work this example.

EXAMPLE

For the equation $x - 2y = 6$:

a.   transform the equation so that y is given in terms of x;

b.   pick four values of x, and evaluate y;

c.   plot the graph.

- - - - -   - - - - -

	Think These Reasons

a. $x - 2y = 6$ Write the given equation.

$\qquad -2y = -x + 6$ Add $-x$ to each member.

$\qquad y = \dfrac{1}{2}x - 3$ Multiply each member by $-\dfrac{1}{2}$.

- - - - -   - - - - -

b.

x	y	Make a
0	−3	table of
2	−2	values.
4	−1	
6	0	

c.   Plot the graph.

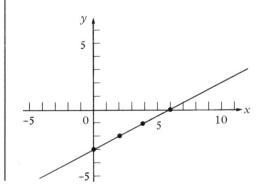

ORAL PRACTICE

For A through L, give the coordinates of the ordered pairs.

A. (6, 8) **B.** (3, 6) **C.** (0, 4) **D.** (−3, 2)
E. (−6, 0) **F.** (−9, −2) **G.** (−10, 9)
H. (−6, 6) **I.** (−2, 3) **J.** (2, 0)
K. (6, −3) **L.** (10, −6)

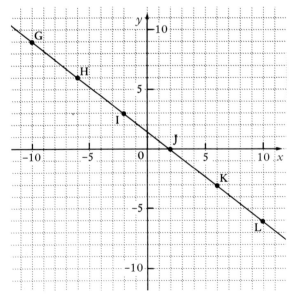

M. $y = -4x + 9$ **N.** $y = -7x - 10$
O. $y = 8x - 6$ **P.** $y = 5x + 7$
Q. $y = -\dfrac{3}{2}x + \dfrac{5}{2}$ **R.** $y = -3x - 5$
S. $y = \dfrac{7}{3}x - \dfrac{4}{3}$ **T.** $y = 4x + 5$
U. $y = -\dfrac{1}{4}x - \dfrac{11}{4}$ **V.** $y = \dfrac{1}{5}x - 4$
W. $y = -x + 6$ **X.** $y = x + 9$

Transform the equation so that y is given in terms of x.

M. $4x + y = 9$ N. $7x + y = -10$ O. $8x - y = 6$

P. $5x - y = -7$ Q. $3x + 2y = 5$ R. $6x + 2y = -10$

S. $7x - 3y = 4$ T. $12x - 3y = -15$ U. $x + 4y = -11$

V. $x - 5y = 20$ W. $x + y = 6$ X. $x - y = -9$

EXERCISE 8-3

For Problems 1 through 8, draw a graph of the indicated set of points. Connect the points with a straight line.

1. (x, y)
    $(5, 8)$
    $(3, 5)$
    $(1, 2)$
    $(-1, -1)$

2. (x, y)
    $(7, 5)$
    $(4, 3)$
    $(1, 1)$
    $(-2, -1)$

3. (x, y)
    $(-3, 7)$
    $(0, 4)$
    $(3, 1)$
    $(6, -2)$

4. (x, y)
    $(-2, 7)$
    $(0, \quad 3)$
    $(2, -1)$
    $(4, -5)$

5. | x | y |
    |----|----|
    | -5 | 3 |
    | -1 | 1 |
    | 3 | -1 |
    | 7 | -3 |

6. | x | y |
    |----|----|
    | -5 | 7 |
    | -2 | 2 |
    | 1 | -3 |
    | 4 | -8 |

7. | x | y |
    |----|----|
    | -5 | -7 |
    | 0 | -4 |
    | 5 | -1 |
    | 10 | 2 |

8. | x | y |
    |----|----|
    | -1 | -5 |
    | 0 | -2 |
    | 1 | 1 |
    | 2 | 4 |

1.–14. See Additional Answers.

For Problems 9 through 20:

a. transform the equation so that y is given in terms of x;
b. pick four numbers, substitute them for x, and evaluate y.
c. plot the graph of the equation.

9. $3x + y = 12$

10. $2x + y = 10$

11. $2x - y = 6$

12. $3x - y = 6$

13. $4x + 5y = 40$

14. $3x + 5y = 30$

15. $3x - 2y = -18$

16. $2x - 3y = -12$

17. $x + y = 7$

18. $x - y = 4$

19. $x - 3y = 0$

20. $x + 2y = 0$

15–20. See Additional Answers.

Problem Notes:

In Problems 9–20, the most prevalent error in dividing each member by the coefficient of y on the left is forgetting to distribute the division to *both* terms on the right.

Insist that students label the two axes with the variable names and show enough numbers on the axes for you to be able to determine the scale. Marking every 5 units is reasonable.

9. **a.** $y = -3x + 12$
    b.
x	y
-1	15
0	12
1	9
2	6
3	3
4	0

10. **a.** $y = -2x + 10$
    b.
x	y
0	10
1	8
2	6
3	4
4	2
5	0

11. **a.** $y = 2x - 6$
    b.
x	y
0	-6
1	-4
2	-2
3	0
4	2

12. **a.** $y = 3x - 6$
    b.
x	y
0	-6
1	-3
2	0
3	3
4	6

13. **a.** $y = -\frac{4}{5}x + 8$
    b.
x	y
0	8
5	4
10	0
-5	12

14. **a.** $y = -\frac{3}{5}x + 6$
    b.
x	y
-5	9
0	6
5	3
10	0

15. **a.** $y = \frac{3}{2}x + 9$
    b.
x	y
-6	0
-4	3
-2	6
0	9

16. **a.** $y = \frac{2}{3}x + 4$
    b.
x	y
-6	0
-3	2
0	4
3	6

17. **a.** $y = -x + 7$
    b.
x	y
7	0
6	1
5	2
4	3
3	4
2	5
1	6
0	7

18. **a.** $y = +x - 4$
    b.
x	y
0	-4
1	-3
2	-2
3	-1
4	0

8-4 | INTERCEPTS AND RAPID GRAPHING

19. a. $x - 3y = 0$ **20. a.** $x + 2y = 0$

$y = \dfrac{1}{3}x$ $y = -\dfrac{1}{2}x$

b.

x	y
−3	−1
0	0
3	1
6	2

b.

x	y
−2	1
0	0
2	−1
4	−2

Time: 4 days, including test

Chalkboard Examples:

First day:
Find the intercepts and plot.
$3x + 4y = 24$
Ans.: $x = 8$, $y = 6$
(Graph below.)

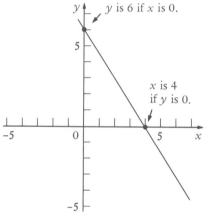
y is 6 if x is 0.
x is 4 if y is 0.

Second day:
1. Plot the points (1, 7) and (5, 2). Find the two intercepts of the line through these two points. Ans.: $x = 6.6$, $y = 8.2$ or 8.3

In the last section you observed that equations such as

$$3x + 2y = 12$$

have graphs that turn out to be straight lines. You can use this fact to draw these graphs with very little work! All you need to do is find *two* points and draw the line.

The easiest two points to find are usually the points where the graph crosses the two coordinate axes. A graph crosses the y-axis where $x = 0$. Substituting 0 for x in $3x + 2y = 12$ gives

$$0 + 2y = 12$$
$$y = 6.$$

Similarly, substituting 0 for y gives

$$3x + 0 = 12$$
$$x = 4.$$

You can plot the two ordered pairs $(0, 6)$ and $(4, 0)$ and draw the line, as shown in the figure.

The numbers 6 and 4 have special names. The 6 is called the *y-intercept*. The 4 is called the *x-intercept*. These names come from the fact that the graph "intercepts" the two axes at these values.

DEFINITION

> **INTERCEPTS**
> The **y-intercept** is the value of y when x is 0.
> The **x-intercept** is the value of x when y is 0.

Objective:
Given an equation of a line, find the x- and y-intercepts, and use these to draw the graph *quickly*.

Cover the answers as you work this example.

EXAMPLE

For the equation $5x - 3y = -30$:
a.   find the x- and y-intercepts;
b.   plot the graph.

- - - - -

a.   Let $x = 0$.

$$0 - 3y = -30$$

$$y = 10$$

y-intercept is 10.

Let $y = 0$.

$$5x - 0 = -30$$

$$x = -6$$

x-intercept is -6.

b.

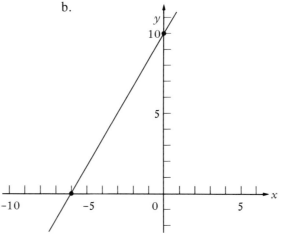

ORAL PRACTICE

Give the y-intercept.

EXAMPLE

	Answer
$3x - 2y = 18$	-9

A. $4x + 3y = 24$ 8

B. $2x + 5y = -100$ -20

C. $3x - 4y = 36$ -9

D. $5x - 8y = -80$ 10

E. $2x + y = 10$ 10

F. $6x - y = -18$ 18

Tell the x-intercept.

G. $4x + 3y = 24$ 6

H. $2x + 5y = -100$ -50

I. $3x - 4y = 36$ 12

J. $5x - 8y = -80$ -16

K. $x + 2y = 10$ 10

L. $x - 6y = -18$ -18

2. *Notebooks and Lab Manuals Problem*—A store sells notebooks for $3 each and lab manuals for $4 each.
   a.   Write an expression for the total number of dollars received.
   b.   The store sells 17 notebooks and 20 lab manuals. How much money does it receive?
   c.   The store's daily quota is $60 from selling notebooks and lab manuals. Write an equation stating this fact.
   d.   Find the intercepts for the equation in part (c).
   e.   Plot an accurate graph of the equation in part (c). Use one square space for each 1 unit on each axis.
   f.   From the graph, find all possible combinations of notebooks and lab manuals that cause the quota to be met exactly.

Solutions:

a.   Let x = no. of notebooks.
     Let y = no. of lab manuals.
     $3x + 4y$ = no. of dollars.
b. $3x + 4y$
        $= 3(17) + 4(20)$
        $= 131$
        $131
c. $3x + 4y = 60$
d. $x = 20$, $y = 15$
e.   (Graph.)

f.   Ordered pairs are:
     (0, 15), (4, 12), (8, 9),
     (12, 6), (16, 3), (20, 0)
3.   You go 20 mi/h for x hours and 15 mi/h for y hours. Write an expression for the total number of miles you have gone.
     Ans.: $20x + 15y$ = no. of miles.

Assignment:

Day 1: Exercise 8–3, #13–19 odd
       Exercise 8–4, #1–9 odd
Day 2: Exercise 8–4, #11–25 odd
Day 3: Exercise 8–4, #12, 16, 20, 22, 26, 27
       in preparation for test
Day 4: (after test) Exercise 8–4, 28 (It is better not to have students try to work ahead in Section 8–5 before class discussion.)

Give the *x*- and *y*-intercepts of each line.

M. *x* : −7
    y : 5
N. *x* : 3
    y : 2

O. *x* : −6
    y : −7
P. *x* : 4
    y : −3

Q. *x* : None
    y : 4
R. *x* : 6
    y : None

EXERCISE 8-4

For Problems 1 through 20, calculate the x- and y-intercepts. Use them to plot the graph.

1. $4x + 3y = 24$ $x:6$ $y:8$

2. $3x + 4y = 36$ $x:12$ $y:9$

3. $2x + 5y = -20$ $x:-10$ $y:-4$

4. $5x + 3y = -15$ $x:-3$ $y:-5$

5. $3x - 4y = 36$ $x:12$ $y:-9$

6. $4x - 3y = 24$ $x:6$ $y:-8$

7. $5x - 8y = -40$ $x:-8$ $y:5$

8. $6x - 5y = -30$ $x:-5$ $y:6$

9. $2x + y = 10$ $x:5$ $y:10$

10. $3x + y = 6$ $x:2$ $y:6$

11. $6x - y = -12$ $x:-2$ $y:12$

12. $4x - y = -8$ $x:-2$ $y:8$

13. $x + 3y = 6$ $x:6$ $y:2$

14. $x + 5y = 10$ $x:10$ $y:2$

15. $x + y = 4$ $x:4$ $y:4$

16. $x + y = -7$ $x:-7$ $y:-7$

17. $x - y = -3$ $x:-3$ $y:3$

18. $x - y = 5$ $x:5$ $y:-5$

19. $2x + 3y = 15$ $x:7.5$ $y:5$

20. $3x + 2y = 9$ $x:3$ $y:4.5$

Problem Notes:

Problems 1–20 are designed to give students a quick and easy way to plot linear graphs. All except 19 and 20 have integer intercepts.

In Problems 21–24 the points are close enough to the axes for students to get the intercepts ± 0.1 unit with a reasonable amount of care. They should use a scale of 1 space for 1 unit. Normal, inexpensive quadrille graph paper with spacing of 0.4 to 0.5 cm or $\frac{3}{16}$ to $\frac{1}{4}$ inch works well.

Starting in this chapter, word problems are distributed through the chapter, where appropriate, rather than being concentrated at the end. Problems 25–28 show use of two-variable expressions in relatively easy situations with highly structured formats.

1.–24. See Additional Answers for graphs.

Note: Answers to Problems 21 through 24 are by *calculation*, rounded to 1 decimal place.

For Problems 21 through 24, plot the two points carefully on graph paper. Connect the points with a straight line, using a ruler and a *sharp* pencil. Then read the x- and y-intercepts, correct to the nearest 0.1 unit, from the graph. Your answer will be considered to be correct if it is no more than ± 0.1 unit from the correct answer.

21. $(-3, 9)$ and $(10, -2)$ $x:7.6$ $y:6.5$

22. $(-5, -1)$ and $(3, 6)$ $x:-3.9$ $y:3.4$

23. $(7, 1)$ and $(-2, -4)$ $x:5.2$ $y:-2.9$

24. $(-3, 3)$ and $(2, -5)$ $x:-1.1$ $y:-1.8$

25. *Tickets Problem* Reserved tickets for the basketball game cost $3 each and general admission tickets cost $2 each. Let x be the number of reserved tickets a person sells and let y be the number of general admission tickets that person sells.

```
┌─────────────────────────────┐
│        TICKET SALES          │
│                              │
│   Reserved:                  │
│      x @ $3  .  .  .  _____  │
│                              │
│   Gen. Admission:            │
│      y @ $2  .  .  .  _____  │
│                              │
│         Total .  .  .  _____ │
└─────────────────────────────┘
```

a. Write an expression for the total number of dollars the person gets for tickets sold. $3x + 2y$
b. How much money is received for:
    i.   8 reserved, 10 general admission; $44
    ii. 10 reserved, 8 general admission? $46
c. A member of the pep squad must sell $30 worth of tickets. Write an equation stating this. $3x + 2y = 30$
d. Find the intercepts of the equation in part (c) and use these to plot the graph of the equation. $x : 10$ $y : 15$
e. Since only whole numbers of tickets can be sold, x and y must be integers. From your graph, find all possible ordered pairs (x, y) that have nonnegative integer coordinates.
    $(0, 15), (2, 12), (4, 9), (6, 6), (8, 3), (10, 0)$

25d.

26. ***Socks and Scarves Problem***   Socks cost $3 a pair and scarves cost $5 each. Natalie Attired buys some of each. Let x be the number of pairs of socks and let y be the number of scarves she buys.

NATALIE'S BILL
Socks:
x pr. @ $3 . . _____
Scarves:
y @ $5   .   .   . _____
Total .   .   . ======

a. Write an expression for the total number of dollars she pays. $3x + 5y$
b. How much would she pay for:
    i.   7 pairs of socks, 4 scarves; $41
    ii. 4 pairs of socks, 7 scarves? $47
c. Write an equation stating that Natalie spends a total of $60 for socks and scarves. $3x + 5y = 60$
d. Find the intercepts for the equation in part (c) and use these to plot the graph of the equation. $x : 20$ $y : 12$
e. You can buy only a whole number of pairs of socks and a whole number of scarves. Use your graph to find all possible numbers of pairs of socks and scarves Natalie could have bought for $60 total. $(0, 12), (5, 9), (10, 6), (15, 3), (20, 0)$

26d.

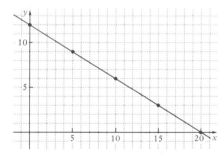

27. ***Walking and Cycling Problem***   Ida Liver can walk at a rate of 100 yards per minute and can ride her bike at 300 yards per minute. Let x be the number of minutes she walks and let y be the number of minutes she rides.
a. Write an expression for the total number of yards she goes. $100x + 300y$
b. How far does she go if she:
    i.   walks for 7 minutes and rides for 3 minutes;   1600 yd
    ii. walks for 3 minutes and rides for 7 minutes?   2400 yd

c.   Ida must deliver a package to a destination 6000 yards away. Write an equation stating this. $100x + 300y = 6000$

d.   Find the intercepts for the equation in part (c). Use these numbers to plot the graph of the equation. $x:60$ $y:20$

e.   If Ida walks for 12 minutes on her 6000-yard delivery, how many minutes must she ride her bike? Show that this ordered pair is *on* your graph in part (d).   16 min

27d.

28.   ***Train and Bus Problem***   A train averages 80 miles per hour (mi/h), and a bus averages 50 mi/h. Let x be the number of hours you ride the train and let y be the number of hours you ride the bus.

a.   Write an expression for the total number of miles you ride. $80x + 50y$

b.   How far do you go if you ride:
  i.   3 hours on the train and 6 hours on the bus;   540 mi
  ii.   6 hours on the train and 3 hours on the bus?   630 mi

c.   You make a 400-mile trip, part by train and part by bus. Write an equation stating this fact. $80x + 50y = 400$

d.   Find the intercepts of the equation and use them to plot the graph of the equation. $x:5$ $y:8$

e.   If you go for 2 hours on the train, how many hours must you ride the bus to complete the 400-mile trip? Show that this ordered pair is *on* your graph in part (d).   4.8 h

28d.

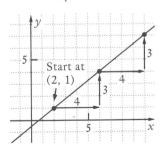

8-5 | SLOPE AND RAPID GRAPHING

Time: 2 days

Chalkboard Examples:

First day:
Draw point $(2, 1)$ on the graph board. From this point, run across 4 spaces to the right, then rise up 3 spaces. The point is $(6, 4)$. Repeat. The point is $(10, 7)$. Connect the points. The result is a straight line. The ratio $\frac{3}{4}$ is called the *slope*.

If you go from the point $(2, 1)$ to the point $(7, 3)$, as in the figure, you must run across 5 units in the x-direction and rise up 2 units in the y-direction. These distances are given the (obvious!) names *run* and *rise*.

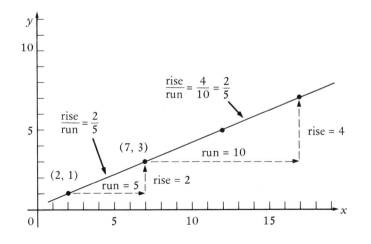

Alternate approach: Use computer graphics to plot $y = mx + b$ with varying values of m and b. Have students discover slope and intercept. Have students work Examples 1 and 2 in class so that they can uncover misconceptions before they start their homework.

Second day:
Put homework on board. Overhead projector transparencies of Problems 1–10 are effective.

Use Oral Practice problems. For Q–V, give students a few minutes to work the problems on their own, then ask specific students for answers.

Assignment:

Day 1: Exercise 8–5, #1–15 odd
Day 2: Exercise 8–5, #12–26 even

DEFINITION

> **RUN AND RISE**
> In going from one point to another in a Cartesian coordinate system, the **run** is the change in x and the **rise** is the change in y.

For any two points on the same straight line, the ratio

$$\frac{\text{rise}}{\text{run}}$$

is *constant*. For the line in the figure, the ratio rise/run is always equal to $\frac{2}{3}$, no matter what pair of points you pick. Since this number indicates how "steep" the line is, it is called the *slope* of the line.

DEFINITION

> **SLOPE**
> The slope of a line is the ratio
> $$\frac{\text{rise}}{\text{run}}.$$

The slope shows up in the equation of a line if you write the equation so that y is in terms of x. Suppose that you plot

$$y = \frac{2}{3}x + 4.$$

as you did in Section 8-3. By substituting various values for x, you can evaluate y and make a table.

x	y
−6	0
−3	2
0	4
3	6
6	8
9	10

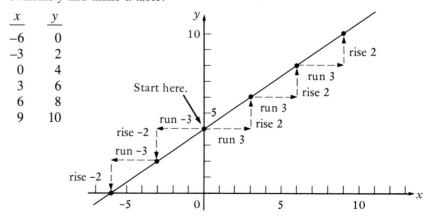

For each pair of points, the slope is $\frac{2}{3}$. And this number is the coefficient of x in the equation! From the table or the graph, you can see that this is true; each time x increases by 3, y increases by 2.

This fact reveals the reason a linear equation has a straight-line graph. It also provides a quick way to draw the graph. You start at any point on the graph, run 3 and rise 2, and you will be at another point on the graph.

All you need is a convenient starting point. The y-intercept is easy to find. Substituting 0 for x in the equation gives

$$y = \frac{2}{3}(0) + 4 = 4.$$

So the y-intercept is 4. Note that this number also shows up in the equation.

$$y = \frac{2}{3}x + 4$$

$$\text{slope} \qquad \text{y-intercept}$$

Any linear equation with y by itself on the left and a linear binomial on the right is said to be in *slope-intercept form*. The letter m is usually used for the slope and b is used for the y-intercept.

CONCLUSION

SLOPE-INTERCEPT FORM
An equation of the form $y = mx + b$, where m and b are constants, is in **slope-intercept form.**
The constant m is the *slope*.
The constant b is the y-intercept.

For the equation $y = \frac{2}{3}x + 4$, $m = \frac{2}{3}$ and $b = 4$.

Objectives:
1. Given two points in a Cartesian coordinate system, find the slope of the line connecting them.
2. Given a linear equation with two variables, find the slope and the y-intercept and use these numbers to plot the graph quickly.

Cover the answers as you work these examples.

EXAMPLE 1

Find the slope of each line.

a.   Line A   b.   Line B   c.   Line C   d.   Line D

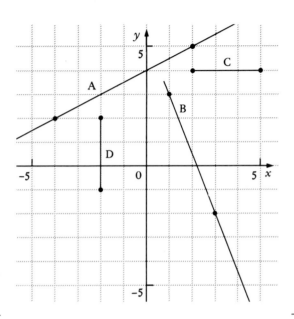

	Think These Reasons

a. $m = \dfrac{\text{rise}}{\text{run}}$ Definition of slope

$= \dfrac{3}{6}$ Count squares. Rise is *up* 3. Run is 6.

$= \dfrac{1}{2}$ Simplify the fraction, if possible.

b. $m = \dfrac{\text{rise}}{\text{run}}$ Definition of slope

$= \dfrac{-5}{2}$ Rise is *down* 5. Run is 2.

$= -\dfrac{5}{2}$ Negative divided by positive is negative.

c. $m = \dfrac{\text{rise}}{\text{run}}$ Definition of slope

$$= \frac{0}{3}$$ Zero squares up or down 3 squares across

$$= \underline{\underline{0}}$$ Arithmetic

- - - - -   - - - - -

d. $m = \dfrac{\text{rise}}{\text{run}}$ Definition of slope

$$= \frac{3}{0}$$ 3 squares up. Zero squares across

$$\underline{\underline{\text{No value!}}}$$ No answer for division by zero!

The line in part (c) is *horizontal*. The line in part (d) is *vertical*. From the answers to these examples you can draw the conclusion shown.

CONCLUSION

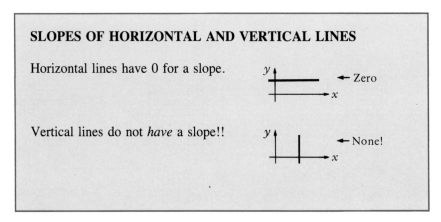

SLOPES OF HORIZONTAL AND VERTICAL LINES

Horizontal lines have 0 for a slope.   ← Zero

Vertical lines do not *have* a slope!!   ← None!

EXAMPLE 2

Write the slope and y-intercept and plot the graph.

$$y = -\frac{3}{5}x + 7$$

- - - - -   - - - - -

$$\underline{\underline{m = -\frac{3}{5}}}$$ $\left(\text{Also equals } \dfrac{-3}{5} \text{ and } \dfrac{3}{-5}.\right)$

$$\underline{\underline{b = 7}}$$ Let $x = 0$. Find y.

For the graph, start at the y-intercept. Count *across* 5 and *down* 3. Or count *back* 5 and *up* 3. Repeat until you have enough points to draw the graph.

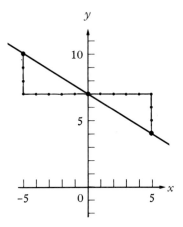

ORAL PRACTICE

Give the slope.

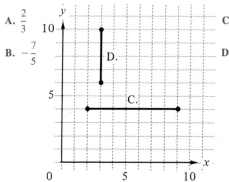

A. $\dfrac{2}{3}$

B. $-\dfrac{7}{5}$

C. 0

D. None

Give the slope.

E. $y = \dfrac{3}{4}x + 7$ $\dfrac{3}{4}$ **F.** $y = \dfrac{9}{5}x - 4$ $\dfrac{9}{5}$ **G.** $y = -\dfrac{3}{2}x + 8$ $-\dfrac{3}{2}$

H. $y = -4x + 9$ $_{-4}$ **I.** $y = x + 6$ $_{1}$ **J.** $y = -x + 2$ $_{-1}$

Give the y-intercept.

K. $y = \dfrac{3}{4}x + 7$ $_{7}$ **L.** $y = \dfrac{9}{5}x - 4$ $_{-4}$ **M.** $y = -\dfrac{3}{2}x + 8$ $_{8}$

N. $y = -4x + 9$ $_{9}$ **O.** $y = x - 6$ $_{-6}$ **P.** $y = 3x$ $_{0}$

Transform to slope-intercept form.

EXAMPLE

                    Answer

$3x + 4y = 24$ $y = -\dfrac{3}{4}x + 6$

Q. $3x + y = 7$ $y = -3x + 7$ R. $5x - y = 8$ $y = 5x - 8$

S. $6x + 5y = 20$ $y = -\frac{6}{5}x + 4$ T. $2x - 3y = 15$ $y = \frac{2}{3}x - 5$

U. $x + 2y = 6$ $y = -\frac{1}{2}x + 3$ V. $-x + 3y = -12$ $y = \frac{1}{3}x - 4$

EXERCISE 8-5

For Problems 1 and 2, find the slope of each line. Simplify as much as possible.   See Additional Answers

1.   2.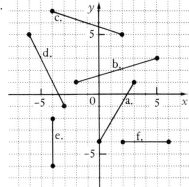

For Problems 3 through 10, plot the points on a Cartesian coordinate system and connect them with a straight line. Find the slope and simplify it if possible.   See Additional Answers.

3. $(-2, 4)$ and $(5, -1)$. $m = -\frac{5}{7}$ 4. $(-2, 1)$ and $(3, 5)$. $m = \frac{4}{5}$

5. $(-2, 1)$ and $(1, -3)$. $m = -\frac{4}{3}$ 6. $(-1, 4)$ and $(3, -4)$. $m = -2$

7. $(-1, 2)$ and $(-4, -6)$. $m = \frac{8}{3}$ 8. $(-3, -4)$ and $(3, -1)$. $m = \frac{1}{2}$

9. $(-6, 1)$ and $(1, -3)$. $m = -\frac{4}{7}$ 10. $(-3, 3)$ and $(-1, -2)$. $m = -\frac{5}{2}$

For Problems 11 through 22, plot the graph using the slope and the y-intercept. Label the axes and show the scale.

Problem Notes:

Problems 11–14 have slopes that are already fractions. For Problems 15–22, students must make fractions. Problems 21 and 22 have slopes of -1 and 1, respectively.

Problems 27–30 have equations in the *point-slope* form. You can point out to students that in Problem 27, for example, the point $(6, 3)$ is on the graph. This point makes the equation true because each member equals zero.

1.   a. $m = \dfrac{7 - 3}{2 - (-7)} = \dfrac{4}{9}$

     b. $m = \dfrac{-2 - 2}{-1 - (-4)} = \dfrac{-4}{3} = -\dfrac{4}{3}$

     c. $m = \dfrac{6}{3} = 2$

     d. $m = \dfrac{-8}{4} = -2$

     e. $m = \dfrac{0}{3} = 0$

     f. $m = \dfrac{3}{0}$ no slope

2.   a. $m = \dfrac{5}{3}$

     b. $m = \dfrac{2}{7}$

     c. $m = \dfrac{-2}{6} = -\dfrac{1}{3}$

     d. $m = \dfrac{-6}{3} = -2$

     e. $m = \dfrac{4}{0}$ no slope!

     f. $m = \dfrac{0}{4} = 0$

11. $y = \dfrac{3}{5}x + 3$ 12. $y = \dfrac{5}{2}x - 1$ 13. $y = -\dfrac{3}{2}x - 4$

14. $y = -\dfrac{1}{4}x + 3$ 15. $y = 2x - 5$ 16. $y = 3x - 2$

17. $y = -3x + 1$ 18. $y = -2x + 6$ 19. $y = 3x$

20. $y = -2x$ 21. $y = -x + 4$ 22. $y = x - 5$

11.–30. See Additional Answers.

In Problems 23 through 30, transform the equation to the slope-intercept form ($y = mx + b$). Then give the slope and the y-intercept. Finally, plot the graph.

23. $7x + 2y = 10$ 24. $3x + 5y = 10$

25. $x - 4y = 12$ 26. $2x - 5y = 15$

27. $y - 3 = \frac{2}{3}(x - 6)$ 28. $y - 5 = \frac{3}{7}(x - 7)$

29. $y + 2 = -\frac{1}{4}(x + 8)$ 30. $y + 3 = -\frac{5}{2}(x - 4)$

For Problems 31 through 34, find the equation of the line described. To do this, you need to recall where the slope and y-intercept appear in the equation $y = mx + b$.

31. Slope = 3, y-intercept = 5   32. Slope = -6, y-intercept = 9

33. Slope = $\dfrac{2}{3}$, y-intercept = -1 34. Slope = -7, y-intercept = 0

23. $y = -\dfrac{7}{2}x + 5$

24. $y = -\dfrac{3}{5}x + 2$

25. $y = \dfrac{1}{4}x - 3$ **26.** $y = \dfrac{2}{5}x - 3$

27. $y = \dfrac{2}{3}x - 1$

28. $y = \dfrac{3}{7}x + 2$

29. $y = -\dfrac{1}{4}x - 4$

30. $y = -\dfrac{5}{2}x + 7$

31. $y = 3x + 5$ **33.** $y = \dfrac{2}{3}x - 1$

32. $y = -6x + 9$ **34.** $y = -7x$

8-6 | FINDING AN EQUATION FROM THE GRAPH

Time: 0 or 2 days

Chalkboard Examples:

Day 1: Find the equation:

1. Slope is 5 and y-intercept is $\dfrac{2}{3}$.

    Ans.: $y = 5x + \dfrac{2}{3}$

2. Slope is -6, line contains $(3, 8)$.

    Ans.: $y - 8 = -6(x - 3)$

    or: $y = -6x + 26$

3. Line contains $(3, 7)$ and $(-5, 11)$

    Ans.: Slope is $\dfrac{(11 - 7)}{(-5 - 3)} = \dfrac{4}{(-8)} = -0.5$

    $y - 7 = -0.5(x - 3)$ or

    $y - 11 = -0.5(x + 5)$

In the last section you plotted graphs of lines using the y-intercept and slope. Suppose someone says, "Find an equation of the line shown in Figure 8-6a." "That's easy!" you reply. "The y-intercept is -4. Counting squares, the run is 2 and rise is 3. So the slope is $\frac{3}{2}$." You can then just substitute these numbers for the literal constants in

$$y = mx + b$$

and get

$$y = \dfrac{3}{2}x - 4.$$

In this section you will learn how to get an equation of a line either from the graph or from information about the graph.

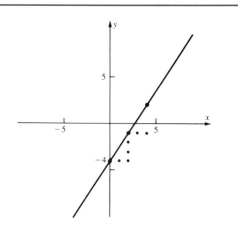

Figure 8-6a _____

Objective:
Given the graph of a line, or information about the graph, write an equation for the line.

There is another form of the equation of a line that helps when the y-intercept is not known. Think about the equation

$$y - 4 = \frac{2}{5}(x - 3).$$

If y is 4, the left member of the equation is zero. If x is 3, the right member is 0. So the ordered pair $(x, y) = (3, 4)$ satisfies the equation. This fact means that the point $(3, 4)$ is on the graph. If you distribute the $\frac{2}{5}$ on the right, it becomes the coefficient of x. So $\frac{2}{5}$ is the slope of the line. The graph is shown in Figure 8-6b.

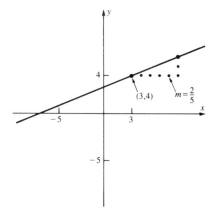

Figure 8-6b _____

4. Line is horizontal and contains $(-2, 6)$.
   Ans.: $y = 6$
5. Line is vertical and contains $(3, -8)$.
   Ans.: $x = 3$

Day 2: Present parallel and perpendicular lines. Have students work some of the trickier problems in Exercise 8–6, particularly those involving the x-intercept.

Assignments:

Day 1: Exercise 8–6, #1 through 21 odd
Exercise 8–5, #28
Exercise 8–4, #28
Day 2: Exercise 8–6, #2 through 22 even, 23 through 45 odd, and 51

Problem Notes:

If you like, you can have students transform the equation they get so that it is in point-slope form. This transformation is as in Problems 23 through 30 of Exercise 8–5. Since the transformation takes about as much time as getting the equation in the first place, you must be judicious about how many problems you assign at a time.

An equation written in the form

$$y - 4 = \frac{2}{5}(x - 3)$$

is said to be in *point-slope form*. The slope, $\frac{2}{5}$, and the coordinates of a point, $(3, 4)$, show up in the equation. The coordinates of the point are the values of x and y that make the right and left members equal zero.

POINT-SLOPE FORM OF A LINEAR EQUATION
An equation in the form

$$y - y_1 = m(x - x_1)$$

is said to be in **point-slope form.** The slope is m, and a fixed point on the line is (x_1, y_1). The variables x and y stand for coordinates of a variable point on the line.

Armed with the point-slope form, you can find an equation of a line, as long as you know the value of the slope and the coordinates of one point.

Cover the answers as you work these examples.

EXAMPLE 1

Write an equation of a line with slope -3 and y-intercept 5.

– – – – –   – – – – –

| | *Think These Reasons* |

$y = -3 + 5$ Use the slope-intercept form since you know the slope and the y-intercept.

EXAMPLE 2

Write an equation of the line with slope $-\frac{3}{4}$ if $(5, -1)$ is on the line.

– – – – –   – – – – –

$y + 1 = -\dfrac{3}{4}(x - 5)$ Use point-slope form since you know the slope and the coordinates of a point. The left member is $y + 1$ because substituting -1 for y must make the left member equal zero.

EXAMPLE 3

Write an equation of the line containing (3, 7) and (5, 1).

- - - - -   - - - - -

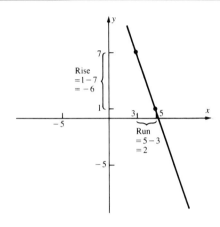

Figure 8-6c _____

Draw the two points, as shown in Figure 8-6c. For the points (3, 7) and (5, 1),

$$\text{run} = 5 - 3 = 2$$
$$\text{rise} = 1 - 7 = -6.$$

So the slope is

$$m = \frac{-6}{2} = -3.$$

Using the point-slope form with either point gives

$$\underline{\underline{y - 7 = -3(x - 3)}} \quad \text{or}$$
$$\underline{\underline{y - 1 = -3(x - 5)}}.$$

EXAMPLE 4

Show that the two answers in Example 3 are equivalent equations.

- - - - -   - - - - -

Transform each equation to slope-intercept form, and compare.

$$y - 7 = -3(x - 3) \qquad\qquad y - 1 = -3(x - 5)$$
$$y - 7 = -3x + 9 \qquad\qquad y - 1 = -3x + 15$$
$$y = -3x + 16 \longleftarrow \text{same!} \longrightarrow y = -3x + 16$$

EXAMPLE 5

Find an equation of each line shown in Figure 8-6d.

- - - - -   - - - - -

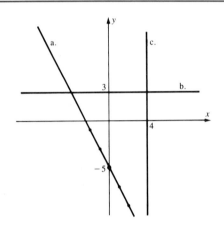

Figure 8-6d

a. The y-intercept is -5. y is -5 when x is 0.

   The slope is -2.   Run 1, rise -2

   Equation is $\underline{\underline{y = -2x - 5}}$.   Use slope-intercept form.

- - - - -   - - - - -

b. The y-intercept is 3.   The graph crosses the y-axis at 3.

   The slope is 0.   No matter what the run equals, the rise is zero.

   Equation is $y = 0x + 3$.   Use slope-intercept form.

   $\underline{\underline{y = 3}}$ Simplify.

Note: The final equation, $y = 3$, says, "No matter what x is, y is always 3." This fact is useful in part (c), below.

- - - - -   - - - - -

c. There is no number for   The graph is parallel to the y-axis.
   the y-intercept.

   There is no number for   The run is zero. If you run at all, you will
   the slope.   be off the line no matter how high or low
                                  you rise.

   Equation is $\underline{\underline{x = 4}}$.   Observe that no matter what y is, x is
                                  always 4. Since there is no number for the
                                  slope, you cannot use either point-slope or
                                  slope-intercept form.

The last two parts of Example 5 lead to the following conclusions about equations of horizontal and vertical lines.

EQUATIONS OF HORIZONTAL AND VERTICAL LINES
If y = constant, the graph is a **horizontal line.**
If x = constant, the graph is a **vertical line.**

ORAL PRACTICE

Name a point on the line.

A. $y - 8 = 5(x - 11)$

B. $y + 5 = -4(x - 2)$

C. $y - 3 = 6(x + 4)$

D. $y + 1 = 0.17(x + 9)$

E. $y - 2 = x - 5$

F. $y - 0 = 4(x - 7)$

G. $y + 0.3 = 15(x - 0)$

H. $y = \left(\dfrac{2}{3}\right)(x + 1)$

I. $y - \dfrac{3}{5} = 4x$

J. $y = 4.5x$

K. $y = 3$

L. $x = 17$

A. $(11, 8)$ B. $(2, -5)$
C. $(-4, 3)$ D. $(-9, -1)$
E. $(5, 2)$ F. $(7, 0)$
G. $(0, -0.3)$ H. $(-1, 0)$
I. $(0, \frac{3}{5})$ J. $(0, 0)$
K. $(0, 3)$ L. $(17, 0)$
M. $\frac{9}{2}$ N. $-\frac{3}{7}$
O. $\frac{1}{3}$ P. $-\frac{7}{3}$
Q. $\frac{5}{3}$ R. $-\frac{4}{3}$
S. $\frac{8}{5}$ T. 0
U. no slope   V. -2

Tell the slope of the line containing the two points. Simplify any fractions.

M.   (3, 7) and (5, 16)

N.   (8, 2) and (1, 5)

O.   (200, 300) and (500, 400)

P.   (5, −1) and (2, 6)

Q.   (−4, 3) and (2, 13)

R.   (−8, 7) and (4, −9)

S.   (5, −3) and (0, −11)

T.   (3, 8) and (7, 8)

U.   (5, 1) and (5, 3)

V.   (0, 0) and (−4, 8)

EXERCISE 8-6

For Problems 1 through 8,
a.   Write the slope and a point on the graph,
b.   Plot the graph.

1-8.a. Points may vary.
1a. $\frac{2}{5}$; (1, 4)
2a. $\frac{3}{5}$; (4, 2)
3a. 4; (3, −2)
4a. 2; (−4, 3)
5a. $-\frac{1}{3}$; (−4, 5)
6a. $\frac{1}{4}$; (3, −5)
7a. $\frac{3}{2}$; (−5, −1)
8a. $-\frac{5}{3}$; (−1, −4)
9. $y = 2x + 5$
10. $y = 6x - 2$
11. $y = -5x + \frac{2}{3}$
12. $y = -1.9x + 0.3$
13. $y - 9 = -3(x - 4)$
15. $y - 18 = 7(x - 3)$
16. $y - 6 = -\frac{2}{7}(x - 5)$
17. $y - 2 = -13(x + 7)$
18. $y + 3.7 = 15(x - 14)$
19. $y + 4 = \frac{1}{8}(x + 2)$
20. $y + 0.3 = -0.007(x + 0.8)$
21. $y - 5 = \frac{7}{2}(x - 4)$
22. $y - 3 = \frac{2}{3}(x - 8)$
23. $y - 2 = -(x + 1)$
24. $y + 3 = -\frac{7}{11}(x - 6)$
25. $y + 1 = -\frac{1}{3}(x + 8)$
26. $y - 4 = -\frac{3}{4}(x + 6)$
27. $x = 3$
28. $y = 1$
29. $y = -7$
30. $x = -5$

1. $y - 4 = \frac{2}{5}(x - 1)$ 2. $y - 2 = \frac{3}{5}(x - 4)$

3. $y + 2 = 4(x - 3)$ 4. $y - 3 = 2(x + 4)$

5. $y - 5 = -\frac{1}{3}(x + 4)$ 6. $y + 5 = \frac{1}{4}(x - 3)$

7. $y + 1 = \frac{3}{2}(x + 5)$ 8. $y + 4 = -\frac{5}{3}(x + 1)$

For Problems 9 through 38, write an equation of the line described.

9.   Has y-intercept 5 and slope 2.

10.   Has y-intercept −2 and slope 6.

11.   Has y-intercept $\frac{2}{3}$ and slope −5.

12.   Has y-intercept 0.3 and slope −1.9.

13.   Has slope −3 and contains (4, 9).

15.   Has slope 7 and contains (3, 18).

16.   Has slope $-\frac{2}{7}$ and contains (5, 6).

17.   Has slope −13 and contains (−7, 2).

18.   Has slope 15 and contains (14, −3.7).

19.   Has slope $\frac{1}{8}$ and contains (−2, −4),

20.   Has slope −0.007 and contains (−0.8, −0.3).

21.   Contains (4, 5) and (6, 12).

22.   Contains (8, 3) and (11, 5).

23.   Contains (−1, 2) and (5, −4).

24.   Contains (6, −3) and (−5, 4).

25.   Contains (−8, −1) and (4, −5).

26.   Contains (−6, 4) and (−2, 1).

27.   Is vertical, and contains (3, 8).

28.   Is horizontal, and contains (−4, 1).

29.   Is horizontal, and contains (2, −7).

30.   Is vertical, and contains (−5, −6).

31.

32.

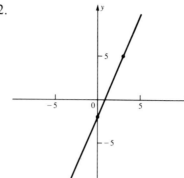

31. $y = -\frac{3}{5}x + 4$

32. $y = \frac{7}{3}x - 2$

33. $y - 5 = \frac{4}{3}(x - 2)$

34. $y - 1 = -\frac{1}{2}(x - 3)$

35. $y - 6 = -2(x + 5)$

36. $y + 2 = \frac{3}{4}(x - 1)$

37. $y = -7$

38. $x = 3$

33.

34.

35.

36.

37.

38.

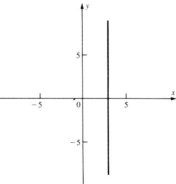

Two lines are *parallel* to each other if their slopes are equal. See Figure 8-6e. For Problems 39 through 44, write an equation of the line described.

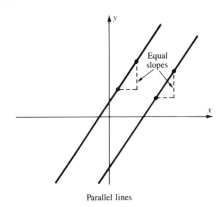

Parallel lines

Figure 8-6e

39. $y + 1 = \frac{2}{7}(x - 6)$
40. $y - 8 = 0.8(x + 3)$
41. $y = 7x + 4$
42. $y = 4x - 2$
43. $y = -\frac{3}{7}x + 5$
44. $y + 3 = \frac{2}{5}(x + 4)$

45. $y = -\frac{7}{5}x + 4$
46. $y = \frac{9}{4}x - 1$

39. Contains $(6, -1)$, and is parallel to the graph of $y = \left(\frac{2}{7}\right)x + 3$.

40. Contains $(-3, 8)$, and is parallel to the graph of $y = 0.8x - 7$.

41. Has y-intercept 4, and is parallel to the graph of $y = 7x - 3$.

42. Has y-intercept -2, and is parallel to the graph of $y = 4x + \frac{3}{8}$.

43. Has y-intercept 5, and is parallel to the graph of $3x + 7y = 42$.

44. Contains $(-4, -3)$, and is parallel to the graph of $2x - 5y = 40$.

Two lines are *perpendicular* to each other if the slope of one line equals the *opposite* of the *reciprocal* of the slope of the other. For instance, the graphs of

$$y = \frac{3}{5}x + 7 \quad \text{and} \quad y = -\frac{5}{3}x + 20$$

are perpendicular since $-\frac{5}{3}$ is the opposite of the reciprocal of $\frac{3}{5}$.

For Problems 45 through 50, write an equation of the line described.

45. Has y-intercept 4, and is perpendicular to the graph of
$y = \left(\frac{5}{7}\right)x - 2$.

46. Has y-intercept -1, and is perpendicular to the graph of
$y = \left(-\frac{4}{9}\right)x + 11$.

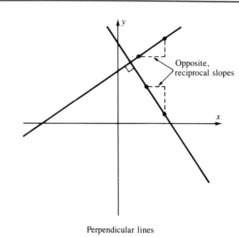

Perpendicular lines

Figure 8-6f _____

47. Contains (4, 9), and is perpendicular to the graph of $y = 7x + \dfrac{3}{8}$.

48. Contains (−6, 1), and is perpendicular to the graph of
    $y = -2x + 0.83$.

49. Contains (−3, −10), and is perpendicular to the graph of
    $4x - 5y = 1$.

50. Has y-intercept −4, and is perpendicular to the graph of
    $8x + 7y = 112$.

The following are intended to make you think hard! Find an equation of
the line described.

51. Has x-intercept 5 and slope 4.

52. Has x-intercept 2 and y-intercept 5.

53. Has x-intercept 3, and is horizontal.

54. Has y-intercept 8, and is vertical.

55. Has x-intercept 0 and y-intercept 0.

47. $y - 9 = -\frac{1}{7}(x - 4)$
48. $y - 1 = \frac{1}{2}(x + 6)$
49. $y + 10 = -\frac{5}{4}(x + 3)$
50. $y = \frac{7}{8}x - 4$

51. $y = 4(x - 5)$
52. $y = -\frac{5}{2}x + 5$
53. No such line
54. No such line
55. $y = kx$ for any real k.

8-7 | FINDING THE INTERSECTION OF TWO GRAPHS BY ACCURATE PLOTTING

This section ties together what you have been learning and prepares you
for the rest of the chapter. You should be able to read it and work the
problems without help from your teacher.

Time: 1 day

Chalkboard Examples:

Plot on the same Cartesian coordinate system:
   $3x + 5y = -15$
   $2x - y = 6$
Find the coordinates of the intersection to the nearest 0.1 unit.

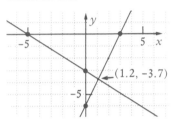

Ans.: Intercepts:
   $x = -5, y = -3;$
   $x = 3, y = -6.$
   Intersection:
   $(1.2, -3.7)$ from the graph.
   $[(\frac{15}{13}, -\frac{48}{13})$ by calculation]

Assignment:

Exercise 8–7, #1–11 odd or 2–12 even

If you draw the graphs of two linear equations on the same coordinate system, they will probably intersect each other somewhere. In the next few sections you will learn how to calculate this point of intersection. For now, you will just plot the graphs and *see* where they intersect.

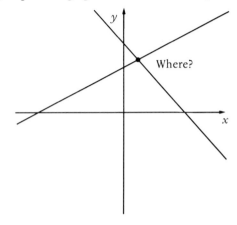

Objective:

Given two linear equations in two variables, to plot the graphs accurately enough to read the coordinates of the point of intersection correct to 0.1 unit.

Cover the answers as you work this example.

EXAMPLE

Plot the graphs and read the coordinates of the point of intersection correct to 0.1 unit.

$$x + 2y = 4$$

$$4x - 5y = -20$$

- - - - -

Find the intercepts.   Plot the graphs.

For $x + 2y = 4$:

   x-intercept:
      $x + 0 = 4$
          $x = 4$

   y-intercept:
      $0 + 2y = 4$
            $y = 2$

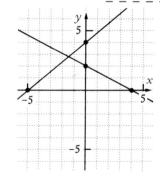

For $4x - 5y = -20$:

x-intercept:
$$4x - 0 = -20$$
$$x = -5$$

y-intercept:
$$0 - 5y = -20$$
$$y = 4$$

Read the point of intersection.

$(-1.5, 2.8)$

Note: In order to get accurate answers, you must draw accurate graphs! So sharpen your pencil, use a good ruler, and be careful. Your answers will be considered to be right if they are no more than ± 0.1 unit from the correct answer. For instance, the y-coordinate could be 2.7, 2.8, or 2.9 and still be counted right.

EXERCISE 8-7

For each pair of equations, find the intercepts and draw both graphs on the same set of axes. Then read the coordinates of the point where the two graphs intersect. Write the answer to the nearest 0.1 unit. Your answer will be counted correct if it is no more than ± 0.1 unit from the right answer.

1. $2x + 3y = 18$ (6.6, 1.6)
    $x - y = 5$

2. $x - 2y = -10$ (1.6, 5.8)
    $4x + 3y = 24$

3. $2x + y = 8$ (3.6, 0.9)
    $5x - 3y = 15$

4. $3x + 4y = 12$ (0.7, 2.5)
    $2x - 3y = -6$

5. $8x - 5y = -40$ (−3.9, 1.8)
    $2x + y = -6$

6. $2x - y = -6$ (−1.6, 2.8)
    $x + 2y = 4$

7. $3x + 2y = -12$ (−3.2, −1.2)
    $x - y = -2$

8. $5x + 7y = -35$ (−0.9, −4.4)
    $3x - 2y = 6$

9. $2x + 3y = -12$ (1.8, −5.2)
    $8x - 5y = 40$

10. $5x + 2y = 20$ (4.4, −1.1)
    $3x - 7y = 21$

11. $3x + 5y = 15$ No intersection.
    $3x + 5y = 30$ The lines are
    (Surprising?)   parallel.

12. $x - 3y = 6$ No intersection.
    $x - 3y = -3$ The lines are
    (Surprising?)   parallel.

Problem Notes:

All problems have equations with integer intercepts for ease of plotting. All graphs are nearly perpendicular to minimize inaccuracies in reading the intersection points. Students can get ± 0.1 unit accuracy with reasonable care using sharp pencils and normal, inexpensive quadrille graph paper.

In Problems 11 and 12, the graphs are parallel.

Note: The intersections were calculated algebraically, and are correct to 1 decimal place.

1.–12. See Additional Answers for graphs.

1. $2x + 3y = 18$: $x = 9$, $y = 6$
    $x - y = 5$: $x = 5$, $y = -5$

2. $x - 2y = -10$: $x = -10$, $y = 5$
    $4x + 3y = 24$: $x = 6$, $y = 8$

3. $2x + y = 8$: $x = 4$, $y = 8$
    $5x - 3y = 15$: $x = 3$, $y = -5$

4. $3x + 4y = 12$: $x = 4$, $y = 3$
    $2x - 3y = -6$: $x = -3$, $y = 2$

5. $6x - 5y = 0$: $x = -5$, $y = 8$
    $2x + y = -6$: $x = -3$, $y = -6$

6. $2x - y = -6$: $x = -3$, $y = 6$
    $x + 2y = 4$: $x = 4$, $y = 2$

7. $3x + 2y = -12$: $x = -4$, $y = -6$
    $x - y = -2$: $x = -2$, $y = 2$

8. $5x + 7y = -35$: $x = -7$, $y = -5$
    $3x - 2y = 6$: $x = 2$, $y = -3$

9. $2x + 3y = 12$: $x = -6$, $y = -4$
    $8x - 5y = 40$: $x = 5$, $y = -8$

10. $5x + 2y = 20$: $x = 4$, $y = 10$
    $3x - 7y = 21$: $x = 7$, $y = -3$

11. $3x + 5y = 15$: $x = 5$, $y = 3$
    $3x + 5y = 30$: $x = 10$, $y = 6$

12. $x - 3y = 6$: $x = 6$, $y = -2$
    $x - 3y = -3$: $x = -3$, $y = 1$

8-8 | SOLVING SYSTEMS OF EQUATIONS BY SUBSTITUTION

Time: 2 days

Chalkboard Examples:

First day:
1. Graph the system
    $2x + 3y = 18$
    $x - y = 5$,
    which is Problem 1 in Exercise 8–7. This will illustrate the meaning of the solution of a system.

2. Solve by substitution
    $5x - 2y = 43$
    $3x + y = 17$.
    Ans.: $(7, -4)$

Second day:
Homework problems on board.
Work Exercise 8–8, #29 or 30, as an example.

Assignment:

Day 1: Exercise 8–7, one problem not previously worked, Exercise 8–8, #1–15 odd or 2–16 even

Day 2: Exercise 8–8, #17–27 odd and 31 or 18–28 even and 32

In the last section you learned how to plot graphs of two equations and find their intersection point. For instance, if you plot

$$2x + 5y = -10$$

and

$$3x - y = 4$$

on the same Cartesian plane, the graphs intersect at approximately

$$(0.6, -2.2),$$

as shown in the figure.

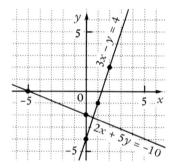

Finding intersection points by actual graphing has two disadvantages. It is tedious, and it is of limited accuracy. In this section you will learn how to *calculate* such intersection points.

A pair of equations with the same two variables is called a *system* of equations. The ordered pair where the graphs intersect each other makes *both* equations true. It is called the *solution* of the system. For future reference, here are definitions of these words.

DEFINITIONS

SYSTEM OF EQUATIONS
A **system of equations** is two or more equations with the same variables.

SOLUTION OF A SYSTEM
A **solution** of a system of equations is an ordered pair that satisfies *all* the equations in the system.

To solve the system

$$2x + 5y = -10 \qquad\qquad (1)$$

$$3x - y = 4 \qquad\qquad (2)$$

you can transform one equation so that a variable is *by itself*. Solving Equation (2) for y in terms of x gives

$$-y = -3x + 4 \qquad \text{Add } -3x \text{ to each member.}$$

$$y = 3x - 4 \qquad \text{Multiply each member by } -1. \qquad (3)$$

Where the graphs intersect, the y in one equation stands for the *same* number as the y in the other. So you may *substitute* $(3x - 4)$ for the y in Equation (1).

$$2x + 5(3x - 4) = -10$$

The result is an equation with only *one* variable. Solve it for x.

$$2x + 15x - 20 = -10 \qquad\qquad \text{Distribute the 5.}$$

$$17x = 10 \qquad\qquad \text{Combine like terms; add 20 to each member.}$$

$$x = \frac{10}{17} \qquad\qquad \text{Divide each member by 17.}$$

$$x = 0.5882 \ldots \qquad \text{Save this in memory.}$$

Substituting $0.5882 \ldots$ for x in Equation (3) gives

$$y = 3(0.5882 \ldots) - 4$$

$$y = -2.2359 \ldots$$

Rounding the values of x and y gives the approximate solution

$$(0.59, -2.24).$$

As you can see, the $(0.6, -2.2)$ from the graph is quite close to this more accurate value.

The process above is called solving a system by **substitution.** Sometimes the equations in a system are called **simultaneous equations** because you solve both equations at the same time.

Objective:

Be able to solve a system of two linear equations with two variables by the substitution method.

Cover the answer as you work the example.

EXAMPLE

Solve.

$$5x + 3y = 17$$
$$x - 2y = 6$$

- - - - -   - - - - -

		Think These Reasons
$5x + 3y = 17$	(1)	Write the given system. Number each equation for future reference.
$x - 2y = 6$	(2)	
$x = 2y + 6$	(3)	Solve (2) for x in terms of y. This is the easiest way, since x has a coefficient of 1.
$5(2y + 6) + 3y = 17$		Substitute $2y + 6$ for x in (1). (*Do not* substitute it back in (2)!)
$10y + 30 + 3y = 17$		Distribute 5.
$13y = -13$		Combine like terms; add -30.
$y = -1$		Divide each member by 13.
$x = 2(-1) + 6$		Substitute -1 for y in (3).
$x = 4$		Do the computation.
Solution: $\underline{\underline{(4, -1)}}$		Write the answer.

Note: Checking the answer requires substituting it into *both* equations. It is possible for an ordered pair to satisfy one equation but not the other.

Check: $5(4) + 3(-1) \overset{?}{=} 17$ $4 - 2(-1) \overset{?}{=} 6$

$20 - 3 \overset{?}{=} 17$ $4 + 2 \overset{?}{=} 6$

$17 = 17$ ✔ $6 = 6$ ✔

ORAL PRACTICE

Solve for x in terms of y or for y in terms of x, whichever is easier.

EXAMPLES

Answers

i. $x + 3y = 7$ i. $x = 7 - 3y$
ii. $4x - y = 9$ ii. $y = 4x - 9$

A. $x + 2y = 5$ $x = 5 - 2y$ B. $x - 6y = 8$ $x = 6y + 8$

C. $2x + y = 10$ $y = 10 - 2x$ D. $6x - y = 12$ $y = 6x - 12$

E. $x - 5y = -15$ $x = 5y - 15$ F. $6x + y = -24$ $y = -6x - 24$

G. $x - 3y = 30$ $x = 3y + 30$ H. $10x - y = 70$ $y = 10x - 70$

I. $x - y = 8$ $\begin{array}{l} x = y + 8 \text{ or} \\ y = x - 8 \end{array}$ J. $x + y = 6$ $x = 6 - y$ or $y = 6 - x$

K. $x - 2y = 0$ $x = 2y$ L. $x + 3(y + 2) = 10$ $x = 4 - 3y$

EXERCISE 8-8

For Problems 1 through 30, solve the system by substitution.

1. $y = 2x$
    $3x + y = 10$ $(2, 4)$

2. $y = 3x$
    $2x - y = 2$ $(-2, -6)$

3. $y = 3x$
    $5x - 2y = 1$ $(-1, -3)$

4. $y = 2x$
    $4x + 3y = 30$ $(3, 6)$

5. $y = x + 4$
    $3x + y = 16$ $(3, 7)$

6. $y = x - 3$
    $4x + y = 32$ $(7, 4)$

7. $x = y - 5$
    $3x + 2y = 3$ $(-1.4, 3.6)$

8. $x = y + 8$
    $5x + 3y = 12$ $(4.5, -3.5)$

9. $4x + 3y = 31$
    $y = 2x + 7$ $(1, 9)$

10. $4x + 5y = 48$
    $y = 3x + 2$ $(2, 8)$

11. $x + 2y = 2$
    $5x - 3y = -29$ $(-4, 3)$

12. $3x + y = 13$
    $2x - 4y = 18$ $(5, -2)$

13. $6x - y = 31$
    $4x + 3y = 17$ $(5, -1)$

14. $x - 7y = -22$
    $5x + 2y = 1$ $(-1, 3)$

15. $7x - 6y = -30$
    $x - 4y = -20$ $(0, 5)$

16. $2x - 9y = 14$
    $6x - y = 42$ $(7, 0)$

17. $x + y = 23$
    $9x - 8y = 27$ $(12.41, 10.59)$

18. $x - y = 6$
    $10x + 11y = 149$ $(10.24, 4.24)$

19. $x - 3y = 13$
    $5x + 3y = 2$ $(2.5, -3.5)$

20. $7x - 3y = -23$
    $x + 5y = 32$ $(-0.5, 6.5)$

Problem Notes:

All problems in this section have systems in which at least one variable has a coefficient of 1 or −1. Substitution is an efficient method for such systems. The addition-subtraction method of the next section is more appropriate for systems in which no coefficient is 1 or −1.

Problems 1–10 already have one variable in terms of the other. Problems 11–20 require a simple addition or subtraction transformation. Problems 21–26 involve distributing.

Problems 27–30 are similar to the systems that will arise in applications in Problems 33–36 of Section 8–10. They arise in certain problems where the value of x must be known before y can be calculated, and vice versa.

Problems 31–34 combine solving by graphing and solving by substitution.

31.

32.

33.

34.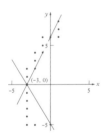

Time: 4 days, including test

Chalkboard Examples:

First day:
1. Solve:
$2x + 5y = 14$ Ans.: $(4.5, 1)$
$2x - 8y = 1$

21. $3(x - 2) + y = -4$
    $4x - 7y = 36$ $(2, -4)$

22. $4(x - 3) + y = -11$
    $6x - 2y = -16$ $(-1, 5)$

23. $x + 6y = 19$
    $5(x - 7) + 2y = -24$ $(1, 3)$

24. $x + 5y = 22$
    $3(x - 9) + 4y = -5$ $(2, 4)$

25. $2(x + 3) - y = 7$
    $7x - 3(y - 1) = 9$ $(3, 5)$

26. $6(x + 2) - y = 31$
    $5x - 2(y - 3) = 23$ $(3, -1)$

For Problems 27 through 30, find the solution correct to two decimal places for each coordinate.

27. $x = 0.6(300 + y)$ $(245.45,$
    $y = 0.2(300 + x)$ $109.09)$

28. $x = 0.8(500 + y)$ $(1545.45,$
    $y = 0.7(500 + x)$ $1431.82)$

29. $x = 0.9(1000 - y)$ $(729.73,$
    $y = 0.7(1000 - x)$ $189.19)$

30. $x = 0.3(200 - y)$ $(51.06,$
    $y = 0.2(200 - x)$ $29.79)$

For Problems 31 through 34, solve the system by substitution. Then plot the graphs of the two equations, using the rise-and-run technique of Section 8.5 or the two-intercept technique of Section 8.4. Show that the two graphs do intersect at the point you calculated.

31. $2x - y = -3$
    $x + y = 9$ $(2, 7)$

32. $3x + y = 1$
    $x - y = 7$ $(2, -5)$

33. $x - 3y = -18$
    $2x + 3y = 9$ $(-3, 5)$

34. $2x - y = -6$
    $5x + 3y = -15$ $(-3, 0)$

8-9 | SOLVING SYSTEMS BY THE LINEAR COMBINATION METHOD

Suppose that you must solve the system

$$5x + 3y = 25 \qquad (1)$$

$$7x - 3y = -1 \qquad (2)$$

None of the variable terms has a coefficient of 1. Thus to solve for y in terms of x or for x in terms of y, you must divide by a coefficient. The resulting fractions would make the substitution method of the last section tedious to use.

There is another method that works very easily for this system. Observe that the coefficients of y in the two equations are *opposites* of each other. If you add $7x - 3y$ to the left member of Equation (1) and add -1 to the right member, the y-terms have a sum of *zero*. (They "cancel out!")

$$(5x + 3y) + (7x - 3y) = 25 + (-1)$$
$$12x = 24$$

An efficient way to do this addition is simply to draw a line under the two equations and add like terms.

$$5x + 3y = 25$$
$$\underline{7x - 3y = -1}$$

$12x \qquad = 24$	Add the two equations.
$x = 2$	Divide each member by 12.

Substituting 2 for x in either equation lets you find y. Using the first one, you get the following value.

$5(2) + 3y = 25$	Substitute 2 for x.
$3y = 15$	Subtract 10 from each member.
$y = 5$	Divide each member by 3.
Solution: $\underline{\underline{(2, 5)}}$	Write the answer.

If neither variable has opposite coefficients, you can *transform* each equation first so that they will. Here's how you would solve the following system.

$$5x + 3y = 9$$
$$2x - 4y = 40$$

Multiplying each member of the first by 2 makes the coefficient of x equal 10. Multiplying each member of the second by -5 makes its x-coefficient equal -10. The terms $10x$ and $-10x$ are opposites of each other. You can draw arrows from each equation with the symbols m 2 and m -5 to indicate what you are doing. The entire solution looks like this:

$5x + 3y = 9$	$\xrightarrow{\text{m } 2}$	$10x + 6y = 18$	Multiply by 2.
$2x - 4y = 40$	$\xrightarrow{\text{m } -5}$	$\underline{-\ 10x + 20y = -200}$	Multiply by -5.
		$26y = -182$	Add the equations.
		$y = -7$	Divide by 26.

$5x + 3(-7) = 9$	Substitute -7 for y in the first equation.
$5x = 30$	Add 21 to each member.
$x = 6$	Divide by 5.
Solution: $\underline{\underline{(6, -7)}}$	Write the answer.

To check the solution, you must substitute $(6, -7)$ into *each* equation. It is possible for an ordered pair to satisfy one of the equations but not the other.

Check: $5(6) + 3(-7) \overset{?}{=} 9$ $2(6) - 4(-7) \overset{?}{=} 40$

$\qquad\qquad\quad 30 - 21 \overset{?}{=} 9$ $\quad 12 + 28 \overset{?}{=} 40$

$\qquad\qquad\qquad\quad 9 = 9$ ✔ $\qquad 40 = 40$ ✔

Note that you could have eliminated y first, instead of x. You would multiply the first equation by 4 and the second by 3, getting the following:

$$5x + 3y = 9 \quad \xrightarrow{\text{m } 4} \quad 20x + 12y = 36$$
$$2x - 4y = 40 \quad \xrightarrow{\text{m } 3} \quad \underline{6x - 12y = 120}$$
$$26x \qquad\quad = 156$$
$$x = 6$$

Then y would be found by substituting 6 for x in the first or second equation.

This method is called the **linear combination** method for solving a system of equations. A linear combination of two quantities is what you get by multiplying each quantity by a constant, then adding the results. The method is also called **addition-subtraction.**

Objective:

Given a system of two linear equations with two variables, solve it by the linear combination method, transforming the equations first as needed.

Cover the answers as you work the examples.

EXAMPLE 1

Solve:

$4x + 9y = 75$

$4x + 3y = 33$

– – – – –   – – – – –

	Think These Reasons

$4x + 9y = 75 \quad \longrightarrow \qquad 4x + 9y = 75$ Write an equation.

$4x + 3y = 33 \quad \xrightarrow{\text{m } -1} \quad \underline{-4x - 3y = -33}$ Multiply by -1.

$\qquad\qquad\qquad\qquad\qquad\quad 6y = 42$ Add the equations.

$\qquad\qquad\qquad\qquad\qquad\quad\; y = 7$ Divide by 7.

$4x + 3(7) = 33$ Substitute 7 for y in the second equation.

     $4x = 12$ Subtract 21 from each member.

       $x = 3$ Divide each member by 4.

Solution: (3, 7)   Write the solution.

EXAMPLE 2

Solve:

$2x - 3y = -8$

$11x + 5y = -1$

- - - - -   - - - - -

$2x - 3y = -8$ $\xrightarrow{\text{m } 5}$ $10x - 15y = -40$ Multiply by 5.

$11x + 5y = -1$ $\xrightarrow{\text{m } 3}$ $\underline{33x + 15y = -3}$ Multiply by 3.

                                        $43x \qquad\quad = -43$ Add the equations.

                                               $x = -1$ Divide by 43.

$2(-1) - 3y = -8$ Substitute -1 for x in the first equation.

        $-3y = -6$ Add 2 to each member.

            $y = 2$ Divide each member by -3.

Solution: (-1, 2)   Write the solution.

Note: There are other ways you could have started. To eliminate x instead of y, you could multiply the first equation by 11 and the second by -2, making the x-coefficients 22 and -22. Then you would eliminate x by adding the equations.

ORAL PRACTICE

Give the equation that results after you add to eliminate a variable.

EXAMPLE

                   Answer

$3x + 2y = 2$

$5x - 2y = 9$ $8x = 11$

A. $2x + 3y = 7$

     $4x - 3y = 5$ $6x = 12$

B. $7x - 4y = 9$

     $2x + 4y = 3$ $9x = 12$

C. $2x + 8y = -3$

     $-2x + 5y = 10$ $13y = 7$

D. $3x + 4y = 8$

     $-3x + 5y = -1$ $9x = 7$

E. $4x - 5y = 9$
$-3x + 5y = -7$ $x = 2$

F. $-4x - 3y = -1$
$4x + 8y = 5$ $5y = 4$

Tell the number by which each equation should be multiplied to eliminate x by linear combination.

EXAMPLE

$$\begin{array}{ll} & \textit{Answer} \\ 5x + 3y = 9 & \text{m } 2 \\ 2x - 8y = 4 & \text{m } 5 \end{array}$$

G. $2x + 5y = 7$ m 3
$3x + 4y = 9$ m -2

H. $4x - 3y = 2$ m 5
$-5x + 8y = 1$ m 4

I. $2x + 10y = 9$ m 4
$8x + 5y = 7$ m -1

Tell the number by which each equation should be multiplied to eliminate y by linear combination.

J. $2x + 5y = 7$ m 4
$3x + 4y = 9$ m -5

K. $4x - 3y = 2$ m 8
$-5x + 8y = 1$ m 3

L. $2x + 10y = 9$ m 1
$8x + 5y = 7$ m -2

EXERCISE 8-9

Problem Notes:

Problems 1–20 require no preliminary transformations or only multiplication by -1. Problems 21–40 require one or both equations to be multiplied by constants to make a variable have opposite coefficients.

For Problems 1 through 20, solve the system by the linear combination method.

1. $3x - y = 5$
$2x + y = 15$ $(4, 7)$

2. $4x + y = 10$
$6x - y = 20$ $(3, -2)$

3. $x + 4y = 17$
$-x + 7y = 38$ $(-3, 5)$

4. $-x + 5y = 6$
$x + 3y = 18$ $(9, 3)$

5. $8x + y = 21$
$3x + y = 13$ $(1.6, 8.2)$

6. $7x + y = 47$
$2x + y = 19$ $(5.6, 7.8)$

7. $x - 4y = 23$
$x + 5y = -4$ $(11, -3)$

8. $x - 6y = 13$
$x + 2y = 5$ $(7, -1)$

9. $5x + 3y = 27$
$7x - 3y = 45$ $(6, -1)$

10. $2x + 5y = 14$
$7x - 5y = -41$ $(-3, 4)$

11. $-2x + 7y = 8.7$
$2x + 3y = 18.3$ $(5.1, 2.7)$

12. $-4x + 8y = -3.6$
$4x - 3y = 13.1$ $(4.7, 1.9)$

13. $10x + 7y = -30$
$8x + 7y = -24$ $(-3, 0)$

14. $6x + 11y = -48$
$x + 11y = -8$ $(-8, 0)$

15. $5x - y = 22$
    $5x + 4y = -63$ $(1, -17)$

16. $3x - 5y = 61$
    $3x - y = 17$ $(2, -11)$

17. $2.3x - 1.7y = 3.5$
    $4.7x - 1.7y = 10.7$ $(3, 2)$

18. $4.1x - 1.3y = 7.1$
    $2.9x - 1.3y = 3.5$ $(3, 4)$

19. $10x - 4y = 35$
    $3x + 4y = 21$ $(4.31, 2.02)^*$

20. $9x + 2y = 59$
    $-2x - 2y = -8$ $(7.29, -3.29)$ *Done *without* roundoff at intermediate steps.

For Problems 21 through 40, first transform the equations so that either the x-coefficients or the y-coefficients are opposite. Then solve by the linear combination method.

21. $3x + 5y = 17$
    $2x + 3y = 11$ $(4, 1)$

22. $5x + 2y = 24$
    $4x + 3y = 29$ $(2, 7)$

23. $4x - 5y = -19$
    $3x + 7y = 18$ $(-1, 3)$

24. $6x - 5y = 28$
    $4x + 9y = -6$ $(3, -2)$

25. $6a - 7b = 12$
    $5a - 4b = 10$ $(2, 0)$

26. $8r - 3s = 15$
    $7r - 4s = 20$ $(0, -5)$

27. $2x + 9y = 12.5$
    $6x + 5y = 8.9$ $(0.4, 1.3)$

28. $3x + 5y = 4.7$
    $6x + 2y = 6.2$ $(0.9, 0.4)$

29. $7u + 8v = 23$
    $3u - 2v = -1$ $(1, 2)$

30. $7c + 10d = -13$
    $3c - 2d = 7$ $(1, -2)$

31. $4x - 3y = 2.7$
    $8x + 5y = 13.1$ $(1.2, 0.7)$

32. $5x - 6y = 2.7$
    $10x + 7y = 1.6$ $(0.3, -0.2)$

33. $3x - 5y = -29$
    $2x - 10y = -42$ $(-4, 3.4)$

34. $7x - 2y = -26$
    $5x - 12y = -45$ $(-3, 2.5)$

35. $4x + y = 42$
    $6x - 5y = 50$ $(10, 2)$

36. $2x + 9y = 39$
    $5x - y = -20$ $(-3, 5)$

37. $x + 12y = -8$
    $8x - 5y = 37$ $(4, -1)$

38. $7x - 8y = 51$
    $x + 10y = -15$ $(5, -2)$

39. $5x + 7y = 18.9$
    $2x - 3y = -8.1$ $(0, 2.7)$

40. $6x + 5y = 5.1$
    $4x - 2y = -1.4$ $(0.1, 0.9)$

For Problems 41 through 44, find an equation of the line connecting the two given points. You can find the slope by first finding the rise and run. The y-intercept can be found from $y = mx + b$ by substituting the slope for m, and one of the ordered pairs for x and y.

41. (3, 4) and (6, 10) $y = 2x - 2$ 42. (1, 7) and $(-3, -5)$ $y = 3x + 4$

43. (8, 5) and $(-4, 2)$ $y = \frac{1}{4}x + 3$ 44. (3, 9) and (15, 1) $y = -\frac{2}{3}x + 11$

8-10 | PROBLEMS INVOLVING TWO VARIABLES

Time: 4 or 5 days

Chalkboard Examples:

First day:
Use Exercise 8–10, 1, as an example. It helps if students have been assigned this problem as homework prior to class.

Second day:
Use Exercise 8–10, 11, as an example.

Third day:
Use Exercise 8–10, 23, as an example.

Fourth day:
Use Exercise 8–10, 33, as an example.

Fifth day:
Consolidate work done so far.

Assignment:

Day 1: Exercise 8–10, two to four problems from 2–10.

Day 2: Exercise 8–10, #13, 15, 17 or 14, 16, 18 (Problems 17 or 18 begin mixture problems.)

Day 3: Exercise 8–10, #19, 25, 27 or 20, 26, 28 (Problems 19 or 20 review mixture problems.)

Day 4: Exercise 8–10, #29, 31, 35 or 30, 32, 34

Day 5: Exercise 8–11, selected problems in preparation for test

Suppose that hamburgers cost \$2.00 each and hot dogs cost \$1.50 each. The amount of money you spend on burgers and dogs depends on how many of each you buy.

$$\text{Let } x = \text{ the number of burgers.}$$

$$\text{Let } y = \text{ the number of hot dogs.}$$

The amount of money spent is

$$2x + 1.5y.$$

This two-variable expression represents a number of dollars. If you know values of x and y, you can easily find the cost. For instance, if x is 5 and y is 3, then

$$2x + 1.5y$$
$$= 2(5) + 1.5(3)$$
$$= 14.50.$$

But the reverse problem is not so simple. If you know that the total spent is \$14.50, you can write the equation

$$2x + 1.5y = 14.50. \tag{1}$$

But you cannot say for sure that x is 5 and y is 3. It is possible that x is 2 and y is 7, because

$$2(2) + 1.5(7)$$
$$= 14.50.$$

You need a second equation to form a *system* that can be solved for both variables. For instance, if you know that the total number of burgers and hot dogs is 8, the second equation would be

$$x + y = 8. \tag{2}$$

You solve this system as follows.

$$2x + 1.5y = 14.5 \quad\longrightarrow\quad 2x + 1.5y = 14.5$$
$$x + y = 8 \quad\xrightarrow{m\ -2}\quad -2x - 2y = -16$$

$$2x + 1.5y = 14.5 \qquad\qquad \overline{-0.5y = -1.5} \quad \text{Add.}$$
$$\underline{2x + 2y = 16}$$
$$-0.5y = -1.5 \qquad\qquad y = 3 \qquad \text{Divide by } -0.5$$

$$x + 3 = 8 \qquad \text{Substitute 3 for } y \text{ in the second equation.}$$
$$x = 5$$

<u>5 hamburgers and 3 hot dogs</u>

In this section you will solve similar problems involving expressions with two variables.

Objective:

Given a problem involving two variables, write and solve a system of two equations and answer the question asked.

Cover the answers as you work the examples.

EXAMPLE 1

Swiss and Limburger Cheese Problem   Swiss cheese and Limburger cheese cost different amounts per kilogram, but you do not know how much. A box containing 3 kilograms (kg) of Swiss and 2 kg of Limburger costs $24.40. Another box containing 4 kg of Swiss and 5 kg of Limburger costs $47.70. Assuming that these figures are for cheese only (not for the box), how much is each kind of cheese worth per kilogram? $- - - - -$

> **Think These Reasons**

Let x = number of dollars
       per kilogram for Swiss.   Define the variables.
Let y = number of dollars
       per kilogram for Limburger.

First write two equations involving x and y. Then solve the system.

$$3x + 2y = 24.40 \xrightarrow{\text{m } 5} \quad 15x + 10y = 122.00$$

$$4x + 5y = 47.70 \xrightarrow{\text{m } -2} \quad -\ \underline{\ 8x - 10y = -95.40\ }$$

$$7x \qquad\quad = 26.60 \qquad \text{Add.}$$

$$x = 3.80 \qquad \text{Divide by 7.}$$

$3(3.80) + 2y = 24.40$ Substitute 3.80 for x in the first equation.

$11.40 + 2y = 24.40$ Do the arithmetic.

$2y = 13.00$ Subtract 11.40.

$y = 6.50$ Divide by 2.

$\underline{\$3.80/\text{kg for Swiss},}$ Answer the question.
$\underline{\$6.50/\text{kg for Limburger}}$

EXAMPLE 2

Cereal Sugar Problem   According to information on the labels, cereal A contains about 38% sugar. Cereal B contains about 46% sugar.

a. What percent sugar would there be in a mixture of 100 g of cereal A and 200 g of cereal B?

b. How many grams of each cereal would be needed to make a kilogram of a mixture containing 40% sugar?

– – – – –   – – – – –

a. Let x = number of grams of cereal A.   Define the variables.
    Let y = number of grams of cereal B.

$0.38x + 0.46y$ = number of grams of sugar.   Write an expression.

If $x = 100$ and $y = 200$, then   Evaluate the expression.

$0.38x + 0.46y$

$= 38 + 92$

$= 130$

130 g of sugar

Total mass is $100 + 200$, or 300 g.

Percent of sugar is $\dfrac{130}{300} \times 100$ $\text{Percent} = \dfrac{\text{number}}{\text{total}} \times 100.$

≈ 43.3

43.3% sugar.   Answer the question.

b. First, write two equations.
$$x + y = 1000$$ Total is 1000 g (1 kg).
$$0.38x + 0.46y = 0.4(1000)$$ Sugar is 40% of 1000 g.

Then simplify and linearly combine.

$x + y = 1000 \xrightarrow{\ \text{m} \ -0.38\ } -0.38x - 0.38y = -380$

$\underline{0.38x + 0.46y = 400 \longrightarrow \quad 0.38x + 0.46y = 400}$

$0.08y = 20$

$y = 250$

$x + 250 = 1000$ Substitute 250 for y in the first equation.

$x = 750$ Subtract 250.

Cereal A: 750 g,
cereal B: 250 g   Answer the question.

EXAMPLE 3

Submarine Problem   A submarine sails submerged for a distance of 150 nautical miles against a current of unknown speed, taking a total of 10 hours. It returns to the starting point, going with the current, in 6 hours.

For both trips it moves the same speed through the water. How many knots (nautical miles per hour) does the sub travel through the water, and how many knots is the current?

－ － － －   － － － － －

Let x = number of knots sub goes. Let y = number of knots current flows.	Define variables.
$x - y$ = net rate *against* the current. $x + y$ = net rate *with* the current.	Subtract the speeds when the motions oppose each other. Add the speeds when the motions help each other.
$(x - y)(10) = 150$ $(x + y)(6) = 150$	Rate × time = distance.
$x - y = 15$ $x + y = 25$	Divide each member by 10. Divide each member by 6.
$2x \quad\;\; = 40$	Add the two equations.
$x = 20$	Divide each member by 2.
$20 + y = 25$	Substitute 20 for x in $x + y = 25$.
$y = 5$	Subtract 5 from each member.

Sub goes at 20 knots.
Current is 5 knots.   Answer the question.

EXAMPLE 4

Insurance Problem   The Joneses have two insurance policies. The first one pays 80% of those expenses not covered by the second. The second pays 70% of those expenses not covered by the first. Mrs. Jones has an operation that costs $3000 and is covered by *both* policies. How much do the Joneses get from each policy? Is the total more than 100% of the $3000?

Let x = number of dollars paid by the first policy.
Let y = number of dollars paid by the second policy.

$3000 - x$ = number of dollars *not* paid by the first policy.
$3000 - y$ = number of dollars *not* paid by the second policy.

$x = 0.8(3000 - y)$	(1)	Because x is 80% of what is *not*
$y = 0.7(3000 - x)$	(2)	paid by the second and y is 70% of what is *not* paid by the first.
$x = 2400 - 0.8y$		Distribute 0.8 in (1).
$x = 2400 - 0.8[0.7(3000 - x)]$		Substitute $0.7(3000 - x)$ for y.
$x = 2400 - 1680 + 0.56x$		Distribute $(0.8)(0.7)$, or 0.56.
$0.44x = 720$		Subtract $0.56x$ from each member and do the arithmetic.
$x = 1636.3636...$		Divide by 0.44.
$y = 0.7(3000 - 1636.36...)$		Substitute $1636.36...$ for x in (2).
$y = 954.5454...$		Do the arithmetic.

First policy pays $1636.36.
Second policy pays $954.55.   Answer the question.

The total paid is $2590.91, which is *less* than 100% of $3000.

Note: The substitution technique is better for this system, since you already have x in terms of y and y in terms of x.

EXERCISE 8-10

Problem Notes:

Various blocks of problems have slightly different themes, progressing from relatively easy to quite hard. The first two problems in each block are highly structured, telling students exactly what to do. For others, students must figure out on their own to define variables, write expressions, solve equations, and answer the question.

Problems 1 through 10 involve finding unknown prices or rates. The first two problems lead you step by step through the problem. For the others, *you* must think of the steps.

1. *Mexican Dinner Problem*   Suppose that you are helping set the prices for the menu at a new Mexican restaurant. The regular dinner contains 2 tacos and 3 enchiladas. The special dinner contains 4 tacos and 5 enchiladas.
    a. Let x be the number of cents charged for each taco and let y be the number of cents charged for each enchilada. Write two expressions, one for the price of a regular dinner and the other for the price of a special dinner.

b. How much would each dinner cost if:
    i.   tacos are 35¢ each and enchiladas are 60¢ each?
    ii. tacos are 45¢ each and enchiladas are 50¢ each?
c. The boss sets prices of $2.39 for the regular dinner and $4.23 for the special dinner. How many cents did she assume per taco and how many cents per enchilada?

```
┌─────────────────────────────┐
│                             │
│       HOLLY PEÑA'S          │
│      MEXICAN FOOD           │
│                             │
│  Regular . . .  $ _____     │
│     2 tacos                 │
│     3 enchiladas            │
│                             │
│  Special  . . . $ _____     │
│     4 tacos                 │
│     5 enchiladas            │
│                             │
└─────────────────────────────┘
```

2. *Scuba Diving Problem*   A scuba diving resort hotel offers divers two plans. Plan A gives 3 nights' lodging and 4 dives. Plan B gives 5 nights' lodging and 8 dives.

```
┌─────────────────────────────┐
│                             │
│       LAST RESORT           │
│     SCUBA DIVING!!          │
│                             │
│  Plan A  . . .  $ _____     │
│     3 nights                │
│     4 dives                 │
│                             │
│  Plan B  . . .  $ _____     │
│     5 nights                │
│     8 dives                 │
│                             │
└─────────────────────────────┘
```

a. Let x be the number of dollars they charge per night and let y be the number of dollars per dive. Write two expressions, one for the amount you would pay for plan A and the other for plan B.
b. Evaluate the expressions in part (a) if lodging is $50 per night and dives are $40 each.
c. If lodging is increased to $80 per night and dives are reduced to $20 each, do the two plans increase or decrease in cost? By how much?
d. A new price list comes out in which plan A costs $440 and plan B costs $780. What prices are now being assumed per night and per dive?

1. a. $2x + 3y$, $4x + 5y$
    b. i. $2.50 regular, $4.40 special
        ii. $2.40 regular, $4.30 special
    c. 37¢ for taco, 55¢ for enchilada

2. a. $3x + 4y$, $5x + 8y$
    b. $310 for A, $570 for B
    c. A goes up $10, B goes down $10
    d. $100 per night, $35 per dive

3. a. 70¢ for an egg, 83¢ for a sausage
b. $9.31

3. *Eggs and Sausage Problem*   A breakfast menu lists 2 eggs with 1 sausage patty for $2.23 and 3 eggs with 2 sausage patties for $3.76.
 a.   Assuming that these amounts pay only for the eggs and sausage, how much do you pay for an egg and how much do you pay for a sausage?
 b.   How much would you expect to pay for the Glutton's Breakfast of 5 eggs and 7 sausage patties?

4. *Artist's Kit Problem*   A beginner's artist kit costs $6.35 and contains 2 brushes and 5 jars of paint. The standard kit has 4 brushes and 12 jars of paint and costs $13.20.
 a.   Assuming that all brushes cost the same and that all jars of paint cost the same, what are the prices of a brush and of a jar of paint? $2.55 for a brush, $.25 for a jar of paint.
 b.   How much would you expect to pay for a deluxe kit containing 7 brushes and 20 jars of paint? $22.85

Problems 5 and 6 show that identical mathematics can represent completely different situations from the real world.

5. *Regular and Unleaded Gas Problem 1*   Regular gas and unleaded gas sell for different prices per liter. Suppose that 2 liters of regular and 3 liters of unleaded cost a total of 252 cents. Five liters of regular and 4 liters of unleaded cost a total of 448 cents. What is the price per liter for each kind of gas?   48¢/liter for regular, 52¢/liter for unleaded

6. *Worm and Snail Relay Problem*   A worm and a snail enter the relay races. If the worm goes for 5 hours and then the snail goes for 4 hours, they cover a total of 448 inches. If the worm goes for 2 hours and the snail goes for 3 hours, they cover a total of 252 inches. How fast does each one slither?   Worm goes 48 in./h, snail goes 52 in./h

7. *Ice Cream Cone Problem*   A well-known chain of ice cream stores sells a cone with 3 scoops of ice cream for $1.28 and a cone with 2 scoops of ice cream for $.87.
 a.   Assuming that these amounts pay only for the ice cream and for the cone, how much do you spend for each scoop of ice cream, and how much for the cone?   41¢/scoop for ice cream, 5¢ for cone
 b.   How much would you expect to pay for a cone with 4 scoops of ice cream? $1.69

8. a. $120 per cord for wood, $20 to deliver
b. $200

8. *Firewood Problem*   It costs $140 to have a cord of firewood delivered to your house and $80 to have one-half cord delivered. Assume that you pay a certain number of dollars per cord for the wood, plus a fixed number of dollars for delivery.
 a.   How much do you pay per cord and how much for delivery?
 b.   How much would you expect to pay to have $1\frac{1}{2}$ cords delivered? (The answer is *not* $220!)

9. *Regular and Unleaded Gas Problem 2*   A gas station has just raised its prices. The attendant resets the pump but forgets to record the old prices. Rather than revealing her forgetfulness by asking her boss, she

consults yesterday's sales report. She finds that 450 liters of regular and 320 liters of unleaded were sold, for a total of $384.83. Regular was 5 cents per liter cheaper than unleaded. What were the two prices per liter yesterday?   47.9¢/liter for regular, 52.9¢/liter for unleaded

10.   **Regular and Unleaded Gas Problem 3**   Unleaded gas costs 5¢ per liter more than regular gas. A dealer buys 1000 liters of unleaded and 3000 liters of regular, for a total of $1870. How many cents per liter does each kind of gas cost?   45.5¢/liter for regular, 50.5¢/liter for unleaded

Problems 11 through 16 involve finding various numbers of items for which the prices are known. The first two lead you step by step through the problem. For the others, *you* must think of the steps.

11.   **Carwash Problem**   The Math Club raised money for its summer trip by washing cars. They charged $3 for a car and $5 for a truck.

CARWASH ACCOUNTING			
Kind	Price	No.	$
Cars	$3	_____	_____
Trucks	$5	_____	_____
Totals	. .	_____	_____

a.   Define variables for the number of cars washed and for the number of trucks washed. Then write an expression for the total number of dollars received. $3x + 5y$

b.   Evaluate the expression in part (a) for:
    i.   27 cars and 13 trucks;   146
    ii.   41 cars and 8 trucks;   163
    iii. 16 cars and 23 trucks. (Surprising?)   163

c.   Suppose the club earned a total of $181 for washing a total of 49 vehicles. Write a system of two equations stating these facts, and solve the system to find out how many of each kind of vehicle they washed.   32 cars, 17 trucks

12.   **Yogurt Problem**   Mel Ting sells half-gallons of frozen yogurt for $4 each and gallons for $7 each.

MEL'S FROZEN YOGURT			
Size	Price	No.	$
½ gal.	$4	_____	_____
1 gal.	$7	_____	_____
Totals	. .	_____	_____

a. Define variables for the number of half-gallons and for the number of gallons sold. Then write an expression for the total number of dollars received. $4x + 7y$

b. Evaluate the expression in part (a) for:
   i.   33 half-gallons and 19 gallons;   265
   ii. 57 half-gallons and 30 gallons;   438
   iii. 36 half-gallons and 42 gallons. (Surprising?)   438

c. One day Mel sells a total of 50 containers of yogurt, for a total of $287. Write a system of equations expressing these facts. Then solve the system to find out how many of each kind of container he sold.   21 half-gallon, 29 gallon

13. **Football Tickets Problem**   Suppose that you are collecting tickets at a football game. Reserved seat tickets cost $4.00 each and general admission tickets costs $3.00 each. After the game is over, the turnstile count shows that 1787 people paid admission. You count a total of $5792 from the sale of tickets. You are just about ready to leave for your postgame date when your boss says, "By the way, how many of each kind of ticket were there?" Rather than spending half an hour sorting and counting all the ticket stubs, you decide to use algebra. What do you tell your boss?   431 reserved, 1356 general admission

14. 7234 reserved, 10,172 general admission

14. **Basketball Tickets Problem**   At a professional basketball game, the turnstile count showed that 17,406 people paid admission. The total cash received for tickets was $133,372. Without actually counting the ticket stubs, find out how many paid for reserved seats ($10.00 each) and how many paid general admission ($6.00 each).

15. **Cars and Trucks Problem**   A trainload of cars and trucks is en route to an automobile dealer for whom you work. Before they arrive, the dealer receives an invoice showing a total of 160 vehicles. But the part of the invoice showing how many of each kind of vehicle has been torn off and lost. Your boss desperately needs to know how many of each there are before they arrive. Since you know algebra, she comes to you for aid. The invoice shows a total mass of 182,800 kilograms of vehicles, and each truck is 1400 kg and each car is 1000 kg. How many of each kind are there?   103 cars, 57 trucks

16. **New-and-Old Oil Problem**   In the 1970s the government held down the price of oil from old wells but allowed a higher price for oil from new wells. One month the oil company that was producing from a particular field paid $28,832.10 for a total of 1395 barrels of oil. But there was no indication of how many of these barrels were "new" oil and how many were "old" oil. Figure out these numbers using the fact that new oil sold for $23.70 per barrel and old oil sold for $12.30 per barrel.   1024 barrels of new oil, 371 barrels of old oil

Problems 17 through 22 involve mixtures of varying quantities of sub-
stances with known compositions. The first two problems lead you step by
step through the problem. For the others, *you* must think of what to do.

17. ***Exhaust Gas Problem***   Carbon monoxide is a gas that is 43%
carbon. Carbon dioxide is only 27% carbon. Suppose that the
Environmental Protection Agency (EPA) analyzes exhaust from cars,
a mixture of carbon monoxide and carbon dioxide.

EPA EXHAUST REPORT			
Gas	%C	mg gas	mg C
CO	43%	————	————
CO_2	27%	————	————
Totals		════	════

Percent C = ____ × 100 = _____

a.   Define variables for the number of milligrams (mg) of each gas
in a sample. Then write an expression for the number of mg of
carbon in the sample. $0.43x + 0.27y$
b.   Evaluate the expression in part (a) if one mixes 2000 mg of
carbon monoxide and 3000 mg of carbon dioxide.   1670
c.   What is the percent of carbon in the mixture of part (b)?   33.4%
d.   If the EPA finds that a 1600-mg sample of exhaust gas has 32%
carbon, how many mg of the sample were carbon monoxide,
and how many were carbon dioxide?   500 mg CO, 1100 mg CO_2

18. ***Gasoline Octane Problem***   The *octane number* of gasoline can be
thought of as the percent of the compound octane in the gasoline.
For instance, 89-octane gas would be 89% octane and 11%
something else. Suppose that a wholesaler has 84-octane gas and
91-octane gas.
a.   The wholesaler mixes x gallons of 84-octane gas and y gallons
of 91-octane gas. Write an expression for the number of gallons
of octane in the mixture. $0.84x + 0.91y$
b.   Evaluate the expression in part (a) if 1000 gallons of 84-octane
gas is mixed with 2000 gallons of 91-octane gas.   2660
c.   What will be the octane number of the mixture in part (b)?   88.7
d.   If the wholesaler receives an order for 15,000 gallons of
89.7-octane gas, how much of each kind should be mixed to fill
the order?   About 2786 gallons of 84-octane; about 12,214 gallons of 91-octane

19. ***Silver Alloy Problem***   Old silver coins contain 90% silver. Silver
solder contains 63% silver. If you wanted to make 200 kilograms of

an alloy containing 82% silver, how many kilograms of old coins and how many kilograms of silver solder could you melt together to do this?   140.74 kg coins, 59.26 kg silver solder

20. *Brass Alloy Problem*   Suppose that you operate a junk yard. You have vast quantities of yellow brass (67% copper, 33% zinc) and red brass (85% copper, 15% zinc) on hand. Al Oye sends an order for 500 tons of brass containing 80% copper and 20% zinc. How many tons of each kind of brass would you have to melt together to fill Al's order?   138.89 tons yellow brass, 361.11 tons red brass

21. *Regular and Advanced Students' Test Problem*   Assume that advanced students would average 93% on an achievement test and that regular students would average 75% on it.
    a. If 100 advanced students and 300 regular students took the test, what would you expect the average to be?   79.5%
    b. How many of each kind of student would be needed to get a group of 90 students who would average 87% on the test?
        60 advanced, 30 regular

22. *Pitcher and Catcher's Batting Problem*   Carl Catcher has a batting average of .370, meaning that he makes a hit 37% of the times he is at bat. Pete Pitcher has a batting average of only .110. Let x be the number of times Carl comes to bat and let y be the number of times Pete comes to bat.
    a. If Carl bats 7 times and Pete bats 3 times, what should their overall batting average be?   .292
    b. In a total of 50 times at bat, how many times may Pete bat in order for their combined average to be as close as possible to .300?   Pete bats 13 times.

Problems 23 through 32 involve motion with and against a current. The first two lead you step by step through the problem. For others, you must think of what to do.

23. *Shark Problem*   A shark takes 20 minutes to swim with the current from its cave to the feeding grounds. Later, it returns against the current, taking 30 minutes.

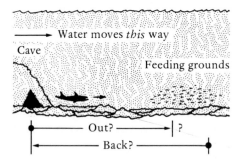

a. Define variables for the shark's speed through the water and for the speed of the current (the speed at which the water is moving). Use feet per minute (ft/min). Then write two expressions, one for the distance the shark swims out and the other for the distance it swims back.

b. Evaluate the expression in part (a) if:
   i.   the shark swims 400 ft/min and the current is 100 ft/min;
   ii. the shark swims 80 ft/min and the current is 50 ft/min.

c. How fast does the shark swim and how fast is the current if both the trip out and the trip back are 2100 feet?

24. **Bee Problem**   The wind blows the smell of a field of flowers to the beehive. A bee flies out to get pollen and then returns to the hive. The outgoing trip takes 70 seconds and the return trip takes 40 seconds.

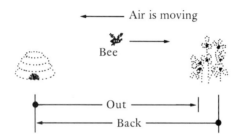

a. Define variables for the rate at which the bee flies through the (still) air and for the rate at which the air is moving (the wind speed) in feet per second. Then write two expressions, one for the distance the bee flew to reach the flower bed and the other for the distance she flies to return to the hive.

b. How far did the bee fly out and how far back if:
   i.   she flies 20 ft/sec and the wind is 5 ft/sec;
   ii. she flies 30 ft/sec and the wind is 20 ft/sec?

c. How fast does the bee fly and what is the wind speed if both the trip out and the return trip are 560 feet?

25. **Snoopy's Dogflight Problem**   Snoopy flies his Sopwith Camel the 120 kilometers from London to Calais in 12 hours, flying into a headwind. The return trip, with the same wind as a tailwind, takes only 2 hours. How fast does Snoopy fly through the air? How fast is the wind blowing?

26. **A. T. Miles's Flight Problem**   A. T. Miles flies his small plane from Tampa to Orlando, a distance of 80 miles, against a headwind. The trip takes 32 minutes. Later, he returns to Tampa with the wind at his back, making the return trip in 20 minutes. How fast does he fly through the air? How fast is the wind blowing?

23. **a.** $20(x + y)$ = number of ft out;
     $30(x - y)$ = number of ft back
   b. i. 10,000 ft out, 9000 ft back
       ii. 2600 ft out, 900 ft back
   c. Shark swims 87.5 ft/min, current is 17.5 ft/min

24. **a.** $70(x - y)$ = number of ft out;
     $40(x + y)$ = number of ft back
   b. i. 1050 ft out, 1000 ft back
       ii. 700 ft out, 2000 ft back
   c. Bee flies 11 ft/sec, wind blows 3 ft/sec.

25. 35 km/h through air; 25 km/h wind
26. 195 mi/h through air; 45 mi/h wind

27. Ann runs 5 ft/sec; escalator moves 1 ft/sec.

31. Aquaman swims about 140.5 m/min; water flows about 73.8 m/min.
32. The boat moves through the water 258 ft/min; current is 306 ft/min.

27. *Escalator Problem*   Ann Tick runs up the "down" escalator in 12 seconds and back down again in 8 seconds. The escalator is 48 feet long. How fast does Ann run? How fast does the escalator move?

28. *Conveyor Belt Problem*   A conveyor belt 420 feet long is moving coal in a strip mine. A rabbit hops on at one end and runs in the same direction the belt is moving. When it gets to the other end, the rabbit turns and runs back, against the motion of the conveyor. The first trip takes 60 seconds and the return trip takes 210 seconds. How fast does the rabbit run and how fast does the conveyor belt move?   Rabbit runs 4.5 ft/sec; conveyor moves 2.5 ft/sec.

29. *Pedalboat Problem*   Eb and Flo are pedalboating on the San Antonio River. Going downstream their speed is 40 meters per minute (m/min). Coming back upstream their speed is only 26 m/min. How fast do they move through the water? How fast is the current going?   They pedal 33 m/min; current is 7 m/min.

30. *Mississippi River Tug Problem*   Going downstream a tugboat averages 17 kilometers per hour (km/h). Coming back upstream its average speed is only 6 km/h. How fast does the current flow? How fast does the tugboat move through the water?   Tug goes 11.5 km/h; current is 5.5 km/h.

31. *Aquaman Problem*   Aquaman swims into a storm drain, from which water is flowing at an unknown rate. He swims 200 meters against the flow in 3 min. Then he returns 150 meters with the flow in 0.7 min, before emerging through a manhole in the top of the drain. How fast does Aquaman swim through the water, and how fast does the water flow in the drain?

32. *Niagara Falls Problem*   Miss Hapse is sailing a remote controlled model boat downstream in the Niagara River. She discovers that at full speed the model can cover 1128 feet in 2 minutes. Suddenly she realizes that the boat is only 240 feet from the falls! She turns it around and runs it at top speed in the other direction. But it is a losing battle. As the boat goes over the falls, she observes that 5 minutes passed since it was turned around. How fast did the boat move through the water? How fast was the water flowing?

Problem 32 is tricky. Because the current is faster than the boat, the boat has a net speed downstream both with and against the current.

Problems 33–36 lead to systems of equations similar to Problems 27–30 of Exercise 8–7. Here, x must be known before y can be found, and vice versa. In deriving the equation $x = 0.2(400 + y)$ in Problem 33, for example, students will argue, "But I don't *know* y!" Your response should convey that they do not know what y *equals*, but they do know what it *stands* for; namely, the amount the father pays. These problems help you convey the concept of the variable as a symbol that stands for a particular number, regardless of whether or not you know its value. Note that these systems are easier to solve by substitution than by addition-subtraction.

Problems 33 through 36 involve equations in which y is in terms of x and x is in terms of y.

33. *Calvin's Vacation Problem*   Calvin Butterball earns $400 working at the supermarket to help pay his share of a vacation trip with Phoebe Small's family. To supplement his earnings, Calvin's mother will give him an additional 20% of what he earns and his father will give him an additional 30% of what he earns.
   a.   How much will he get from each parent?
   b.   Calvin is good at business deals and asks if his mother will give him 20% of the *total* he gets from working and from his father. He also asks if his father will give 30% of the total he gets from working and from his mother. His parents agree, provided Calvin can figure out the right amounts. How much will Calvin get from each parent under these conditions?
   c.   How much more will Calvin get in part (b) than in part (a)?

33. **a.** $80 from mother, $120 from father
    b. $110.64 from mother, $153.19 from father
    c. $63.83

34. *Fund-Raising Problem*   The Student Council conducts a fund-raising project for needy families. The School Board agrees to give an additional amount equal to 70% of what is raised. The Chamber of Commerce agrees to give an additional amount equal to 60% of what is raised. Here is the catch! The Board will pay 70% of the *total* from the project and from the Chamber of Commerce. The Chamber will pay 60% of the *total* from the project and from the School Board. The project makes $2000.
   a.   How much will the School Board give, and how much will the Chamber of Commerce give? $3862.07 from Board, $3517.24 from Chamber
   b.   How much more money will the Student Council get under this plan than they would if the Board and the Chamber just paid 70% and 60%, respectively, of the $2000? $4779.31 more

35. *Income Tax Problem 1*   If a family pays state income tax, they can deduct this amount from their income for federal tax purposes. For instance, if the income is $50,000, and the state tax is $4000, then they pay federal tax on only the remaining $46,000. A mathematical difficulty arises in states that let you deduct the *federal* tax from the income before figuring *state* tax. You need to know each amount of tax before you can figure out the other! Here's how they get around this difficulty. Suppose that the income is $50,000.
   a.   Let f be the number of dollars of federal tax and let s be the number of dollars of state tax. Write two equations, one saying that the state tax is 10% of what is left after paying federal tax and the other saying that the federal tax is 20% of what is left after paying state tax.
   b.   How much state and federal tax does the family pay?
   c.   How much does the family save over what they would pay if the 10% and 20% tax rates applied to the entire $50,000?

35. **a.** $s = 0.1(50,000 - f)$
        $f = 0.2(50,000 - s)$
    b. $4081.63 state tax, $9183.67 federal tax.
    c. $1734.70

36. **a.** $s = 0.4(200,000 - f)$
        $f = 0.6(200,000 - s)$
    b. $42,105.26 state tax; $94,736.84 federal tax.
    c. $63,157.90
    Trouble otherwise, because tax would be entire income!

36. *Income Tax Problem 2*   Repeat Problem 35 if the family's income is $200,000 and the state and federal tax rates are 40% and 60%, respectively. Explain why this family would be in trouble if the 40% and 60% tax rates were applied to the entire $200,000.

For Problems 37 through 40, you must use the concepts of this chapter in clever ways!

37. a. 5.6 min up, 7.4 min down.
  b. 432 m up, 1752 m down.

  Problem 38 involves graphical determination of integer solutions of a single equation with two variables, similar to the problems in Section 8–4.
  Problem 39 is easy if students first realize that the variables should be the numbers of *groups,* not the numbers of band and pep squad members. The equations must say that the total number of band members is 100, and the total number of pep squad members is 80.

38. b. $y = -\dfrac{7}{5}x + 20$

  Integer pts: (0,20), (5, 13), (10, 6).

0 7-pt;	20 5-pt.
5 7-pt;	13 5-pt.
10 7-pt;	6 5-pt.

39. 30 5-member, 10 3-member

  B P B P B P P
               B

40. a. Check student plots.
  b. (5, 13) is not the same as one of the data points.
  c. Answers may vary.
  d. Slope is about 2.
  e. Answers may vary. $y = 2x + 3$
  f. Answers may vary. (3, 9); (7, 17); (30, 63); (48.5, 100)

---

37. *Uphill and Downhill Running Problem*   Suppose that you can run 240 meters per minute (m/min) going downhill, but only 160 m/min going uphill.
  a. One day you run 2672 meters in a total of 13 min. How many minutes did you run uphill and how many minutes down?
  b. Another day you run 2184 meters in a total of 10 min. How far did you run uphill and how far down?

38. *Test Problems Problem*   A test is to contain some questions worth 7 points each and some worth 5 points each. Let x be the number of 7-point questions and let y be the number of 5-point questions.
  a. Write an equation stating that the total number of points on the test is to be 100. $7x + 5y = 100$
  b. Figure out how many of each kind of question there could be. (There is more than one correct answer. Drawing a graph may help you find them.)

39. *Marching Formation Problem*   The marching band and the pep squad do a combined routine in which they divide into 5-member and 3-member groups, as shown in the figure. If the band has a total of 100 members and the pep squad has a total of 80 members, how many of each kind of group can be formed so that no one is left over?

40. *Scattered Data Problem*   In Section 8-6 you found the equation of a line from two points on the graph. In the real world, two variables are often related by a linear graph. When you measure values of x and y, there can be inaccuracies. The points might not quite lie in a straight line. Your purpose is to find the "best" line to represent the data. Suppose the following values of x and y have been measured.

  x: 2   4   5   6   8
  y: 8 11 12 14 20

  a. Plot all six points on graph paper.
  b. The line that fits best goes through the point whose x-coordinate is the average of the x-values, and whose y-coordinate is the average of the y-values. Calculate these average values, and plot the point on your graph. Is it the same as one of the data points?
  c. With a ruler, draw the line through the point in part (b) that you think best fits the six data points.
  d. Approximately what is the slope of the line in part (c)?
  e. Write an equation of the line in part (d). Transform it to the slope-intercept form, $y = mx + b$.
  f. The equation in part (e) can be used to predict other values of x and y. Predict what y would be if $x = 3$, if $x = 7$, and if $x = 30$. Predict the value of x that would make $y = 100$.

41. ***Shoe Size Experiment Problem***   Tall people have longer feet than short people. It seems reasonable to assume that there is a linear relationship between height and shoe size. In this problem you will conduct an experiment to try to determine such a relationship.

    a.   Select a group of people, such as the students in your class. Have each person record height and shoe size on an index card. You may want to measure height in inches or in centimeters rather than in feet and inches. Separate the cards into boys and girls, because shoe sizes are determined differently for each sex.

    b.   Plot two graphs of all the data points, one for boys and one for girls. Use *x* for height and *y* for shoe size. Then draw the best-fitting line as in Problem 40. Find the equation of each line.

    c.   Bob Lanier was a professional basketball player. He wears a size 22 shoe. Based on your equation, how tall do you predict he is?

    d.   Tell at least two ways you could change the way you get data for this problem that would make the line better represent the relationship between shoe size and height.

41. Answers may vary.

8-11 | CHAPTER REVIEW AND TEST

In this chapter you have studied expressions that have two variables, such as $5x + 7y$. To evaluate such expressions, you need to know values for both x and y. Setting such an expression equal to some number gives an equation with two variables, like

$$5x + 7y = 35.$$

These equations have *many* solutions, and you learned how to plot a graph of these solutions on a *Cartesian plane* (see the figures). *Slopes* and *intercepts* helped you plot these graphs quickly. By reversing the graphing process, you found an equation when information about the graph was given.

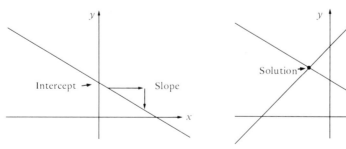

Equation with two variables   System of equations

Time: 1 day

Test Ideas:

If you choose, your test can consist entirely of word problems. This strategy alerts students to the need to learn to work the problems rather than to rely on simple equation-solving techniques to get sufficient points to pass. About four problems of the type in Exercise 8–9 are reasonable for a 50-minute period.

Assignment:

Study Section 9–1 in preparation for starting Chapter 9. Work the five examples. Work Exercise 9–1, #1–49 odd or 2–50 even. Although this sounds like a long assignment, students can finish it in about 20 to 30 minutes.

Problem Notes:

For Problems 6 and 7, make sure students solve by the prescribed method. Give no credit for using the other technique, even though the answer may be right.

Problem 7a is easily solved by either addition-subtraction or substitution. Problem 7b is more easily solved by substitution.

Problem 8 combines all of the plotting and system-solving techniques of this section in the same problem. Students see how graphical and algebraic solutions produce the same answer, although the graphical solution is only approximate. The system is most easily solved by addition-subtraction.

Two such equations form a *system of equations*. The *solution* of a system satisfies both equations and is represented by the point where the graphs cross. You learned how to calculate this ordered pair either by *substitution* or by *linear combination*.

In preparation for the Chapter Test below, go back and make a list of the objectives of each section. If you do not understand what the objective means, rework enough of the examples in that section to refresh your memory. The test itself is a good review but should be tried only after you have looked through your notes. The test may take you longer than a normal classroom test.

CHAPTER TEST

1. a. The ordinate is the *vertical* coordinate. The abscissa is the *horizontal* coordinate.
b. The rise is the *vertical* change. The run is the *horizontal* change.
c. The slope is the rise/run. An intercept is the value of one variable when the other equals zero.
d. An x-intercept is a *value of x* when $y = 0$. A y-intercept is a *value of y* when $x = 0$.
e. A horizontal line has a 0 slope. A vertical line does not have a number for the slope.

4.-5. See Additional Answers.

6a. $y = \frac{2}{7}x + 8$
b, $y + 3 = -\frac{5}{2}(x - 4)$
c. $y - 7 = -\frac{8}{5}(x + 2)$
d. $x = 4$

1. What is the difference in each case?
   a. Ordinate and abscissa.
   b. Rise and run.
   c. Slope and intercept.
   d. x-intercept and y-intercept.
   e. Slope of a horizontal line and slope of a vertical line.

2. a. Who is credited with inventing the xy-coordinate system? Rene Descartes
   b. Draw a coordinate system and show the names of the quadrants.
   c. What is a system of equations? Two or more equations with the same variables
   d. Find the x-intercept of $5x + 3y = 90$. $x = 18$
   e. Write an example of an equation in slope-intercept form. $y = 2x + 3$

3. For the expression $2x + 7y$:
   a. evaluate it if x is 13 and y is -8; -30
   b. find x if the expression equals 73 and y is 5;   19
   c. find y if the expression equals -1 and x is 10. -3

4. Plot the points $(1, 2)$ and $(5, -1)$ on a Cartesian coordinate system. Connect the points with a straight line. Find the slope of the line. $-\frac{3}{4}$

5. Plot the graph:
   a. $y = -\frac{3}{7}x$
   b. $y - 4 = 3(x + 2)$
   c. $y = -3$

6. Find an equation of the line.
   a. Has slope $\frac{2}{7}$ and y-intercept 8.
   b. Contains $(4, -3)$ and has slope $-\frac{5}{2}$.
   c. Contains $(-2, 7)$ and $(3, -1)$.
   d. Is vertical, and contains $(4, 6)$.

7. Solve by the addition-subtraction method.
$$2x + 3y = 8.1$$
$$5x - 2y = -1.6 \quad (0.6, 2.3)$$

8. Solve by substitution.

$$5x - y = -3$$
$$3x + 8y = 24 \quad (0,3)$$

9. Solve by either method.

   a. $x + 4y = 19$ b. $x = 0.7(300 - y)$
       $6x + 5y = 38$ $(3,4)$ $y = 0.8(300 - x)$ $(95.\overline{45}, 163.\overline{63})$

10. Use the system

$$x + 2y = 8$$
$$5x - 2y = 6.$$

10.a. $x:8$; $y:4$. See Additional Answers.

   a. Plot the graph of the first equation by finding the two intercepts.
   b. Transform the second equation to slope-intercept form. Use the slope and intercept to plot the graph on the *same* coordinate system as part (a). $y = \frac{5}{2}x - 3$
   c. Read the intersection point of the two graphs correct to 0.1 unit. $(2.3, 2.8)$
   d. Solve the system of equations either by addition-subtraction or by substitution. Show that the answer agrees with the one you found by graphing in part (c). $(2.\overline{3}, 2.8\overline{3})$

11. *Hamburger and Hot Dog Problem*   As junior employee in your office, you are sent out to get hamburgers and hot dogs for the 23 people who work there. On the way, you forget how many of each to buy. So you decide to figure it out by algebra. Each person gets one burger or one dog (not both!). You have collected a total of $32.10. Burgers cost $1.50 each and dogs cost $1.10 each. How many of each should you buy? 17 hamburgers, 6 hot dogs

Problems 11–13 touch on the three simplest problem types of Section 8–10.

12. *Crow's Flight Problem*   A. Crow flies 10.5 miles against the wind and returns with the wind. The first flight takes 35 minutes and the return flight takes 15 minutes. How many miles per minute does A. Crow fly? How fast is the wind blowing? Crow: 0.5 mi/min; wind: 0.2 mi/min.

13. *Antifreeze Problem*   Brand A antifreeze is 85% ethylene glycol. Brand B is 60% ethylene glycol. The two brands are to be mixed.
   a. Define variables for the numbers of gallons of each kind used. Then write an expression for the number of gallons of ethylene glycol in the mixture. $0.85x + 0.60y$
   b. If 100 gallons of brand A is mixed with 150 gallons of brand B, find:
      i.   the number of gallons of ethylene glycol in the mixture; 175 gal
      ii. the percent of ethylene glycol in the mixture. 70%
   c. If 1000 gallons of mixture is to have 78% ethylene glycol, how many gallons of each brand should be used? 720 gal of A, 280 gal of B

13. a. x = no. gal. A
       y = no. gal. B
       $0.85x + 0.60y$

9

Properties
of Exponents

In Chapter 1 you learned about powers and exponents. For instance, 2^5 means five 2s multiplied together. In this chapter you will learn how to multiply and divide powers quickly by operating with their exponents. For instance, when you divide two powers that have equal bases, you can subtract their exponents. The result leads to a definition of negative exponents. Positive and negative exponents can be used to simplify operations with very large or very small numbers by writing them in scientific notation. *For example, the 8,000,000,000 neurons in a person's brain could be written as* 8×10^9.

Expression:
x^5 means $x \cdot x \cdot x \cdot x \cdot x$.
Operation:
$$\frac{x^5}{x^7} = x^{-2}$$
Application:
8 billion equals 8,000,000,000, which equals 8×10^9.

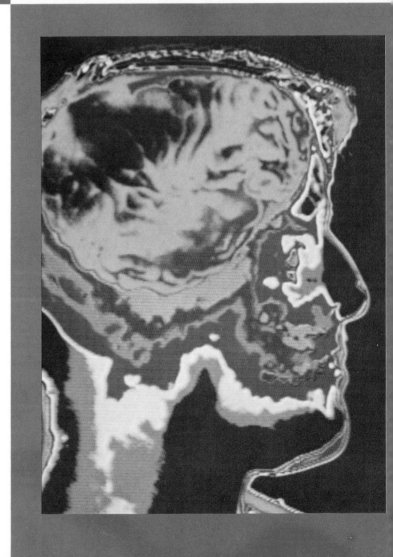

9-1 | PRIME NUMBERS AND PRIME FACTORS

This section reviews information you have probably encountered in earlier mathematics courses. So you should be able to read it and work the problems without help.

The numbers

$$2, 3, 5, 7, 11, 13, \ldots$$

are called *prime* numbers. A prime has only two factors, 1 and itself.

$$2 = 1 \cdot 2$$
$$3 = 1 \cdot 3$$
$$5 = 1 \cdot 5$$
$$7 = 1 \cdot 7$$
$$11 = 1 \cdot 11$$
$$13 = 1 \cdot 13$$

DEFINITION

> **PRIME NUMBER**
> A **prime number** is a positive integer
> that has *no* positive integers as factors
> other than 1 and itself.
> The number 1 is *not* considered to be a prime.

A number such as 144 is called a **composite** number, because it can be factored into a product composed of several primes. For example,

$$144 = 2 \cdot 2 \cdot 2 \cdot 2 \cdot 3 \cdot 3.$$

Time: $\frac{1}{2}$ day, with Section 9–2

Chalkboard Examples:

Write as a product of primes:
a. 72   Ans.: $2^3 \cdot 3^2$
b. 600   Ans.: $2^3 \cdot 3 \cdot 5^2$

Assignment:

Problems 1–19 odd or 2–20 even should have been assigned as preparation for this section. If not, assign Problems 1, 5, 9, 13, and 17 along with the assignment for Section 9–2.

These primes can be found by using the "upside-down, short-division" process explained in Section 1-3.

Prime factors of 144

$$2\overline{)144}$$
$$2\overline{)72}$$
$$2\overline{)36}$$
$$2\overline{)18}$$
$$3\overline{)9}$$
$$3$$

Ask yourself, "What prime goes into 144?", then, "What prime goes into 72?", and so forth.

The product $2 \cdot 2 \cdot 2 \cdot 2 \cdot 3 \cdot 3$ can be written using *powers*. Since 2^4 means $2 \cdot 2 \cdot 2 \cdot 2$ and 3^2 means $3 \cdot 3$, you can write

$$144 = 2^4 \cdot 3^2.$$

In the next few sections you will learn some properties of powers. In this section, you concentrate on factoring integers into primes.

Objective:
Be able to factor a given integer into a product of primes. If a prime occurs more than once, write the product in terms of powers.

Cover the answers as you work these examples.

EXAMPLE 1

Write 1125 as a product of powers of primes.

– – – – –   – – – – –

$$1125$$ Work: $3\overline{)1125}$
                                   $3\overline{)375}$
$$= 3 \cdot 3 \cdot 5 \cdot 5 \cdot 5$$ $5\overline{)125}$
                                   $5\overline{)25}$
$$= 3^2 \cdot 5^3$$ 5

EXAMPLE 2

Write 7007 as a product of powers of primes.

– – – – –   – – – – –

$$7007$$ Work: $7\overline{)7007}$
$$= 7 \cdot 7 \cdot 11 \cdot 13$$ $7\overline{)1001}$
                                   $11\overline{)143}$
$$= 7^2 \cdot 11 \cdot 13$$ 13

Note: You may want to use a calculator to do the actual division and then write the results in the upside-down, short-division form.

EXERCISE 9-1

For Problems 1 through 20, write as a product of powers of primes.

Problem Notes:

Problem 21 shows the reason why 1 is not considered prime. If it were, the fundamental theorem of arithmetic would be false. Mathematicians consider paying the price of excluding 1 from the set of primes to be well worth the gain of having this theorem. Note that 1 *does* have a unique set of prime factors—the *empty* set.

1. 40 $2^3 \cdot 5$
2. 63 $3^2 \cdot 7$
3. 225 $3^2 \cdot 5^2$
4. 351 $3^3 \cdot 13$
5. 252 $2^2 \cdot 3^2 \cdot 7$
6. 360 $2^3 \cdot 3^2 \cdot 5$
7. 784 $2^4 \cdot 7^2$
8. 500 $2^2 \cdot 5^3$
9. 891 $3^4 \cdot 11$
10. 800 $2^5 \cdot 5^2$
11. 2057 $11^2 \cdot 17$
12. 3211 $13^2 \cdot 19$
13. 2700 $2^2 \cdot 3^3 \cdot 5^2$
14. 3528 $2^3 \cdot 3^2 \cdot 7^2$
15. 6125 $5^3 \cdot 7^2$
16. 8575 $5^2 \cdot 7^3$
17. 15,379 $7 \cdot 13^3$
18. 12,005 $5 \cdot 7^4$
19. 30,030 $2 \cdot 3 \cdot 5 \cdot 7 \cdot 11 \cdot 13$
20. 75,600 $2^4 \cdot 3^3 \cdot 5^2 \cdot 7^1$

21. *1 is Not a Prime Problem*   the number 1 fits the definition of prime numbers, because

$$1 = 1 \cdot 1.$$

That is, 1 has no other factors besides 1 and itself. Yet the definition includes the restriction that the number 1 is *not* considered to be a prime. The reason for this restriction is the following conclusion, called the *fundamental theorem of arithmetic*.

21. b. If 1 were a prime then these would *also* be prime factorizations of 12:
$1 \cdot 2 \cdot 2 \cdot 3$
$1 \cdot 1 \cdot 2 \cdot 2 \cdot 3$
$1 \cdot 1 \cdot 1 \cdot 2 \cdot 2 \cdot 3$
$1 \cdot 1 \cdot 1 \cdot 1 \cdot 2 \cdot 2 \cdot 3,$
etc.
c. The set of prime factors of 1 is $\emptyset$, the *empty* set!

FUNDAMENTAL THEOREM OF ARITHMETIC
Each positive integer has exactly *one* set of prime factors.

---

a. Write the set of prime factors of 12. $2 \cdot 2 \cdot 3$
b. Explain why 12 would have *other* sets of prime factors if 1 were considered to be a prime.
c. What is the set of prime factors of 1 itself?

9-2   THE OPERATION EXPONENTIATION

You recall that a power is an expression involving repeated multiplication. For instance, 5^3 means three 5s multiplied together.

$$5^3 = 5 \times 5 \times 5$$

The operation *raising to powers* is called *exponentiation*.

DEFINITION

EXPONENTIATION
x^a means a x's multiplied together. That is, for any real number x and for any positive integer a,

$$x^a = x \cdot x \cdot x \cdots x \quad (a \text{ factors}).$$

In this section you use this definition to evaluate and operate with powers. For instance, x^4 means four x's multiplied together. If x is 6, you would evaluate x^4 as follows.

$$x^4$$
$$= 6^4$$
$$= 6 \times 6 \times 6 \times 6$$
$$= 1296$$

The operations are straightforward. A calculator will help when the numbers are large.

Objective:
Given an expression involving a power of a variable, use the definition of exponentiation to evaluate or simplify the expression.

Cover the answers as you work these examples.

EXAMPLE 1
Evaluate x^4y^2 if $x = 3$ and $y = -5$.

- - - - -   - - - - -

	Think These Reasons
x^4y^2	Write the given expression.
$= 3^4 \times (-5)^2$	Substitute for x and y.
$= 3 \times 3 \times 3 \times 3 \times (-5) \times (-5)$	Use the definition of exponentiation.
$= 2025$	Do the arithmetic. (Negative times negative is *positive*.)

EXAMPLE 2

Write x^5x^2 as a single power of x.

- - - - -   - - - - -

x^5x^2	Write the given expression.
$= x \cdot x \cdot x \cdot x \cdot x \cdot x \cdot x$	Use the definition of exponentiation.
$= \underline{\underline{x^7}}$	There are seven x's multiplied together.

EXAMPLE 3

Write $(x^4)^3$ as a single power of x.

- - - - -   - - - - -

$(x^4)^3$	Write the given expression.
$= x^4 \cdot x^4 \cdot x^4$	Use the definition of exponentiation.
$= x \cdot x \cdot x \cdot x \cdot x \cdot x \cdot x \cdot x \cdot x \cdot x \cdot x \cdot x$	Use the definition again.
$= \underline{\underline{x^{12}}}$	There are 12 x's multiplied together.

EXAMPLE 4

Write $(5x)^3$ without parentheses.

- - - - -   - - - - -

$(5x)^3$	Write the given expression.
$= 5x \cdot 5x \cdot 5x$	Use the definition of exponentiation.
$= (5 \cdot 5 \cdot 5)(x \cdot x \cdot x)$	Commute and associate.
$= \underline{\underline{125x^3}}$	$5 \cdot 5 \cdot 5 = 125; \ x \cdot x \cdot x = x^3$.

ORAL PRACTICE

Tell what the expression would be if written using powers.

A. $x \cdot x \cdot x \cdot x$ x^4 B. $y \cdot y \cdot y$ y^3

C. $z \cdot z \cdot z \cdot z \cdot z$ z^5 D. $x \cdot x \cdot x \cdot y \cdot y$ x^3y^2

E. $a \cdot a \cdot b \cdot b \cdot c \cdot c$ $a^2b^2c^2$ F. $x \cdot x \cdot x \cdot x \cdot y$ x^4y

G. $r \cdot c \cdot c \cdot c$ rc^3 H. $7 \cdot a \cdot a \cdot a \cdot a$ $7a^4$

I. $5 \cdot x \cdot x \cdot y \cdot y \cdot y$ $5x^2y^3$

J. $3 \cdot x \cdot x \cdot x \cdot x \cdot y \cdot y \cdot y \cdot y \cdot y \cdot z \cdot z \cdot z \cdot z \cdot z \cdot z \cdot z$ $3x^4y^5z^7$

Evaluate these powers.

K. 2^3 8   L. 3^2 9

M. 3^3 27   N. 2^2 4

O. 4^2 16   P. 2^4 16

Q. $(-2)^3$ -8 R. $(-2)^4$ 16

S. 3^1 3   T. 1^3 1

U. 0^3 0   V. $(-1)^5$ -1

EXERCISE 9-2

Problem Notes:

These problems are intended to reinforce the definition of exponentiation. Sharper students will see, for example, that the answer can be obtained by adding exponents. Wait until the next section, though, to hold students responsible for the properties.

For Problems 1 through 10, evaluate the power for the given values of the variable.

1. x^3
    a. $x = 2$ 8
    b. $x = 5$ 125
    c. $x = -3$ -27

2. x^4
    a. $x = 2$ 16
    b. $x = 3$ 81
    c. $x = -4$ 256

3. x^6
    a. $x = 2$ 64
    b. $x = 4$ 4096
    c. $x = -1$ 1

4. x^5
    a. $x = 2$ 32
    b. $x = 4$ 1024
    c. $x = -1$ -1

5. $3x^4$
    a. $x = 2$ 48
    b. $x = 6$ 3888
    c. $x = 10$ 30,000

6. $5x^3$
    a. $x = 2$ 40
    b. $x = 4$ 320
    c. $x = 10$ 5000

7. x^2y^3
    a. $x = 4, y = 5$ 2000
    b. $x = -1, y = 2$ 8
    c. $x = 3, y = -2$ -72

8. x^3y^4
    a. $x = 2, y = 5$ 5000
    b. $x = -1, y = 2$ -16
    c. $x = 5, y = -2$ 2000

9. $(x^2)^5$
    a. $x = 3$ 59,049
    b. $x = -2$ 1024
    c. $x = 4$ 1,048,576

10. $(x^3)^2$
    a. $x = 4$ 4096
    b. $x = -5$ 15,625
    c. $x = 10$ 1,000,000

For Problems 11 through 20, write the expression as a single power of *x*.

11. x^3x^4 x^7

12. x^5x^3 x^8

13. x^2x^7 x^9

14. x^4x^6 x^{10}

15. x^5x^8 x^{13}

16. x^2x^9 x^{11}

17. $(x^2)^4$ x^8

18. $(x^3)^2$ x^6

19. $(x^3)^5$ x^{15}

20. $(x^5)^3$ x^{15}

For Problems 21 through 30, write the expression without parentheses.

21. $(xy)^3$ x^3y^3

22. $(xy)^4$ x^4y^4

23. $(ab)^6$ a^6b^6

24. $(rt)^5$ r^5t^5

25. $(3x)^4$ 3^4x^4 or $81x^4$

26. $(2x)^5$ $2^5x^5 = 32x^5$

27. $(5x)^2$ $5^2 \cdot x^2 = 25x^2$

28. $(3x)^3$ $3^3x^3 = 27x^3$

29. $(x^2y)^4$ x^8y^4

30. $(xy^2)^3$ x^3y^6

31. ***Definition of Exponentiation Problem***   Dee Student loses points on a test for saying, "5^3 means 5 multiplied by itself 3 times." Explain to Dee what her mistake is.

31. $5^3 = 5 \cdot 5 \cdot 5$. There are three 5's, not 3 "times" signs.

32. ***Computer Program for Evaluating Powers***   The following is a BASIC program for doing exponentiation. The input is the values of the base and exponent. The computer then uses the base as a factor the right number of times. Do the following.
   a. Trace the program, showing the simulated memory and the output, if the base is 4 and the exponent is 3.
   b. Run the program on a computer. Use it to evaluate:
      i. 8^5;   ii. 5^8;   iii. 7^9;   iv. 9^7;   v. 10^7.
   c. Which is bigger, 7^8 or 8^7?
   d. Evaluate 10^{20}. What does the computer print? What is the largest power of 10 your computer will handle without overflowing?

Problem 32a can be done as a homework assignment without access to a computer. The program uses the definition of exponentiation to evaluate the power. See Additional Answers for the results.

```
10   INPUT "BASE: ";X
20   INPUT "EXPONENT: ";N
30   LET P = 1
40   FOR C = 1 TO N
50   LET P = P * X
60   NEXT C
70   PRINT
80   PRINT X;"^";N;" = ";P
90   END
```

9-3 | EXPONENTS, PRODUCTS, AND POWERS

Time: 1 day

Chalkboard Examples:

Evaluate two ways.
a. Parentheses first.
b. Transform first.
1. $(7^2)(7^3)$ Ans.: 16,807
2. $(2 \times 5)^3$ Ans.: 1000
3. $(4^3)^2$ Ans.: 4096
From these examples, infer the three properties. Then have students work Examples 1–5.

Note: The words "Product of powers with *equal* bases" are used in this text rather than the more customary words ". . . powers with the same base." It is important for students to realize that there are two separate powers and that their bases happen to be equal.

Assignments:

Exercise 9–3, #1–29 odd,
Exercise 9–2, #6, 12, 18, 22 for review

In the last section you learned the formal definition of exponentiation as repeated multiplication. For instance, 5^3 means three 5s multiplied together, as shown.

$$5^3 = 5 \times 5 \times 5.$$

Because of this definition, there are some interesting things that happen to exponents when you multiply or divide two powers. In this section you will learn three properties of exponentiation, and in the next section you will learn two more.

PRODUCT OF TWO POWERS

The expressions 5^3 and 5^4 are two powers that have equal bases, 5, and different exponents, 3 and 4. If you multiply these two powers together, you get

$$(5^3)(5^4)$$
$$= (5 \times 5 \times 5)(5 \times 5 \times 5 \times 5)$$
$$= 5 \times 5 \times 5 \times 5 \times 5 \times 5 \times 5$$
$$= 5^7.$$

The last step is true because there are seven 5s multiplied together, which is what 5^7 really means. A quick way to get the answer is to *add* the exponents.

$$(5^3)(5^4) = 5^{3+4} = 5^7$$

This shortcut will work as long as the two powers have equal bases. If the bases are different, such as in $(5^3)(6^4)$, there is no way to simplify the expression (other than to evaluate it); $(5^3)(6^4)$ equals $5 \times 5 \times 5 \times 6 \times 6 \times 6 \times 6$, which is neither a power of 5 nor a power of 6.

PRODUCT OF TWO POWERS WITH EQUAL BASES
If you multiply two powers, and both bases are equal, then you can *add* the exponents (and use the same base). That is, for any real number x and for any positive integers a and b,
$$(x^a)(x^b) = x^{a+b}.$$

POWER OF A PRODUCT

The parentheses in the expression $(3 \times 5)^4$ mean to multiply 3 by 5 first, then raise the answer to the fourth power.

$$(3 \times 5)^4 = 15^4 = 50{,}625$$

However, you can use the definition of exponentiation first and write

$$(3 \times 5)^4 = (3 \times 5)(3 \times 5)(3 \times 5)(3 \times 5).$$

Commuting and associating factors gives

$$(3 \times 3 \times 3 \times 3)(5 \times 5 \times 5 \times 5),$$

which results in

$$3^4 \times 5^4.$$

The exponent has been *distributed* to each factor, 3 and 5. In other words, exponentiation distributes over multiplication. Carrying out the multiplication shows that you really do get the same answer.

$$3^4 \times 5^4 = 81 \times 625 = 50{,}625$$

POWER OF A PRODUCT
Exponentiation distributes over multiplication. That is, for any real numbers x and y, and for any positive integer a,

$$(xy)^a = x^a y^a.$$

Be careful that you do not try to distribute exponentiation over addition or subtraction! Recall from Section 5.8 that

$$(x + y)^2 = x^2 + 2xy + y^2.$$

There are middle terms when you raise *sums* to powers.

POWER OF A POWER

The parentheses in the expression $(2^3)^4$ mean to raise 2 to the third power first, then raise the answer to the fourth power.

$$(2^3)^4 = 8^4 = 4096$$

Again, the definition of exponentiation could be used to write

$$(2^3)^4$$

$$= (2^3)(2^3)(2^3)(2^3)$$

$$= (2 \times 2 \times 2)(2 \times 2 \times 2)(2 \times 2 \times 2)(2 \times 2 \times 2)$$

$$= 2 \times 2 \times 2 \times 2 \times 2 \times 2 \times 2 \times 2 \times 2 \times 2 \times 2 \times 2$$

$$= 2^{12}.$$

The last step is true because there are 12 2s multiplied together, which is what 2^{12} means. A quick way to get the answer is to *multiply* the exponents.

$$(2^3)^4 = 2^{3 \cdot 4} = 2^{12}$$

This property is summarized as follows.

POWER OF A POWER
If you raise a power to a power, then you can *multiply* the exponents. That is, for any real number x and for any positive integers a and b,

$$(x^a)^b = x^{ab}.$$

If the expressions with which you are dealing contain only constants, these three properties are not really needed. However, if the expressions contain *variables*, the properties allow you to *simplify* the expressions. What you must learn is when to *add* the exponents, when to *multiply* them, and when to *distribute* them.

Objective:
Given an expression containing powers and variables, simplify the expression using the three properties of exponentiation.

Cover the answers as you work these examples.

EXAMPLE 1

Simplify $(x^8)(x^{20})$.

— — — — —   — — — — —

	Think These Reasons
$(x^8)(x^{20})$	Write the given expression.
$= x^{8+20}$	Add the exponents. Use x as the base.
$= x^{28}$	Do the arithmetic.

Note: You can probably do the whole problem in your head and just write

$$(x^8)(x^{20}) = x^{28}.$$

EXAMPLE 2

Simplify $(5r^7)(6r^2)$.

- - - - -

$(5r^7)(6r^2)$	Write the given expression.
$= 30r^9$	Commute, associate, and multiply the coefficients. Add the exponents and use r as the base.

EXAMPLE 3

Simplify $(5xy^7)^3$.

- - - - -

$(5xy^7)^3$	Write the given expression.
$= (5)^3(x)^3(y^7)^3$	Distribute the exponentiation to *all three* factors. Do not forget the coefficient, 5.
$= 125x^3y^{21}$	$5^3 = 125$; multiply the exponents since a power is raised to a power.

EXAMPLE 4

Simplify $3x^5 + 9x^5$.

- - - - -

$3x^5 + 9x^5$	Write the given expression.
$= 12x^5$	Combine like terms. (There are *no* operations performed on the exponents.)

EXAMPLE 5

Simplify $5x^3 + 4x^9$.

- - - - -

Cannot be simplified.	The powers are *added,* not multiplied. There are no properties for a *sum* of two powers, even if the bases are equal.

ORAL PRACTICE

Simplify each expression.

A. $(x^3)(x^2)$ x^5 B. $(x^3)^2$ x^6

C. $(x^4)(x^5)$ x^9 D. $(x^4)^5$ x^{20}

E. $(x^5)^4$ x^{20} F. $(xy)^3$ x^3y^3

G. $(ab)^7$ a^7b^7 H. $(3x)^2$ $9x^2$

I. $(2x)^3$ $8x^3$ J. $(x^2y)^3$ x^6y^3

K. $(xy^2)^3$ x^3y^6 L. $(x^2y^3)^4$ x^8y^{12}

M. $(x)(x^3)$ x^4 N. $x^3 + x^3$ $2x^3$

O. $x^3 + x^4$ $x^3 + x^4$ (same)   P. $4x^5 - x^5$ $3x^5$

EXERCISE 9-3

Problem Notes:

In this chapter it is particularly important for students to remember earlier techniques while working new problems. To increase student contact time with a particular topic, it is recommended that problems from previous sections be assigned along with those from the present section. The assignments prescribed herein show one way this can be accomplished.

There are more problems in this section than are required for mastery. You may assign fewer problems, increasing the number of problem types, especially for better students who might become bored with repetitive work. The ample number of problems is provided so that plenty will be available to assign for review when students are working later sections.

For Problems 1 through 6, evaluate the expression two ways:
a. by doing what is in parentheses first;
b. by using the appropriate property of exponentiation first.
Use a calculator (if necessary) to do the final operations, and thus show that the two answers are the same.

1. $(2^4)(2^2)$ $2^6 = 64$ 2. $(3^4)(3^5)$ $3^9 = 19{,}683$

3. $(4 \times 5)^3$ $20^3 = 8000$ 4. $(2 \times 5)^3$ $10^3 = 1000$

5. $(3^2)^5$ $3^{10} = 59{,}049$ 6. $(2^4)^3$ $2^{12} = 4096$

For Problems 7 through 60, simplify the expression.

7. $(x^5)(x^{13})$ x^{18} 8. $(x^8)(x^{12})$ x^{20}

9. $(y^{30})(y^{50})$ y^{80} 10. $(z^{40})(z^{60})$ z^{100}

11. $(z)(z^7)$ z^8 12. $(r^5)(r)$ r^6

13. $(a^{41})(a^{29})(a^{17})$ a^{87} 14. $(y^{70})(y^{17})(y^{13})$ y^{100}

15. $(3x^6)(5x^7)$ $15x^{13}$ 16. $(2x^8)(9x^3)$ $18x^{11}$

17. $(9r^{20})(7r^{32})$ $63r^{52}$ 18. $(8s^{30})(7s^{20})$ $56s^{50}$

19. $(-8s^{12})(6s^{47})$ $-48s^{59}$ 20. $(-5x^9)(11x^{21})$ $-55x^{30}$

21. $(-10x^8)(-20x^{80})$ $200x^{88}$ 22. $(-30a^{19})(-10a^{17})$ $300a^{36}$

23. $(5x^7)(2x^9)(3x^{11})$ $30x^{27}$ 24. $(6x^5)(2x^{10})(7x^{13})$ $84x^{28}$

25. $(7b^{10})(-11b^{20})(13b)$ $-1001b^{31}$ 26. $(3y)(-23y^8)(-29y^{31})$ $2001y^{40}$

27. $(x^9)^6$ x^{54} 28. $(x^7)^8$ x^{56}

29. $(p^{12})^5$ p^{60}

30. $(y^{10})^5$ y^{50}

31. $(y^2)^7$ y^{14}

32. $(s^4)^8$ s^{32}

33. $(5r^6)^3$ $125r^{18}$

34. $(3x^5)^4$ $81x^{20}$

35. $(-2x^{10})^5$ $-32x^{50}$

36. $(-7x^8)^2$ $49x^{16}$

37. $(-3x^7)^4$ $81x^{28}$

38. $(-2y^6)^3$ $-8y^{18}$

39. $[(x^5)^7]^4$ x^{140}

40. $[(x^6)^7]^{10}$ x^{420}

41. $(xy)^9$ x^9y^9

42. $(ab)^{10}$ $a^{10}b^{10}$

43. $(ab)^{17}$ $a^{17}b^{17}$

44. $(pj)^{52}$ $p^{52}j^{52}$

45. $(3rs)^5$ $243r^5s^5$

46. $(2xy)^5$ $32x^5y^5$

47. $(0.1x^3y^5)^3$ $0.001x^9y^{15}$

48. $(0.1r^2s^6)^4$ $0.0001r^8s^{24}$

49. $(-6c^5d^6)^2$ $36c^{10}d^{12}$

50. $(-9m^3n^8)^2$ $81m^6n^{16}$

51. $(-2x^6y^7)^3$ $-8x^{18}y^{21}$

52. $(-5x^4y^{11})^3$ $-125x^{12}y^{33}$

53. $(10xy^{10})^4$ $10,000x^4y^{40}$

54. $(10cd^6)^3$ $1000c^3d^{18}$

55. $(3^x5^y)^z$ $3^{xz}5^{yz}$

56. $(4^a7^b)^c$ $4^{ac}7^{bc}$

57. $8x^6 + 3x^6$ $11x^6$

58. $7x^9 + 11x^9$ $18x^9$

59. $13y^7 - 21y^7$ $-8y^7$

60. $14a^3 - 50a^3$ $-36a^3$

In Problems 33–40 and others, be alert for the common error
$$(5x^6)^3 = 5x^{18},$$
in which students distribute the exponent to the variable factors but forget to distribute it to the constant coefficient.

For Problems 61 through 100, either simplify the expression or state that it cannot be simplified.

61. $(3x^9)(3x^5)$ $9x^{14}$

62. $(4x^7)(4x^9)$ $16x^{16}$

63. $(9x^3)(5x^3)$ $45x^6$

64. $(7x^4)(9x^4)$ $63x^8$

65. $9x^3 + 5x^3$ $14x^3$

66. $7x^4 + 9x^4$ $16x^4$

67. $x^5 \cdot y^7$ Cannot be simplified

68. $x^8 \cdot y^3$ Cannot be simplified

69. $x^5 \cdot x^7$ x^{12}

70. $x^8 \cdot x^3$ x^{11}

71. $x^5 + x^7$ Cannot be simplified

72. $x^8 + x^3$ Cannot be simplified

73. $x^5 + x^5$ $2x^5$

74. $x^8 + x^8$ $2x^8$

75. $x^5 - x^5$ 0

76. $x^8 - x^8$ 0

77. $3x^5 - x^5$ $2x^5$

78. $5x^8 - x^8$ $4x^8$

79. $(x^5)^2$ x^{10}

80. $(x^8)^3$ x^{24}

81. $(-2x)^3$ $-8x^3$

82. $(-4x)^3$ $-64x^3$

83. $(-2x)^4$ $16x^4$

84. $(-3x)^4$ $81x^4$

85. $-(2x)^4$ $-16x^4$

86. $-(3x)^4$ $-81x^4$

Problems 61–100 have sequences of expressions that involve changes that look minor but actually are of crucial importance. These problems force the students to distinguish among the properties based on the operation sign and the nature of the variables rather than on such extraneous clues as the placement among similar-looking expressions.
Problems 77, 78, 95, and 96 are intended to help students overcome the common mistake
$$3x^5 - x^5 = 3.$$

87. $(x^2)^4$ x^8 88. $(x^3)^4$ x^{12}

89. $(xy)^4$ x^4y^4 90. $(xy)^5$ x^5y^5

91. $(2x^2y^3)^4$ $16x^8y^{12}$ 92. $(2x^3y^2)^5$ $32x^{15}y^{10}$

93. $(x^4y^2)^6(x^2y^3)^4$ $x^{32}y^{24}$ 94. $(x^5y^6)^2(x^3y^2)^5$ $x^{25}y^{22}$

95. $5x^3 - x^3$ $4x^3$ 96. $7x^5 - x^5$ $6x^5$

97. $3x^5 - x^3$ Cannot be simplified   98. $5x^7 - x^5$ Cannot be simplified

99. $3x^5(x^2 - y^3)$ $3x^7 - 3x^5y^3$ 100. $4x^9(x^7 + y^5)$ $4x^{16} + 4x^9y^5$

9-4 | EXPONENTS AND QUOTIENTS

Time: 1 day

Chalkboard Examples:

1. Transform without evaluating:
   $\left(\dfrac{3}{5}\right)^4$ Ans.: $\dfrac{3^4}{5^4}$

2. Simplify:
   $\dfrac{x^5}{x^3}$ Ans.: x^2

From these examples, infer the two properties. Then have students work Examples 1–5.

Assignment:

Exercise 9–4, #1–39 odd,
Exercise 9–3, #61–99 odd

Recall from earlier work in mathematics that you multiply fractions by multiplying their numerators together and multiplying their denominators together. For instance,

$$\frac{3}{7} \times \frac{4}{5} = \frac{3 \times 4}{7 \times 5} = \frac{12}{35}.$$

Later in your mathematical career you will learn how to prove this multiplication property of fractions.

MULTIPLICATION PROPERTY OF FRACTIONS
To multiply two fractions, multiply their numerators and multiply their denominators. That is, for any real numbers a, b, x, and y, with $b \neq 0$ and $y \neq 0$,

$$\frac{a}{b} \cdot \frac{x}{y} = \frac{ax}{by}.$$

This property gives a way to transform a quotient that is raised to a power, such as

$$\left(\frac{2}{3}\right)^5.$$

Using the definition of exponentiation, you can write this as

$$\left(\frac{2}{3}\right)^5 = \left(\frac{2}{3}\right)\left(\frac{2}{3}\right)\left(\frac{2}{3}\right)\left(\frac{2}{3}\right)\left(\frac{2}{3}\right).$$

Using the multiplication property of fractions (repeatedly) gives

$$\frac{2 \times 2 \times 2 \times 2 \times 2}{3 \times 3 \times 3 \times 3 \times 3},$$

which equals

$$\frac{2^5}{3^5}.$$

As you can see, the exponent, 5, has been *distributed* to the 2 in the numerator and to the 3 in the denominator.

POWER OF A QUOTIENT
Exponentiation *distributes* over division. That is, for any real numbers x and y ($y \neq 0$), and for any integer a,

$$\left(\frac{x}{y}\right)^a = \frac{x^a}{y^a}.$$

The multiplication property of fractions can be used in the other direction to simplify fractions. For instance, to simplify $\frac{24}{36}$, you could write the following.

$$\frac{24}{36}$$

$$= \frac{12 \times 2}{12 \times 3} \qquad \text{24 equals 12 times 2.}$$
$$\qquad\qquad\qquad \text{36 equals 12 times 3.}$$

$$= \frac{12}{12} \times \frac{2}{3} \qquad \text{Multiplication property of fractions}$$

$$= 1 \times \frac{2}{3} \qquad \text{A number divided by itself equals 1.}$$

$$= \frac{2}{3} \qquad \text{1 times a number equals that number.}$$

The same technique can be used to simplify quotients with *variables* in the numerator or denominator. For instance, $\frac{x^7}{x^4}$ can be simplified as follows.

$$\frac{x^7}{x^4}$$

$$= \frac{x \cdot x \cdot x \cdot x \cdot x \cdot x \cdot x}{x \cdot x \cdot x \cdot x} \qquad \text{Use the definition of exponentiation.}$$

$$= \frac{x \cdot x \cdot x \cdot x}{x \cdot x \cdot x \cdot x} \times \frac{x \cdot x \cdot x}{1}$$ Use the multiplication property of fractions.

$$= 1 \times \frac{x \cdot x \cdot x}{1}$$ A number divided by itself equals 1.

$$= \underline{\underline{x^3}}$$ Multiplying or dividing by 1 leaves the number unchanged, and $x \cdot x \cdot x$ equals x^3.

From this example you should see a *quick* way to get the answer. The exponent in the answer, 3, is the *difference* between 7 and 4. Once you know this, you can write simply

$$\frac{x^7}{x^4} = x^{7-4} = \underline{\underline{x^3}}.$$

In fact, the middle step can be done in your head. The general property is as follows.

QUOTIENT OF TWO POWERS WITH EQUAL BASES
If you divide two powers, and they have equal bases, then you can *subtract* the exponents (numerator minus denominator) and use that same base. That is, for any nonzero number x and for any positive integers a and b,

$$\frac{x^a}{x^b} = x^{a-b}.$$

The fact that 1 times a number equals that number is an axiom. It is sometimes called the *multiplication property of 1*. Another name for this property is the *multiplicative identity axiom*. The answer after multiplying a number by 1 is identical to the original number.

MULTIPLICATIVE IDENTITY AXIOM
(or **Multiplication Property of 1**)
Multiplying a number by 1 does not change its value. That is, for any real number x,

$$x \cdot 1 = x.$$

In this section you will use these properties to simplify expressions involving powers and division.

Objective:
Be able to simplify powers of quotients and quotients of powers using the properties of exponentiation.

Cover the answers as you work these examples.

EXAMPLE 1

Transform to remove the parentheses: $\left(\dfrac{x}{y}\right)^{7}$.

– – – – –   – – – – –

	Think These Reasons

$\left(\dfrac{x}{y}\right)^{7}$ Write the given expression.

$=\dfrac{x^{7}}{y^{7}}$ Power of a quotient property

EXAMPLE 2

Simplify $\dfrac{x^{10}}{x^{4}}$.

– – – – –   – – – – –

$\dfrac{x^{10}}{x^{4}}$ Write the given expression.

$= x^{6}$ Subtract the exponents.

EXAMPLE 3

Simplify $\dfrac{15x^{6}y^{7}}{5x^{2}y^{4}}$.

– – – – –   – – – – –

$\dfrac{15x^{6}y^{7}}{5x^{2}y^{4}}$ Write the given expression.

$=\dfrac{15}{5} \times \dfrac{x^{6}}{x^{2}} \times \dfrac{y^{7}}{y^{4}}$ Use the multiplication property of fractions to separate the x's, y's, and constants.

$= 3x^{4}y^{3}$ Simplify the coefficient. Subtract exponents of powers with equal bases.

EXAMPLE 4

Simplify $\dfrac{x^9}{y^3}\left(\dfrac{y}{x}\right)^5$.

– – – – –   – – – – –

$\dfrac{x^9}{y^3}\left(\dfrac{y}{x}\right)^5$ Write the given expression.

$=\dfrac{x^9}{y^3}\times\dfrac{y^5}{x^5}$ Distribute exponentiation over division.

$=\dfrac{x^9 y^5}{y^3 x^5}$ Use the multiplication property of fractions to make *one* fraction.

$=\dfrac{x^9 y^5}{x^5 y^3}$ Commute the multiplication in the denominator.

$=\dfrac{x^9}{x^5}\times\dfrac{y^5}{y^3}$ Use the multiplication property of fractions to separate the x's and y's.

$=\underline{\underline{x^4 y^2}}$ Subtract the exponents of powers with equal bases.

Note: Once you understand the reasons in this example, you can shorten the work, as follows.

$\dfrac{x^9}{y^3}\left(\dfrac{y}{x}\right)^5$ Write the given expression.

$=\dfrac{x^9 y^5}{y^3 x^5}$ Distribute the exponentiation. Combine the fractions.

$=\underline{\underline{x^4 y^2}}$ Subtract the exponents of powers with *equal* bases.

EXAMPLE 5

Simplify $\dfrac{x^7}{y^5}$.

– – – – –   – – – – –

$\dfrac{x^7}{y^5}$ Write the given expression.

<u>Cannot be simplified.</u>   The bases are not *equal*.

ORAL PRACTICE

Give the expression as a *single* power.

A. $\dfrac{2^7}{2^3}$ $\quad 2^4$

B. $\dfrac{3^9}{3^4}$ $\quad 3^5$

C. $\dfrac{5^8}{5^2}$ $\quad 5^6$

D. $\dfrac{7^5}{7^4}$ $\quad 7$ or 7^1

E. $\dfrac{6^8}{6}$ $\quad 6^7$

F. $\dfrac{x^8}{x^3}$ $\quad x^5$

G. $\dfrac{y^9}{y^7}$ $\quad y^2$

H. $\dfrac{z^5}{z^2}$ $\quad z^3$

I. $\dfrac{a^3}{a^2}$ $\quad a$ or a^1

J. $\dfrac{b^7}{b}$ $\quad b^6$

Transform to remove the parentheses.

K. $\left(\dfrac{x}{y}\right)^5$ $\quad \dfrac{x^5}{y^5}$

L. $\left(\dfrac{a}{b}\right)^3$ $\quad \dfrac{a^3}{b^3}$

M. $\left(\dfrac{c}{d}\right)^8$ $\quad \dfrac{c^8}{d^8}$

N. $\left(\dfrac{4}{5}\right)^2$ $\quad \dfrac{4^2}{5^2}$ or $\dfrac{16}{25}$

O. $\left(\dfrac{3}{7}\right)^1$ $\quad \dfrac{3}{7}$

Do the following.

P.   Evaluate 2^7.   128

Q.   Evaluate 2^4.   16

R.   Evaluate $\dfrac{2^7}{2^4}$ by dividing the answers to P and Q.   8

S.   Simplify $\dfrac{2^7}{2^4}$ using the properties of exponentiation. 2^3

T.   Evaluate the answer to S.   8

U.   Tell one reason why people transform expressions using the properties of exponentiation.   Properties make expressions easier to evaluate.

EXERCISE 9-4

For Problems 1 through 40, simplify the expression.

1. $\dfrac{x^{11}}{x^7}$ $\quad x^4$

2. $\dfrac{x^{15}}{x^8}$ $\quad x^7$

3. $\dfrac{s^{22}}{s^8}$ $\quad s^{14}$

4. $\dfrac{r^{31}}{r^{19}}$ $\quad r^{12}$

Problem Notes:

All problems in this section are written so that the denominator exponent of a variable never exceeds the numerator exponent. The issue of what happens when the reverse is true is deliberately ignored until the next section where negative exponents are defined. Thus, students are not forced to learn a property for this case, which will be immediately superceded in the next section.

5. $\dfrac{3x^6}{x^2}$ $3x^4$

6. $\dfrac{5x^7}{x^5}$ $5x^2$

7. $\dfrac{6c^9}{2c^4}$ $3c^5$

8. $\dfrac{10p^8}{5p^4}$ $2p^4$

9. $\dfrac{x^9}{x^8}$ x

10. $\dfrac{x^5}{x^4}$ x

11. $\dfrac{y^5}{y}$ y^4

12. $\dfrac{z^7}{z}$ z^6

13. $\dfrac{x^5}{x^5}$ 1

14. $\dfrac{x^7}{x^7}$ 1

15. $\dfrac{3z^8}{z^8}$ 3

16. $\dfrac{4y^9}{y^9}$ 4

Problems 17–20 and others have expressions for which students must divide the coefficients and subtract the exponents. The denominator exponent was deliberately chosen to be a factor of the numerator exponent. Thus, students are forced to distinguish between handling of exponents and coefficients based strictly on the properties rather than on whether one number divides another.

Be alert for the common error

$\dfrac{x^a}{x^b} = 1^{(a-b)}$.

The students subtract the exponents and divide the bases. It is to help avoid this error that the words ". . . and use that same base" appear in the statements of the properties.

17. $\dfrac{-8x^9}{4x^3}$ $-2x^6$

18. $\dfrac{-12x^8}{3x^2}$ $-4x^6$

19. $\dfrac{20x^{12}}{-5x^3}$ $-4x^9$

20. $\dfrac{32x^{10}}{-8x^5}$ $-4x^5$

21. $\dfrac{x^5y^7}{x^2y^5}$ x^3y^2

22. $\dfrac{x^9y^5}{x^5y^2}$ x^4y^3

23. $\dfrac{a^{12}b^8}{a^4b^4}$ a^8b^4

24. $\dfrac{c^9d^{15}}{c^3d^3}$ c^6d^{12}

25. $\dfrac{40x^9y^8}{10x^4y^7}$ $4x^5y$

26. $\dfrac{70x^5y^{11}}{7x^3y^9}$ $10x^2y^2$

27. $\dfrac{24x^{10}y^{15}}{8x^2y^5}$ $3x^8y^{10}$

28. $\dfrac{36x^{15}y^{20}}{12x^3y^5}$ $3x^{12}y^{15}$

29. $\dfrac{56x^4y^6}{8x^4}$ $7y^6$

30. $\dfrac{72x^2y^5}{9y^5}$ $8x^2$

31. $\dfrac{28x^3y^7}{7y^6}$ $4x^3y$

32. $\dfrac{54x^8y^4}{6x^7}$ $9xy^4$

33. $\dfrac{x^{10}}{y^5}\left(\dfrac{y}{x}\right)^8$ x^2y^3

34. $\dfrac{x^8}{y^3}\left(\dfrac{y}{x}\right)^4$ x^4y

35. $\dfrac{r^7}{t^4}\left(\dfrac{t}{r}\right)^5$ r^2t

36. $\dfrac{p^9}{f^3}\left(\dfrac{f}{p}\right)^6$ p^3f^3

37. $\dfrac{x^5}{4}\left(\dfrac{2}{x}\right)^3$ $2x^2$

38. $\dfrac{x^7}{9}\left(\dfrac{3}{x}\right)^4$ $9x^3$

39. $\dfrac{5^8}{3^4}\left(\dfrac{3}{5}\right)^7$ $5 \cdot 3^3 = 135$

40. $\dfrac{2^{10}}{3^6}\left(\dfrac{3}{2}\right)^7$ $2^3 \cdot 3 = 24$

For Problems 41 through 60, simplify the expression using the properties of exponentiation in this section and the last.

41. $\left(\dfrac{x^5}{y^4}\right)^2$ $\dfrac{x^{10}}{y^8}$

42. $\left(\dfrac{x^7}{y^5}\right)^3$ $\dfrac{x^{21}}{y^{15}}$

43. $\left(\dfrac{a^4}{b^2}\right)^3$ $\dfrac{a^{12}}{b^6}$

44. $\left(\dfrac{c^{10}}{d^5}\right)^2$ $\dfrac{c^{20}}{d^{10}}$

45. $\dfrac{(xy)^5}{x^3}$ x^2y^5

46. $\dfrac{(xy)^7}{y^5}$ x^7y^2

47. $\dfrac{(xy)^9}{x^2y^3}$ x^7y^6

48. $\dfrac{(xy)^8}{x^4y^5}$ x^4y^3

49. $\dfrac{(2x)^5}{2x^5}$ 16

50. $\dfrac{(3x)^4}{3x^4}$ 27

51. $\dfrac{(x^3y)^2}{x^2y}$ x^4y

52. $\dfrac{(xy^5)^3}{x^2y}$ xy^{14}

53. $\dfrac{(x^2y^3)^4}{x^5y^6}$ x^3y^6

54. $\dfrac{(x^3y^4)^2}{x^2y^5}$ x^4y^3

55. $\dfrac{x^{11}y^{13}}{(xy^3)^2}$ x^9y^7

56. $\dfrac{x^{10}y^{12}}{(x^2y)^3}$ x^4y^9

57. $\dfrac{(3x^6)^4}{(3x^2)^3}$ $3x^{18}$

58. $\dfrac{(2x^4)^5}{(2x^3)^2}$ $8x^{14}$

59. $\dfrac{(5ab^2)^6}{(5a^2b)^3}$ $125b^9$

60. $\dfrac{(3c^2d)^{10}}{(3cd^5)^2}$ $3^8 \cdot c^{18} = 6561c^{18}$

9-5 | NEGATIVE AND ZERO EXPONENTS

Time: 4 days, including test

Note: Negative and zero exponents are presented here primarily to aid in understanding scientific notation in the next two sections. If you do not plan to present scientific notation, you may choose to give a test, then branch directly to Chapter 10 following completion of Section 9–4.

In the last section you learned that when you divide two powers with equal bases, you can subtract their exponents. For instance,

$$\frac{x^5}{x^3} = x^{5-3} = x^2.$$

This property leads to difficulties if the exponent of the denominator is larger than the exponent of the numerator. What would $\frac{x^4}{x^7}$ equal? Using the property, you would get

$$\frac{x^4}{x^7} = x^{4-7} = x^{-3.}$$

Chalkboard Examples:

First day:
Simplify by
a. using the definition of exponentiation and

b. subtracting the exponents.

1. $\dfrac{x^3}{x^5}$ Ans.: a. $\dfrac{1}{x^2}$ b. $x^{(-2)}$

2. $\dfrac{x^4}{x^4}$ Ans.: a. 1   b. x^0

From these examples, infer the two definitions.

Have students work Examples 1, 2, and 3.

Oral Practice Problems A–T can be used here.

Second day:
Homework problems at the board
Examples 4 and 5
Oral Practice Problems U–Y

Third day:
Consolidate previous work.

Fourth day:
Test.

Assignments:

Day 1: Exercise 9–5, #1–23 odd,
Exercise 9–4, #41–59 odd,
Day 2: Exercise 9–5, #65–99 odd,
Day 3: Exercise 9–5, #10, 20, 30, 40, 50,
60, 70, 80, 90, 100, in preparation for
test; 9–3, #62–100 even
Day 4: (Following test):
Study Section 9–6,
work Examples 1 and 2, and
work Exercise 9–6, #1, 5, 9, 15, 21.
or:
Study Section 10-1
Work Exercise 10-1 #1–21 odd

The answer has a *negative* exponent, which does not make sense in terms of repeated multiplication of x's. However, you can find an answer by going back to the definition of exponentiation.

$$\frac{x^4}{x^7}$$

$$= \frac{x \cdot x \cdot x \cdot x}{x \cdot x \cdot x \cdot x \cdot x \cdot x \cdot x}$$ Use the definition of exponentiation.

$$= \frac{x \cdot x \cdot x \cdot x \cdot 1}{x \cdot x \cdot x \cdot x \cdot x \cdot x \cdot x}$$ Use the multiplicative identity axiom to multiply by 1.

$$= \frac{x \cdot x \cdot x \cdot x}{x \cdot x \cdot x \cdot x} \cdot \frac{1}{x \cdot x \cdot x}$$ Use the multiplication property of fractions to get *two* fractions

$$= 1 \cdot \frac{1}{x \cdot x \cdot x}$$ A number divided by itself equals 1.

$$\underline{\underline{= \frac{1}{x^3}}}$$ Use the multiplicative identity axiom and the definition of exponentiation.

In order to subtract exponents, you must *define* x^{-3} to be the same thing as $\frac{1}{x^3}$.

DEFINITION

NEGATIVE EXPONENTS
For any nonzero number x and for any integer n,

$$x^{-n} = \frac{1}{x^n}.$$

A similar difficulty arises with a power divided by itself.

$$\frac{x^5}{x^5} = x^{5-5} = x^0$$

Since any nonzero number divided by itself equals 1, x^0 must be defined to be 1.

DEFINITION

ZERO EXPONENT
For any nonzero number x,

$$x^0 = 1.$$

In this section you will use positive and negative exponents along with the properties of exponentiation to simplify expressions involving powers.

Objective:
Be able to simplify expressions involving powers with positive, negative, and zero exponents.

Cover the answers as you work the examples.

EXAMPLE 1

Simplify $\dfrac{x^5}{x^7}$.

– – – – –   – – – – –

Think These Reasons

$\dfrac{x^5}{x^7}$ Write the given expression.

$= \underline{\underline{x^{-2}}}$ Subtract the exponents: $5 - 7 = -2$.

EXAMPLE 2

Simplify $\dfrac{r^{-3}}{r^4}$.

– – – – –   – – – – –

$\dfrac{r^{-3}}{r^4}$ Write the given expression.

$= \underline{\underline{r^{-7}}}$ Subtract the exponents: $-3 - 4 = -7$.

EXAMPLE 3

Simplify $x^{-7}x^4$.

– – – – –   – – – – –

$x^{-7}x^4$ Write the given expression.

$= \underline{\underline{x^{-3}}}$ *Add* the exponents: $-7 + 4 = -3$.

EXAMPLE 4

Simplify $(3x^{-5})^2$.

– – – – –   – – – – –

$(3x^{-5})^2$ Write the given expression.

$= \underline{\underline{9x^{-10}}}$ Distribute exponentiation over multiplication; multiply the exponents.

EXAMPLE 5

Simplify $\dfrac{x^7}{y^5}\left(\dfrac{x^3}{y}\right)^{-2}$.

- - - - -   - - - - -

$\dfrac{x^7}{y^5}\left(\dfrac{x^3}{y}\right)^{-2}$ Write the given expression.

$=\dfrac{x^7 x^{-6}}{y^5 y^{-2}}$ Distribute exponentiation over division. Combine the resulting fractions.

$=\dfrac{x}{y^3}$ Add the exponents in the numerator and denominator.

$=\underline{\underline{xy^{-3}}}$ Dividing by y^3 is equivalent to multiplying by its reciprocal, y^{-3}.

ORAL PRACTICE

Evaluate each expression.

EXAMPLES

Answers

i. 2^{-3} i. $\dfrac{1}{8}$

ii. 5^0 ii. 1

A. 3^{-2} $\frac{1}{9}$ B. 5^{-3} $\frac{1}{125}$

C. 4^{-3} $\frac{1}{64}$ D. 7^0 1

E. 0^7 0

Transform to a single power with a positive or negative exponent.

F. $\dfrac{x^4}{x^9}$ x^{-5} G. $\dfrac{a^5}{a^7}$ a^{-2}

H. $\dfrac{y^{-3}}{y^5}$ y^{-8} I. $\dfrac{z^6}{z^{-4}}$ z^{10}

J. $\dfrac{p^{-8}}{p^{-11}}$ p^3 K. $\dfrac{x^3}{x^{-3}}$ x^6

L. $\dfrac{x^{-5}}{x^5}$ x^{-10} M. $\dfrac{x^{-7}}{x^{-7}}$ 1

N. $\dfrac{x^0}{x^4}$ x^{-4} O. $\dfrac{x^{-5}}{x^0}$ x^{-5}

P. x^5x^{-7} x^{-2}

Q. $x^{-2}x^5$ x^3

R. $x^{-6}x^{-7}$ x^{-13}

S. x^0x^{-4} x^{-4}

T. x^8x^{-8} 1

U. $(x^{-3})^2$ x^{-6}

V. $(x^2)^{-3}$ x^{-6}

W. $(x^{-5})^{-2}$ x^{10}

X. $(x^3y^{-2})^4$ $x^{12}y^{-8}$

Y. $(2x^{-4}y)^{-3}$ $\frac{1}{8}x^{12}y^{-3}$

EXERCISE 9-5

For Problems 1 through 10, evaluate the expression *without* using a calculator.

Problem Notes:

The problems in this section are similar to those in Exercise 9–4, except that the exponents can be negative. In order to make students comfortable operating with negative exponents, the answer is specified to contain no powers in the denominator.

1. 3^{-2} $\frac{1}{9}$

2. 2^{-3} $\frac{1}{8}$

3. 4^{-3} $\frac{1}{64}$

4. 4^{-2} $\frac{1}{16}$

5. 5^{-2} $\frac{1}{25}$

6. 7^{-3} $\frac{1}{343}$

7. 1^{-5} 1

8. 1^{-8} 1

9. $(-2)^{-3}$ $-\frac{1}{8}$

10. $(3)^{-2}$ $\frac{1}{9}$

For Problems 11 through 40, a. write powers with positive or negative exponents, leaving no powers in denominators; b. write the powers *without* negative exponents.

11. $\dfrac{x^3}{x^8}$ a. x^{-5} b. $\dfrac{1}{x^5}$

12. $\dfrac{x^5}{x^7}$ a. x^{-2} b. $\dfrac{1}{x^2}$

13. $\dfrac{y^5}{y^9}$ a. y^{-4} b. $\dfrac{1}{y^4}$

14. $\dfrac{z^6}{z^8}$ a. z^{-2} b. $\dfrac{1}{z^2}$

15. $\dfrac{a}{a^5}$ a. a^{-4} b. $\dfrac{1}{a^4}$

16. $\dfrac{b}{b^4}$ a. b^{-3} b. $\dfrac{1}{b^3}$

17. $\dfrac{c^5}{c^6}$ a. c^{-1} b. $\dfrac{1}{c}$

18. $\dfrac{d^7}{d^8}$ a. d^{-1} b. $\dfrac{1}{d}$

19. $\dfrac{x^5}{x^0}$ a. x^5 b. x^5

20. $\dfrac{x^0}{x^7}$ a. x^{-7} b. $\dfrac{1}{x^7}$

21. $\dfrac{x^{-3}}{x^{-3}}$ a. 1 b. 1

22. $\dfrac{x^4}{x^4}$ a. 1 b. 1

23. x^5x^{-3} a. x^2 b. x^2

24. x^7x^{-2} a. x^5 b. x^5

25. $x^{-8}x^2$ a. x^{-6} b. $\dfrac{1}{x^6}$

26. $x^{-6}x^2$ a. x^{-4} b. $\dfrac{1}{x^4}$

27. $x^{-6}x^{-7}$ a. x^{-13} b. $\dfrac{1}{x^{13}}$

28. $x^{-3}x^{-5}$ a. x^{-8} b. $\dfrac{1}{x^8}$

29. x^7y^{-3} a. x^7y^{-3} b. $\dfrac{x^7}{y^3}$

30. x^5y^{-2} a. x^5y^{-2} b. $\dfrac{x^5}{y^2}$

31. x^5x^0 a. x^5 b. x^5

32. x^0x^6 a. x^6 b. x^6

33. x^0x^{-7} a. x^{-7} b. $\dfrac{1}{x^7}$

34. $x^{-3}x^0$ a. x^{-3} b. $\dfrac{1}{x^3}$

35. $\dfrac{r^2s^3}{r^6s^9}$ a. $r^{-4}s^{-6}$ b. $\dfrac{1}{r^4s^6}$

36. $\dfrac{a^5b^2}{a^8b^6}$ a. $a^{-3}b^{-4}$ b. $\dfrac{1}{a^3b^4}$

37. $\dfrac{a^5b^6}{a^7b^6}$ a. a^{-2} b. $\dfrac{1}{a^2}$

38. $\dfrac{m^9k^7}{m^4k^7}$ a. m^5 b. m^5

39. $\dfrac{c^5d^0}{c^2d^7}$ a. c^3d^{-7} b. $\dfrac{c^3}{d^7}$

40. $\dfrac{r^6s^0}{r^4s^8}$ a. r^2s^{-8} b. $\dfrac{r^2}{s^8}$

For Problems 41 through 110, simplify the expression. Use negative exponents, and leave no variables in denominators.

41. $\dfrac{t^{15}v^7}{t^0v^{10}}$ $t^{15}v^{-3}$

42. $\dfrac{c^{19}d^{13}}{c^0d^{18}}$ $c^{19}d^{-5}$

43. $\dfrac{x^7y}{xy^5}$ x^6y^{-4}

44. $\dfrac{x^6z}{xz^9}$ x^5z^{-8}

45. $\dfrac{x^7y}{(xy)^5}$ x^2y^{-4}

46. $\dfrac{(xy)^6}{x^5y}$ xy^5

47. $(x^2y^{-3})^5$ $x^{10}y^{-15}$

48. $(x^{-2}y^4)^6$ $x^{-12}y^{24}$

49. $(2x^{-3})^4$ $16x^{-12}$

50. $(3x^{-5})^2$ $9x^{-10}$

51. $(x^{-3}y^4)^{-2}$ x^6y^{-8}

52. $(x^5y^{-2})^{-3}$ $x^{-15}y^6$

53. $(3x^{-4})^{-2}$ $\frac{1}{9}x^8$

54. $(2x^{-6})^{-3}$ $\frac{1}{8}x^{18}$

55. $\dfrac{x^{-8}}{x^2}$ x^{-10}

56. $\dfrac{x^{-7}}{x^3}$ x^{-10}

57. $\dfrac{a^3}{a^{-10}}$ a^{13}

58. $\dfrac{y^4}{y^{-13}}$ y^{17}

59. $\dfrac{h^{-4}}{h^{-6}}$ h^2

60. $\dfrac{z^{-2}}{z^{-7}}$ z^5

61. $\dfrac{p^0}{p^{-5}}$ p^5

62. $\dfrac{a^0}{a^{-3}}$ a^3

63. $\dfrac{y^7}{y^0}$ y^7

64. $\dfrac{b^{11}}{b^0}$ b^{11}

65. $\dfrac{x^5 y^{-7}}{x^3 y^9}$ $x^2 y^{-16}$

66. $\dfrac{x^6 y^{-3}}{x^2 y^8}$ $x^4 y^{-11}$

67. $\dfrac{r^{-2} y^5}{r^{10} y^7}$ $r^{-12} y^{-2}$

68. $\dfrac{t^{-3} u^7}{t^9 u^{12}}$ $t^{-12} u^{-5}$

69. $\dfrac{c^{-3} d^{-7}}{c^5 d^{-7}}$ c^{-8}

70. $\dfrac{y^{-5} z^{-9}}{y^{-5} z^3}$ z^{-12}

71. $\dfrac{15 x^9}{3 x^7}$ $5 x^2$

72. $\dfrac{20 x^7}{5 x^2}$ $4 x^5$

73. $\dfrac{12 a^{10}}{15 a^7}$ $\frac{4}{5} a^3$

74. $\dfrac{18 y^{12}}{12 y^4}$ $\frac{3}{2} y^8$

75. $\dfrac{6 r^9}{12 r^{-4}}$ $\frac{1}{2} r^{13}$

76. $\dfrac{5 z^2}{10 z^{-3}}$ $\frac{1}{2} z^5$

77. $\dfrac{51 m^6 p}{17 m^4 p^{-9}}$ $3 m^2 p^{10}$

78. $\dfrac{57 k^7 p}{19 k^3 p^{-5}}$ $3 k^4 p^6$

79. $\dfrac{2 t^5 v^{-7}}{10 t^6 v^{-8}}$ $\frac{1}{5} t^{-1} v^1$

80. $\dfrac{4 r^8 s^{-6}}{40 r^7 s^{-7}}$ $\frac{1}{10} rs$

81. $\dfrac{x^5}{y^4}\left(\dfrac{y}{x}\right)^3$ $x^2 y^{-1}$

82. $\dfrac{x^9}{y^5}\left(\dfrac{y}{x}\right)^4$ $x^5 y^{-1}$

83. $\left(\dfrac{m}{x}\right)^5 \times \dfrac{x^6}{m^{-11}}$ $m^{16} x$

84. $\left(\dfrac{n}{d}\right)^5 \times \dfrac{d^7}{n^{-4}}$ $n^9 d^2$

85. $\left(\dfrac{a}{b}\right)^{-5} \times \dfrac{a^5}{b^7}$ b^{-2}

86. $\left(\dfrac{x}{y}\right)^{-7} \times \dfrac{x^7}{y^5}$ y^2

87. $\dfrac{r^{-3}}{s^5}\left(\dfrac{r}{s}\right)^7$ $r^4 s^{-12}$

88. $\dfrac{k^{-2}}{r^4}\left(\dfrac{k}{r}\right)^8$ $k^6 r^{-12}$

89. $\left(\dfrac{x}{y}\right)^0 \times \dfrac{1}{x^3}$ x^{-3}

90. $\left(\dfrac{a}{b}\right)^0 \times \dfrac{1}{a^5}$ a^{-5}

91. $\left(\dfrac{x^5}{y^4}\right)^2$ $x^{10} y^{-8}$

92. $\left(\dfrac{x^7}{y^5}\right)^3$ $x^{21} y^{-15}$

93. $\left(\dfrac{x^{-2}}{y^5}\right)^3$ $x^{-6} y^{-15}$

94. $\left(\dfrac{x^{-4}}{y^3}\right)^2$ $x^{-8} y^{-6}$

95. $\left(\dfrac{x^2}{y^3}\right)^4 \left(\dfrac{y^5}{x^3}\right)^2$ $x^2 y^{-2}$

96. $\left(\dfrac{x^4}{y^5}\right)^2 \left(\dfrac{y^2}{x^3}\right)^5$ x^{-7}

97. $\left(\dfrac{a^{-2}}{b^3}\right)^5\left(\dfrac{b^{-3}}{a^4}\right)^{-2}$ $a^{-2}b^{-9}$

98. $\left(\dfrac{t^{-3}}{u^4}\right)^3\left(\dfrac{u^{-4}}{t^6}\right)^{-5}$ $t^{21}u^8$

99. $\dfrac{(x^6y^2)^3}{(x^4y^3)^5}$ $x^{-2}y^{-9}$

100. $\dfrac{(x^4y^3)^2}{(x^5y^2)^4}$ $x^{-12}y^{-2}$

101. $\dfrac{(r^{-3}s^4)^2}{(r^5s^{-2})^3}$ $r^{-21}s^{14}$

102. $\dfrac{(m^{-2}p^5)^2}{(m^4p^{-3})^3}$ $m^{-16}p^{19}$

103. $\dfrac{(3x^6)^4}{(3x^{-2})^3}$ $3x^{30}$

104. $\dfrac{(2x^4)^5}{(2x^{-1})^3}$ $4x^{23}$

105. $\dfrac{(2tp^2)^3}{(2t^2p)^4}$ $\frac{1}{2}t^{-5}p^2$

106. $\dfrac{(3ab^3)^2}{(3a^2b)^4}$ $\frac{1}{9}a^{-6}b^2$

107. $\dfrac{(5rs^{-2})^6}{(5r^3s)^2}$ $625s^{-14}$

108. $\dfrac{(5cd^{-3})^5}{(5c^2d)^3}$ $25c^{-1}d^{-18}$

109. $\dfrac{(3r^6)^3}{9r^6}$ $3r^{12}$

110. $\dfrac{(4a^5)^3}{4a^{15}}$ 16

9-6 | POWERS OF 10 AND SCIENTIFIC NOTATION

Time: 2 days

Chalkboard Examples:

First day:
1. Multiply:
   8.7654 × 10³   Ans.: 8765.4
   34.5 × 10³   Ans.: 34,500
   0.000019 × 10³   Ans.: 0.019

2. Divide:
   234.5 ÷ 10²   Ans. 2.345
   7.8 ÷ 10⁵   Ans. 0.000078
   500,000 ÷ 10⁴   Ans. 50

3. Multiply:
   345.67 × 10⁻²   Ans.: 3.4567

4. Transform to scientific notation.
   2,340,000   Ans. 2.34 × 10⁶
   0.00078   Ans. 7.8 × 10⁻⁴
   56 million Ans.: 5.6 × 10⁷
Have students work Examples 1 and 2.

Oral Practice Problems A–P are appropriate.

Second day:
Do the operation. Write in scientific notation.

Multiplying or dividing a number by 10 is easy. For instance,

$$37.29 \times 10 = 372.9 \quad \text{and} \quad 37.29 \div 10 = 3.729.$$

All you need do is move the decimal point one place. To tell which way to move it, remember that *multiplying* by 10 makes a number *bigger* and *dividing* by 10 makes a number *smaller*.

It is just as easy to multiply or divide by a *power* of 10. For instance, multiplying a number by 10^3 moves the decimal point *three* places.

$$9.2153 \times 10^3 = 9215.3$$

$$13.7 \times 10^3 = 13,700$$

$$0.000025 \times 10^3 = 0.025$$

Dividing by a power of 10 moves the decimal point in the other direction. Again, the number of places it moves is equal to the exponent of 10. For instance,

$$413.2 \div 10^2 = 4.132 \qquad \text{Moves 2 places.}$$

$$6.1 \div 10^5 = 0.000061 \qquad \text{Moves 5 places.}$$

$$300,000 \div 10^4 = 30. \qquad \text{Moves 4 places.}$$

In each case, dividing by a power of 10 makes the number *smaller*.

Suppose that you multiply a number by 10^{-2}, which has a *negative* exponent. To figure out what happens, use the following reasoning.

$$21.584 \times 10^{-2}$$

$= 21.584 \times \dfrac{1}{10^2}$ Definition of negative exponents

$= 21.584 \div 10^2$ Definition of division

$= 0.21584$ Dividing by 10^2 makes the number *smaller*.

When you multiply a number by 10^{-2}, the decimal point moves *two* places and the number gets *smaller*. Using this observation, the answer to such a problem can be written in one step. For instance,

$$98.74 \times 10^{-3} = 0.09874.$$

Your thought process should be: Move the decimal point *three* places in the direction that makes the number *smaller*.

Powers of 10 provide a compact way to write very large or very small numbers. It is hard to read a number such as

$$5380000000$$

because it is impossible for the human brain to comprehend this many digits without actually counting them. It is much easier to read this number if it is written as 5.38 times the appropriate power of 10.

$$5380000000 = 5.38 \times 10^9$$

To find out what the exponent should be, you must count how far the decimal point moves.

Decimal point starts here.
5380000000.
Decimal point moves 9 spaces.

Very small numbers (close to zero) can be treated the same way. For instance, 0.000002345 can be written as 2.345 times a power of 10. Again, the exponent is found by counting how far the decimal point moves.

$$0.000002345 = 2.345 \times 10^{-6}$$
Decimal point moves 6 spaces.

The most reliable way to tell whether the exponent will be positive or negative is to realize that large numbers (absolute value larger than 10) will have *positive* exponents, and small numbers, or decimals (absolute value less than 1), will have *negative* exponents.

Round.
$(2.3 \times 10^8)(8.21 \times 10^{-5})$
Ans. 1.9×10^4
$\dfrac{6.789 \times 10^4}{4.56 \times 10^{-5}}$ Ans. 1.49×10^9
Have students work Examples 3–6.
Oral Practice Problems Q–Z are appropriate.

Assignments:

Day 1: Exercise 9–6, #1–29 odd and
Exercise 9–5, #42, 52, 62, 72 for
review
Day 2: Exercise 9–6, #16–36 even and 37–59
odd

Numbers such as 5.38×10^9 and 2.345×10^{-6} are said to be in **scientific notation.** The factor on the left has the decimal point after the *first* (non-zero) digit. This factor is called the **mantissa.** The factor on the right is a power of 10. Its exponent is called the **characteristic.**

$$5.38 \times 10^9 \qquad 2.345 \times 10^{-6}$$

Characteristic

Mantissa

Numbers too great or too small to put into a calculator can be multiplied or divided easily if they are first transformed to scientific notation. For instance,

$(5380000000)(0.000002345)$

$= (5.38 \times 10^9)(2.345 \times 10^{-6})$	Transform to scientific notation.
$= (5.38 \times 2.345)(10^9 \times 10^{-6})$	Commute and associate the mantissas and the powers of 10.
$= 12.6161 \times 10^3$	Multiply.
$= 1.26161 \times 10^4$	Move the decimal point so the number is in scientific notation.
$\approx 1.26 \times 10^4.$	Round the answer.

The next-to-last step is taken so that the mantissa will have the decimal point after the *first* digit—12.6161 equals 1.26161×10^1, and $10^1 \times 10^3 = 10^4$.

The answer is rounded off because the given numbers are only approximate. The number of digits in the mantissa is called the number of **significant digits.** The answer is no more accurate than the factor with the *least* number of significant digits. In this case, the answer is rounded off to three significant digits. When there are several numbers to be multiplied or divided, you round off only the *final* answer. Rounding off at intermediate steps would make the final answer less precise.

Dividing numbers in scientific notation is also relatively easy. For instance,

$$\frac{5.38 \times 10^9}{2.345 \times 10^{-6}}$$

$= \dfrac{5.38}{2.345} \times \dfrac{10^9}{10^{-6}}$	Use the multiplication property of fractions.
$\approx 2.29 \times 10^{15}.$	Divide the mantissas and round off to three significant digits. Subtract the exponents: $9 - (-6) = 9 + 6 = 15$.

Objective:
Given large or small numbers, transform them to scientific notation (and vice versa), and multiply or divide them.

Cover the answers as you work the examples.

EXAMPLE 1

Transform to decimal form.

a. 8.49×10^6

– – – – –   – – – – –

$$8.49 \times 10^6$$
$$= 8{,}490{,}000$$

b. 6.291×10^{-4}

– – – – –   – – – – –

$$6.291 \times 10^{-4}$$
$$= 0.0006291$$

EXAMPLE 2

Transform to scientific notation.

a. 374,100

– – – – –   – – – – –

$$374{,}100$$
$$= 3.741 \times 10^5$$

b. 0.0029

– – – – –   – – – – –

$$0.0029$$
$$= 2.9 \times 10^{-3}$$

c. 34 billion

– – – – –   – – – – –

$$34 \text{ billion}$$
$$= 34{,}000{,}000{,}000$$
$$= 3.4 \times 10^{10}$$

In the United States, the following numbers are named as shown.

NAMES FOR LARGE NUMBERS

10^3	thousand
10^6	million
10^9	billion
10^{12}	trillion
10^{15}	quadrillion
10^{18}	quintillion

Each number is 1000 times the previous one. In Europe, a million is also 10^6, but a billion is 10^{12}, a trillion is 10^{18}, and so forth. There, each named number is 1,000,000 times the previous one.

EXAMPLE 3

Multiply $(7.82 \times 10^4)(3.4 \times 10^{-9})$. Round your answer to the appropriate number of significant digits.

– – – – –   – – – – –

	Think These Reasons
$(7.82 \times 10^4)(3.4 \times 10^{-9})$	Write the given expression.
$= 26.588 \times 10^{-5}$	Multiply the mantissas. Add the exponents.
$= 2.6588 \times 10^{-4}$	Write the answer with the decimal point after the first digit.
$\approx \underline{2.7 \times 10^{-4}}$	Round off to two significant digits.

Note: The whole computation can be done in one step. The minimum you should write is

$$(7.82 \times 10^4)(3.4 \times 10^{-9}) \approx \underline{2.7 \times 10^{-4}}.$$

EXAMPLE 4

Divide: $\dfrac{4.378 \times 10^{13}}{7.91 \times 10^4}$. Round your answer.

– – – – –   – – – – –

$\dfrac{4.378 \times 10^{13}}{7.91 \times 10^4}$	Write the given expression.
$\approx 0.553 \times 10^9$	Divide the mantissas and round off to three significant digits. Subtract the exponents.

$= \underline{5.53 \times 10^8}$ 　　　　Write the answer with the decimal point after the first nonzero digit.

Note: The last sign is $=$ rather than $\approx$ because it connects 0.553×10^9 and 5.53×10^8. These two numbers are *exactly* equal, not just approximately equal.

EXAMPLE 5

Find the reciprocal of 3.49×10^{-7}. Round your answer.

- - - - - 　　　　　　　　　　　 - - - - -

$\dfrac{1}{3.49 \times 10^{-7}}$ 　　　　Write the *reciprocal* of the given expression.

$= \dfrac{1 \times 10^0}{3.49 \times 10^{-7}}$ 　　　　Write the numerator in scientific notation. 10^0 is equal to 1.

- - - - - 　　　　　　　　　　　 - - - - -

Think These Reasons

$= \dfrac{1}{3.49} \times \dfrac{10^0}{10^{-7}}$ 　　　　Use the multiplication property of fractions to separate the mantissas and the powers.

$\approx 0.287 \times 10^7$ 　　　　$1 \div 3.49 \approx 0.287$. Subtract the exponents: $0 - (-7) = 7$.

$= \underline{2.87 \times 10^6}$ 　　　　Write the answer in scientific notation.

EXAMPLE 6

Evaluate $(9.43 \times 10^{-4})^3$. Round your answer.

- - - - - 　　　　　　　　　　　 - - - - -

$(9.43 \times 10^{-4})^3$ 　　　　Write the given expression.

$= 9.43^3 \times (10^{-4})^3$ 　　　　Distribute exponentiation over multiplication.

$\approx 839 \times 10^{-12}$ 　　　　$9.43 \times 9.43 \times 9.43 \approx 839$. Multiply the exponents.

$= \underline{8.39 \times 10^{-10}}$ 　　　　Write the answer in scientific notation.

ORAL PRACTICE

Give the number in scientific notation.

A.   358 3.58×10^2 　　　　　　B.   7290 7.29×10^3

C.   0.0743 7.43×10^{-2} D.   0.000045 4.5×10^{-5}

E. 23×10^5 2.3×10^6 F. 42×10^{-7} 4.2×10^{-6}

G. 0.51×10^8 5.1×10^7 H. 0.19×10^{-3} 1.9×10^{-4}

Give the number in words.

EXAMPLES

Answers

i.   48,500,000   i.   48.5 million
ii. 6.3×10^{11} ii.   630 billion

I.   294,000   294 thousand   J.   1,500,000   1.5 million

K.   32,000,000   32 million   L. 413×10^5 41.3 million

M. 5×10^9 5 billion   N. 8.2×10^{13} 82 trillion

O. 7.2×10^{14} 720 trillion   P. 6.8×10^0 6.8

Evaluate. Give the answer in scientific notation.

Q. $(2 \times 10^4)(3 \times 10^2)$ 6×10^6 R. $(4 \times 10^{-3})(2 \times 10^7)$ 8×10^4

S. $(1 \times 10^4)(8 \times 10^{-9})$ 8×10^{-5} T. $(3 \times 10^{-5})(2 \times 10^{-6})$ 6×10^{-11}

U. $(4 \times 10^3)(5 \times 10^6)$ 2×10^{10} V. $(6 \times 10^{-4})(3 \times 10^{-2})$ 1.8×10^{-5}

W. $\dfrac{6 \times 10^8}{2 \times 10^5}$ 3×10^3 X. $\dfrac{8 \times 10^3}{4 \times 10^9}$ 2×10^{-6}

Y. $(3 \times 10^7)^2$ 9×10^{14} Z. $(2 \times 10^4)^3$ 8×10^{12}

EXERCISE 9-6

Problem Notes:

The greatest difficulty students have with scientific notation is figuring which direction to move the decimal point. They seek some magic rule to memorize, such as, "When the exponent is negative, the decimal moves left." Unfortunately, such rules work in opposite directions, depending whether you are going from scientific to decimal or vice versa. The most reliable thing to remember is that

1.   Write a number that is 10 times as large as
   a.   5.73   57.3   b.   29.1   291
   c.   304   3040   d.   0.068   0.68
   e.   0.00907   0.0907

2.   Write a number that is 10 times as large as
   a.   6.03   60.3   b.   427.9   4279
   c.   2214   22,140   d.   0.53   5.3
   e.   0.000998   0.00998

3. Write a number that is $\frac{1}{10}$ as large as
    a. 63.9 6.39   b. 7.91 0.791
    c. 82 8.2   d. 0.48 0.048
    e. 0.00014 0.000014

4. Write a number that is $\frac{1}{10}$ as large as
    a. 47.2 4.72   b. 6.85 0.685
    c. 943 94.3   d. 0.025 0.0025
    e. 3 0.3

the = sign must tell the truth. The two numbers on either side of the = sign must really be equal. Application of this principle requires some thought, but the reward is a better understanding of the process.
Students can be taught to use scientific notation keys on the calculator. They should first spend several days operating with powers of 10 in their heads so that they will appreciate what the calculator is doing.

For Problems 5 through 14, transform the number to decimal form.

5. 7.1×10^3 7100   6. 3.6×10^4 36,000

7. 4.65×10^5 465,000   8. 9.24×10^5 924,000

9. 3.8×10^{-4} 0.00038   10. 4.83×10^{-6} 0.00000483

11. 8.6×10^1 86   12. 7.4×10^{-1} 0.74

13. 9.8×10^{-1} 0.98   14. 6.02×10^1 60.2

For Problems 15 through 36, transform the number to scientific notation.

15. 43,800 4.38×10^4 16. 715,200 7.152×10^5

17. 291.7 2.917×10^2 18. 49.63 4.963×10^1

19. 34,500,000 3.45×10^7 20. 517,000 5.17×10^5

21. 0.00739 7.39×10^{-3} 22. 0.000281 2.81×10^{-4}

23. 0.00000114 1.14×10^{-6} 24. 0.0000000192 1.92×10^{-8}

25. 27.5 million 2.75×10^7 26. 44.2 thousand 4.42×10^4

27. 200 thousand 2.00×10^5 28. 30 billion 3.0×10^{10}

29. 62.4×10^3 6.24×10^4 30. 73.6×10^5 7.36×10^6

31. 548×10^{-7} 5.48×10^{-5} 32. 295×10^{-8} 2.95×10^{-6}

33. 0.07×10^8 7×10^6 34. 0.0034×10^9 3.4×10^6

35. 97.1×10^{-4} 9.71×10^{-3} 36. 84.6×10^{-2} 8.46×10^{-1}

For Problems 37 through 60, do the operations in your *head,* without using a calculator. Write the answer in scientific notation.

37. $(2 \times 10^7)(3 \times 10^8)$ 6×10^{15} 38. $(2 \times 10^5)(4 \times 10^8)$ 8×10^{13}

39. $(4 \times 10^9)(2 \times 10^{-3})$ 8×10^6 40. $(3 \times 10^{-4})(2 \times 10^{11})$ 6×10^7

41. $(7 \times 10^4)(5 \times 10^{11})$ 3.5×10^{16} 42. $(5 \times 10^7)(9 \times 10^8)$ 4.5×10^{16}

43. $(6 \times 10^3)(7 \times 10^{-8})$ 4.2×10^{-4} 44. $(9 \times 10^6)(7 \times 10^{-13})$ 6.3×10^{-6}

45. $(9 \times 10^{-5})(6 \times 10^5)$ 5.4×10^1 46. $(8 \times 10^{-7})(6 \times 10^7)$ 4.8×10^1

47. $(8 \times 10^{-4})(7 \times 10^{-20})$ 5.6×10^{-23} 48. $(4 \times 10^{-5})(7 \times 10^{-10})$ 2.8×10^{-14}

49. $\dfrac{8 \times 10^{15}}{2 \times 10^4}$ 4×10^{11} 50. $\dfrac{8 \times 10^{17}}{4 \times 10^8}$ 2×10^9

51. $\dfrac{6 \times 10^4}{3 \times 10^{11}}$ 2×10^{-7} 52. $\dfrac{6 \times 10^5}{2 \times 10^{12}}$ 3×10^{-7}

53. $\dfrac{5 \times 10^{-2}}{1 \times 10^4}$ 5×10^{-6} 54. $\dfrac{7 \times 10^{-3}}{1 \times 10^5}$ 7×10^{-8}

55. $\dfrac{7 \times 10^5}{2 \times 10^{-3}}$ 3.5×10^8 56. $\dfrac{9 \times 10^3}{2 \times 10^{-7}}$ 4.5×10^{10}

57. $\dfrac{2 \times 10^{-3}}{4 \times 10^{-12}}$ 5×10^8 58. $\dfrac{2 \times 10^{-9}}{8 \times 10^{-7}}$ 2.5×10^{-3}

59. $\dfrac{4 \times 10^{-8}}{5 \times 10^8}$ 8×10^{-17} 60. $\dfrac{3 \times 10^{-4}}{6 \times 10^4}$ 5×10^{-9}

For Problems 61 through 76, use a calculator to multiply or divide the mantissas. Write the answer in scientific notation, with the appropriate number of significant digits.

61. 6.40×10^{13} **62.** 7.43×10^{11} 61. $(2.05 \times 10^6)(3.12 \times 10^7)$ 62. $(3.52 \times 10^4)(2.11 \times 10^7)$

63. 6.6×10^{12} **64.** 5.5×10^7 63. $(4.9 \times 10^{17})(1.345 \times 10^{-5})$ 64. $(1.3 \times 10^{-5})(4.253 \times 10^{12})$

65. 1.99×10^{-14} **66.** 4.73×10^{-5} 65. $(8.65 \times 10^3)(2.296 \times 10^{-18})$ 66. $(9.06 \times 10^{-9})(5.224 \times 10^3)$

67. 1.7×10^{-12} **68.** 6.2×10^{-16} 67. $(1.79 \times 10^{-4})(9.7 \times 10^{-9})$ 68. $(1.72 \times 10^{-5})(3.6 \times 10^{-11})$

69. $\dfrac{3.75 \times 10^8}{2.93 \times 10^5}$ 1.28×10^3 70. $\dfrac{4.28 \times 10^6}{1.94 \times 10^2}$ 2.21×10^4

71. $\dfrac{4.976 \times 10^{-8}}{8.2 \times 10^5}$ 6.1×10^{-14} 72. $\dfrac{7.732 \times 10^{-7}}{9.63 \times 10^3}$ 8.03×10^{-11}

73. $\dfrac{7.6 \times 10^4}{9.83 \times 10^{-9}}$ 7.7×10^{12} 74. $\dfrac{1.07 \times 10^4}{8.3 \times 10^{-2}}$ 1.3×10^5

75. $\dfrac{6.802 \times 10^{-7}}{5.1996 \times 10^{-11}}$ 1.308×10^4 76. $\dfrac{7.41 \times 10^{-12}}{6.94 \times 10^{-5}}$ 1.07×10^{-7}

For Problems 77 through 80, find the reciprocal of the given number.

77. 5.87×10^4 1.70×10^{-5} 78. 2.93×10^5 3.41×10^{-6}

79. 1.62×10^{-7} 6.17×10^6 80. 7.8×10^{-9} 1.3×10^8

For Problems 81 through 86, raise the number to the indicated power.

81. $(2.34 \times 10^5)^2$ 5.48×10^{10} 82. $(1.29 \times 10^7)^2$ 1.66×10^{14}

83. $(4.08 \times 10^{-5})^2$ 1.66×10^{-9} 84. $(6.13 \times 10^{-6})^2$ 3.76×10^{-11}

85. $(8.97 \times 10^4)^3$ 7.22×10^{14} 86. $(7.21 \times 10^5)^3$ 3.75×10^{17}

9-7 | PROBLEMS INVOLVING NUMBERS IN SCIENTIFIC NOTATION

As you might expect from the name, numbers in scientific notation occur in problems from science! More generally, they occur in problems from the real world. In this section you work problems involving arithmetic performed on very large or very small numbers. As in the previous section, the properties of exponentiation are the key to operating with such numbers.

Objective:

Given a problem from the real world involving very large or very small constants, do the arithmetic using scientific notation.

Cover the answer as you work the example.

EXAMPLE

Louisiana Purchase Problem   In 1803, when Thomas Jefferson was president, the United States purchased about 5×10^8 acres of land from the French for 15 million dollars. About how much per acre did the land cost?

- - - - -   - - - - -

Think These Reasons

15 million $= 1.5 \times 10^7$ 1 million $= 10^6$

$\$ \text{ per acre} = \dfrac{1.5 \times 10^7}{5 \times 10^8}$ *Per* means *divided by.* So \$ per acre $= \$ \div$ acres.

$= 0.3 \times 10^{-1}$ Divide the mantissas. Subtract the exponents.

$= 3 \times 10^{-2}$ Write in scientific notation.

About 3 cents per acre   Answer the question.

Time: 3 days

Chalkboard Examples:

First day:
People Problem—There are about 4.5 billion people in the world.
a. Write this number in scientific notation.
   Ans.: 4.5×10^9
b. Assuming that the average mass of a person is 53,000 grams, about how many grams of people are there in the world?
   Ans.: 2.4×10^{14}

c. There are about 1.49×10^{14} square meters of land on the earth's surface. How many square meters per person is this?
   Ans.: 3.3×10^4, or about 33,000
Have students work the example, then start the assignment.

Second and third days:
Work previous homework problems at the board.
Work new homework problems individually.

Assignments:

Day 1: Exercise 9–7, #1, 3, 5,
        Exercise 9–6, #31–35 odd and 61–85 odd
Day 2: Exercise 9–7, #7–17 odd,
        Exercise 9–6, #62, 70, 78, 82

EXERCISE 9-7

1. *National Debt Problem*   In 1980 the national debt of the United States was about 970 billion dollars. The 1980 census showed 226,504,825 people. About how many dollars per person was the national debt? $4280 per person

2. *Average Ocean Depth Problem*   The total area of the world's oceans is about 360.928 million square kilometers. The total volume of water in the oceans is about 1.32 billion cubic kilometers. The average depth equals the volume divided by the area. What is the average depth? How many meters is this?   3660 meters

3. *Continental Drift Problem*   Measurements show that Europe and Africa are separating from the Americas at a rate of about 1 inch per year. The continents are presently about 4000 miles apart. Assuming that the rate has remained constant, how many years has it been since the continents split apart and started drifting?   253 million years

They used to *fit!*

4. *Clothing Industry Problem*   There are about 230 million people in the United States. Assume that each person buys 6 pairs of socks a year and that socks cost about $4 a pair. How much money can the clothing industry expect to take in each year from selling socks? Give the answer in words.   About 5.5 billion dollars!

5. *Automotive Batteries Problem*   There are about 120 million cars and trucks in the United states. Each one uses a battery, which needs replacing about once every 3 years. If an average battery costs $80, how much money can the battery manufacturing industry expect to make each year?   About 3.2 billion dollars!

6. *Brain Cell Problem*   The brain of a normal adult weighs about 3 pounds. It has about 8 billion neurons (brain cells). How many pounds per neuron is that? Answer in scientific notation. 3.75×10^{-10} lbs/neuron

7. *Earth's Land Area Problem*   The total area of the earth's surface is about 5.1007×10^8 square kilometers. The area of all land is about 1.49141×10^8 square kilometers. What percent of the earth's sur-

face is land? (Divide land area by total area and multiply by 100.) 29.239%

8. *Gold Plated Pinhead Problem*   An atom of gold has an area of about 6.6×10^{-16} square centimeter. How many atoms would it take to cover the head of a pin of area 3.2×10^{-2} square centimeter, with a layer of gold 1 atom thick? 4.8×10^{13} atoms

9. *Glacier Problem*   A typical glacier moves downhill at about 5 inches per day. Suppose that the glacier is 4 miles long.
    a. Recalling that 1 mile is 5280 feet, how many days will it take for snow that falls at the top of the glacier to move downhill to the bottom? 50688 days
    b. How many years is this? 139 years

10. *Numbers on a Calculator Problem*   A normal calculator can handle numbers as big as 9.99×10^{99}. To see how big a number this is, answer the following questions.
    a. The volume of the earth is 2.59×10^{11} cubic miles. One cubic mile is 5280^3 cubic feet. What is the volume of the earth in cubic feet? 3.81×10^{22}
    b. One grain of sand has a volume of about 1.3×10^{-9} cubic feet. Divide the answer in part (a) by 1.3×10^{-9} to find the number of grains of sand the earth could hold. 2.93×10^{31} grains
    c. Which is bigger, the number of grains of sand the earth could hold or the largest number a calculator can hold?

    c. The calculator number is *much* greater than the number of sand grains the earth could hold.

11. *Paper Consumption Problem*   A school uses 150 cartons of paper in a year. Each carton has 10 reams, and each ream has 500 sheets.
    a. How many sheets of paper does the school use in a year? 750,000
    b. If there are 2000 students in the school, how many sheets of paper per student is this? 375

12. *Speed of Light Problem*   Light travels at a speed of 299,792 kilometers per second. How long does it take light to get from:
    a. New York to Los Angeles, 3900 km; 1.301×10^{-2} sec
    b. the sun to the earth, 150 million km; 500 sec
    c. Earth to Pluto at its closest point of approach, 4.44 billion km? Answer in hours. 4.11 hours

    In Problem 12a, the light of course cannot go directly from New York to Los Angeles because of the curvature of the earth. Dramatic evidence of the speed of light appears in cable television broadcasts, in which the signal is relayed by a satellite about 23,000 miles out in space. If an event such as a sportscast is also broadcast on the radio, the sound from the television will lag by about a quarter of a second, the time for the signal to get to the satellite and back to earth at the speed of light.

13. *Light-Year Problem*   Light travels 299,792 kilometers per second. How far does light travel in a year? This distance is called a **light-year.** Answer in words. About 9.5 trillion km

14. *Life in Seconds Problem*   The average life expectancy in the United States is about 71 years. About how many seconds is this? Answer in words. About 2.2 billion seconds

15. *Leaky Faucet Problem*   A leaking faucet drips 1 drop per second.
    a. How many drops does it leak in a year? About 32 million
    b. There are about 76,000 drops of water in a gallon. How many gallons per year would be leaked at one drop per second? 415

16. *Water Bill Problem*   The Dupp family goes on vacation. They are gone for month. Near the end, Fess admits that he left the water running in the back yard. Phil estimates that the faucet runs at 4 gallons per minute. Bill knows that water costs about 0.1 cent per gallon. Mae thinks up a reason for their auntie to pay the bill. How much will the bill be?   About $173

Problem 17 shows that significant savings can be realized by turning off lights or by using smaller bulbs.

17. *Power Consumption Problem*   Suppose that a house has 12 100-watt light bulbs.
    a.   A *kilowatt* (kw) of electrical power is 1000 watts. How many kilowatts do the 12 bulbs require in all?   1.2 kw
    b.   If the lights stay on an average of 8 hours a day, how many hours in all will they be on in a year?   2920
    c.   The amount of energy used by the lights is measured in *kilowatt-hours,* abbreviated kwh. This number is found by multiplying the number of kilowatts by the number of hours. How many kilowatt-hours in all will the bulbs use in a year?   3504
    d.   Suppose that electricity costs 7.8 cents per kwh. How much would be spent on lighting in a year? $273.31
    e.   How much could be saved by:
        i.   using 60-watt bulbs instead of 100-watt; $109.32
        ii. burning the lights (100-watt) 6 hours a day instead of 8? $68.33

18. *Computer Calculations Problems*   A popular brand of personal computer can do a computation in 5×10^{-7} second.
    a.   How many computations can it do in one second? Answer in words.   Two million
    b.   How long would it take the computer to do a billion computations?   500 sec
    c.   If a program takes 30 seconds to run, how many computations were done?   60 million

19. *Sahara Desert Problem*   The Sahara Desert covers about 3 million square miles.
    a.   Write this number in scientific notation. 3×10^6
    b.   One square mile is 5280^2 square feet. About how many square feet is the Sahara Desert? 8×10^{13}
    c.   Assume that the Sahara Desert is covered with sand to an average depth of 200 feet. The volume of this sand in cubic feet is the area in square feet times the depth in feet. How many cubic feet of sand are there? 1.7×10^{16}*
    d.   A grain of sand has a volume of about 1.3×10^{-9} cubic foot. Divide the volume in cubic feet by 1.3×10^{-9} to find out approximately how many grains of sand there are in the Sahara Desert. 1.3×10^{25}*

*Found *without* round-off at intermediate steps.

20. *Ocean Water Molecules Problem*   According to the World Book Encyclopedia, there are about 326 million cubic miles of water on the earth.

a. Write this number in scientific notation. 3.26×10^8
b. One cubic mile is 5280^3 cubic feet. About how many cubic feet of water are there on the earth? 4.80×10^{19}
c. A thimble holds about 5×10^{-5} cubic foot of water. Divide the answer to part (b) by 5×10^{-5} to find out how many thimblefuls of water there are on the earth. 9.6×10^{23}
d. A cubic foot of water has about 9.47×10^{26} water molecules. Which is greater, the number of water molecules in a thimbleful of water or the number of thimblefuls of water on the earth? How many *times* as great? Number of molecules is 9.9×10^2, or about 1000 times greater.

Problem 20 leads to the remarkable conclusion that there are more molecules in a thimbleful of water than there are thimblefuls of water in the entire world! One need only stand at the beach with thimble in hand to appreciate the significance of this fact.

| 9-8 | CHAPTER REVIEW AND TEST |

In this chapter you have returned to an old concept, raising numbers to powers (*exponentiation*). Based on the definition of exponentiation, there are properties that allow you to operate on powers by operating on their exponents. These properties are useful for operating on numbers in scientific notation.

There are four operations you do with exponents.

1. Add.
2. Subtract.
3. Multiply.
4. Distribute.

Your main task is to remember which thing you do at which time. There is a memory aid that may help. List the operations according to the order of operations.

Exponentiation
Multiplication
Addition
Nothing

When you do an operation to a *power*, you do the operation *below* to its exponent! For instance,

Exponentiation: $(2^3)^4 = 2^{3 \cdot 4}$ ⟵ *Multiply* the exponents.

Addition: $x^3 + y^4$ ⟵ Do *nothing* to the exponents.

If you understand the concepts of this chapter, you should be able to work the following test in a length of time equal to one class period.

Time: 1 day

Test Ideas:

Your test can be over either the entire chapter or scientific notation. For problems involving scientific notation, the most effective ones are those involving things with which your students are familiar.

Assignment:

Study Section 10–1.
Work Exercise 10–1, #1–21 odd.

CHAPTER TEST

1. **a.** A prime number has no integer factors besides 1 and itself. A composite number is a product of 2 or more primes.

b. A power is an entire expression, such as 2^3. The exponent is just the superscript, such as 3 in 2^3.

e. A mantissa is the number multiplied by a power of 10, such as 3.6 in 3.6×10^4. A characteristic is the exponent of 10 in scientific notation.

2. **a.** $x^0 = 1$ for all non-zero numbers x.

b. $x^{-n} = \dfrac{1}{x^n}$ for all non-zero numbers x.

c. $a^x \cdot a^y = a^{x+y}$

d. $\left(\dfrac{x}{y}\right)^a = \dfrac{x^a}{y^a}$

e. $(a^x)^y = a^{xy}$

1. What is the difference in each case?
   a. A prime number and a composite number.
   b. A power and an exponent.
   c. 3^0 and 0^3. $3^0 = 1 \; 0^3 = 0$
   d. 2^3 and 2^{-3}. $2^3 = 8,\ 2^{-3} = \frac{1}{8}$
   e. A mantissa and a characteristic.

2. State each.
   a. The definition of zero exponent.
   b. The definition of negative exponents.
   c. The property of a product of two powers with equal bases.
   d. The property of a power of a quotient.
   e. The property of a power of a power.

3. Calvin Butterball and Phoebe Small give the following answers on an algebra test. Who is right? Write *Calvin*, *Phoebe*, *both*, or *neither*.

Problem		Calvin's answer	Phoebe's answer
a. Simplify $x^6 x^8$.	Phoebe	x^{48}	x^{14}
b. Simplify $(x^6)^8$.	Calvin	x^{48}	x^{14}
c. Simplify $(2y^3)^5$.	Neither	$2y^{15}$	$10y^{15}$
d. Simplify $\left(\dfrac{3x^5}{4}\right)^3$.	Both	$\dfrac{27x^{15}}{y^{12}}$	$27x^{15}y^{-12}$
e. Simplify $\dfrac{x^5 y}{x^3 y^7}$.	Phoebe	$x^2 y^{-7}$	$\dfrac{x^2}{y^6}$
f. Simplify x^0.	Calvin	1	x
g. Significant digits in 7.89×10^5.	Phoebe	2	3
h. One trillionth.	Neither	$0.000,000,001$	10^{-9}

4. Simplify, or state that the expression cannot be simplified.
   a. $(5x^8)(7x^9)$ $35x^{17}$
   b. $(5a^7)^3$ $125a^{21}$
   c. $\dfrac{r^5 s^{-2}}{r^8 s^5}$ $r^{-3}s^{-7}$
   d. $\left(\dfrac{x^{13}y^0}{x^8 y^{-5}}\right)^2$ $x^{10}y^{10}$
   e. $\dfrac{1}{a^2 b^{-6}}$ $a^{-2}b^6$
   f. $\dfrac{81b^5}{27c^3}$ $3b^5 c^{-3}$
   g. $\dfrac{x^5}{x}$ x^4
   h. $\dfrac{5x}{x}$ 5
   i. $3x^7 \cdot 3x^9$ $9x^{16}$
   j. $3x^7 + 3x^9$ Cannot be simplified.
   k. $7x^3 + 9x^3$ $16x^3$
   l. $7x^3 - 7x^3$ 0
   m. $7x^3 - x^3$ $6x^3$

5. Do the following operations. Write the answers in scientific notation, rounded off to the appropriate number of significant digits.
   a. (32.4 billion)(5.7 million) 1.8×10^{17}
   b. $(7.91 \times 10^{-7})(6.43 \times 10^{25})$ 5.09×10^{19}
   c. $\dfrac{1.873 \times 10^5}{7.64 \times 10^{-7}}$ 2.45×10^{11}
   d. $\dfrac{4.73 \times 10^{-17}}{6.02 \times 10^{-8}}$ 7.86×10^{-10}
   e. $(7.46 \times 10^9)^2$ 5.57×10^{19}
   f. $\dfrac{1}{2.5 \times 10^{-7}}$ (*Exact* answer) 4×10^6

6. *Government Spending Rate Problem*   The United States Government's budget for 1981 called for spending about 635 billion dollars. There are 5.256×10^5 minutes in a year. About how many dollars per minute did the Government spend that year?

   1.21×10^6, or over a *million* dollars a minute.

10

More Operations
With Polynomials

In Chapter 5 you learned how to multiply two binomials and how to factor quadratic trinomials. In this chapter you will learn some more ways to factor polynomials. You will also find out a quick way to solve certain quadratic equations by factoring. The speed you gain will help you do better on standardized tests or in contest mathematics. On that kind of test you might do such things as finding the exact time at which the hands of a clock coincide.

Expression:
$15x^2 - 6ax - 2cx + 8ac$
Factored form:
$(5x - 2a)(3x - 4c)$
Equation:
$2x^2 - x - 3 = 0$
Factored form:
$(2x - 3)(x + 1) = 0$
Solution:
$S = \{\frac{3}{2}, -1\}$

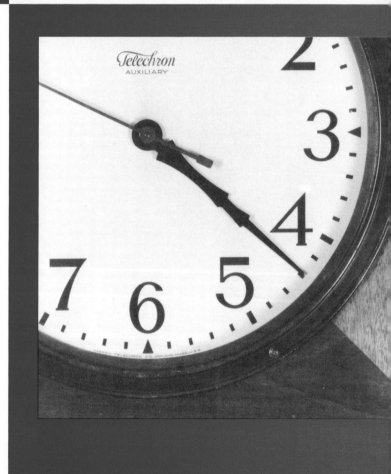

10-1 REVIEW OF MULTIPLYING AND FACTORING POLYNOMIALS

Since this section is a review of things you learned in Chapter 5, you should be able to read it quickly and work the problems without prior classroom discussion. If you are rusty on the techniques, go back to Chapter 5 and look things up!

You should remember how to multiply two binomials. To find

$$(3x + 2)(x - 7),$$

you multiply each term of the first binomial by each term of the second one.

$$(3x + 2)(x - 7)$$

$= 3x^2 - 21x + 2x - 14$ Multiply $3x$ by x and by -7.
                            Multiply 2 by x and by -7.

$= \underline{\underline{3x^2 - 19x - 14}}$ Combine like terms.

To factor a quadratic trinomial, you reverse this process. For example, to factor $3x^2 - 19x - 14$ you first write

$3x^2 - 19x - 14$
$= ($ $)($ $)$.   Write empty parentheses.

The first terms in the binomials must be $3x$ and x, because their product is $3x^2$. So you fill in these numbers.

$3x^2 - 19x - 14$
$= (3x$ $)(x$ $)$ Fill in the first terms.

The other terms in the binomials must have a product equal to -14. The possibilities are as follows.

$$+1, -14 \qquad +7, \ -2$$
$$-1, +14 \qquad -7, \ +2$$

Time: $\frac{1}{2}$ day, with Section 10–2

Chalkboard Examples:

Use selected problems from Exercise 10–1 as refresher examples.

Assignment:

Exercise 10–1, #1–21 odd should have been assigned after the last test on Chapter 9. If not, assign 10–1, #3, 5, 11, and 19 with the assignment for 10–2.

$$+2, -7 \qquad +14, -1$$
$$-2, +7 \qquad -14, +1$$

You simply *try* these possibilities until you find one that works. The correct pair is the one that gives $-19x$ for the middle term when the binomials are multiplied together again. That pair turns out to be $+2, -7$. So you finish by filling in these numbers. The complete problem looks like this:

$$3x^2 - 19x - 14$$

$$= \underline{\underline{(3x + 2)(x - 7)}} \qquad \text{Fill in the constants that give } -19x \text{ for the middle term and } -14 \text{ for the last term.}$$

Objective :

Recall how to multiply two binomials and how to factor quadratic trinomials.

The following problems give you practice doing this.

EXERCISE 10-1

Problem Notes:

Problems 1–20 review previously learned factoring and multiplying techniques.

For Problems 1 through 10, multiply the binomials.

1. $(x + 3)(x + 11)$ $x^2 + 14x + 33$ 2. $(x + 5)(x + 9)$ $x^2 + 14x + 45$

3. $(2x + 5)(x - 4)$ $2x^2 - 3x - 20$ 4. $(3x - 7)(x + 2)$ $3x^2 - x - 14$

5. $(3x - 8)(2x - 7)$ $6x^2 - 37x + 56$ 6. $(5x - 3)(7x - 4)$ $35x^2 - 41x + 12$

7. $(x + 5)(x - 5)$ $x^2 - 25$ 8. $(3x - 4)(3x + 4)$ $9x^2 - 16$

9. $(3x + 4)(3x + 4)$ $9x^2 + 24x + 16$ 10. $(x - 6)(x - 6)$ $x^2 - 12x + 36$

For Problems 11 through 20, factor the polynomial.

11. $x^2 + 14x + 45$ $(x + 9)(x + 5)$ 12. $x^2 + 14x + 33$ $(x + 11)(x + 3)$

13. $x^2 - 4x - 21$ $(x + 3)(x - 7)$ 14. $x^2 + 6x - 16$ $(x + 8)(x - 2)$

15. $x^2 - 12x + 20$ $(x - 2)(x - 10)$ 16. $x^2 - 13x + 36$ $(x - 9)(x - 4)$

17. $4x^2 - 49$ $(2x + 7)(2x - 7)$ 18. $x^2 + 14x + 49$ $(x + 7)(x + 7)$ or $(x + 7)^2$

19. $2x^2 + 9x - 5$ $(2x - 1)(x + 5)$ 20. $3x^2 - 20x - 7$ $(x - 7)(3x + 1)$

21. The answer to a factoring problem is

$$x^2 - 2x - 15 = (x + 3)(x - 5).$$

a. Show that the answer is correct by evaluating both
$x^2 - 2x - 15$ and $(x + 3)(x - 5)$ if:
i. $x = 3$;   ii. $x = -4$.
b. Which expression is easier to evaluate? $(x+3)(x-5)$ is easier to evaluate.

22. The answer to a multiplication problem is

$$(3x + 2)(x + 1) = 3x^2 + 5x + 2.$$

a. Show that the answer is correct by evaluating both
$(3x + 2)(x + 1)$ and $3x^2 + 5x + 2$ if:
i. $x = 4$;   ii. $x = -1$.
b. Which expression is easier to evaluate? $(3x+2)(x+1)$ is easier to evaluate.

Problems 21 and 22 reinforce the fact that the expanded form and the factored form really do stand for equal numbers. Students should find the factored form slightly easier to evaluate.

21. a. i. $-12 = -12$ **ii.** $9 = 9$

22. a. i. $70 = 70$ **ii.** $0 = 0$

10-2 | THE GREATEST COMMON FACTOR

In Section 10.1 you factored integers as products of primes. For instance,

$$108 = 2 \cdot 2 \cdot 3 \cdot 3 \cdot 3$$

$$120 = 2 \cdot 2 \cdot 2 \cdot 3 \cdot 5.$$

Since 2 is a factor of both 108 and 120, it is called a **common factor** of these two numbers. So are 3 and 6, as you can check by dividing 108 and 120 by 3 and by 6.

$$\frac{108}{3} = 36 \qquad \frac{108}{6} = 18$$

$$\frac{120}{3} = 40 \qquad \frac{120}{6} = 20$$

The quotient is an *integer*.

For what you will be doing next in algebra, it is important to find the *greatest* common factor (GCF) of two numbers.

DEFINITION

> **GREATEST COMMON FACTOR**
> The **greatest common factor** (GCF) of two positive integers a and b is the greatest integer for which
>
> $$a/\text{GCF} = \text{integer},$$
>
> and
>
> $$b/\text{GCF} = \text{integer}.$$

Time: $\frac{1}{2}$ day, with Section 10–1

Chalkboard Examples:

Find the GCF:
1. 18 and 24   Ans.: 6
2. 1500 and 360   Ans.:
$2 \cdot 2 \cdot 3 \cdot 5 = 60$
3. 24 and 55   Ans.: 1 (relatively prime)
4. x^3 and x^8 Ans.: x^3
5. y^6z^6 and y^5z^9 Ans.: y^5z^6
Conclusion: GCF has the power with the *smaller* exponent.
6. x^3y^5 and y^4z^6 Ans.: y^4
7. $24x^4y$ and $30x^3y^5$ Ans.: $6x^3y$
8. Two terms in
$15x^5 + 20xy^3$ Ans.: $5x$

Assignment:

Exercise 10–2, #1–49 odd or 2–50 even and Exercise 10–1, #3, 5, 11, 19, if not previously assigned

The GCF of two integers can be found by factoring them into primes. For 108 and 120 you would think

$$108 = 2 \cdot 2 \cdot 3 \cdot 3 \cdot 3$$

$$120 = 2 \cdot 2 \cdot 2 \cdot 3 \cdot 5$$

$$\therefore \text{GCF} = 2 \cdot 2 \cdot 3 = 12$$

The GCF is formed by multiplying all common prime factors as many times as they occur.

If two integers have *no* common prime factors, their GCF is 1. Such numbers are said to be **relatively prime.** For example,

$$10 = 2 \cdot 5$$

$$21 = 3 \cdot 7.$$

Both 10 and 21 are composite. But they have no *common* prime factors. Their GCF is 1.

Expressions with variables can have common factors, too. For instance,

$$x^5 = x \cdot x \cdot x \cdot x \cdot x$$

$$x^3 = x \cdot x \cdot x$$

$$\text{GCF} = x \cdot x \cdot x = x^3.$$

In this section you will practice finding the greatest common factor of given pairs of expressions.

Objective :

Given two integers or two expressions with powers of variables, write the greatest common factor of the expressions.

Cover the answers as you work these examples.

EXAMPLE 1

Find the GCF of 12 and 15.

– – – – –   – – – – –

Think These Reasons

GCF = 3 $12 = 2 \cdot 2 \cdot 3$ The 3s are common factors.

$15 = 3 \cdot 5$

EXAMPLE 2

Find the GCF of 540 and 2250.

$- - - - -$ $- - - - -$

$540 = 2 \cdot 2 \cdot 3 \cdot 3 \cdot 3 \cdot 5$ $2 \overline{)540}$ $2 \overline{)2250}$

$2250 = 2 \cdot 3 \cdot 3 \cdot 5 \cdot 5 \cdot 5$ $2 \overline{)270}$ $3 \overline{)1125}$

                               $3 \overline{)135}$ $3 \overline{)375}$

GCF $= 2 \cdot 3 \cdot 3 \cdot 5$ $3 \overline{)45}$ $5 \overline{)125}$

      $= \underline{\underline{90}}$ $3 \overline{)15}$ $5 \overline{)25}$

                                   5   5

EXAMPLE 3

Find the GCF of 32 and 45.

$- - - - -$ $- - - - -$

   $32 = 2 \cdot 2 \cdot 2 \cdot 2 \cdot 2$

   $45 = 3 \cdot 3 \cdot 5$

$\underline{\underline{\text{GCF} = 1}}$ 32 and 45 are relatively prime.

EXAMPLE 4

Find the GCF of y^7 and y^4.

$- - - - -$ $- - - - -$

   $y^7 = y \cdot y \cdot y \cdot y \cdot y \cdot y \cdot y$

   $y^4 = y \cdot y \cdot y \cdot y$

$\underline{\underline{\text{GCF} = y^4}}$

Note: You could do this problem more quickly by observing that the GCF always contains the power with the *smaller* exponent.

EXAMPLE 5

Find the GCF of $x^4 y^7$ and $x^5 y^3$.

$- - - - -$ $- - - - -$

$\underline{\underline{\text{GCF} = x^4 y^3}}$ $x^4 y^7 = x \cdot x \cdot x \cdot x \cdot y \cdot y \cdot y \cdot y \cdot y \cdot y \cdot y$

                          $x^5 y^3 = x \cdot x \cdot x \cdot x \cdot x \cdot y \cdot y \cdot y$

                          There are 4 common *x*-factors and 3 common *y*-factors.

EXAMPLE 6

Find the GCF of $x^7 y^5$ and $x^2 z^4$.

$$\text{GCF} = x^2$$

There are 2 common x-factors.
The y and z are not *common* factors.

EXAMPLE 7

Find the GCF of $24x^3y^5$ and $36x^4y$.

$$\text{GCF} = 12x^3y$$

The GCF of 24 and 36 is 12.
There are 3 common x-factors and 1 common y-factor.

EXAMPLE 8

Find the GCF of the two terms in $12x^3 - 18xy^2$.

$$\text{GCF} = 6x$$

The GCF of 12 and 18 is 6.
There is one common x-factor.
y is not a common factor.

ORAL PRACTICE

Give the GCF of these numbers. If the GCF is 1, also give *relatively prime*.

A. 8 and 12   4

B. 9 and 15   3

C. 10 and 15   5

D. 12 and 15   3

E. 12 and 16   4

F. 9 and 16   1 Rel. Prime

G. 4 and 10   2

H. 5 and 10   5

I. 6 and 10   2

J. 6 and 12   6

K. 6 and 15   3

L. 8 and 15   1 Rel. Prime

EXERCISE 10-2

1. (See text definition.)
2. Two numbers are relatively prime if they have no common prime factors. 15 and 14 are composite, but are relatively prime since they have no *common* prime factors.

1. Write from memory the definition of greatest common factor.

2. Tell what it means for two numbers to be relatively prime. Explain why two composite numbers can be relatively prime to each other.

For Problems 3 through 20, write the GCF of the given pair of numbers. Do the work mentally wherever possible. If the GCF equals 1, also write *relatively prime*.

Problem Notes:

Problems 3–50 parallel the examples.

3. 12 and 18   6

4. 16 and 20   4

5. 20 and 24   4

6. 24 and 30   6

7. 22 and 33   11

8. 18 and 21   3

9. 35 and 12   1, relatively prime

10. 22 and 9   1, relatively prime

11. 54 and 36   18

12. 56 and 32   8

13. 600 and 450   150

14. 252 and 588   84

15. 270 and 225   45

16. 315 and 189   63

17. 189 and 220   1, relatively prime

18. 225 and 308   1, relatively prime

19. 1000 and 1500   500

20. 2000 and 2100   100

For Problems 21 through 40, write the GCF of the two expressions.

21. x^5 and x^3 x^3

22. x^6 and x^5 x^5

23. a^7 and a^9 a^7

24. r^3 and r^7 r^3

25. b^6 and b^9 b^6

26. c^8 and c^{12} c^8

27. x^2y^3 and x^5y^2 x^2y^2

28. x^4y^2 and x^3y^7 x^3y^2

29. $r^{10}s^{11}$ and r^9s^{13} r^9s^{11}

30. $a^{12}h^{13}$ and a^9h^7 a^9h^7

31. $10x^6$ and $5x^4$ $5x^4$

32. $12x^5$ and $6x^8$ $6x^5$

33. $16m^2$ and $20m^3$ $4m^2$

34. $20m^4$ and $24m^3$ $4m^3$

35. $18a^3b^8$ and $21ab^6$ $3ab^6$

36. $18c^3d^4$ and $12c^6d$ $6c^3d$

37. $56c^3d^2$ and $32c^3e^2$ $8c^3$

38. $54x^4z^2$ and $36y^2z^3$ $18z^2$

39. $24x^2y^3z^4$ and $30x^5y^4z^3$ $6x^2y^3z^3$

40. $22a^3b^5c$ and $55ab^4c^7$ $11ab^4c$

For Problems 41 through 50, find the GCF of the two terms in the expression.

41. $6x^3 + 9x^2$ $3x^2$

42. $10x^2 + 15x^3$ $5x^2$

43. $4a^2 - 8a^5$ $4a^2$

44. $7b^5 - 14b^6$ $7b^5$

45. $3c^8 - 12c^5$ $3c^5$

46. $7d^9 - 21d^4$ $7d^4$

47. $10x^2y^4 + 15x^3y$ $5x^2y$

48. $8x^5y^2 + 12xy^3$ $4xy^2$

49. $x^{12} - x^8$ x^8

50. $y^{15} - y^{10}$ y^{10}

Problems 51–60 extend the GCF concept to three numbers, in anticipation of finding the GCF of the three terms of a trinomial to be factored in Section 10–3.

For Problems 51 through 60, find the GCF of the three numbers. In order to be a common factor, a number must be a factor of all three given numbers. If there are no factors common to all three, also write *relatively prime*.

51. 24, 18, and 42   6   52. 24, 32, and 40   8

53. 50, 75, and 60   5   54. 36, 54, and 60   6

55. 12, 15, and 35   1, relatively prime 56. 50, 65, and 39   1, relatively prime

57. 100, 120, and 150   10   58. 200, 300, and 250   50

59. 720, 108, and 1800   36   60. 324, 540, and 1080   108

10-3 | **FACTORING POLYNOMIALS THAT HAVE COMMON FACTORS**

Time: 1 day

Chalkboard Examples:

Factor completely.
1. $4x^2 + 28x + 40$
    Ans.: $4(x + 5)(x + 2)$
2. $6x^2 + 9x - 60$
    Ans.: $3(x + 4)(2x - 5)$
3. $5x^2 - 45y^2$
    Ans.: $5(x + 3y)(x - 3y)$
4. $2x^4 - 6x^3 - 20x^2$
    Ans.: $2x^2(x + 2)(x - 5)$
Use Oral Practice.

Assignment:

Exercise 10–3, #1–29 odd and
Exercise 10–2, #8, 18, 28, 38, 48 (for review)

Suppose you had to factor $4x^2 + 40x + 84$. The x^2-coefficient does not equal 1. So you might start by writing $(4x +$ $)(x +$ $)$ or $(2x +$ $)$ $(2x +$ $)$ and looking for the right factors of 84 to fill in the spaces.

However, if you *think* before you start to work, you will see that each term of $4x^2 + 40x + 84$ has 4 as a common factor. Using the distributive axiom, you can factor 4 from each term, as you did in Section 3.4.

$$4x^2 + 40x + 84$$
$$= 4(x^2 + 10x + 21)$$

The trinomial $x^2 + 10x + 21$ is much easier to factor than the original polynomial. You get

$$4(x + 3)(x + 7).$$

In this form the polynomial is said to be *completely factored*. The operations with fractions in the next chapter rely upon factoring polynomials completely.

TECHNIQUE

FIRST STEP IN FACTORING
The first step in factoring any polynomial is to factor the GCF of the terms from the polynomial.

Objective:
Given a polynomial whose terms have common factors, be able to factor the polynomial completely.

Cover the answers as you work these examples.

EXAMPLE 1

Factor completely: $3x^2 + 30x + 48$.

– – – – –   – – – – –

	Think These Reasons

$3x^2 + 30x + 48$ Write the given expression.

$= 3(x^2 + 10x + 16)$ Factor out the GCF of the three terms.

$= 3(x + 2)(x + 8)$ 2 and 8 are the two *factors* of 16 whose *sum* is 10.

EXAMPLE 2

Factor completely: $15x^2 - 5x - 10$.

– – – – –   – – – – –

$15x^2 - 5x - 10$ Write the given expression.

$= 5(3x^2 - x - 2)$ Factor out 5.

$= 5(3x + 2)(x - 1)$ First terms are $3x$ and x. Last terms, 2 and -1, give $-x$ and -2 when the binomials are multiplied.

EXAMPLE 3

Factor completely: $7x^2 - 63$.

– – – – –   – – – – –

$7x^2 - 63$ Write the given expression.

$= 7(x^2 - 9)$ Factor out 7.

$= 7(x + 3)(x - 3)$ Factor a difference of two squares. (See Section 5-7.)

EXAMPLE 4

Factor completely: $3x^5 + 6x^4y - 45x^3y^2$.

– – – – –   – – – – –

$$3x^5 + 6x^4y - 45x^3y^2 \qquad \text{Write the given expression.}$$

$$= 3x^3(x^2 + 2xy - 15y^2) \qquad \text{Factor out the GCF, } 3x^3. \text{ (The GCF may contain a variable!)}$$

$$= \underline{\underline{3x^3(x - 3y)(x + 5y)}} \qquad -3 \text{ and } 5 \text{ are two factors of } -15 \text{ whose sum is 2. (Do not forget } y \text{ in the second terms.)}$$

Problem Notes:

Throughout this chapter, problems should be assigned from previous sections along with ones from the current section. This strategy both helps students remember previous techniques and gives them old problems on which they can be successful if they have not yet mastered the new technique. The assignments for each section show a way this can be done.

   Problems 1–20 reduce to quadratic trinomials with the leading coefficient equal to 1.
   Problems 21–30 reduce to differences of two squares.
   Problems 31–40 are a mixture of the above.

1. $2(x + 3)(x + 5)$
2. $3(x + 5)(x + 2)$
3. $3(x + 6)(x + 4)$
4. $4(x + 3)(x + 4)$
5. $4(x - 2)(x + 3)$
6. $5(x + 8)(x - 1)$
7. $5(r - 7)(r + 5)$
8. $10(s - 7)(s + 3)$
9. $2(x + 3y)(x + 4y)$
10. $2(x + 2y)(x + 4y)$
11. $6(x - 3)(x - 1)$
12. $6(x - 5)(x - 4)$
13. $10(s + 12)(s - 1)$
14. $8(p + 6)(p - 2)$
15. $8(a - 5b)(a + 3b)$
16. $7(r - 8s)(r + 2s)$
17. $x^2(x - 6)(x - 2)$
18. $x^4(x - 6)(x - 3)$
19. $2c^3(c - 1)(c + 4)$
20. $3a^3(a + 5)(a - 1)$
21. $4(x + 5)(x - 5)$
22. $2(x + 7)(x - 7)$
23. $5(x + 6)(x - 6)$

ORAL PRACTICE

Give the result of factoring out the GCF.

EXAMPLE

                                  Answer
$2x^3 + 6x^2 - 8x$ $2x$ times the quantity $x^2 + 3x - 4$.

A. $3x^2 + 12x + 9$ $3(x^2 + 4x + 3)$ B. $4x^2 + 8x + 20$ $4(x^2 + 2x + 5)$

C. $4x^2 + 10x + 20$ $2(2x^2 + 5x + 10)$ D. $6x^2 + 9x + 30$ $3(2x^2 + 3x + 10)$

E. $6x^2 + 8x + 30$ $2(3x^2 + 4x + 15)$ F. $7x^2 - 14x + 28$ $7(x^2 - 2x + 4)$

G. $x^3 - 4x^2 + 3x$ $x(x^2 - 4x + 3)$ H. $y^3 + 8y^2 - 7y$ $y(y^2 + 8y - 7)$

I. $x^5 + 7x^4 + 9x^3$ $x^3(x^2 + 7x + 9)$ J. $a^8 - 5a^7 - 4a^6$ $a^6(a^2 - 5a - 4)$

K. $x^3y^3 - xy$ $xy(x^2y^2 - 1)$ L. $x^3y - xy^3$ $xy(x^2 - y^2)$

EXERCISE 10-3

Factor completely.

1. $2x^2 + 16x + 30$ 2. $3x^2 + 21x + 30$

3. $3x^2 + 30x + 72$ 4. $4x^2 + 28x + 48$

5. $4x^2 + 4x - 24$ 6. $5x^2 + 35x - 40$

7. $5r^2 - 10r - 175$ 8. $10s^2 - 40s - 210$

9. $2x^2 + 14xy + 24y^2$ 10. $2x^2 + 12xy + 16y^2$

11. $6x^2 - 24x + 18$ 12. $6x^2 - 54x + 120$

13. $10s^2 + 110s - 120$ 14. $8p^2 + 32p - 96$

15. $8a^2 - 16ab - 120b^2$ 16. $7r^2 - 42rs - 112s^2$

17. $x^4 - 8x^3 + 12x^2$

18. $x^6 - 9x^5 + 18x^4$

19. $2c^5 + 6c^4 - 8c^3$

20. $3a^5 + 12a^4 - 15a^3$

21. $4x^2 - 100$

22. $2x^2 - 98$

23. $5x^2 - 180$

24. $10x^2 - 250$

25. $7x^3 - 7x$

26. $11a^3 - 11a$

27. $10x^2 - 90y^2$

28. $3x^2 - 27y^2$

29. $x^3y - xy^3$

30. $r^3s - rs^3$

31. $6x^2 - 48x + 96$

32. $7x^2 - 70x + 175$

33. $2m^2 + 20mp + 50p^2$

34. $9b^2 + 72bc + 144c^2$

35. $3ax^2 + 36ax + 60a$

36. $5dx^2 + 50dx + 80d$

37. $6c^2x^2 - 600d^2x^2$

38. $8p^2x^2 - 392p^2s^2$

39. $2x^4y^3 - 18x^3y^4 - 72x^2y^5$

40. $3x^6y^2 - 15x^5y^3 - 150x^4y^4$

41. $6x^2 + 21x + 15$

42. $6x^2 + 44x + 14$

43. $15x^2 + 40x - 15$

44. $12x^2 + 18x - 30$

45. $20e^2 - 28e + 8$

46. $15c^2 - 48c + 9$

47. $18x^2 - 24xy - 24y^2$

48. $16x^2 - 24xy - 72y^2$

49. $4y^6 - 18y^5 + 8y^4$

50. $15z^5 - 65z^4 + 20z^3$

24. $10(x + 5)(x - 5)$
25. $7x(x + 1)(x - 1)$
26. $11a(a + 1)(a - 1)$
27. $10(x + 3y)(x - 3y)$
28. $3(x + 3y)(x - 3y)$
29. $xy(x + y)(x - y)$
30. $rs(r + s)(r - s)$
31. $6(x - 4)^2$
32. $7(x - 5)^2$
33. $2(m + 5p)^2$
34. $9(b + 4c)^2$

Problems 41–50 reduce to quadratic trinomials with the leading coefficient greater than 1.

35. $3a(x + 10)(x + 2)$
36. $5d(x + 8)(x + 2)$
37. $6x^2(c + 10d)(c - 10d)$
38. $8p^2(x + 7s)(x - 7s)$
39. $2x^2y^3(x - 12y)(x + 3y)$
40. $3x^4y^2(x - 10y)(x + 5y)$
41. $3(2x + 5)(x + 1)$
42. $2(3x + 1)(x + 7)$
43. $5(3x - 1)(x + 3)$
44. $6(2x + 5)(x - 1)$
45. $4(5e - 2)(e - 1)$
46. $3(5c - 1)(c - 3)$
47. $6(3x + 2y)(x - 2y)$
48. $8(2x + 3y)(x - 3y)$
49. $2y^4(2y - 1)(y - 4)$
50. $5z^3(3z - 1)(z - 4)$

Time: 2 days

Chalkboard Examples:

First day:
Factor completely.
1. $(x + 3)x + (x + 3)(7)$
   Ans.: $(x + 3)(x + 7)$
2. $x(x - 4) + 5(x - 4)$
   Ans.: $(x - 4)(x + 5)$
   Note: Preferred order of factors has the expression factored out written *first*. This form helps students see that what they are actually doing is removing a common factor and not simply rearranging parentheses.
3. $4c(5p - 2) - 7d(5p - 2)$
   Ans.: $(5p - 2)(4c - 7d)$
4. $5x(x - 2) + (x - 2)$
   Ans.: $(x - 2)(5x + 1)$
   Note: Factoring $(x - 2)$ out of $(x - 2)$ leaves 1.
5. $(x^2)(3x - 7) - 16(3x - 7)$
   Ans.: $(3x - 7)(x + 2)(x - 2)$
Do Oral Practice.

<table>
<tr><td>10-4</td><td>COMMON BINOMIAL FACTORS</td></tr>
</table>

You have learned how to use the distributive properties to factor out common factors. For instance,

$$3x + 12 = 3(x + 4).$$

The number 3 is a common factor of each term. Sometimes, terms of an expression have common factors that are binomials, such as in

$$(x - 5)x + (x - 5)(4).$$

In this case the binomial $(x - 5)$ is a common factor of each term. It can be factored out in the same way 3 was in the first example.

$$(x - 5)x + (x - 5)(4)$$
$$= (x - 5)(x + 4).$$

Factoring $(x - 5)$ out of the first term leaves x and factoring $(x - 5)$ out of the second term leaves 4. So the other factor is $(x + 4)$, just as it was in the first example.

Second day:
Homework problems at the board.
Work one of Problems 32–50 even as an example.

Assignments:

Day 1: Exercise 10–4, #1–29 odd,
        Exercise 10–3, #31–39 odd, and
        Exercise 10–2, #20, 40
Day 2: Exercise 10–4, #31–53 odd,
        Exercise 10–3, #41–49 odd, and
        Exercise 10–2, #51

Objective :

Be able to factor a polynomial that has common binomial factors.

Cover the answers as you work these examples.

EXAMPLE 1

Factor $(x + 7)x - (x + 7)(12)$.

– – – – –   – – – – –

Think These Reasons

$(x + 7)x - (x + 7)(12)$ Write the given expression.

$= (x + 7)(x - 12)$ Factor out $(x + 7)$ from each term. x remains from one term and -12 remains from the other.

EXAMPLE 2

Factor $x(x - 2) + 6(x - 2)$.

– – – – –   – – – – –

$x(x - 2) + 6(x - 2)$ Write the given expression.

$= (x - 2)(x + 6)$ Factor out $(x - 2)$ from each term. x remains from one term and 6 remains from the other.

EXAMPLE 3

Factor $2a(3r + 5) - 7b(3r + 5)$.

– – – – –   – – – – –

$2a(3r + 5) - 7b(3r + 5)$ Write the given expression.

$= (3r + 5)(2a - 7b)$ Factor out $(3r + 5)$. $2a$ remains from one term and $-7b$ remains from the other.

EXAMPLE 4

Factor $3x(5x - 8) - (5x - 8)$.

– – – – –   – – – – –

$3x(5x - 8) - (5x - 8)$ Write the given expression.

$= (5x - 8)(3x - 1)$ Factor out $(5x - 8)$. $3x$ remains from one term. -1 remains from the other, because $-(5x - 8) \div (5x - 8)$ equals -1.

EXAMPLE 5

Factor completely: $x^2(2x + 5) - 36(2x + 5)$.

– – – – –   – – – – –

$x^2(2x + 5) - 36(2x + 5)$ Write the given expression.

$= (2x + 5)(x^2 - 36)$ Factor out $(2x + 5)$.

$= \underline{\underline{(2x + 5)(x + 6)(x - 6)}}$ Factor $x^2 - 36$ as a difference of two squares. Each factor is now prime, so the expression is factored completely.

ORAL PRACTICE

Give the common binomial factor.

EXAMPLES

Answers

i. $(x + 5)x + (x + 5)y$ ii.   The quantity $x + 5$.

ii. $(x + 6)x + (x + 5)y$ ii.   No common factors.

A. $(x + 3)x + (x + 3)y$ $(x + 3)$ B. $(x - 7)x + (x - 7)y$ $(x - 7)$

C. $a(x + 2) - b(x + 2)$ $(x + 2)$ D. $c(x - 4) - d(x - 4)$ $(x - 4)$

E. $k(x - 6) + (x - 6)p$ $(x - 6)$ F. $(x + 9)j - k(x + 9)$ $(x + 9)$

G. $(x - 3)y + (x - 4)z$ H. $(x + 5)r - (x - 5)s$ No common factors   G.   No common factors

I. $x(x - 1) + 6(x - 1)$ $(x - 1)$ J. $x(x + 8) - 7(x + 8)$ $(x + 8)$

K. $(x + 2)(x + 3) + 5(x + 2)$ L. $(x - 4)(x - 1) - 6(x - 1)$ $(x - 1)$ K. $(x + 2)$

EXERCISE 10-4

For Problems 1 through 30, factor the polynomial completely.

1. $(x + 2)x + (x + 2)(10)$ 2. $(x + 3)x + (x + 3)(5)$

3. $(x - 5)x - (x - 5)(8)$ 4. $(x - 7)x + (x - 7)(9)$

5. $x(x + 4) - 7(x + 4)$ 6. $x(x + 8) - 2(x + 8)$

7. $3x(x - 21) + 4(x - 21)$ 8. $5x(x - 6) + 3(x - 6)$

9. $6r(2r - 9) - 3(2r - 9)$ 10. $6b(3s - 2) - 4(3s - 2)$

11. $7a(4a + b) - 6(4a + b)$ 12. $4p(3p + j) - 7(3p + j)$

Problem Notes:

Problems 1–30 are similar to the examples.
  Problems 31–50 involve the same concept in a more complicated setting.

1. $(x + 2)(x + 10)$ 2. $(x + 3)(x + 5)$
3. $(x - 5)(x - 8)$ 4. $(x - 7)(x + 9)$
5. $(x + 4)(x - 7)$ 6. $(x + 8)(x - 2)$
7. $(x - 21)(3x + 4)$ 8. $(x - 6)(5x + 3)$
9. $3(2r - 9)(2r - 1)$ 10. $2(3s - 2)(3b - 2)$
11. $(4a + b)(7a - 6)$ 12. $(3p + j)(4p - 7)$

13. $(3x - 1)(12 + x)$
14. $(2x - 5)(13 + x)$
15. $(x + 3)(6x + 1)$
16. $(x - 4)(3x + 1)$
17. $(8m - 5)(m - 1)$
18. $(6k - 1)(k - 1)$
19. $(3x - 7)(1 + 2x)$
20. $(4x - 5)(1 + 3x)$
21. $(x - j)(p - k)$
22. $(r + c)(y - k)$
23. $(x + 4)(x + 3)(x - 3)$
24. $(x - 7)(x + 7)(x - 7)$
25. $(r - 5)(a + b)(a - b)$
26. $(s - 2)(c + d)(c - d)$
27. $(a + 2)(a - 2)(x + y)(x - y)$
28. $(y + 5)(y - 5)(x + z)(x - z)$
29. $(4 + r)(4 - r)(x + 1)(x - 1)$
30. $(3 + v)(3 - v)(x + 1)(x - 1)$
31. $(x + 3)(2x - 5)$
32. $(x + 2)(2x - 3)$
33. $2(2x - 7)(x + 3)$
34. $2(3x - 5)(x + 2)$
35. $(3a + 4)(5x - 3)$
36. $(2r + 11)(x - 4)$
37. $(x + 7)(x + 2)(x + 3)$
38. $(x - 4)(x + 2)(x + 7)$
39. $(2x - 1)(x + 1)(x - 4)$
40. $(5x + 1)(x - 1)(x - 2)$
41. $(5y - z)(x - 2)(x - 10)$
42. $(a - 2b)(x - 2)(x - 5)$
43. $(x + 1)(x + 5)(x + 2)$
44. $(x + 4)(x - 7)(x - 3)$
45. $(x - 3)^3$ **46.** $(x + 2)^3$
47. $x(x + 3)(x + 5)(x - 5)$
48. $x^3(x - 7)(x + 3)(x - 3)$
49. $x(x + 2)(x + 1)$
50. $x(x - 3)(x + 3)$

13. $12(3x - 1) + x(3x - 1)$ **14.** $13(2x - 5) + x(2x - 5)$

15. $6x(x + 3) + (x + 3)$ **16.** $3x(x - 4) + (x - 4)$

17. $m(8m - 5) - (8m - 5)$ **18.** $k(6k - 1) - (6k - 1)$

19. $(3x - 7) + 2x(3x - 7)$ **20.** $(4x - 5) + 3x(4x - 5)$

21. $p(x - j) - k(x - j)$ **22.** $y(r + c) - k(r + c)$

23. $x^2(x + 4) - 9(x + 4)$ **24.** $x^2(x - 7) - 49(x - 7)$

25. $a^2(r - 5) - b^2(r - 5)$ **26.** $c^2(s - 2) - d^2(s - 2)$

27. $x^2(a^2 - 4) - y^2(a^2 - 4)$ **28.** $x^2(y^2 - 25) - z^2(y^2 - 25)$

29. $x^2(16 - r^2) - (16 - r^2)$ **30.** $x^2(9 - v^2) - (9 - v^2)$

For Problems 31 through 50, factor out the common polynomial factor and simplify the result as much as possible. Factor further, if possible.

31. $x(x + 3) + (x - 5)(x + 3)$ **32.** $x(x + 2) + (x - 3)(x + 2)$

33. $x(2x - 7) + (2x - 7)(x + 6)$ **34.** $x(3x - 5) + (3x - 5)(x + 4)$

35. $(3a + 4)(5x - 2) - (3a + 4)$ **36.** $(2r + 11)(x - 3) - (2r + 11)$

37. $x^2(x + 7) + (5x + 6)(x + 7)$ **38.** $x^2(x - 4) + (9x + 14)(x - 4)$

39. $x^2(2x - 1) - (2x - 1)(3x + 4)$ **40.** $x^2(5x + 1) - (5x + 1)(3x - 2)$

41. $x^2(5y - z) - (12x - 20)(5y - z)$

42. $x^2(a - 2b) - (7x - 10)(a - 2b)$

43. $x(x^2 + 6x + 5) + 2(x^2 + 6x + 5)$

44. $x(x^2 - 3x - 28) - 3(x^2 - 3x - 28)$

45. $x(x^2 - 6x + 9) - 3(x^2 - 6x + 9)$

46. $x(x^2 + 4x + 4) + 2(x^2 + 4x + 4)$

47. $x^3(x + 3) - 25x(x + 3)$

48. $x^5(x - 7) - 9x^3(x - 7)$

49. $(x + 2)(x^2 + x + 1) - (x + 2)$

50. $(x - 3)(x^2 + 3x + 1) - (x - 3)$

For Problems 51 through 60, factor the polynomials (if necessary). Then give the greatest common factor (GCF) of the two polynomials.

EXAMPLE

$(x + 4)(x - 1)$ and $(x - 1)(x + 2)$
GCF $= (x - 1)$

51. $x^2 + 3x + 2$ and $x + 1$

52. $x^2 + 5x + 6$ and $x + 3$

53. $x^2 + 2x - 8$ and $x^2 - 3x + 2$

54. $x^2 - 7x + 10$ and $x^2 - x - 2$

55. $x^2 - x - 6$ and $x^2 + x - 6$

56. $x^2 - 7x + 12$ and $x^2 + 3x - 4$

57. $x^2 - 9$ and $x^2 + 2x - 15$

58. $x^2 - 25$ and $x^2 - 8x + 15$

59. $(x + 1)(x - 2)(x + 3)$ and $(x + 1)(x + 3)(x - 5)$

60. $(x + 2)(x - 2)(x - 7)$ and $(x - 7)(x + 7)(x - 2)$

Problems 51–60 anticipate the techniques needed for operations with algebraic fractions in Chapter 11.

Problems 55 and 56 have factors that are conjugates but that have no common factors.

51. $(x + 1)$ **52.** $(x + 3)$
53. $(x - 2)$ **54.** $(x - 2)$
55. 1 (Relatively prime)
56. 1 (Relatively prime)
57. $(x - 3)$ **58.** $(x - 5)$
59. $(x + 3)(x + 1)$ **60.** $(x - 7)(x - 2)$

10-5   FACTORING BY GROUPING (ASSOCIATING)

In the last section you learned how to factor polynomials that have common binomial factors, such as

$$2a(3r + 5) - 7b(3r + 5)$$

$$= (3r + 5)(2a - 7b).$$

Suppose that you are asked to factor

$$6ar + 10a - 21br - 35b.$$

The first two terms have $2a$ as a common factor. The last two terms have $-7b$ as a common factor. Associating terms and then doing the factoring gives

$6ar + 10a - 21br - 35b$	Given expression.
$= (6ar + 10a) + (-21br - 35b)$	Associate terms.
$= 2a(3r + 5) - 7b(3r + 5)$	Factor out $2a$ and $-7b$.
$= (3r + 5)(2a - 7b).$	Factor out $(3r + 5)$.

As you can see, the next-to-last line is the same as the first example. All that is new is associating pairs of terms and factoring out their greatest common factor. This technique is called **factoring by grouping,** or **factoring by associating**.

Objective :
Given a polynomial with four terms, be able to factor it by grouping (associating).

Cover the answers as you work these examples.

EXAMPLE 1

Factor completely: $x^2 + 2x + xy + 2y$.

– – – – –

Time: 3 days, including test

Chalkboard Examples:

First day:
Factor completely, by grouping.
1. $x^2 + 3x + xz + 3z$
    Ans.: $(x + 3)(x + z)$
    Note: See note for Section 10–4 concerning preferred order of factors.

2. $10x^2 - 15bx - 14ex + 21be$
    Ans.: $(2x - 3b)(5x - 7e)$

3. $xy + 2y - x - 2$
    Ans.: $(x + 2)(y - 1)$
    Note: Factor out -1 from the last two terms.

4. $x^3 - 2x^2 - 25x + 50$
    Ans.: $(x - 2)(x + 5)(x - 5)$

5. $6x^2 + 8x + 15x + 20$
    Ans.: $(3x + 4)(2x + 5)$
    Note: Anticipates splitting the middle term in Section 10–6.

Do Oral Practice.

Second day:
Review in preparation for test.

Third day:
Test.

Assignments:

Day 1: Exercise 10–5, #1–19 odd,
         Exercise 10–4, #18, 28, 38, 48, 54,
         and Exercise 10–3, #20

Day 2: In preparation for test:
         Exercise 10–5, #21–35 odd,
         Exercise 10–4, #30, 40, 55,

Exercise 10–3, #30, and
Exercise 10–2, #36, 53
Day 3: After test: Exercise 10–5, #37, 39, 41

	Think These Reasons

$x^2 + 2x + xy + 2y$ — Write the given expression.

$= x(x + 2) + y(x + 2)$ — Factor x from $x^2 + 2x$ and factor y from $xy + 2y$.

$= \underline{\underline{(x + 2)(x + y)}}$ — Factor out $(x + 2)$.

EXAMPLE 2

Factor completely: $15x^2 - 6ax - 20cx + 8ac$.

– – – – –   – – – – –

$15x^2 - 6ax - 20cx - 8ac$ — Write the given expression.

$= 3x(5x - 2a) - 4c(5x - 2a)$ — Factor $3x$ from $15x^2 - 6ax$ and factor $-4c$ from $-20cx + 8ac$. (When you factor $-4c$ out of $+8ac$, you get $-2a$, not $+2a$!)

$= \underline{\underline{(5x - 2a)(3x - 4c)}}$ — Factor out $(5x - 2a)$.

EXAMPLE 3

Factor completely: $ax + 3a + x + 3$.

– – – – –   – – – – –

$ax + 3a + x + 3$ — Write the given expression.

$= a(x + 3) + 1(x + 3)$ — Factor a from $ax + 3a$ and factor 1 from $x + 3$.

$= \underline{\underline{(x + 3)(a + 1)}}$ — Factor out $(x + 3)$.

EXAMPLE 4

Factor completely: $x^3 - 5x^2 - 9x + 45$.

– – – – –   – – – – –

$x^3 - 5x^2 - 9x + 45$ — Write the given expression.

$= x^2(x - 5) - 9(x - 5)$ — Factor x^2 from $x^3 - 5x^2$ and factor -9 from $-9x + 45$.

$= (x - 5)(x^2 - 9)$ — Factor out $(x - 5)$.

$= \underline{\underline{(x - 5)(x + 3)(x - 3)}}$ — To factor completely, factor $x^2 - 9$ as a difference of two squares.

EXAMPLE 5

Factor completely: $15x^2 - 12x + 10x - 8$.

– – – – –   – – – – –

$$15x^2 - 12x + 10x - 8$$

Write the given expression.

$$= 3x(5x - 4) + 2(5x - 4)$$

Factor $3x$ from $15x^2 - 12x$ and factor 2 from $10x - 8$. Do *not* combine like terms.

$$= \underline{\underline{(5x - 4)(3x + 2)}}$$

Factor out $(5x - 4)$.

ORAL PRACTICE

Tell what you would factor out of the first two terms and what you would factor out of the last two terms to factor by grouping.

EXAMPLES

                                    Answers
i. $3ax + ab - 6x - 2b$ i. $a, -2$
ii. $6x - 2c - 3x + c$ ii. $2, -1$

A. $ax + bx + ay + by$ x and y B. $x^2 + xy + xz + yz$ x and z
C. $ax - 2x + ay - 2y$ x and y D. $3x - 3y - ax + ay$ 3 and $-a$
E. $ac + bc - a^2 - ab$ c and $-a$ F. $a^2c + a^2d + b^2c + b^2d$ a^2 and b^2
G. $x^3 + 3x^2 + 2x + 6$ x^2 and 2 H. $x^3 - 5x^2 - 3x + 15$ x^2 and -3
I. $2a + ax - 2x^2 - x^3$ a and $-x^2$ J. $x^2 - 2x + xy - 2y$ x and y
K. $5ax + 10a - x - 2$ $5a$ and -1 L. $6a^2 + 5ab + 6a + 5b$ a and 1

EXERCISE 10-5

In Problems 1 through 34, factor the polynomial completely.

1. $a^2 + 3a + ab + 3b$
2. $r^2 + 7r + rc + 7c$
3. $8x^2 + 12xy + 10xz + 15yz$
4. $15x^2 + 20xy + 18nx + 24ny$
5. $bx + 3cx - 2br - 6cr$
6. $ax + 4ex - 3ad - 12de$
7. $6ax - 14x + 15a - 35$
8. $9hx - 21x + 6h - 14$
9. $mc - 6cv - 5m + 30v$
10. $rv - 2vx - 6r + 12x$
11. $x^2 + 5xy + x + 5y$
12. $x^2 + 8xz + x + 8z$
13. $5rz + 2sz - 5r - 2s$
14. $6dt + 5ct - 6d - 5c$

Problem Notes:

Problems 1–34 combine all of the factoring techniques students have been learning in this chapter—in particular, factoring out common monomial and binomial factors.

1. $(a + 3)(a + b)$
2. $(r + 7)(r + c)$
3. $(2x + 3y)(4x + 5z)$
4. $(3x + 4y)(5x + 6n)$
5. $(b + 3c)(x - 2r)$
6. $(a + 4e)(x - 3d)$
7. $(3a - 7)(2x + 5)$
8. $(3h - 7)(3x + 2)$
9. $(m - 6v)(c - 5)$
10. $(r - 2x)(v - 6)$
11. $(x + 5y)(x + 1)$
12. $(x + 8z)(x + 1)$
13. $(5r + 2s)(z - 1)$
14. $(6d + 5c)(t - 1)$

15. $2(5b + 6)(3a + 7)$
16. $3(2x + 3)(4m + 5)$
17. $(2x - 3)(x^2 - 2)$
18. $(2x - 3)(5x^2 + 1)$
19. $(4x + 15)(3x^2 + 8)$
20. $(2x - 7)(x^2 - 5)$
21. $3(4x - 3)(2x^2 + 5)$
22. $4(2x - 5)(8x^2 + 3)$
23. $(2x + 1)(x + 3)(x - 3)$
24. $(3x + 1)(x + 5)(x - 5)$
25. $5(x - 2)(x + 4)(x - 4)$
26. $6(x - 1)(x + 2)(x - 2)$
27. $(2x + 3)(6x + 5)$
28. $(5x + 7)(3x + 5)$
29. $(2x - 3)(x + 7)$
30. $(4x - 3)(2x + 3)$
31. $(5x - 2)(3x + 1)$
32. $(8x - 5)(2x + 1)$
33. $(8x - 3)(x - 1)$
34. $(10x - 7)(x - 1)$

Problems 35–50 are suitable for better students. They involve grouping the terms in ways other than 2 and 2.

35. $(x + 3 + y)(x + 3 - y)$
36. $(x + 4 + c)(x + 4 - c)$
37. $(x - 5 + 3a)(x - 5 - 3a)$
38. $(x - 7 + 4y)(x - 7 - 4y)$
39. $(x + y + 4)(x - y - 4)$
40. $(x + a + 5)(x - a - 5)$
41. $(5x + a - 2)(5x - a + 2)$
42. $(10x + y - 3)(10x - y + 3)$
43. $(x - 5 + 7c)(x - 5 - 7c)$
44. $(x - 4 + 5b)(x - 4 - 5b)$
45. $(x + 3)(x + 2 - a)$
46. $(x + 4)(x + 5 - r)$
47. $(x + 3)(x - 1 + r)$
48. $(x + 5)(x - 1 + s)$
49. $(x + 5)(3s + x - 2)$
50. $(x + 3)(2m + x - 2)$
51. $(x - 2)(x^3 + x + 5)$
52. $(x - 5)(x^3 + x + 6)$
53. $(x + 5)(c(x + 3) + d(x - 7))$
54. $(x + 2)(u(x + 7) + z(x - 5))$

15. $30ab + 36a + 70b + 84$

16. $24mx + 36m + 30x + 45$

17. $2x^3 - 3x^2 - 4x + 6$

18. $10x^3 - 15x^2 + 2x - 3$

19. $12x^3 + 45x^2 + 32x + 120$

20. $2x^3 - 7x^2 - 10x + 35$

21. $24x^3 - 18x^2 + 60x - 45$

22. $64x^3 - 160x^2 + 24x - 60$

23. $2x^3 + x^2 - 18x - 9$

24. $3x^3 + x^2 - 75x - 25$

25. $5x^3 - 10x^2 - 80x + 160$

26. $6x^3 - 6x^2 - 24x + 24$

27. $12x^2 + 18x + 10x + 15$

28. $15x^2 + 21x + 25x + 35$

29. $2x^2 - 3x + 14x - 21$

30. $8x^2 - 6x + 12x - 9$

31. $15x^2 - 6x + 5x - 2$

32. $16x^2 - 10x + 8x - 5$

33. $8x^2 - 3x - 8x + 3$

34. $10x^2 - 7x - 10x + 7$

In Problems 35 through 54, some of the polynomials can be arranged in groups of three terms and one term, or one term and three terms. For instance,

$$x^2 + 6x + 9 - y^2 = (x + 3)^2 - y^2,$$

which is a difference of two squares. Other polynomials have more than four terms. For instance,

$$x^2 + 5x + 6 - ax - 3a = (x + 3)(x + 2) - a(x + 3),$$

which has $(x + 3)$ as a common binomial factor. Factor each of these polynomials completely.

35. $x^2 + 6x + 9 - y^2$

36. $x^2 + 8x + 16 - c^2$

37. $x^2 - 10x + 25 - 9a^2$

38. $x^2 - 14x + 49 - 16y^2$

39. $x^2 - (y^2 + 8y + 16)$

40. $x^2 - (a^2 + 10a + 25)$

41. $25x^2 - a^2 + 4a - 4$

42. $100x^2 - y^2 + 6y - 9$

43. $x^2 - 10x + 25 - 49c^2$

44. $x^2 - 8x + 16 - 25b^2$

45. $x^2 + 5x + 6 - ax - 3a$

46. $x^2 + 9x + 20 - rx - 4r$

47. $x^2 + 2x - 3 + rx + 3r$

48. $x^2 + 4x - 5 + sx + 5s$

49. $3sx + 15s + x^2 + 3x - 10$

50. $2mx + 6m + x^2 + x - 6$

51. $x^4 - 2x^3 + x^2 + 3x - 10$

52. $x^4 - 5x^3 + x^2 + x - 30$

53. $cx^2 + 8cx + 15c + dx^2 - 2dx - 35d$

54. $ux^2 + 9ux + 14u + zx^2 - 3zx - 10z$

10-6 | FACTORING HARDER QUADRATIC TRINOMIALS

Suppose you have to factor

$$6x^2 + 31x + 35.$$

There are so many possible factors to try that you could spend a whole evening on one set of problems! What you need is a systematic way to factor these harder quadratic trinomials.

In Problems 27 through 34 of the last section, you factored polynomials like

$$6x^2 + 10x + 21x + 35$$

by grouping. Associating the first two terms and the last two terms gives

$$(6x^2 + 10x) + (21x + 35).$$

Factoring out $2x$ from $6x^2 + 10x$ and 7 from $21x + 35$ gives

$$2x(3x + 5) + 7(3x + 5).$$

Now, $(3x + 5)$ is a common binomial factor and can be factored out, giving

$$(3x + 5)(2x + 7).$$

Suppose that you have to factor the quadratic trinomial

$$6x^2 + 31x + 35.$$

If you could split the middle term, $31x$, into $10x + 21x$, you could factor as above. Observe that $(10)(21)$ equals 210, and that $(6)(35)$ also equals 210. This is true because when you multiply $(3x + 5)(2x + 7)$, you get

$$(3x + 5)(2x + 7) = (3 \cdot 2)x^2 + (5 \cdot 2)x + (3 \cdot 7)x + (5 \cdot 7).$$

$$5, \quad 2, \quad 3, \quad 7$$
$$3, \quad 2, \quad 5, \quad 7$$

All four coefficients—3, 2, 5, and 7—appear in the 6 and 35. All four also appear in the 10 and 21. So 10 and 21 are two *factors* of 210 that *add* up to 31. To factor

$$6x^2 + 31x + 35$$

from scratch, you would first *multiply* (6)(35), getting 210. Then you would look for *other* factors of 210—specifically, factors that add up to 31. A systematic way of looking for these factors is to make a table.

Time: 0 or 2 days (optional section)

Chalkboard Examples:

First day:
To introduce the technique, use text example $6x^2 + 31x + 35 = (3x + 5)(2x + 7)$, or other trinomial-giving factors with four relatively prime coefficients. Then have students try:

$$2x^2 + 11x + 15$$
$$= 2x^2 + 5x + 6x + 15$$
$$= x(2x + 5) + 3(2x + 5)$$
$$= (2x + 5)(x + 3)$$

From here on, the most effective strategy is to let students start on their homework in class. Give enough time for them to get at least through Problem 7 in class so they can discover for themselves what to do when negative signs appear. If possible, students should reach 11 before leaving class to encounter a problem that is prime.

Second day:
Homework at the board.
Have students work Examples 5 and 6 to recognize those easier to do mentally.
Oral Practice can be used here.

Assignments:

Day 1: Exercise 10–6, #1–19 odd and
        Exercise 10–5, #20, 30
Day 2: Exercise 10–6, #2–10 even and
        Exercise 10–6, #21–29 odd, and
        Exercise 10–5, #22, 32

Factors	Sum	31?
1, 210	211	No.
2, 105	107	No.
3, 70	73	No.
5, 42	47	No.
6, 35	41	No.
7, 30	37	No.
10, 21	31	Yes!

So you split the middle term, $31x$, into $10x + 21x$, write

$$6x^2 + 10x + 21x + 35,$$

and factor by grouping as shown above.

TECHNIQUE

SPLITTING THE MIDDLE TERM
To factor a quadratic trinomial of the form

$$ax^2 + bx + c:$$

1. Multiply a by c.

2. Look for two factors of ac whose sum is b.

3. Split the middle term and factor by grouping.

(If there are *no* factors of ac whose sum is b, then $ax^2 + bx + c$ is *prime*.)

You should always be alert for easier ways of working problems. For instance,

$$3x^2 + 5x + 2$$

is easy to factor by inspection, without splitting the middle term. You just write empty parentheses and then fill in the binomials that give $3x^2 + 5x + 2$ when they are multiplied back together.

$$3x^2 + 5x + 2$$
$$= (3x + 2)(x + 1)$$

Objective:
Given a quadratic trinomial, such as $6x^2 + 31x + 35$, factor it by inspection or by splitting the middle term.

Cover the answers as you work the examples.

EXAMPLE 1

Factor $8x^2 + 26x + 15$.

– – – – –   – – – – –

	Think These Reasons
$(8)(15) = 120$	Multiply the x^2-coefficient by the constant term.
$1 + 120 = 121$	Seek two factors of 120 whose sum is
$2 + 60 = 62$	26.
$3 + 40 = 43$	
$4 + 30 = 34$	
$5 + 24 = 29$	
$6 + 20 = 26$ This is it!	
$8x^2 + 26x + 15$	Write the given expression.
$= 8x^2 + 6x + 20x + 15$	Split the middle term.
$= 2x(4x + 3) + 5(4x + 3)$	Factor $2x$ from $8x^2 + 6x$ and factor 5 from $20x + 15$.
$= \underline{\underline{(4x + 3)(2x + 5)}}$	Factor out $(4x + 3)$.

EXAMPLE 2

Factor $18x^2 - 23x - 6$.

– – – – –   – – – – –

$(18)(-6) = -108$	Multiply the x^2-coefficient by the constant term.
$1 - 108 = -107$	Seek two factors of -108 whose sum is
$2 - 54 = -52$	-23.
$3 - 36 = -33$	
$4 - 27 = -23$ This is it!	
$18x^2 - 23x - 6$	Write the given expression.
$= 18x^2 + 4x - 27x - 6$	Split the middle term
$= 2x(9x + 2) - 3(9x + 2)$	Factor out $2x$ and -3.
$= \underline{\underline{(9x + 2)(2x - 3)}}$	Factor out $(9x + 2)$.

EXAMPLE 3

Factor $3x^2 - 19x + 16$.

– – – – –   – – – – –

$$(3)(16) = 48$$

Multiply the x^2-coefficient by the constant term.

$$-1 - 48 = -49$$
$$-2 - 24 = -26$$
$$-3 - 16 = -19 \quad \text{This is it!}$$

Seek two factors of $+48$ whose sum is -19. Both must be *negative*.

$$3x^2 - 19x + 16$$

Write the given expression.

$$= 3x^2 - 3x - 16x + 16$$

Split the middle term.

$$= 3x(x - 1) - 16(x - 1)$$

Factor out $3x$ and -16.

$$= \underline{\underline{(x - 1)(3x - 16)}}$$

Factor out $x - 1$.

EXAMPLE 4

Factor $10x^2 + 21x + 6$.

– – – – –   – – – – –

$$(10)(6) = 60$$

Multiply the x^2-coefficient by the constant term.

$$1 + 60 = 61$$

Seek two factors of 60 whose sum is 21.

$$2 + 30 = 32$$
$$3 + 20 = 23$$
$$4 + 15 = 19 \quad \text{Skips 21!}$$

$$\therefore \underline{\underline{10x^2 + 21x + 6 \text{ is prime.}}}$$

No integer factors of 60 add up to 21.

Note: This is how to use the technique of splitting the middle term to tell whether or not a quadratic trinomial will factor.

EXAMPLE 5

Factor $2x^2 + 9x - 5$.

– – – – –   – – – – –

$$2x^2 + 9x - 5$$

Write the given expression.

$$= \underline{\underline{(2x - 1)(x + 5)}}$$

Factor by inspection. This one is easy to do without splitting the middle term.

EXAMPLE 6

Factor $20x^2 + 30x - 200$.

– – – – –   – – – – –

$$20x^2 + 30x - 200$$

Write the given expression.

$$= 10(2x^2 + 3x - 20)$$ Factor out 10, the GCF of the terms. (Remember, factor out *common* factors *first*!)

$$= \underline{\underline{10(2x - 5)(x + 4)}}$$ Factor $2x^2 + 3x - 20$ by inspection.

ORAL PRACTICE

Are these middle terms split correctly? Explain.

EXAMPLES

i. $2x^2 - 5x + 3 = 2x^2 - 3x - 2x + 3$
     Yes; $(2)(3) = 6$, $(-3)(-2) = 6$, and $-3 - 2 = -5$.
ii. $2x^2 - 5x + 3 = 2x^2 - 3x + 2x + 3$
     No; $(2)(3) = 6$, but $(-3)(2) = -6$, or
     no; $-3 + 2$ equals -1, not -5.

A. $3x^2 + 7x + 2 = 3x^2 + x + 6x + 2$

B. $3x^2 + 7x + 2 = 3x^2 + 6x + x + 2$

C. $2x^2 + 11x + 15 = 2x^2 + 5x + 6x + 15$

D. $3x^2 + 10x - 8 = 3x^2 - 2x + 12x - 8$

E. $3x^2 - 10x - 8 = 3x^2 + 2x + 12x - 8$

F. $6x^2 + 11x + 5 = 6x^2 + 5\tilde{x} + 6x + 5$

G. $6x^2 + 13x + 5 = 6x^2 + 10x + 3x + 5$

H. $6x^2 + 17x + 5 = 6x^2 + 10x + 3x + 5$

I. $6x^2 + 17x + 5 = 6x^2 + 3x + 14x + 5$

J. $6x^2 + 17x + 5 = 6x^2 + 2x + 15x + 5$

A.   Yes. $(3)(2) = 6$ and $(1)(6) = 6$, and $1 + 6 = 7$

B.   Yes. $(3)(2) = 6$ and $(6)(1) = 6$, and $6 + 1 = 7$

C.   Yes. $(2)(15) = 30$ and $(5)(6) = 30$, and $5 + 6 = 11$

D.   Yes. $(3)(-8) = -24$ and $(-2)(12) = -24$, and $-2 + 12 = 10$

E.   No. $2 + 12 \neq -10$, or $(3)(-8) = -24$, but $(2)(12) = +24$

F.   Yes. $(6)(5) = 30$ and $(5)(6) = 30$, and $5 + 6 = 11$

G.   Yes. $(6)(5) = 30$ and $(10)(3) = 30$, and $10 + 3 = 13$

H.   No. $10 + 3 \neq 17$

I.   No. $(6)(5) = 30$, but $(3)(14) = 42$

J.   Yes. $(6)(5) = 30$ and $(2)(15) = 30$, and $2 + 15 = 17$

Problem Notes:

Problems 6 and 11 are prime polynomials.
   Problems 17–20 and certain ones from 39–50 have common factors that should be factored out first.
   Problems 21–50 allow students to factor by inspection. You may find that weaker students prefer to stick with splitting the middle term.

1. $(3x + 4)(x + 4)$
2. $(2x + 3)(x + 6)$
3. $(3x + 4)(2x + 5)$
4. $(2x + 5)(3x + 5)$
5. $(2x - 9)(x + 10)$
6. Prime

EXERCISE 10-6

For Problems 1 through 20, use the technique of splitting the middle term to factor the polynomial completely or show it is prime.

1. $3x^2 + 16x + 16$ 2. $2x^2 + 15x + 18$

3. $6x^2 + 23x + 20$ 4. $6x^2 + 25x + 25$

5. $2x^2 + 11x - 90$ 6. $3x^2 + 20x + 40$

7. $(4x + 1)(5x - 12)$
8. $(5x - 12)(6x + 1)$
9. $(3x - 8)(3x - 5)$
10. $(3x - 5)(x + 14)$
11. Prime
12. $(5x - 18)(2x - 3)$
13. $(8x + y)(3x + 2y)$
14. $(x + 12y)(12x + y)$
15. $(r - s)(4r - 5s)$
16. $(8p - 9j)(p - j)$
17. $8(3x + 2)(2x - 3)$
18. $6(4x + 1)(x - 3)$
19. $-3(x - 1)(4x + 15)$
20. $-10(8x - 3)(x + 4)$
21. $(2x + 1)(x + 3)$
22. $(3x + 1)(x + 2)$
23. $(3x + 4)(x + 2)$
24. $(3x + 8)(x + 1)$
25. $(5x - 1)(x - 4)$
26. $(7x - 2)(x - 2)$
27. $(3x + 5)(2x - 1)$
28. $(3x + 4)(2x - 1)$
29. $(6x + 5)(x - 1)$
30. $(6x + 1)(x - 3)$
31. $(3r + 2s)(2r + 3s)$
32. $(3a + 4b)(2a + b)$
33. $(5a + 2b)(3a + 2b)$
34. $(3x + 5y)(2x + 3y)$
35. $(m - 4)(6m - 1)$
36. $(4r - 1)(r - 6)$
37. $(2m - 5)(m + 10)$
38. $(5p + 2)(p - 2)$
39. $4(x + 1)(x + 8)$
40. $6(x + 2)(x + 4)$
41. $(7x + y)(x - y)$
42. $(9c + d)(c - d)$
43. $x^3(4x + 3)(2x - 1)$
44. $x^5(6x + 1)(3x - 2)$
45. $ax(a - 5x)(2a - 3x)$
46. $uv(2u - 3v)(2u - 3v) = uv(2u - 3v)^2$
47. $3r(3u + 2)^2$
48. $5s(n - 9)(2n + 3)$
49. $2(x + 3)(3x - 2)(2x + 1)$
50. $3(x - 2)^2(4x + 1)$

7. $20x^2 - 43x - 12$
8. $30x^2 - 67x - 12$
9. $9x^2 - 39x + 40$
10. $3x^2 + 37x - 70$
11. $4x^2 + 7x + 18$
12. $10x^2 - 51x + 54$
13. $24x^2 + 19xy + 2y^2$
14. $12x^2 + 145xy + 12y^2$
15. $4r^2 - 9rs + 5s^2$
16. $8p^2 - 17pj + 9j^2$
17. $48x^2 - 40x - 48$
18. $24x^2 - 66x - 18$
19. $-12\check{x}^2 - 33x + 45$
20. $-80x^2 - 290x + 120$

For Problems 21 through 50, factor the polynomial completely, either by inspection (preferably) or by splitting the middle term.

21. $2x^2 + 7x + 3$
22. $3x^2 + 7x + 2$
23. $3x^2 + 10x + 8$
24. $3x^2 + 11x + 8$
25. $5x^2 - 21x + 4$
26. $7x^2 - 16x + 4$
27. $6x^2 + 7x - 5$
28. $6x^2 + 5x - 4$
29. $6x^2 - x - 5$
30. $6x^2 - 17x - 3$
31. $6r^2 + 13rs + 6s^2$
32. $6a^2 + 11ab + 4b^2$
33. $15a^2 + 16ab + 4b^2$
34. $6x^2 + 19xy + 15y^2$
35. $6m^2 - 25m + 4$
36. $4r^2 - 25r + 6$
37. $2m^2 + 15m - 50$
38. $5p^2 - 8p - 4$
39. $4x^2 + 36x + 32$
40. $6x^2 + 36x + 48$
41. $7x^2 - 6xy - y^2$
42. $9c^2 - 8cd - d^2$
43. $8x^5 + 2x^4 - 3x^3$
44. $18x^7 - 9x^6 - 2x^5$
45. $2a^3x - 13a^2x^2 + 15ax^3$
46. $4u^3v - 12u^2v^2 + 9uv^3$
47. $27ru^2 + 36ru + 12r$
48. $10sn^2 - 75sn - 135s$
49. $12(x + 3)x^2 - 2(x + 3)x - 4(x + 3)$
50. $12(x - 2)x^2 - 21(x - 2)x - 6(x - 2)$

10-7   SOLVING QUADRATIC EQUATIONS BY FACTORING

In Chapter 6 you learned how to use the Quadratic Formula to solve equations like

$$x^2 - x - 2 = 0.$$

You also know how to factor quadratic trinomials like

$$x^2 - x - 2.$$

It is time to put these two ideas together and come up with a quick way to solve certain kinds of quadratic equations.

Starting with

$$x^2 - x - 2 = 0,$$

you can factor the left member to get

$$(x - 2)(x + 1) = 0.$$

In this form, the equation says that a *product* of two numbers equals *zero*. But the only way a product can equal zero is for one of its *factors* to be zero. So the equation can be transformed to

$$x - 2 = 0 \quad \text{or} \quad x + 1 = 0.$$

This transformation changes one hard problem into two easy problems. Adding 2 in the first clause and subtracting 1 in the second gives

$$x = 2 \quad \text{or} \quad x = -1.$$
$$\therefore S = \{2, -1\}$$

The fact that zero times a number equals zero is called the *multiplication property of zero*.

MULTIPLICATION PROPERTY OF ZERO

If one factor of a product is 0, then the product equals 0.
That is, for any real number n,

$$n \cdot 0 = 0 \quad \text{or} \quad 0 \cdot n = 0.$$

The fact that a product can be zero *only* if one of its factors is zero is called the *converse of the multiplication property of zero*.

CONVERSE OF THE MULTIPLICATION PROPERTY OF ZERO

If a product of real numbers equals zero, then one of its factors equals zero. That is, for real numbers n and p, if $np = 0$, then $n = 0$ or $p = 0$.

Unfortunately, the factoring scheme above does not work if the trinomial cannot be factored. There is a quick way to tell whether or not it will factor. You recall that for the equation

$$ax^2 + bx + c = 0,$$

the Quadratic Formula says that

$$x = \frac{-b \pm \sqrt{b^2 - 4ac}}{2a}.$$

You recall that $b^2 - 4ac$ under the radical sign is called the *discriminant*. For $x^2 - x - 2$, the discriminant is

$$(-1)^2 - 4(1)(-2) = 9.$$

The number 9 happens to be a *perfect square*, 3^2. So $\sqrt{9} = 3$, and the solutions for x will not involve any radicals. This is also the case whenever a trinomial $ax^2 + bx + c$ can be factored.

CONCLUSION

DISCRIMINANT TEST FOR FACTORABILITY
A quadratic trinomial $ax^2 + bx + c$ can be factored if and only if the discriminant, $b^2 - 4ac$, is a perfect square.

Objective:
Given a quadratic equation, solve it by factoring, if practical. Otherwise, solve it by the Quadratic Formula.

Cover the answers as you work these examples.

EXAMPLE 1

Solve $(7x - 3)(2x + 5) = 0$.

- - - - -   - - - - -

	Think These Reasons
$(7x - 3)(2x + 5) = 0$	Write the given equation.
$7x - 3 = 0$ or $2x + 5 = 0$	A product is 0 only if a factor is 0.
$7x = 3$ or $2x = -5$	Add 3 and add -5.
$x = \dfrac{3}{7}$ or $x = -\dfrac{5}{2}$	Divide by 7 and divide by 2.

$$\therefore S = \left\{ \frac{3}{7}, -\frac{5}{2} \right\}$$ Write the solution set.

EXAMPLE 2

Solve $2x^2 - x - 3 = 0$.

– – – – –   – – – – –

$2x^2 - x - 3 = 0$	Write the given equation.
$(2x - 3)(x + 1) = 0$	Factor (by inspection, if you can).
$2x - 3 = 0$ or $x + 1 = 0$	A product is 0 only if a factor is 0.
$2x = 3$ or $x = -1$	Add 3 and add -1.
$x = \dfrac{3}{2}$ or $x = -1$	Divide by 2.
$\therefore S = \left\{ \dfrac{3}{2}, -1 \right\}$	Write the solution set.

EXAMPLE 3

Solve $2x^2 + 15x + 12 = 0$.

– – – – –   – – – – –

$2x^2 + 15x + 12 = 0$	Write the given expression.
$b^2 - 4ac = 15^2 - 4(2)(12)$	Calculate the discriminant.
$= 129$	129 is not a perfect square, so the trinomial cannot be factored.
$x = \dfrac{-15 \pm \sqrt{129}}{2(2)}$	Use the Quadratic Formula.
$x \approx -0.91$ or -6.59	Do the arithmetic.
$\therefore S = \{-0.91, -6.59\}$	Write the solution set.

EXAMPLE 4

Solve $10x^2 - 83x + 24 = 0$.

– – – – –   – – – – –

$10x^2 - 83x + 24 = 0$	Write the given equation.
$x = \dfrac{83 \pm \sqrt{6889 - 4(10)(24)}}{2(10)}$	Use the Quadratic Formula. (It would be impractical to factor a trinomial with such big coefficients!)
$x = \dfrac{83 \pm \sqrt{5929}}{20}$	Do the computation.

$$x = \frac{83 \pm 77}{20}$$

Take the square root. (The trinomial *would* have factored, since 5929 is a perfect square.)

$$x = 8 \quad \text{or} \quad \frac{3}{10}$$

Finish the computation.

$$\therefore S = \left\{ 8, \frac{3}{10} \right\}$$

Write the solution set.

ORAL PRACTICE

Can the equation at the top of the next page be solved by factoring? Explain.

EXAMPLES

Answers.

i. $3x^2 - 10x - 8 = 0$ i.   Yes; $b^2 - 4ac = 196$, a perfect square.
ii. $5x^2 - 11x + 3 = 0$ ii. No; $b^2 - 4ac = 61$, not a perfect square.

A. Yes. $b^2 - 4ac = 4$, a perf. sq.
B. Yes. $b^2 - 4ac = 25$, a perf. sq.
C. No. $b^2 - 4ac = 13$, not a perf. sq.
D. No. $b^2 - 4ac = -11$, not a perf. sq.
E. Yes. $b^2 - 4ac = 49$, a perf. sq.
F. No. $b^2 - 4ac = -31$, not a perf. sq.
G. Yes. $b^2 - 4ac = 1$, a perf. sq.
H. Yes. $b^2 - 4ac = 4$, a perf. sq.
I. Yes. $b^2 - 4ac = 196$, a perf. sq.
J. No. $b^2 - 4ac = 105$, not a perf. sq.
K. No. $b^2 - 4ac = -4$, not a perf. sq.
L. Yes. $b^2 - 4ac = 0$, a perf. sq.

A. $x^2 + 8x + 15 = 0$ B. $x^2 - x - 6 = 0$
C. $x^2 + 5x + 3 = 0$ D. $x^2 + 3x + 5 = 0$
E. $x^2 + 3x - 10 = 0$ F. $x^2 + 3x + 10 = 0$
G. $2x^2 + 7x + 6 = 0$ H. $3x^2 - 8x + 5 = 0$
I. $3x^2 + 10x - 8 = 0$ J. $2x^2 + 5x - 10 = 0$
K. $x^2 + 6x + 10 = 0$ L. $4x^2 - 12x + 9 = 0$

EXERCISE 10-7

Problem Notes:

Problems 3–16 are already factored.
  Problems 17–40 must be factored first.
  Problems 25, 26, 35, and 36 require use of the Quadratic Formula.

3. $S = \{3, 7\}$ 4. $S = \{9, 2\}$
5. $S = \{\frac{5}{3}, -4\}$ 6. $S = \{\frac{7}{4}, -3\}$

1. State the multiplication property of zero.   (See text.)

2. State the converse of the multiplication property of zero.   (See text.)

For Problems 3 through 16, solve the equation.

3. $(x - 3)(x - 7) = 0$ 4. $(x - 9)(x - 2) = 0$

5. $(3x - 5)(x + 4) = 0$ 6. $(4x - 7)(x + 3) = 0$

7. $(7x + 8)(2x - 11) = 0$

8. $(11x + 17)(2x - 13) = 0$

9. $(5x + 13)(4x + 21) = 0$

10. $(5x + 24)(4x + 37) = 0$

11. $(x - 3)(x + 4)(x - 5) = 0$

12. $(x - 6)(x - 5)(x + 1) = 0$

13. $(6x - 5)(x + 7)(2x - 9) = 0$

14. $(2x - 9)(x + 8)(6x - 7) = 0$

15. $(x - 1)(x + 2)(x + 3)(x - 4) = 0$

16. $(x + 6)(x - 7)(x - 8)(x + 9) = 0$

For Problems 17 through 40, solve by factoring, if practical. Otherwise, solve by the Quadratic Formula. Round off irrational solutions to two decimal places.

17. $x^2 + 7x + 10 = 0$

18. $x^2 + 10x + 21 = 0$

19. $x^2 - x - 12 = 0$

20. $x^2 - 3x - 10 = 0$

21. $x^2 + 4x - 5 = 0$

22. $x^2 + 5x - 6 = 0$

23. $x^2 - 5x + 6 = 0$

24. $x^2 - 6x + 8 = 0$

25. $x^2 + 7x + 5 = 0$

26. $x^2 + 9x + 7 = 0$

27. $2x^2 + 5x + 3 = 0$

28. $2x^2 + 11x + 5 = 0$

29. $3x^2 + 2x - 8 = 0$

30. $3x^2 + 7x - 20 = 0$

31. $5x^2 - 7x - 6 = 0$

32. $5x^2 - 8x - 4 = 0$

33. $6x^2 - 11x + 5 = 0$

34. $5x^2 - 24x + 16 = 0$

35. $5x^2 - 14x - 6 = 0$

36. $2x^2 - 15x - 5 = 0$

37. $6x^2 - 5x - 6 = 0$

38. $6x^2 - 7x - 20 = 0$

39. $16x^2 - 46x + 15 = 0$

40. $12x^2 - 20x + 7 = 0$

For Problems 41 through 46, the left member can be factored as a product of *three* linear binomials. Solve the equations. Each has three solutions.

41. $x^3 - 3x^2 - 4x + 12 = 0$

42. $x^3 - 2x^2 - 9x + 18 = 0$

43. $x^3 + 4x^2 - 25x - 100 = 0$

44. $x^3 + 5x^2 - 36x - 180 = 0$

45. $3x^3 + 4x^2 - 3x - 4 = 0$

46. $4x^3 + 24x^2 - x - 6 = 0$

For Problems 47 through 50, each equation has three solutions. However, you must be very clever to find all three. Try factoring, first!

47. $x^3 + 6x^2 - 5x - 30 = 0$

48. $x^3 + 2x^2 - 7x - 14 = 0$

49. $6x^3 - 3x^2 - 8x + 4 = 0$

50. $5x^3 - 20x^2 - 3x + 12 = 0$

7. $S = \{-\frac{8}{7}, \frac{11}{2}\}$
8. $S = \{\frac{-17}{11}, \frac{13}{2}\}$
9. $S = \{\frac{-13}{5}, \frac{-21}{4}\}$
10. $S = \{\frac{-24}{5}, \frac{-37}{4}\}$
11. $S = \{3, -4, 5\}$
12. $S = \{6, 5, -1\}$
13. $S = \{\frac{5}{6}, -7, \frac{9}{2}\}$
14. $S = \{\frac{9}{2}, -8, \frac{7}{6}\}$
15. $S = \{1, -2, -3, 4\}$
16. $S = \{-6, 7, 8, -9\}$
17. $S = \{-2, -5\}$
18. $S = \{-3, -7\}$
19. $S = \{-3, 4\}$
20. $S = \{-2, 5\}$
21. $S = \{1, -5\}$
22. $S = \{1, -6\}$
23. $S = \{2, 3\}$
24. $S = \{2, 4\}$
25. $S = \{-0.81, -6.19\}$
26. $S = \{-0.86, -8.14\}$

Problems 39 and 40 may be easier if done by the Quadratic Formula.

27. $S = \{-\frac{3}{2}, -1\}$
28. $S = \{-\frac{1}{2}, -5\}$
29. $S = \{\frac{4}{3}, -2\}$
30. $S = \{\frac{5}{3}, -4\}$
31. $S = \{-\frac{3}{5}, 2\}$
32. $S = \{-\frac{2}{5}, 2\}$
33. $S = \{\frac{5}{6}, 1\}$
34. $S = \{\frac{4}{5}, 4\}$
35. $S = \{3.18, -0.38\}$
36. $S = \{7.82, -0.32\}$
37. $S = \{-\frac{2}{3}, \frac{3}{2}\}$
38. $S = \{2.5, -\frac{4}{3}\}$
39. $S = \{\frac{3}{8}, \frac{5}{2}\}$
40. $S = \{\frac{1}{2}, \frac{7}{6}\}$

Problems 41–50 are suitable for better students. The polynomials must be factored by grouping. Problems 49 and 50 require students to be able to solve equations like $3x^2 - 4 = 0$, getting $x = \pm\sqrt{\frac{4}{3}}$ or $\pm\frac{2}{\sqrt{3}}$.

41. $S = \{3, -2, 2\}$
42. $S = \{2, -3, 3\}$
43. $S = \{-4, -5, 5\}$
44. $S = \{-5, -6, 6\}$
45. $S = \{\frac{-4}{3}, -1, 1\}$
46. $S = \{-6, \frac{-1}{2}, \frac{1}{2}\}$
47. $S = \{-6, -\sqrt{5}, \sqrt{5}\}$
48. $S = \{-2, -\sqrt{7}, \sqrt{7}\}$
49. $S = \{\frac{1}{2}, \sqrt{\frac{4}{3}}, -\sqrt{\frac{4}{3}}\}$
50. $S = \{4, \sqrt{\frac{3}{5}}, -\sqrt{\frac{3}{5}}\}$

10-8 | CONTEST AND STANDARDIZED TEST PROBLEMS

Time: 2 to 6 days

Note: If time is short, you may spend just a few days on this section. The most effective way for students to master these problems is to work one or two every day for the rest of the course. Consequently, subsequent chapters refer back to this section.

Chalkboard Examples:

First day:
1. A is 5 years older than B. The product of their ages is 1554. How old is each?
   Ans.: A is 42, B is 37.

2. Find two consecutive positive integers whose product is 90.
   Ans.: 9 and 10

3. Find two consecutive negative integers whose product is 121,452.
   Ans.: −349, −348

4. Find two consecutive odd integers if the sum of their squares is 290.
   Ans.: 11 and 13 or −13 and −11
Oral Practice is appropriate here.

Second day:
1. The units digit of a two-digit number is twice the tens digit. If the digits are reversed, the resulting number is 36 more than the original number. What is the original number?
   Ans.: 48

2. Twenty pennies and nickels have a total value of 48 cents. How many of each are there?
   Ans.: 13 pennies, 7 nickels
Third day:
1. A leaves home walking 200 meters per minute. Six minutes later, B leaves home and rides a bike after A at 500 meters per minute. How long does it take for B to catch up with A?
   Ans.: 4 minutes

2. The length of a rectangle is 5 feet more than its width. The area of the rectangle is 204 square feet. What are its dimensions?
   Ans. 12 feet by 17 feet
Fourth day:
1. A rectangle 5 inches by 8 inches is enlarged by adding an L-shaped strip around

Problems on contests, aptitude tests, and achievement tests are designed to measure your understanding of numbers rather than to show how mathematics is applied in realistic situations. Sometimes you can work these problems in your head without writing expressions and equations. Sometimes there are clever shortcuts you may be able to think up! You can always use algebra if no easier ways come to mind.

Suppose a question asks you to find two consecutive integers whose product is 56. You might choose 7 and 8, because you remember that $7 \times 8 = 56$, and 7 and 8 are consecutive. You might just *try* some possibilities.

$$
\begin{array}{lll}
3 \times 4 = 12 & & \text{No} \\
4 \times 5 = 20 & & \text{No} \\
5 \times 6 = 30 & & \text{No} \\
6 \times 7 = 42 & & \text{No} \\
7 \times 8 = 56 & & \text{Yes!}
\end{array}
$$

This process is called *trial and error*. It is the process you have used to factor quadratic trinomials.

Trial and error is tedious if the numbers are big. But there may be other shortcuts. Faced with the problem of finding two consecutive integers whose product is 5402, Pamela Duke thought, "They must be about the same size. So I will find $\sqrt{5402}$ by calculator; it is 73.498299 . . . . The answer must be 73 and 74, the integers on either side." Upon multiplying, she found $73 \times 74 = 5402$, so her answer was right.

This problem could also be worked by algebra.

	Think These Reasons
Let x = smaller integer.	Define variables.
Let y = larger integer.	
$xy = 5402$	The product is 5402.
$y = x + 1$	The integers are consecutive.
$x(x + 1) = 5402$	Substitute $x + 1$ for y.
$x^2 + x = 5402$	Distribute x.

$$x^2 + x - 5402 = 0$$ Subtract 5402 from each member.

$$x = \frac{-1 \pm \sqrt{1 - 4(1)(5402)}}{2(1)}$$ Use the Quadratic Formula.

$$x = \frac{-1 \pm 147}{2}$$ Do the arithmetic.

$$x = 73 \quad \text{or} \quad -74$$ Finish the arithmetic.

$$y = 74 \quad \text{or} \quad -73$$ Substitute into $y = x + 1$.

$$\underline{73, 74 \quad \text{or} \quad -74, -73}$$ Answer the question.

The algebraic solution takes a fairly long time. But it is *reliable*. Also, it uncovers another possible answer, -74 and -73, which you might otherwise miss. Finally, algebra will tell you if there is *no* answer. Had the values of x and y turned out not to be integers, then there would have been no such numbers.

The main purpose of this section is to make you familiar with some kinds of problems that appear on contests and standardized tests so that you can score higher on these tests. There are also some problems that are more realistic.

Objective :
Be able to work problems involving ages, consecutive integers, digits, coins, relative rates, and rectangles.

The following examples show an algebraic solution as well as some shortcuts that might be used.

EXAMPLE 1

Age Problem R is 4 years younger than S. The product of their ages is 96. Find each one's age.

– – – – –   – – – – –

Think These Reasons

Trial and error:

$5 \times 9 = 45$ No
$6 \times 10 = 60$ No
$7 \times 11 = 77$ No
$8 \times 12 = 96$ Yes!

two of the sides. The area of the L is 48 square inches. How wide is the strip? Ans.: 3 inches (Can be done by trial and error.)

2. A rectangle 5 inches by 8 inches is enlarged by adding an L-shaped strip around two of the sides. The area of the L is 34 square inches. How wide is the strip? Ans.: approximately 2.23 inches (requires Quadratic Formula)

Fifth day:
1. A strip of uniform width is cut from around all four sides of a 6 cm by 8 cm rectangle. The strip has area 13 square centimeters. What is the width of the strip? Ans.: 0.5 cm

Sixth day:
Review in preparation for test.

Assignments:
(You may assign the corresponding even-numbered problems.)
Day 1: Exercise 10–8, #1, 13, 17, 21, 25 and Exercise 10–7, #18–26 even
Day 2: Exercise 10–8, #3, 15, 19, 35, 37, 45, Exercise 10–7, #28, and Exercise 10–6, #16

Day 3: Exercise 10–8, #5, 18, 39, 41, 49, 55, 61, Exercise 10–7, #30, and Exercise 10–6, #18
Day 4: Exercise 10–8, #9, 29, 43, 51, 57, 63, 69
Day 5: Exercise 10–8, #11, 31, 36, 53, 59, 65, 73
Day 6: Exercise 10–9, #selected problems (in preparation for test)

R is 8, S is 12 because 8 × 12 is 96 and 8 is 4 less than 12.

Answer the question. This is all you need to write! *Justify* your answer to show why it is right.

– – – – –

Algebraic method:

Let r = R's age.
Let s = S's age.

$r = s - 4$ (1)

R | is | 4 years younger than S.

Write an equation using one given piece of information.

$rs = 96$ (2)

Product of ages | is | 96.

Write another equation using the other piece of given information.

$(s - 4)(s) = 96$
$s^2 - 4s - 96 = 0$

Substitute $s - 4$ for r in (2).
Distribute s. Subtract 96.

$(s + 8)(s - 12) = 0$

Factor.

$s + 8 = 0$ or $s - 12 = 0$

Set each factor equal to 0.

$s = -8$ or $s = 12$
Impossible.

Solve the equations. Discard any meaningless answers.

$r = 12 - 4$

Substitute 12 for s in (1).

$= 8$

Do the arithmetic.

R is 8, S is 12.

Answer the question.

EXAMPLE 2

Digits Problem   The units digit of a two-digit number is 2 more than the tens digit. If the digits are reversed, the new number is 39 less than twice the original number. Find the original number.

– – – – –   – – – – –

| *Think These Reasons* |

Algebraic method:

Let t = tens digit.
Let u = units digit.

Define the variables.

$u = t + 2$ (1)

Units digit | is | 2 more than tens digit.

Write one equation using one known fact.

$10t + u$ is original number.
$10u + t$ is reversed number.

(For instance, 39 means 30 + 9.)

$10u + t = 2(10t + u) - 39$ (2)

Reversed number | is | 39 less than twice the number.

Write another equation using the other known fact

$10u + t = 20t + 2u - 39$	Distribute 2.
$8u - 19t = -39$	Subtract $20t$ and $2u$.
$8(t + 2) - 19t = -39$	Substitute $t + 2$ for u.
$8t + 16 - 19t = -39$	Distribute 8.
$-11t = -55$	Combine like terms; subtract 16.
$t = 5$	Divide by -11.
$u = 5 + 2$	Substitute 5 for t in (1).
$u = 7$	Add.
Number is 57.	Write the answer.

− − − − −   − − − − −

Trial and error:

Possible Numbers	×2	Reverse	Difference	
13	26	31	−5	
24	48	42	6	
35	70	53	17	
46	92	64	28	
→ 57	114	75	39	This is it!
68	136	86	50	
79	158	97	61	

Number is 57 because 7 is 2   Answer the question. Justify
more than 5 and 114 is 39 more   your answer.
than 75.

In Example 2, the trial-and-error method takes a bit of work. But it *is* practical because there are only seven possible two-digit numbers that have a units digit two more than the tens digit.

EXAMPLE 3

Coin (Total Value) Problem   Eleven dimes and quarters have a total value of $2.15. How many of each are there?
Algebraic method:

− − − − −   − − − − −

Let d = number of dimes.   Define the variables. Use letters
Let q = number of quarters.   that sound like what they represent.

$d + q = 11$ (1)   There are 11 coins in all.

$10d + 25q = 215$ (2)   Total value is $2.15.

$2d + 5q = 43$ Divide (2) by 5.

$\underline{2d + 2q = 22}$ Multiply (1) by 2.

$\quad 3q = 21$ Subtract.

$\qquad q = 7$ Divide each member by 3.

$\ d + 7 = 11$ Substitute 7 for q in (1).

$\qquad d = 4$ Subtract 4 from each member.

$\underline{\underline{\text{4 dimes, 7 quarters.}}}$ Answer the question.

– – – – –   – – – – –

Trial and error:

Dimes	Quarters	Value
0	11	2.75
1	10	2.60
2	9	2.45
3	8	2.30
4	7	2.15

$\underline{\underline{\text{4 dimes, 7 quarters,}}}$ because
$\overline{4 \times 10 \text{ plus } 7 \times 25}$ is 215 and
$4 + 7$ is 11.

– – – – –   – – – – –

Pattern method: If all 11 are quarters, the total is $2.75. Each time you substitute a dime for a quarter, the total goes *down* by 15¢. The total has to go down 60¢ to get from $2.75 to $2.15. So there must be 4 dimes because 4×15 is 60.

$\underline{\underline{\text{4 dimes, 7 quarters,}}}$ because
$\overline{4 \times 10 \text{ plus } 7 \times 25}$ is 215 and
$4 + 7$ is 11.

EXAMPLE 4

Train Problem   A freight train leaves point A going 50 km/h. Two hours later, a passenger train leaves A going in the same direction at 80 km/h. How long will it take the passenger train to catch the freight train?

– – – – –   – – – – –

This is a *relative rate* problem.

Let t = number of hours for the passenger train to catch up.

In two hours, the freight train has gone $2 \times 50 = 100$ km.
The passenger train *catches up* at a rate of $80 - 50 = 30$ km/h.
So the passenger train must catch up 100 km at 30 km/h.

$$\text{distance} = \text{rate} \times \text{time}$$

$$100 = 30t$$

$$3\tfrac{1}{3} = t$$

$$\underline{\underline{\text{3 h 20 min.}}}$$

This example shows a shortcut, using the concept of relative rate. The passenger train catches up 100 kilometers at a relative rate of 30 km/h. There are other algebraic ways to do this problem, but the relative rate technique is far superior.

EXAMPLE 5

Rectangle Problem   A 7-inch by 10-inch rectangle has a strip of uniform width, x inches, around its outside. If the area of the strip is 50 square inches, what is the width of the strip?

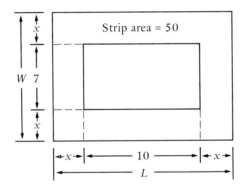

- - - - -   - - - - -

Think These Reasons

Algebraic method:

x = number of inches of strip width.	Rewrite the definition of x.
Let L = number of inches in total length.	Define variables for length and width.
Let W = number of inches in total width.	
Area of inner rectangle = $7(10) = 70$.	Area = length × width.
Total area = $70 + 50 = 120$	Add the area of the strip.
$\therefore LW = 120$	Area = length × width.
$L = 10 + 2x$ $\;\;\;\;$ $W = 7 + 2x$	See the diagram. For example, $L = x + 10 + x = 10 + 2x$.
$\therefore (10 + 2x)(7 + 2x) = 120$	Substitute for L and W.
$70 + 34x + 4x^2 = 120$	Multiply the binomials.

$$4x^2 + 34x - 50 = 0$$ Commute terms. Subtract 120 from each member.

$$x = \frac{-34 \pm \sqrt{1156 - 4(4)(-50)}}{2(4)}$$ Use the Quadratic Formula.

$$x = \frac{-34 \pm \sqrt{1956}}{8}$$ Do the computation.

$x \approx 1.28$ or -9.78 Discard any irrelevant answers.

Impossible

<u>About 1.28 in. wide</u>   Answer the question.

Since the answer to this problem is not an integer, the problem would be impractical to do by the trial-and-error method.

ORAL PRACTICE

Do these problems in your head. Give the answer.

A.   Two consecutive positive integers whose product is 20.   4, 5

B.   Two consecutive negative integers whose product is 20.   −4, −5

C.   Two consecutive positive integers whose product is 42.   6, 7

D.   Two odd consecutive positive integers whose product is 35.   5, 7

E.   Two even consecutive positive integers whose product is 48.   6, 8

F.   Two even consecutive negative integers whose product is 80.   −8, −10

G.   Two positive integers that differ by 3 and whose product is 70.   7, 10

H.   Two negative integers that differ by 3 and whose product is 54.   −6, −9

I.   Two consecutive positive integers whose squares have a sum of 25.   3, 4

J.   Two consecutive negative integers whose squares have a sum of 13.   −2, −3

EXERCISE 10-8

Age Problems

1.   A is 4 years older than B. The product of their ages is 45. How old is each?   A is 9, B is 5

2. C is 3 years younger than D. The product of their ages is 88. How old is each?   C is 8, D is 11

3. E is twice as old as F. The product of their ages is 72. How old is each?   E is 12, F is 6.

4. G is 4 times as old as H. The product of their ages is 1600. How old is each?   G is 80, H is 20.

5. J is 3 years older than K. If you square K's age and add twice J's age, the result is 69. What are their ages?   J is 10, K is 7.

6. L is 2 years younger than M. The difference between the squares of their ages is 28. How old is each?   M is 8, L is 6.

7. N's age is 70% of M's age. Four years ago M was 1.6 times as old as N. What are their ages now?   M is 20, N is 14.

8. Q's age is 80% of R's age. Five years from now Q's age will be 90% of R's age. How old is each now?   R is 5, Q is 4.

9. Olivia, Newt, and John were each born 3 years apart, with Olivia the youngest and John the oldest. The sum of the squares of their ages is 606. How old is each?   O is 11, N is 14, J is 17.

10. April, Mae, June, and Julie were born in consecutive years, in that order, with April being the oldest. All they will tell you is that the sum of the squares of their ages is 534. How old are they?

11. Manny Moore is 5 years older than his brother, Les. All they will tell you is that the sum of the squares of their ages is 773. How old are they?   M is 22, L is 17.

12. Mr. Rhee is 4 years older than Ms. Rhee, but their actual ages are a mystery. If they tell you that the sum of the squares of their ages is 3706, how old are they?   Mr. Rhee is 45, Ms. Rhee is 41.

Consecutive Integers Problems

13. Find two consecutive integers whose product is 72.   8, 9 or −8, −9

14. Find two consecutive integers whose product is 90.   9, 10 or −10, −9

15. Find two consecutive integers whose product is 3422.   58, 59 or −59, −58

16. Find two consecutive integers whose product is 9312.   96, 97 or −97, −96

17. Find two consecutive positive integers if the sum of their squares is 3445.   41, 42

18. Find two consecutive negative integers if the sum of their squares is 1513.   −27, −28

19. Find three consecutive negative integers if the sum of their squares is 12,290.   −63, −64, −65

Problem Notes:

The spirit of these problems is to work them in the head wherever possible. Algebraic solutions should be considered as a last resort. Make sure students justify any answer found mentally, as shown in Example 1. Approached this way, these problems encourage problem-solving skills rather than simply exercise working. Encourage students to share with one another clever shortcuts they find. You may learn some problem-solving techniques yourself!

For Problems 7 and 8, use reasoning such as "N's age is a multiple of 0.7. So the ages could be (7, 10), (14, 20), (21, 30), ... Subtracting 4 from each age gives (3, 6), (10, 16), (17, 26), ... Since 16 = 1.6(10), the answer is (14, 20)."

10. April is 13, Mae is 12, June is 11, Julie is 10.

22.   37, 39, or −39, −37

Problems 25 and 32 have no answer because the values are non-integers. Problem 26 has no answer because the values are even rather than odd.

25.   No such integers
27.   −84, −82

20. Find three consecutive positive integers if the sum of their squares is 1454.   21, 22, 23

21. Find two consecutive odd integers whose product is 7055.   83, 85 or −85, −83

22. Find two consecutive odd integers whose product is 1443.

23. Find three consecutive odd integers if the sum of their squares is 7211.   47, 49, 51 or −47, −49, −51

24. Find three consecutive odd integers if the sum of their squares is 15,995.   71, 73, 75 or −75, −73, −71

25. Find two consecutive odd integers if the sum of their squares is 510.

26. Find two consecutive odd integers if the sum of their squares is 1060.   No such odd integers

27. Find two consecutive even negative integers whose product is 6888.

28. Find two consecutive even positive integers whose product is 2808.   52, 54

29. Find three consecutive even negative integers if the sum of their squares is 5300.   −44, −42, −40

30. Find three consecutive even integers if the sum of their squares is 1208.   18, 20, 22 or −22, −20, −18

31. Find two consecutive even integers if the square of the larger minus the square of the smaller is 348.   86, 88

32. Find two consecutive even integers if the sum of their squares is 2200.   No such integers

33. Find two consecutive even integers if the sum of their squares is 164.   8, 10, or −10, −8

34. Find two consecutive odd integers if the difference between their squares is 16.   3, 5 or −5, −3

Digits Problems

35. The units digit of a two-digit number is 40% of the tens digit. If the digits are reversed, the resulting number is 27 less than the original number. Find the original number.   52

36. A two-digit number is five times its units digit. If the digits are reversed, the resulting number is 27 more than the original number. Find the original number.   25

37. The sum of the digits of a two-digit number is 9. If the digits are reversed, the new number is 9 less than three times the original number. Find the original number.   27

38. The sum of the digits of a two-digit number is 6. If the digits are reversed, the new number is 9 less than four times the original number. Find the original number. 15

39. The units digit of a two-digit number is 1 less than twice the tens digit. The square of the tens digit is 9 more than the units digit. Find the number. 47

40. The tens digit of a two-digit number is 1 less than five times the units digit. The square of the units digit is 5 less than the tens digit. Find the number. 92

41. The tens digit of a two-digit number is 3 less than the square of the units digit. If 27 is subtracted from the number, the result is the number with the digits reversed. Find the original number. 63

42. The units digit of a two-digit number is 2 less than the square of the tens digit. If 36 is added to the number, the result is the number with the digits reversed. Find the original number. 37

43. The tens digit of a two-digit number is 7 times the units digit. What is the number? (Think!) 71

For Problems 43 and 44, there is only one pair of digits that meet the given requirement; therefore, a second equation is unnecessary.

44. The units digit of a two-digit number is $\frac{3}{8}$ of the tens digit. What is the number? (Think!) 83

Coin and Total Value Problems

45. Twelve dimes and quarters have a total value of $1.95. How many of each are there? 7 dimes, 5 quarters

46. Ten nickels and quarters have a total value of $1.70. How many of each are there? 4 nickels, 6 quarters

47. Eighteen pennies and nickels have a total value of 38 cents. How many of each are there? 13 pennies, 5 nickels

48. Twelve pennies and quarters have a total value of $2.52. How many of each are there? 2 pennies, 10 quarters

49. *Bank Teller Problem*   A bank teller has $10,000 in $20 bills and $50 bills. If the teller has a total of 320 bills, how many of each kind are there? 120 $50 bills, 200 $20 bills

50. *Courier Problem*   A courier picks up 1000 small, unmarked bills, some $20 bills and some $50 bills. The total value is $41,000. How many of each kind are there? 700 $50 bills, 300 $20 bills

51. *Sandwich Problem*   Ten sandwiches are purchased at a total cost of $18.50. Some are tuna sandwiches at $2.00 each, and the rest are cheese sandwiches at $1.50 each. How many of each kind are there? 7 tuna sandwiches, 3 cheese sandwiches

52. *City Vehicle Problem*   the city spent $120,000 buying 10 new vehicles. Trucks cost $14,000 each and cars cost $9000 each. How many of each kind were bought?   6 trucks, 4 cars

53. *Plumbers' Wages Problem*   Plumbers earn $160 a day, and plumbers' helpers earn $100 a day. Twenty plumbers and helpers earn a total of $2600 in a day. How many of each are there? 10 and 10

54. *Carnival Problem*   In a carnival game, you gain $2 if you win and lose $1 if you do not win. If someone plays 30 times and has a net loss of $6, how many wins were there?   8

Relative Rate Problems

55. A leaves home going 30 kilometers per hour (km/h). Half an hour later, B starts from the same place and goes after A at 50 km/h. How long does it take B to catch up with A?   45 minutes

56. C leaves home going 40 kilometers per hour (km/h). When C is 9 km from home, D starts after C from the same place, going 58 km/h. How long does it take D to catch up with C?   30 minutes

57. E is approaching F at 20 km/h. When E is 30 km away, F starts out to meet E, going 40 km/h. How long does it take F to meet E?   30 minutes

58. G and H are 370 km apart. At the same instant they start toward each other, G going 50 km/h and H going 60 km/h. How long is it before they meet?   3.36 h

59. J and K start from 600 km apart and approach each other at constant, but different, rates. It takes 12 hours for them to meet. If J goes 10 km/h faster than K, how fast does each one travel?   J; 30 km/h, K; 20 km/h

60. *Clock Hands Problem*   At exactly what time between 4:00 and 5:00 will the minute hand of a clock be directly over the hour hand? (*Note:* The minute hand's rate is 60 minutes per hour and the hour hand's rate is 5 minutes per hour. Find out their *relative* rate and then figure out how long it takes the minute hand to catch up the 20 minutes they are apart at 4:00.) $4:21\frac{9}{11}$ o'clock

Rectangle Problems

In Problems 61–64, the technique for solving the problem directly is the same as the technique for factoring in the equation for the algebraic solution. For instance, in Problem 61, both techniques involve finding two factors of 63 that differ by 2.

61. A rectangle of area 63 has a length 2 more than its width. Find the length and width.   L = 9, W = 7

62. A rectangle of area 90 has a width 9 less than its length. Find the length and width.   L = 15, W = 6

63. The area of a rectangle is 96 square kilometers. Its width is 4 km less than its length. Find its dimensions.   L = 12 km, W = 8 km

64. The area of a rectangle is 567 square centimeters. Its length is 6 cm more than its width. Find its dimensions.   L = 27 cm, W = 21 cm

Problems 65, 66, 76, 77, and 78 must be worked algebraically, because the answers are irrational.

65. The area of a rectangle is 52.7 square meters. Its length is 2 meters more than its width. Find its dimensions.   L = 8.33 m, W = 6.33 m

66. The area of a rectangle is 3247 square millimeters. Its width is 51 mm less than its length. Find its dimensions.   L = 87.93 mm, W = 36.93 mm

67. A rectangle has a perimeter of 34 and an area of 60. Find its dimensions.   L = 12, W = 5

68. A rectangle has a perimeter of 32 and an area of 60. Find its dimensions.   L = 10, W = 6

69. *Larger Field Problem*   Terry Torrey has a rectangular field 3 kilometers by 7 kilometers. He desires to purchase 24 square kilometers more, thus increasing the length and the width by equal amounts (see sketch). Find *x*, the number of kilometers by which length and width are increased.   2 km

Problems 69–78 involve borders around rectangles. Students often have difficulty visualizing the relationship between the width of the strip and the other dimensions. Drawing the dimensions as in Example 5 helps. This way, for example, the two *x*'s and the 7 clearly add up to *W*. Finding *W* is thus equivalent to the problems, "Find the length marked '?'" in Section 1–2 at the beginning of the book.

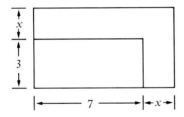

70. *Road and Field Problem*   A rectangular tract of land 20 m by 30 m has part of its area covered by an L-shaped road, which goes around two sides. The road is the same width on both sides, and its area is 184 square meters. What are the dimensions of the part of the tract *not* covered by the road?   16 m by 26 m

71. *Patio Painting Problem*   Patty O'Cover paints a rectangle in one corner of a 24-ft by 18-ft patio. Her instructions are to cover $\frac{1}{6}$ of the area of the patio. The unpainted strip is to be the same width on both sides. What are the dimensions of the painted rectangle?   6 ft by 12 ft

72. *Rug Problem*   A rug 4 m by 5 m covers $\frac{2}{3}$ of the floor area in a room. The rug touches two walls, leaving a strip of uniform width around the other two walls. How wide is the strip?   1 m

73. How wide a strip could be added to all four sides of a 9-by-12 rectangle to form a new rectangle of area 180?   1.5

74. How wide a strip could be added to all four sides of a 20-by-30 rectangle to form a new rectangle one less than half the original area?   3.5

75. *Picture Frame Problem*   Matt Cutter makes a cardboard frame to go around the edges of an 8 cm by 10 cm photograph. The frame has an area of 63 square centimeters and is of equal width all the way around. What is this width?   1.5 cm

76. *Lawn Problem*   A landscape architect plans a rectangular back yard with flower beds of equal width completely surrounding a rectangular lawn. The yard has dimensions of 47 m by 39 m. The lawn is to occupy 90% of the total area. How wide are the flower beds?   1.09 m

77. *Swimming Pool Problem*   A rectangular tract of land 40 m by 46 m is to have a rectangular swimming pool built in the middle of it. The pool is to occupy 60% of the area of the tract. The edges of the pool are all to be the *same* distance from the edges of the tract. What are the dimensions of the pool?   30.36 m by 36.36 m

78. *Oil Lease Problem*   Earl Wells leases a rectangular tract of land 5.3 km by 4.1 km. He can drill for oil on the inner 70% of the tract but must leave a strip of land of uniform width around the edges containing the other 30% of the land. How close can the wells come to the boundaries of the tract?   0.38 km

Time: 1 day

Test Ideas:

Your test can be either over the whole chapter or can concentrate on topics such as splitting the middle term, solving quadratics by factoring, and working problems. It is suggested that you give full credit for problems worked mentally, as long as the student justifies the answer. In fact, you may want to give extra credit for a clever solution if it is well explained. You should also give some problems with simple equation solving by factoring so that the student must demonstrate that technique. Also, there should be some problems with irrational or fractional answers that cannot be found easily by trial and error.

10-9   CHAPTER REVIEW AND TEST

In this chapter you have learned how to operate with polynomials that are more complicated than before. You found the greatest common factor (GCF) for pairs of integers, for pairs of polynomials, and for terms within a polynomial. Next you worked with polynomials with common binomial factors. The factoring-by-grouping technique allowed you to factor harder quadratic trinomials by splitting the middle term. Factoring gave an alternate way to solve quadratic equations without using the Quadratic Formula. This technique gave you a quick way to solve word problems of the type found on standardized tests and on contests.

Try working the following test quickly enough to finish it in the time normally allowed for a classroom test.

CHAPTER TEST

1. What is the:
   a. definition of greatest common factor;
   b. meaning of *relatively prime;*
   c. first step in factoring any polynomial;
   d. converse of the multiplication property of zero;
   e. discriminant test for factorability?

2. Factor completely.
   a. $8x^2 - 16x - 280$ $8(x - 7)(x + 5)$
   b. $x^5 + 13x^4 + 30x^3$ $x^3(x + 10)(x + 3)$
   c. $2x^3 - 50x$ $2x(x + 5)(x - 5)$
   d. $r^2(x + 11) - s^2(x + 11)$ $(x + 11)(r + s)(r - s)$
   e. $ab - 3ax + 2bx - 6x^2$ $(b - 3x)(a + 2x)$
   f. $7x^2 - 15xy + 2y^2$ $(7x - y)(x - 2y)$

3. Use splitting the middle term to factor the polynomial completely or to show that it is prime.
   a. $10x^2 + 7x - 12$ $(5x - 4)(2x + 3)$
   b. $9x^2 - 56x + 12$ $(9x - 2)(x - 6)$
   c. $15x^2 + 80x + 24$ Prime

4. Solve by factoring.
   a. $x^2 - 2x - 15 = 0$ $S = \{-3, 5\}$
   b. $2x^2 - 13x + 20 = 0$ $S = \{\frac{5}{2}, 4\}$
   c. $3x^2 + 4x + 1 = 0$ $S = \{-\frac{1}{3}, -1\}$

5. Factor (if necessary). Then find the GCF.
   a. $x^2 - 4, x + 2$ $(x + 2)$
   b. $x^2 + 6x + 9, x^2 + x - 6$ $(x + 3)$
   c. $(x - 2)(x + 3), (x + 2)(x - 4)$ 1, (Relatively prime)

6. *Age Problem*   A is 5 years older than B. The product of their ages is 84. How old is each?   A is 12, B is 7

7. *Consecutive Integers Problem*   Find two consecutive odd integers if their product is 63.   7, 9, or −7, −9

8. *Digits Problem*   The units digit of a two-digit number is 1 less than the square of the tens digit. The number with the digits reversed is 7 more than twice the original number. Find the original number.   38

9. *Coin Problem*   Twelve dimes and quarters have a total value of $1.65. How many of each are there?   3 quarters, 9 dimes

Assignment:

After test: Study Section 11–1. Work the examples. Work Exercise 11–1, #1–9 odd or 2–10 even.

1. a. The GCF of two positive integers a and b is the greatest integer for which $a/\text{GCF} = $ integer and $b/\text{GCF} = $ integer.
    b. Two integers are relatively prime if they have no common prime factors.
    c. First step: Factor out any common factors.
    d. If a product of real numbers equals zero, then one of its factors is zero.
    e. A quadratic trinomial $ax^2 + bx + c$ can be factored if and only if the discriminant, $b^2 - 4ac$, is a perfect square.

10. *Relative Rate Problem*   C starts out going 40 miles per hour (mi/h). Three hours later, D starts out after C from the same point, going 60 mi/h. How long does it take D to catch up with C?   6 hrs

11. *Rectangle Problem*   A rectangle 8 feet by 6 feet has a border of uniform width around the inside of all four edges. If the border has area 33 square feet, how wide is the border?   1.5 ft

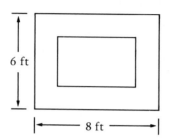

11

Rational Algebraic Expressions

You know how to add, multiply, and simplify fractions. In this chapter you will do these things with fractions that contain variables. You will evaluate them for given values of the variable or solve equations to find the value of the variable. A good example is a problem involving motion with or against a current, where time equals distance divided by rate. The rate is a sum or difference of the boat's rate and the current's rate.

Variable:

x Speed of tugboat in water

Expressions:

$x - 8$ Speeds of tugboat with
$x + 8$ respect to land, upstream
          and downstream

$\dfrac{200}{x - 8} + \dfrac{50}{x + 8}$ Total time for
200 miles up-
stream, 50 miles
downstream

Equation:

$\dfrac{200}{x - 8} + \dfrac{50}{x + 8} = 52.5$

       Total time is 52.5 hours.

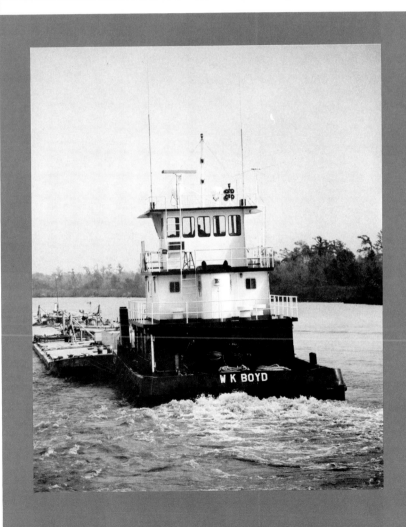

INTRODUCTION TO RATIONAL ALGEBRAIC
EXPRESSIONS AND EQUATIONS

Time: $\frac{1}{2}$ day, with Section 11-2

Chalkboard Examples:

1. Evaluate $\frac{x + 5}{x - 3}$ if:

   a. x is 7;   Ans.: 3

   b. x is 9;   Ans.: $\frac{1}{3}$

   c. x is 3.   Ans.: Undefined. $\left(\frac{8}{0}\right)$

2. For $\frac{x + 5}{x - 3}$, find x if:

   the expression equals 6. Ans.: 4.6

Assignment:

Problems 1–9 odd already should have been
assigned following the test on Chapter 10. If
not, assign Problems 1 and 7 with problems
from Exercise 11-2. The even-numbered problems will be assigned one at a time later on.

A rational algebraic expression is an expression that has a polynomial for
its numerator and a polynomial for its denominator. Two rational expressions are

$$\frac{x + 3}{x - 2} \quad \text{and} \quad \frac{x^2 - 3x + 2}{x - 5}.$$

DEFINITION

RATIONAL ALGEBRAIC EXPRESSION
A **rational algebraic expression** is an expression that can be written
as a ratio of two polynomials,

$$\frac{\text{polynomial}}{\text{polynomial}}.$$

(The denominator polynomial cannot be 0.)

It is easy to evaluate a rational expression such as

$$\frac{x - 5}{x + 4}.$$

All you need to do is substitute a given value of x and do the arithmetic.
For instance, if x is 3, then

$$\frac{x - 5}{x + 4}$$

$$= \frac{3 - 5}{3 + 4}$$

$$= \frac{-2}{7}.$$

Finding x when you know the value of the expression takes a bit more work. For instance, if the expression above equals 9, you write

$$\frac{x - 5}{x + 4} = 9.$$

This equation is called a **fractional equation.** It can be transformed to a simpler one by getting rid of the fraction. To do this, you multiply each member by $(x + 4)$.

$$(x + 4) \cdot \frac{x - 5}{x + 4} = (x + 4)(9)$$

The left member becomes $x - 5$. The 9 can be distributed in the right member. The result is

$$x - 5 = 9x + 36.$$

From here on the problem is easy.

$$-8x = 41$$

$$x = -\frac{41}{8}$$

If you want a decimal answer, you can divide and get

$$\underline{\underline{x = -5.125}}$$

The result can be checked by substituting -5.125 for x and doing the arithmetic.

$$\frac{x - 5}{x + 4}$$

$$= \frac{-5.125 - 5}{-5.125 + 4}$$

$$= \frac{-10.125}{-1.125}$$

$$= 9 \ \blacktriangleright$$

Objective :
Given a rational algebraic expression, find its value when you know what x equals, and find out what x equals when you know the value of the expression.

Cover the answers as you work the examples on the next page.

EXAMPLE 1

Evaluate $\dfrac{x + 7}{x - 2}$ if:

a. x is 5;   b. x is -7;   c. x is 2.

– – – –

Think These Reasons

a.
$$\dfrac{x + 7}{x - 2}$$ Write the given expression.

$$= \dfrac{5 + 7}{5 - 2}$$ Substitute 5 for x.

$$= \dfrac{12}{3}$$ Do the computation.

$$= \underline{4}$$ Divide.

– – – – –

b.
$$\dfrac{x + 7}{x - 2}$$ Write the given expression.

$$= \dfrac{-7 + 7}{-7 - 2}$$ Substitute -7 for x.

$$= \dfrac{0}{-9}$$ Do the computation.

$$= \underline{0}$$ Divide.

– – – – –

c.
$$\dfrac{x + 7}{x - 2}$$ Write the given expression.

$$= \dfrac{2 + 7}{2 - 2}$$ Substitute 2 for x.

$$= \dfrac{9}{0}$$ Do the computation.

$$\underline{\text{No value}}$$ $\dfrac{9}{0}$ is not a real number.

EXAMPLE 2

Find x if $\dfrac{x + 7}{x - 2}$ equals 3. Check your answer.

– – – – –

$$\dfrac{x + 7}{x - 2} = 3$$ Write an equation.

$$x + 7 = 3(x - 2) \qquad \text{Multiply each member by } x - 2.$$

$$x + 7 = 3x - 6 \qquad \text{Distribute 3.}$$

$$-2x = -13 \qquad \text{Subtract } 3x \text{ and subtract 7.}$$

$$\underline{x = 6.5} \qquad \text{Divide by } -2.$$

Check: $\qquad \dfrac{x + 7}{x - 2}$

$$= \dfrac{6.5 + 7}{6.5 - 2} \qquad \text{Substitute 6.5 for } x.$$

$$= \dfrac{13.5}{4.5} \qquad \text{Do the computation.}$$

$$= 3 \quad \text{✔} \qquad \text{Divide. The answer checks.}$$

The following exercise has more problems like these.

EXERCISE 11-1

1. Evaluate $\dfrac{x - 9}{x + 4}$ if:

    a. x is 6; $-\frac{3}{10}$
    b. x is -5; 14
    c. x is 9. 0

2. Evaluate $\dfrac{x - 10}{x + 3}$ if:

    a. x is 2; $-\frac{8}{5}$
    b. x is -5; $\frac{15}{2}$
    c. x is -3. No value

Problem Notes:

These problems carry out the theme of this text—specifically, that there are two things one does with expressions, evaluate them when x is known or find x when the expression's value is known.

3. Evaluate $\dfrac{2x + 7}{x - 5}$ if:

    a. x is 8; $\frac{23}{3}$
    b. x is -3; $-\frac{1}{8}$
    c. x is 5. No value

4. Evaluate $\dfrac{3x + 6}{x - 4}$ if:

    a. x is 7; 9
    b. x is -2; 0
    c. x is 4. No value

5. Evaluate $\dfrac{x^2 + 5x + 6}{x^2 + 7x + 10}$ if:

    a. x is 5; $\frac{4}{5}$
    b. x is -3; 0
    c. x is 0. $\frac{3}{5}$

6. Evaluate $\dfrac{x^2 + 6x + 8}{x^2 + 9x + 20}$ if:

    a. x is 3; $\frac{5}{8}$
    b. x is -5; No value
    c. x is 0. $\frac{2}{5}$

7. For $\dfrac{x - 9}{x + 4}$, find x if:

    a. the expression equals 3; -10.5
    b. the expression equals -4. -1.4

8. For $\dfrac{x - 10}{x + 3}$, find x if:

    a. the expression equals 5; -6.25;
    b. the expression equals -4. -0.4

9. For $\dfrac{2x + 7}{x - 5}$, find x if:

   a. the expression equals 10; 7.125

   b. the expression equals 2.
      (Surprising?) No value

10. For $\dfrac{3x + 6}{x - 4}$, find x if:

   a. the expression equals 8; 7.6

   b. the expression equals 3.
      (Surprising?) No value

11-2 | **SIMPLIFYING RATIONAL ALGEBRAIC EXPRESSIONS**

In Section 9-4, you used the multiplication property of fractions to simplify fractions.

$$\frac{24}{36}$$

$$= \frac{12 \cdot 2}{12 \cdot 3}$$ 12 is the GCF of 24 and 36.

$$= \frac{12}{12} \cdot \frac{2}{3}$$ Use the multiplication property of fractions.

$$= \frac{2}{3}$$ Use the multiplication property of 1. $\dfrac{12}{12}$ equals 1.

The same procedure is used to simplify fractions that contain variables. You factor the numerator and denominator and then get rid of the common factors.

$$\frac{x^2 - 2x - 35}{x^2 + 7x + 10}$$

$$= \frac{(x + 5)(x - 7)}{(x + 5)(x + 2)}$$ Factor the numerator and denominator.

$$= \frac{x + 5}{x + 5} \cdot \frac{x - 7}{x + 2}$$ Use the multiplication property of fractions.

$$= \frac{x - 7}{x + 2}$$ Use the multiplication property of 1: $\dfrac{x + 5}{x + 5}$ equals 1.

The next-to-last line looks like the step in making fractions have common denominators in which you multiplied by an appropriate form of 1. The line above can be thought of as: Multiply the numerator and denominator by the same number. With this in mind, you can go directly from

$$\frac{(x + 5)(x - 7)}{(x + 5)(x + 2)} \quad \text{to} \quad \frac{x - 7}{x + 2}.$$

Your thought process should be: *Divide* the numerator and denominator by the same number. This process is called *canceling,* because the common factor in the numerator and the denominator seems to cancel out.

DEFINITION

> **CANCELING**
> To **cancel** in a fraction means to *divide* the numerator and denominator by the same common factor. That is, for real numbers a, b, and c, with $a \neq 0$ and $c \neq 0$,
>
> $$\frac{ab}{ac} = \frac{b}{c}.$$

Do not read more into the definition of canceling than is there! For instance, in

$$\frac{x - 7}{x + 2},$$

you *cannot* cancel the x's. Since canceling is a *division* process, dividing the numerator and denominator by x would give

$$\frac{1 - \dfrac{7}{x}}{1 + \dfrac{2}{x}},$$

which is not simpler than the original fraction. Canceling can be done only when the numerator and denominator each consists of *one* term with common *factors* or can be written in that form.

Objective:
Be able to cancel common factors from the numerator and denominator of a rational algebraic expression.

Cover the answers as you work these examples.

EXAMPLE 1

Simplify: $\dfrac{15x^8}{25x^2}$.

– – – – –   – – – – –

	Think These Reasons
$$\frac{15x^8}{25x^2}$$	Write the given expression.
$$= \frac{3x^6}{5}$$	Cancel 5 for the coefficients. Subtract exponents for the powers.

EXAMPLE 2

Simplify: $\dfrac{(x + 5)(x - 4)}{(x + 5)(x + 4)}$.

- - - - -   - - - - -

$$\frac{(x + 5)(x - 4)}{(x + 5)(x + 4)}$$	Write the given expression.
$$= \frac{x - 4}{x + 4}$$	Cancel the $(x + 5)$ factors. There are *no* other common factors. Do not cancel the *terms x* or 4!

EXAMPLE 3

Simplify: $\dfrac{2x^2 - 4x - 30}{2x^2 - 7x - 15}$.

- - - - -   - - - - -

$$\frac{2x^2 - 4x - 30}{2x^2 - 7x - 15}$$	Write the given expression.
$$= \frac{2(x^2 - 2x - 15)}{2x^2 - 7x - 15}$$	Factor out any *common* factors *first*.
$$= \frac{2(x - 5)(x + 3)}{(2x + 3)(x - 5)}$$	Factor the trinomials.
$$= \frac{2(x + 3)}{2x + 3} \quad \text{or} \quad \frac{2x + 6}{2x + 3}$$	Cancel the $(x - 5)$ factors. Nothing else cancels.

ORAL PRACTICE

Can canceling be done? If so, *what* can be canceled?

A. Yes. $(x + 3)$

A. $\dfrac{2(x + 3)}{3(x + 3)}$ **B.** $\dfrac{3(x + 4)}{3(x + 5)}$ Yes. 3   **C.** $\dfrac{4(x + 4)}{6(x + 3)}$ Yes. 2

D. $\dfrac{2(x + 3)}{2(y + 3)}$ Yes. 2   E. $\dfrac{2(x + 3)}{2x + 3}$ No   • F. $\dfrac{8x}{12x}$ Yes. 4x

G. $\dfrac{(x + 4)(3)}{12(x + 4)}$ H. $\dfrac{x + 3}{x - 3}$ No   I. $\dfrac{(x + 3)(x + 4)}{(x + 3)(x - 4)}$

J. $\dfrac{(x - 2)(x + 3)}{(x + 3)(x - 2)}$ • K. $\dfrac{x^2 - 9}{x + 3}$ Yes. (x + 3)

G.   Yes. 3(x + 4)
I.   Yes (x + 3)
J.   Yes. (x − 2)(x + 3)

EXERCISE 11-2

For Problems 1 through 30, simplify the expression.

1. $\dfrac{12x^3}{18x^5}$ $\dfrac{2}{3x^2}$

2. $\dfrac{24x^2}{36x^6}$ $\dfrac{2}{3x^4}$

3. $\dfrac{25x^2y^8}{10x^3y^5}$ $\dfrac{5y^3}{2x}$

4. $\dfrac{35x^7y^4}{21x^2y^7}$ $\dfrac{5x^5}{3y^3}$

5. $\dfrac{(x + 3)(x - 2)}{(x + 5)(x - 2)}$ $\dfrac{x + 3}{x + 5}$

6. $\dfrac{(x - 7)(x + 4)}{(x - 6)(x + 4)}$ $\dfrac{x - 7}{x - 6}$

7. $\dfrac{(x - 8)(x + 2)}{(x + 4)(x - 8)}$ $\dfrac{x + 2}{x + 4}$

8. $\dfrac{(x - 12)(x + 6)}{(x + 6)(x - 3)}$ $\dfrac{x - 12}{x - 3}$

9. $\dfrac{(2x + 5)(x + 1)}{(2x - 5)(x + 1)}$ $\dfrac{2x + 5}{2x - 5}$

10. $\dfrac{(3x - 7)(x - 4)}{(3x - 7)(x + 4)}$ $\dfrac{x - 4}{x + 4}$

11. $\dfrac{x^2 + x - 6}{x^2 - 4}$ $\dfrac{x + 3}{x + 2}$

12. $\dfrac{x^2 - 3x - 18}{x^2 - 36}$ $\dfrac{x + 3}{x + 6}$

13. $\dfrac{x^2 + 2x - 3}{x^2 + 7x + 12}$ $\dfrac{x - 1}{x + 4}$

14. $\dfrac{x^2 + 2x - 8}{x^2 - 5x + 6}$ $\dfrac{x + 4}{x - 3}$

15. $\dfrac{x^2 + 2x - 35}{x^2 + x - 30}$ $\dfrac{x + 7}{x + 6}$

16. $\dfrac{x^2 + 9x + 8}{x^2 - 6x - 7}$ $\dfrac{x + 8}{x - 7}$

17. $\dfrac{3x^3 + 5x^2}{6x + 10}$ $\dfrac{x^2}{2}$

18. $\dfrac{3x^2 + 12x}{x^4 + 4x^3}$ $\dfrac{3}{x^2}$

19. $\dfrac{5x^2 - 20}{x^2 + 5x + 6}$ $\dfrac{5(x - 2)}{x + 3}$

20. $\dfrac{7x^2 - 63}{x^2 + 7x + 12}$ $\dfrac{7(x - 3)}{x + 4}$

21. $\dfrac{2x^2 - 5x - 3}{2x^2 - 3x - 2}$ $\dfrac{x - 3}{x - 2}$

22. $\dfrac{3x^2 - 5x - 2}{3x^2 + 7x + 2}$ $\dfrac{x - 2}{x + 2}$

23. $\dfrac{4x^2 - x - 3}{3x^2 + x - 4}$ $\dfrac{4x + 3}{3x + 4}$

24. $\dfrac{5x^2 - 9x - 2}{4x^2 - 7x - 2}$ $\dfrac{5x + 1}{4x + 1}$

Problem Notes:

For Problem 17 on, there is sometimes a common factor that should be factored out first.

Beware of common mistakes such as canceling *terms*. The most mathematically honest way to dispel this misconception is to point out that canceling is a *division* process and that division would have to be distributed to all terms in the numerator and denominator. See the text example after the definition of canceling.

25. $\dfrac{10x^2 - 19x + 6}{10x^2 - 21x + 9}$ $\dfrac{5x - 2}{5x - 3}$

26. $\dfrac{8x^2 + 10x + 3}{8x^2 + 2x - 3}$ $\dfrac{2x + 1}{2x - 1}$

27. $\dfrac{3x^2 + 27x + 60}{3x^2 + 12x - 15}$ $\dfrac{x + 4}{x - 1}$

28. $\dfrac{5x^2 + 10x - 40}{5x^2 + 15x - 20}$ $\dfrac{x - 2}{x - 1}$

29. $\dfrac{12x^2 - 27}{4x^2 - 2x - 12}$ $\dfrac{6x - 9}{2x - 4}$

30. $\dfrac{45x^2 - 20}{9x^2 + 6x - 8}$ $\dfrac{15x + 10}{3x + 4}$

31. Find x if $\dfrac{x + 6}{x + 9} = 4$. -10

32. Find x if $\dfrac{x + 7}{x - 5} = 2$. 17

33. For what value of x is $\dfrac{x - 3}{x + 5}$
    a.   equal to zero?   3
    b.   undefined? -5

34. For what value of x is $\dfrac{x - 6}{x - 7}$
    a.   equal to zero?   6
    b.   undefined?   7

11-3   MULTIPLYING AND DIVIDING RATIONAL EXPRESSIONS

Time: 2 days

Chalkboard Examples:

First day: Use the two examples in the text.

Second day: Homework problems at the board.

Assignments:

Day 1: Exercise 11–3, #1 through 33 odd
Exercise 10–8, one selected word problem

Day 2: Exercise 11–3, #8 through 32, every fourth problem
Exercise 11–3, #35 through 45 odd, and 51

Problem Notes:

Problems 1 through 10 are rather boring since not much canceling can be done. The problems show mainly the technique of multiplying and dividing rational expressions.

Problems 11 through 24 involve only monomials.

Problems 25 through 50 involve progressively trickier expressions involving binomials, factoring, or both.

You should recall that to multiply two fractions you multiply numerator by numerator and denominator by denominator. For instance,

$$\frac{2}{5} \cdot \frac{3}{7} = \frac{2 \cdot 3}{5 \cdot 7} = \frac{6}{35}.$$

Dividing fractions is done by multiplying the first fraction by the reciprocal of the second. For instance,

$$\frac{2}{5} \div \frac{3}{7} = \frac{2}{5} \cdot \frac{7}{3} = \frac{2 \cdot 7}{5 \cdot 3} = \frac{14}{15}.$$

In this section you will do the same thing with algebraic fractions (that is, with rational algebraic expressions).

Objective:

Given two rational expressions, multiply them or divide them, and simplify the answer.

Cover the answers as you work these examples.

EXAMPLE 1

Given $\dfrac{12x}{15}$ and $\dfrac{20x}{18}$:

a.   multiply them;
b.   divide the first by the second.

– – – – –

Problems 51 through 54 give a review of Section 11-1.

– – – – –

	Think These Reasons

a. $\dfrac{12x}{15} \cdot \dfrac{20x}{18}$

Multiply the given expressions.

$= \dfrac{12 \cdot 20x^2}{15 \cdot 18}$

Multiply numerator by numerator and denominator by denominator.

$= \dfrac{8}{9}x^2$

Do the canceling.

b. $\dfrac{12x}{15} \div \dfrac{20x}{18}$

Divide the first by the second.

$= \dfrac{12x}{15} \cdot \dfrac{18}{20x}$

Change dividing to multiplying by the reciprocal.

$= \dfrac{12 \cdot 18x}{15 \cdot 20x}$

Multiply.

$= \dfrac{27}{20}$

Do the canceling.

EXAMPLE 2

Divide and simplify: $\dfrac{x^2 - 2x - 15}{4x^2 + 8x} \div \dfrac{x + 3}{4x - 20}$

– – – – –   – – – – –

$\dfrac{x^2 - 2x - 15}{4x^2 + 8x} \div \dfrac{x + 3}{4x - 20}$

Write the given expression.

$= \dfrac{x^2 - 2x - 15}{4x^2 + 8x} \cdot \dfrac{4x - 20}{x + 3}$

Write dividing as multiplying by the reciprocal.

$= \dfrac{(x - 5)(x + 3)}{4x(x + 2)} \cdot \dfrac{4(x - 5)}{x + 3}$

Factor.

$= \dfrac{(x - 5)(x + 3)(4)(x - 5)}{4x(x + 2)(x + 3)}$

Multiply.

$= \dfrac{(x - 5)(x - 5)}{x(x + 2)}$

Cancel.

$= \dfrac{x^2 - 10x + 25}{x^2 + 2x}$

Multiply.

ORAL PRACTICE

Multiply or divide, and simplify.

A. $\dfrac{2}{3x} \cdot \dfrac{6}{3x}$ $\dfrac{4}{3x^2}$

B. $\dfrac{2}{3x} \div \dfrac{6}{3x}$ $\dfrac{1}{3}$

C. $\dfrac{5}{6a} \cdot \dfrac{3a}{2}$ $\dfrac{5}{4}$

D. $\dfrac{5}{6a} \div \dfrac{3a}{2}$ $\dfrac{5}{9a^2}$

E. $\dfrac{C}{3} \cdot \dfrac{5}{C}$ $\dfrac{5}{3}$

F. $\dfrac{C}{3} \div \dfrac{5}{C}$ $\dfrac{c^2}{15}$

G. $\dfrac{x^3}{4} \cdot \dfrac{8}{x}$ $2x^2$

H. $\dfrac{3}{4p} \div \dfrac{1}{12p^4}$ $9p^3$

I. $\dfrac{3}{2} \cdot \dfrac{x+5}{12}$ $\dfrac{x+5}{8}$

J. $\dfrac{4}{x+1} \div \dfrac{5}{x+1}$ $\dfrac{4}{5}$

K. $\dfrac{2}{x-7} \cdot \dfrac{x-7}{8}$ $\dfrac{1}{4}$

L. $\dfrac{2}{3} \div \dfrac{3}{x-2}$ $\dfrac{2x-4}{9}$

EXERCISE 11-3

1. a. $\dfrac{56}{45x^2}$

   b. $\dfrac{72}{35}$

2. a. $\dfrac{7}{33x^2}$

   b. $\dfrac{77}{12}$

3. a. $\dfrac{55}{216x^2}$

   b. $\dfrac{15}{22}$

4. a. $\dfrac{28}{27x^2}$

   b. $\dfrac{16}{21}$

5. a. $\dfrac{x^2+3x}{48}$

   b. $\dfrac{x}{3x+9}$

6. a. $\dfrac{x^2-3x}{50}$

   b. $\dfrac{x}{2x-6}$

7. a. $\dfrac{x^2-11x+30}{x^2-4x-21}$

   b. $\dfrac{x^2-13x+42}{x^2-2x-15}$

8. a. $\dfrac{x^2+x-12}{x^2+13x+42}$

   b. $\dfrac{x^2+10x+24}{x^2+4x-21}$

9. a. $\dfrac{8x^2+22x+15}{3x^2+5x-2}$

   b. $\dfrac{2x^2+7x+6}{12x^2+11x-5}$

10. a. $\dfrac{15x^2-26x+8}{2x^2-17x+8}$

    b. $\dfrac{3x^2-28x+32}{10x^2-9x+2}$

For Problems 1 through 10:

a. multiply the two expressions;
b. divide the first expression by the second.

1. $\dfrac{8}{5x}, \dfrac{7}{9x}$

2. $\dfrac{7}{6x}, \dfrac{2}{11x}$

3. $\dfrac{5}{12x}, \dfrac{11}{18x}$

4. $\dfrac{8}{9x}, \dfrac{7}{6x}$

5. $\dfrac{x}{12}, \dfrac{x+3}{4}$

6. $\dfrac{x}{10}, \dfrac{x-3}{5}$

7. $\dfrac{x-6}{x+3}, \dfrac{x-5}{x-7}$

8. $\dfrac{x+4}{x+7}, \dfrac{x-3}{x+6}$

9. $\dfrac{2x+3}{3x-1}, \dfrac{4x+5}{x+2}$

10. $\dfrac{3x-4}{2x-1}, \dfrac{5x-2}{x-8}$

For Problems 11 through 50, do the multiplication and division and simplify.

11. $\dfrac{6x}{5y} \cdot \dfrac{10y}{8x}$ $\dfrac{3}{2}$

12. $\dfrac{8x}{3y} \cdot \dfrac{12y}{16x}$ 2

13. $\dfrac{5a}{7b} \div \dfrac{25a}{21b}$ $\dfrac{3}{5}$

14. $\dfrac{9c}{14d} \div \dfrac{12c}{21d}$ $\dfrac{9}{8}$

15. $\dfrac{20p}{49s} \cdot \dfrac{42p}{10s}$ $\quad \frac{12p^2}{7s^2}$

16. $\dfrac{24r}{55k} \cdot \dfrac{66r}{8k}$ $\quad \frac{18r^2}{5k^2}$

17. $\dfrac{30m}{13t} \div \dfrac{15t}{52m}$ $\quad \frac{8m^2}{t^2}$

18. $\dfrac{40e}{17f} \div \dfrac{30f}{51e}$ $\quad \frac{4e^2}{f^2}$

19. $\dfrac{6ab^2}{35b} \cdot \dfrac{42a}{18ab}$ $\quad \frac{2a}{5}$

20. $\dfrac{32xy^3}{9x} \cdot \dfrac{15x}{16xy}$ $\quad \frac{10y^2}{3}$

21. $\dfrac{3p^2c^3}{5c^6} \div \dfrac{12p^4c}{10c^2}$ $\quad \frac{1}{2p^2c^2}$

22. $\dfrac{22xyz}{27x} \div \dfrac{33xz}{5y}$ $\quad \frac{10y^2}{81x}$

23. $\dfrac{5r}{4s} \cdot \dfrac{6r}{10s} \cdot \dfrac{8t}{12t}$ $\quad \frac{r^2}{2s^2}$

24. $\dfrac{10m}{11p} \cdot \dfrac{44p}{20k} \cdot \dfrac{15k}{8m}$ $\quad \frac{15}{4}$

25. $\dfrac{6x+12}{3x-9} \cdot \dfrac{5x-15}{4x+8}$ $\quad \frac{5}{2}$

26. $\dfrac{3x-12}{8x+12} \cdot \dfrac{12x+18}{5x-20}$ $\quad \frac{9}{10}$

27. $\dfrac{c^2-d^2}{4c} \cdot \dfrac{6c^3}{(c+d)^2}$ $\quad \frac{3c^3-3c^2d}{2c+2d}$

28. $\dfrac{3h^4}{(h-p)^2} \cdot \dfrac{h^2-p^2}{12h}$ $\quad \frac{h^4+h^3p}{4h-4p}$

29. $\dfrac{4u^2-1}{u^3-16u} \cdot \dfrac{u^2+4u}{2u-1}$ $\quad \frac{2u+1}{u-4}$

30. $\dfrac{v^2-9}{v^2+3v} \cdot \dfrac{v^3}{v^3-3v^2}$ $\quad 1$

31. $\dfrac{7x-14y}{x+6y} \div \dfrac{21}{3x+9y}$ $\quad \frac{x^2+xy-6y^2}{x+6y}$

32. $\dfrac{24}{a+4b} \div \dfrac{8a+12b}{2a+8b}$ $\quad \frac{12}{2a+3b}$

33. $\dfrac{5a+15}{a^2-9} \div \dfrac{5a-15}{(a-3)^2}$ $\quad 1$

34. $\dfrac{12-4x}{10+5x} \div \dfrac{9-x^2}{4-x^2}$ $\quad \frac{8-4x}{15+5x}$

35. $\dfrac{x^2+2x-35}{6x^3} \cdot \dfrac{2x^2-6x}{x^2+4x-21}$ $\quad \frac{x-5}{3x^2}$

36. $\dfrac{d^2+4d-45}{4d-20} \cdot \dfrac{3d-3}{d^2-81}$ $\quad \frac{3d-3}{4d-36}$

37. $\dfrac{y^2+3y-18}{y^2-8y+12} \cdot \dfrac{2y-4}{y^2-36}$ $\quad \frac{2y-6}{y^2-12y+36}$

38. $\dfrac{x^2-x-2}{x^2-2x+1} \cdot \dfrac{x-1}{x+1}$ $\quad \frac{x-2}{x-1}$

39. $\dfrac{2c^2+5c+2}{2c^2+c-6} \div \dfrac{6c+3}{2c-3}$ $\quad \frac{1}{3}$

40. $\dfrac{3x^2+6x+9}{4x+6} \div \dfrac{4x^2+8x+12}{2x+3}$ $\quad \frac{3}{8}$

41. $\dfrac{a^3+ab^2}{a^3-2a^2b} \div \dfrac{a^2+b^2}{(a-2b)^2}$ $\quad \frac{a-2b}{a}$

42. $\dfrac{k^2v-5k^2}{v^2-4} \div \dfrac{kv-5k}{v+2}$ $\quad \frac{k}{v-2}$

43. $\dfrac{6x+12}{8x-4} \cdot \dfrac{3x-9}{12x+6} \div \dfrac{3x^2-12}{8x^2-2}$ $\quad \frac{x-3}{2x-4}$

44. $\dfrac{5a^2-5a}{4a^3} \cdot \dfrac{a^2-9a-b}{4a-40} \div \dfrac{2a^2-2}{a}$ $\quad \frac{5}{32a}$

45. $\dfrac{x^3-9x}{8} \div \dfrac{x+3}{2} \cdot \dfrac{4}{3x-9}$ $\quad \frac{x}{3}$

46. $\dfrac{b^2 - 7b + 10}{b^2 - 6b + 5} \div \dfrac{1}{b - 2} \cdot \dfrac{b + 1}{b^2 - 4b + 4}$ $\dfrac{b + 1}{b - 1}$

47. $\dfrac{t^2 + 2t - 8}{t + 4} \cdot (t - 2)^{-1}$ 1

48. $\dfrac{x^2 - 2x - 3}{x + 1} \cdot 5(x - 3)^{-1}$ 5

49. $\dfrac{4x + 6}{4x + 5}$

50. $\dfrac{x - 4}{x^3 + 10x^2 + 12x - 72}$

49. $\dfrac{2x + 3}{4x + 5} \div \dfrac{4x + 5}{2x + 3} \cdot \dfrac{8x + 10}{2x + 3}$

50. $(x^2 + 4x - 12)^{-1} \div \dfrac{x + 6}{x - 4}$

51. Find x if $\dfrac{x + 3}{x - 2} = 5$. $\dfrac{13}{4}$

52. Find x if $\dfrac{2x + 5}{x - 11} = 2$.   no solution

53. For what value of x is $\dfrac{x - 7}{x + 2}$

   a. equal to zero?   7
   b. undefined? -2

54. For what value of x is $\dfrac{2x + 7}{x - 4}$

   a. equal to zero? -3.5
   b. undefined?   4

11-4 | LEAST COMMON MULTIPLE

Time: 2 days

Chalkboard Examples:

First day:
Find the LCM:

1. $15r^6m^4$ and $20r^9m^3$ Ans.: $60r^9m^4$

2. $2x + 3$ and $x - 12$
   Ans.: $(2x + 3)(x - 12)$
   There are *no* common factors!

3. $x^2 + 4x - 5$ and $x^2 - 11x - 10$
   Ans.: $(x + 5)(x - 1)(x - 10)$
   $(x - 1)$ is a common factor.

Second day:
Homework problems at the board.

Assignments:

Day 1: Exercise 11–4, #1 through 29 odd.
   Exercise 11–3, selected problems from 34 through 54 even.
   Exercise 10–8, one word problem.
Day 2: Exercise 11–4, #2 through 3 even
   Exercise 11–4, #31 through 47 odd
   Exercise 11–4, #51 and 57.

In order to add two fractions, their denominators must be equal. For instance

$$\frac{2}{5} + \frac{3}{7} = \frac{14}{35} + \frac{15}{35} = \frac{29}{35}$$

The 35 is called a common denominator. It is a special case of a more general idea.

A **multiple** of a given number is an integer multiplied by that number. For instance, 12, 30, and 6000 are multiples of 6. Also, 32, 80, and 88 are multiples of 8. Listing the multiples of 6 and 8 in order shows something interesting.

Common multiples

6: 6 12 18 (24) 30 36 42 (48) 54 60 66 . . .

8: 8 16 (24) 32 40 (48) 56 64 72 80 88 . . .

Some multiples of 6 are also multiples of 8. These are called **common multiples** of 6 and 8. The number 24 is the smallest of the common multiples. It is called the **least common multiple.** This number is abbreviated LCM. When you add two fractions, you use the LCM of the denominators as the common denominator.

DEFINITION

> **LEAST COMMON MULTIPLE (LCM)**
> A **common multiple** of integers a and b is a number that equals
>
> integer $\times$ a and   integer $\times$ b.
>
> The **least common multiple** (LCM) of integers a and b is the *smallest* positive number that is a common multiple of a and b.

Problem Notes:

Problems 1 through 40 are the "bread and butter" problems of this section. They start with two simple monomials, and progress through polynomials that first need factoring.

Problems 41 through 50 get at the *meaning* of LCM, and a property relating LCM and GCF. Problems 47 and 48 are particularly effective in distinguishing among "multiple," "*common* multiple," and "*least* common multiple."

Problems 51 through 62 warm up students for adding and subtracting rational expressions in the next section.

The LCM of two integers can be found by factoring them into primes. For instance,

$$6 = 2 \cdot 3$$
$$8 = 2 \cdot 2 \cdot 2$$

To be a multiple of 6, a number must have at least one 2 and at least one 3 as factors. To be a multiple of 8, a number must have at least three 2's as factors. So the least common multiple of 6 and 8 has three 2's and one 3.

$$\text{LCM} = 2 \cdot 2 \cdot 2 \cdot 3 = 24$$

The diagram shows the set of factors of 6 and set of factors of 8. The overlapping region has factors of both 6 and 8, the *common* factors. The other regions have the rest of the factors of 6 and 8. From the diagram you should be able to see from the figure that the LCM is the *intersection* of the two sets of prime factors.

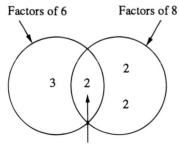

Factors of 6   Factors of 8

Common factors

LCM of 6 and 8 is the
union of the two sets, $2 \cdot 2 \cdot 2 \cdot 3$

In this section you will practice getting LCMs of two polynomials so that you will be prepared to find common denominators for adding rational expressions.

Objective:
Given two polynomials, find their LCM.

Cover the answers as you work the examples.

EXAMPLE 1

Find the LCM of $12a^2b^5$, and $18a^3bc$.

– – – – –   – – – – –

| Think These Reasons |

$12a^2b^5 = 2 \cdot 2 \cdot 3 \cdot a \cdot a \cdot b \cdot b \cdot b \cdot b \cdot b$ Factor.

$18a^3bc = 2 \cdot 3 \cdot 3 \cdot a \cdot a \cdot a \cdot b \cdot c$ Factor.

$\text{LCM} = 2 \cdot 2 \cdot 3 \cdot 3 \cdot a \cdot a \cdot a \cdot b \cdot b \cdot b \cdot b \cdot b \cdot c$ Pick the least number of factors that are needed to cover all of each expression.

$\underline{\text{LCM} = 36a^3b^5c}$ Simplify.

From this example you may be able to see a short cut! Just take each factor with the *highest* exponent in either of the two expressions.

EXAMPLE 2

Find the LCM of $9x^4$ and $6x(x + 5)^3$.

– – – – –   – – – – –

$\underline{\text{LCM} = 18x^4(x + 5)^3}$ LCM of 9 and 6 is 18. Take the highest exponent of x and the highest exponent of $(x + 5)$.

EXAMPLE 3

Find the LCM of $x^2 - 2x - 15$ and $x^2 - 4x - 5$.

– – – – –   – – – – –

$x^2 - 2x - 15 = (x + 3)(x - 5)$

$x^2 - 4x - 5 = (x - 5)(x + 1)$ Factor the two expressions.

$\underline{\text{LCM} = (x + 3)(x - 5)(x + 1)}$ Write the LCM. The $(x - 5)$ is a common factor, so it appears only *once*.

ORAL PRACTICE

Find the LCM of the given pair of integers.

A. 6, 8 24 B. 12, 15 60 C. 12, 9 36 D. 8, 18 72 E. 7, 21 21

F. 4, 12 12 G. 5, 4 20 H. 9, 10 90 I. 4, 30 60 J. 24, 36 72

EXERCISE 11-4

For Problems 1 through 40, find the LCM of the two expressions.

1. a^2bc, ab^2c a^2b^2c

2. $ax^2, 4a^2x$ $4a^2x^2$

3. $4x^3, 6x^5$ $12x^5$

4. $6pc^2, 15p^2c$ $30p^2c^2$

5. $42a^3b, 49b^2c$ $294a^3b^2c$

6. $56r^5t, 54r^3z^2$ $1512r^5tz^2$

7. $4x, 4(a - x)$ $4x(a - x)$

8. $a^2, a(a - b)$ $a^2(a - b)$

9. $2(a - x), 3(a + x)$ $6(a - x)(a + b)$

10. $5(x + 3), 6(x - 3)$ $30(x + 3)(x - 3)$

11. $3(a + x), 7(a + x)$ $21(a + x)$

12. $9(x - 3), 11(x - 3)$ $99(x - 3)$

13. $c^2m(c - m), cm^2(c - m)$

14. $p^3f(p + f), p^2f^4(p + f)$ 13. $c^2m^2(c - m)$ 14. $p^3f^4(p + f)$

15. $xyz(x - y), xy$ $xyz(x - y)$

16. $a^2b, a^3b^2(a - b)$ $a^3b^2(a - b)$

17. $2a - 2b, 4a - 4b$ $4(a - b)$

18. $4a^2 - 9, 6a^2 - 9a$ $3a(2a + 3)(2a - 3)$

19. $j^2 - 9, j^2 + 3j$ $j(j + 3)(j - 3)$

20. $6r + 12t, 8r + 16t$ $24(r + 2t)$

21. $(x - y)^2, x^2 - y^2$ $(x - y)^2(x + y)$

22. $(c + 5)^2, c^2 - 25$ $(c + 5)^2(c - 5)$

23. $(x - 3)(x + 2), (x + 2)(x - 7)$

24. $(x + 4)(x - 5), (x - 1)(x + 4)$ 23. $(x - 3)(x + 2)(x - 7)$
24. $(x + 4)(x - 5)(x - 1)$

25. $(x - 2)^5(x + 3)^2, (x + 2)^4(x + 3)^3$ $(x - 2)^5(x + 3)^3(x + 2)^4$

26. $(x + 1)^7(x - 7)^6, (x - 7)^4(x + 5)$ $(x + 1)^7(x - 7)^6(x + 5)$

27. $x^2 + 6x + 8, x^2 + 7x + 12$

28. $x^2 - 7x + 12, x^2 - 9x + 20$ 27. $(x + 2)(x + 4)(x + 3)$
28. $(x - 3)(x - 4)(x - 5)$

29. $2x^2 + x - 3, x^2 + 4x - 5$

30. $3x^2 + 5x - 2, x^2 + 6x + 8$ 29. $(2x + 3)(x - 1)(x + 5)$
30. $(3x - 1)(x + 2)(x + 4)$

31. $12x^2 + 36x + 24, 18x^2 - 18$ $36(x + 2)(x + 1)(x - 1)$

32. $24x^2 - 96, 18x^2 + 18x - 36$ $72(x - 2)(x + 2)(x - 1)$

33. $x^3 - 2x^2 - x + 2, x^2 - 3x + 2$ $(x - 2)(x + 1)(x - 1)$

34. $x^3 + x^2 - 9x - 9, x^2 - 4x + 3$ $(x - 3)(x + 3)(x - 1)(x + 1)$

35. $x^2 - 4, 4x - 8$ $_{4(x - 2)(x + 2)}$ 36. $9x^2 - 1, 18x + 6$ $_{6(3x + 1)(3x - 1)}$

37. $x^2 + 5x + 6, x^2 - 6x + 8$ $_{(x + 3)(x + 2)(x - 2)(x - 4)}$

38. $2x^2 + 7x + 3, 2x^2 + 7x - 4$ $_{(2x + 1)(2x - 1)(x + 3)(x + 4)}$

39. $x^5 + 2x^4 + x^3, x^7 - x^5$ $_{x^5(x + 1)^2(x - 1)}$

40. $4x^3 - 16x, 6x^4 - 6x^3 - 12x^2$ $_{12x^2(x - 2)(x + 2)(x + 1)}$

For Problems 41 through 46, find the LCM of the *three* expressions.

41. x^3, a^2x^2, a^4 $_{a^4x^3}$ 42. j^5, j^3w, jw^2 $_{j^5w^2}$

43. $10v^4, 12v^2c^2, 4vc^3$ $_{60v^4c^3}$ 44. $15r^3, 21r^25^3, 35s^4$ $_{105r^3s^4}$

45. $6x^3y^2z^4, 4xy^3z^2, 9x^2y^4z$ $_{36x^3y^4z^4}$ 46. $9x^4y, 12x^3y^2, 54x^2y^3$ $_{108x^4y^3}$

47. 2: 2   4 |6| 8   10 (12) 14   16 (18) 20
    3:    3 |6| 9   (12)   15   (18)

47. Write all the integral multiples of 2 and all the integral multiples of 3 that are between 1 and 20. Circle the pairs of *common* multiples. Put a box around the *least* common multiple.

48. 12: 12   24 |36| 38   60 (72) 84   96
    18:    18 |36| 54   (72)   90

48. Write all the integral multiples of 12 and all the integral multiples of 18 that are between 1 and 100. Circle the pairs of *common* multiples. Put a box around the *least* common multiple.

49. LCM = 72
    GCF = 12
    (LCM)(GCF) = (72)(12) = 864 = (24)(36)

49. Find the LCM of 24 and 36. Find the GCF of 24 and 36. Show that (LCM)(GCF) = 24 × 36.

50. LCM = 2352
    GCF = 1
    If two integers have common factors, the difference between them must be a common factor or a product of common factors. When the difference is 1, the GCF must be 1.

50. Find the LCM of 48 and 49. Find the GCF of 48 and 49. Is it possible for two integers like 48 and 49 that are just 1 apart to have any common factors other than 1? If so, *find* two such integers. If not, tell *why* not.

Problems 51 through 62 give you a brief review of adding and subtracting fractions before you go on to Section 11-5. Add or subtract. Simplify the answer, if possible.

51. $\dfrac{3}{5} + \dfrac{1}{5}$ $\dfrac{4}{5}$ 52. $\dfrac{2}{7} + \dfrac{4}{7}$ $\dfrac{6}{7}$

53. $\dfrac{5}{8} - \dfrac{7}{8}$ $-\dfrac{1}{4}$ 54. $\dfrac{3}{10} - \dfrac{9}{10}$ $-\dfrac{3}{5}$

55. $\dfrac{2}{3} + \dfrac{1}{2}$ $\dfrac{7}{6}$ 56. $\dfrac{1}{3} + \dfrac{5}{2}$ $\dfrac{17}{6}$

57. $\dfrac{3}{5} - \dfrac{2}{7}$ $\dfrac{11}{35}$ 58. $\dfrac{3}{5} - \dfrac{4}{11}$ $\dfrac{13}{55}$

59. $\dfrac{5}{6} + \dfrac{3}{4}$ $\dfrac{19}{12}$ 60. $\dfrac{1}{6} + \dfrac{5}{4}$ $\dfrac{17}{12}$

61. $\dfrac{5}{8} - \dfrac{7}{12}$ $\dfrac{1}{24}$ 62. $\dfrac{3}{8} - \dfrac{5}{12}$ $-\dfrac{1}{24}$

11-5 | ADDING AND SUBTRACTING RATIONAL EXPRESSIONS

In order to add two fractions, their denominators must be equal. In the last section, the example given was

$$\frac{2}{5} + \frac{3}{7} = \frac{14}{35} + \frac{15}{35} = \frac{29}{35}$$

In this section you will add rational algebraic expressions. The fractions will have variables in the numerator, denominator, or both. For instance, suppose you must add

$$\frac{7}{6x} + \frac{3}{4}.$$

The easiest common denominator to use is the least common multiple (LCM) of the two denominators. For $6x$ and 4, the LCM is:

$$LCM = 12x.$$

Multiplying $\frac{7}{6x}$ by $\frac{2}{2}$ (which equals 1) and $\frac{3}{4}$ by $\frac{3x}{3x}$ (which also equals 1) gives

$$\frac{7}{6x} \cdot \frac{2}{2} + \frac{3}{4} \cdot \frac{3x}{3x}$$

$$= \frac{14}{12x} + \frac{9x}{12x}$$

$$= \frac{14 + 9x}{12x}$$

Since $12x$ is the LCM of two denominators, it is called the *least common denominator,* or LCD.

DEFINITION

> **LEAST COMMON DENOMINATOR (LCD)**
> The **least common denominator** (LCD) of two fractions is the LCM of the two denominators.

Objective:

Given two rational algebraic expressions, be able to find their LCD, and use the result to add or subtract the two expressions.

Time: 3 days

Chalkboard Examples:

First day:
Have students work the text examples, or use the following:

1. $\dfrac{6}{5x} + \dfrac{7}{4x}$ Ans.: $\dfrac{59}{20x}$

2. $\dfrac{x-2}{x+3} - \dfrac{x+5}{x-4}$ Ans.: $\dfrac{-14x-7}{x^2-x-12}$

Subsequent days:
Homework at the board

Assignments:

Day 1: Exercise 11–5, #1, 5, 9, and 11 through 45 odd.
     Exercise 11–4, selected even problems from 32 on.
     Exercise 10–8, one word problem.
Day 2: Exercise 11–5, #12 through 46 even.
     Exercise 11–5, #47 through 57 odd.
Day 3: Exercise 11–5, #48 through 58 even.
     Exercise 11–5, #59 through 69 odd.

Problem Notes:

The main mistake students make in subtracting algebraic fractions is neglecting to distribute the "−" to each term in the second numerator. The other mistake is canceling when there is a "+" or "−" separating two terms in the numerator, such as in

$$\frac{3(x-2) + 5(x+4)}{(x-2)(x+4)}$$

The author has resorted to such tactics as charging students 5 cents (which is put into the class treasury) each time they make these errors. Both errors are failures to observe the distributive properties. The first is not realizing it applies. The second is not realizing that canceling is a *division* process. You *can* cancel the $(x-2)$'s, if you are willing to pay the price of dividing *both* terms in the numerator by $(x-2)$. The first term comes out "nice," 3. The second term comes out a mess, $\frac{(x+4)}{(x-2)}$, leaving the fraction *worse* than it was when you started. Most people consider this price too high to pay.

Problems 1 through 10 are somewhat tedious, and not very interesting because no canceling can be done. They simply illustrate adding and subtracting algebraic fractions.

Problems 11 through 70 start with simple monomial denominators, and get progressively more difficult as binomials, trinomials, and finally 1, become denominators. Canceling can be done in some, but not all, of these problems.

Cover the answers as you work these examples.

EXAMPLE 1

Do the addition:

Add: $\dfrac{5}{3x} + \dfrac{9}{4x}$.

– – – – –

– – – – –

	Think These Reasons

$\dfrac{5}{3x} + \dfrac{9}{4x}$ — Write the given expression.

$= \dfrac{5}{3x} \cdot \dfrac{4}{4} + \dfrac{9}{4x} \cdot \dfrac{3}{3}$ — Write each fraction with the LCD, $12x$.

$= \dfrac{20}{12x} + \dfrac{27}{12x}$ — Multiply the fractions.

$= \dfrac{47}{12x}$ — Add the fractions.

EXAMPLE 2

Subtract: $\dfrac{5x}{x-y} - \dfrac{5y}{x-y}$

– – – – –

– – – – –

$\dfrac{5x}{x-y} - \dfrac{5y}{x-y}$ — Write the given expression.

$= \dfrac{5x - 5y}{x-y}$ — Denominators are already common.

$= \dfrac{5(x-y)}{x-y}$ — Factor the numerator.

$= 5$ — Cancel the $(x-y)$'s.

EXAMPLE 3

Add: $\dfrac{x+3}{x-7} + \dfrac{x-2}{x-1}$

– – – – –

– – – – –

$= \dfrac{x+3}{x-7} \cdot \dfrac{x-1}{x-1} + \dfrac{x-2}{x-1} \cdot \dfrac{x-7}{x-7}$ — Multiply by suitable forms of 1.

$$= \frac{x^2 + 2x - 3}{x^2 - 8x + 7} + \frac{x^2 - 9x + 14}{x^2 - 8x + 7}$$

Multiply the numerators and the denominators.

$$= \frac{(x^2 + 2x - 3) + (x^2 - 9x + 14)}{x^2 - 8x + 7}$$

Add the numerators; use the common denominator.

$$= \frac{2x^2 - 7x + 11}{x^2 - 8x + 7}$$

Combine like terms.

EXAMPLE 4

Subtract: $\frac{x + 5}{x + 6} - \frac{x - 2}{x + 4}$.

- - - - -   - - - - -

$$\frac{x + 5}{x + 6} - \frac{x - 2}{x + 4}$$

Write the given expression.

$$= \frac{x + 5}{x + 6} \cdot \frac{x + 4}{x + 4} - \frac{x - 2}{x + 4} \cdot \frac{x + 6}{x + 6}$$

Write the fractions with the common denominator.

$$= \frac{x^2 + 9x + 20}{x^2 + 10x + 24} - \frac{x^2 + 4x - 12}{x^2 + 10x + 24}$$

Simplify each fraction.

$$= \frac{(x^2 + 9x + 20) - (x^2 + 4x - 12)}{x^2 + 10x + 24}$$

Subtract the numerators; use the common denominator.

$$= \frac{x^2 + 9x + 20 - x^2 - 4x + 12}{x^2 + 10x + 24}$$

Distribute -1.

$$= \frac{5x + 32}{x^2 + 10x + 24}$$

Combine like terms.

ORAL PRACTICE

Do the indicated operation and give the answer.

A. $\frac{2}{3x} + \frac{6}{3x}$ $\frac{8}{3x}$ B. $\frac{2}{3x} - \frac{6}{3x}$ $-\frac{4}{3x}$ C. $\frac{x}{6} - \frac{x}{3}$ $-\frac{x}{6}$

D. $\frac{x}{6} + \frac{x}{3}$ $\frac{x}{2}$ E. $\frac{5}{6x} + \frac{2}{3x}$ $\frac{3}{2x}$ F. $\frac{5}{6x} - \frac{2}{3x}$ $\frac{1}{6x}$

G. $\frac{1}{8} - \frac{5x + 3}{8}$ H. $\frac{2}{7} - \frac{3x - 4}{7}$ I. $\frac{4}{9} - \frac{x + 1}{9}$ G. $\frac{-5x - 2}{8}$ H. $\frac{-3x + 6}{7}$

J. $\frac{2}{3} + \frac{5x - 2}{3}$ $\frac{5x}{3}$ K. $\frac{2}{3} - \frac{5x - 2}{3}$ I. $\frac{-x + 3}{9}$ K. $\frac{-5x + 4}{3}$

EXERCISE 11-5

For Problems 1 through 10:

a.   add the two expressions;
b.   subtract the second expression from the first.

1. a. $\dfrac{107}{45x}$

   b. $\dfrac{37}{45x}$

2. a. $\dfrac{89}{66x}$

   b. $\dfrac{65}{66x}$

3. a. $\dfrac{37}{36x}$

   b. $-\dfrac{7}{36x}$

4. a. $\dfrac{37}{18x}$

   b. $-\dfrac{5}{18x}$

5. a. $\dfrac{4x+9}{12}$

   b. $\dfrac{-2x-9}{12}$

6. a. $\dfrac{3x-6}{10}$

   b. $\dfrac{-x+6}{10}$

7. a. $\dfrac{2x^2-15x+27}{x^2-4x-21}$

   b. $\dfrac{-11x+57}{x^2-4x-21}$

8. a. $\dfrac{2x^2+14x+3}{x^2+13x+42}$

   b. $\dfrac{6x+45}{x^2+13x+42}$

9. a. $\dfrac{14x^2+18x+1}{3x^2+5x-2}$

   b. $\dfrac{-10x^2-4x+11}{3x^2+5x-2}$

10. a. $\dfrac{13x^2-37x+34}{2x^2-17x+8}$

    b. $\dfrac{-7x^2-19x+30}{2x^2-17x+8}$

1. $\dfrac{8}{5x},\dfrac{7}{9x}$

2. $\dfrac{7}{6x},\dfrac{2}{11x}$

3. $\dfrac{5}{12x},\dfrac{11}{18x}$

4. $\dfrac{8}{9x},\dfrac{7}{6x}$

5. $\dfrac{x}{12},\dfrac{x+3}{4}$

6. $\dfrac{x}{10},\dfrac{x-3}{5}$

7. $\dfrac{x-6}{x+3},\dfrac{x-5}{x-7}$

8. $\dfrac{x+4}{x+7},\dfrac{x-3}{x+6}$

9. $\dfrac{2x+3}{3x-1},\dfrac{4x+5}{x+2}$

10. $\dfrac{3x-4}{2x-1},\dfrac{5x-2}{x-8}$

For Problems 11 through 70, do the indicated operations and simplify.

11. $\dfrac{5}{x}+\dfrac{3}{x}\quad \dfrac{8}{x}$

12. $\dfrac{7}{y}+\dfrac{4}{y}\quad \dfrac{11}{y}$

13. $\dfrac{2x}{3y}-\dfrac{5x}{3y}\quad -\dfrac{x}{y}$

14. $\dfrac{a}{4b}-\dfrac{5a}{4b}\quad -\dfrac{a}{b}$

15. $\dfrac{x}{8}+\dfrac{3x}{8}\quad \dfrac{x}{2}$

16. $\dfrac{c}{9}+\dfrac{5c}{9}\quad \dfrac{2c}{3}$

17. $\dfrac{2}{a}+\dfrac{3}{b}\quad \dfrac{3a+2b}{ab}$

18. $\dfrac{4}{d}+\dfrac{7}{j}\quad \dfrac{4j+7d}{dj}$

19. $\dfrac{3}{r}-\dfrac{4}{s}\quad \dfrac{3s-4r}{rs}$

20. $\dfrac{6}{x}-\dfrac{5}{x}\quad \dfrac{1}{x}$

21. $\dfrac{3}{2a}+\dfrac{1}{4a}\quad \dfrac{7}{4a}$

22. $\dfrac{5}{6z}+\dfrac{2}{3z}\quad \dfrac{3}{2z}$

23. $\dfrac{7}{10p}-\dfrac{3}{5p}\quad \dfrac{1}{10p}$

24. $\dfrac{8}{9x}-\dfrac{2}{3x}\quad \dfrac{2}{9x}$

25. $\dfrac{4}{5a}+\dfrac{2}{3a}\quad \dfrac{22}{15a}$

26. $\dfrac{4}{7m}+\dfrac{3}{2m}\quad \dfrac{29}{14m}$

27. $\dfrac{5}{4x}-\dfrac{2}{3x}\quad \dfrac{7}{12x}$

28. $\dfrac{8}{3b}-\dfrac{2}{5b}\quad \dfrac{34}{15b}$

29. $\dfrac{5}{6x} - \dfrac{1}{4x}$ $\dfrac{7}{12x}$

30. $\dfrac{2}{9y} - \dfrac{5}{6y}$ $-\dfrac{11}{18y}$

31. $\dfrac{3}{ax} + \dfrac{2}{ay}$ $\dfrac{3y+2x}{axy}$

32. $\dfrac{2}{rc} + \dfrac{4}{rd}$ $\dfrac{2d+4c}{crd}$

33. $\dfrac{x-1}{3} + \dfrac{x+1}{6}$ $\dfrac{3x-1}{6}$

34. $\dfrac{p+2}{6} + \dfrac{p-3}{8}$ $\dfrac{7p-1}{24}$

35. $\dfrac{2c-3}{4} - \dfrac{c+2}{6}$ $\dfrac{4c-13}{12}$

36. $\dfrac{3t+4}{8} - \dfrac{t+2}{3}$ $\dfrac{t-4}{24}$

37. $\dfrac{2a-b}{4} - \dfrac{a+4b}{10}$ $\dfrac{8a-13b}{20}$

38. $\dfrac{2x-1}{2} + \dfrac{x+2}{4}$ $\dfrac{5x}{4}$

39. $\dfrac{5m-1}{6} - \dfrac{3m+2}{9}$ $\dfrac{9m-7}{18}$

40. $\dfrac{3k+4}{3} - \dfrac{5k-1}{5}$ $\dfrac{23}{15}$

41. $\dfrac{a}{3} - \dfrac{3a}{7} + \dfrac{a}{21}$ $-\dfrac{a}{21}$

42. $\dfrac{5a}{9} - \dfrac{3a}{2} + \dfrac{a}{6}$ $-\dfrac{7a}{9}$

43. $\dfrac{1}{4x} + \dfrac{1}{2x} - \dfrac{2}{3x}$ $\dfrac{1}{12x}$

44. $\dfrac{2}{xy} + \dfrac{4}{xz} - \dfrac{3}{yz}$ $\dfrac{2z+4y-3x}{xyz}$

45. $\dfrac{a}{2a+2b} + \dfrac{b}{2a+2b}$ $\dfrac{1}{2}$

46. $\dfrac{2a}{a+n} + \dfrac{2n}{a+n}$ 2

47. $\dfrac{x}{3x-3y} - \dfrac{y}{3x-3y}$ $\dfrac{1}{3}$

48. $\dfrac{p}{3p-6} - \dfrac{2}{3p-6}$ $\dfrac{1}{3}$

49. $\dfrac{5}{6r-6s} - \dfrac{3}{4r-4s}$ $\dfrac{1}{12r-12s}$

50. $\dfrac{5}{6x-2y} - \dfrac{3}{9x-3y}$ $\dfrac{3}{6x-2y}$

51. $\dfrac{1}{2a-2b} + \dfrac{1}{4a-4b}$ $\dfrac{3}{4a-4b}$

52. $\dfrac{1}{3a+3b} + \dfrac{1}{12a+12b}$ $\dfrac{5}{12a+12b}$

53. $\dfrac{1}{x-1} + \dfrac{1}{x+1}$ $\dfrac{2x}{x^2-1}$

54. $\dfrac{2}{x+3} + \dfrac{2}{x-3}$ $\dfrac{4x}{x^2-9}$

55. $\dfrac{x}{x+y} - \dfrac{y}{x-y}$ $\dfrac{x^2-2xy-y^2}{x^2-y^2}$

56. $\dfrac{r}{r+7} - \dfrac{r}{r-7}$ $-\dfrac{14r}{r^2-49}$

57. $\dfrac{x}{x+3} - \dfrac{2}{x+4}$ $\dfrac{x^2+2x-6}{x^2+7x+12}$

58. $\dfrac{x}{x-1} - \dfrac{3}{x+5}$ $\dfrac{x^2+2x+3}{x^2+4x-5}$

59. $\dfrac{x-2}{x+4} + \dfrac{x+1}{x-2}$ $\dfrac{2x^2+x+8}{x^2+2x-8}$

60. $\dfrac{x+6}{x+3} + \dfrac{x+3}{x+6}$ $\dfrac{2x^2+18x+45}{x^2+9x+18}$

61. $\dfrac{x+7}{x-1} - \dfrac{x+2}{x+3}$ $\dfrac{9x+23}{x^2+2x-3}$

62. $\dfrac{x-4}{x-2} - \dfrac{x-7}{x+1}$ $\dfrac{6x-18}{x^2-x-2}$

63. $\dfrac{x-5}{x-10} - \dfrac{x-4}{x-2}$ $\dfrac{7x-30}{x^2-12x+20}$

64. $\dfrac{x-6}{x-1} - \dfrac{x-9}{x-3}$ $\dfrac{x+9}{x^2-4x+3}$

65. $x + \dfrac{x + 2}{x - 2} \quad \dfrac{x^2 - x + 2}{x - 2}$ 66. $\dfrac{x - 3}{x + 4} + x \quad \dfrac{x^2 + 5x - 3}{x + 4}$

67. $\dfrac{x^2 - 3x + 4}{x + 2} - x \quad \dfrac{-5x + 4}{x + 2}$ 68. $\dfrac{x^2 + 4x + 1}{x - 3} - x \quad \dfrac{7x + 1}{x - 3}$

69. $\dfrac{x - 3}{x + 5} \cdot \dfrac{x + 5}{x - 1} \quad \dfrac{x - 3}{x - 1}$ 70. $\dfrac{x + 8}{x - 1} \cdot \dfrac{x + 8}{x + 2} \quad \dfrac{x^2 + 16x + 64}{x^2 + x - 2}$

11·6 | COMBINED OPERATIONS AND SPECIAL CASES

Time: 3 or 4 days, including test

Chalkboard Examples:

First day:
Perform the operations and simplify.

1. $\dfrac{(x - 7)(x + 6)(x - 5)}{(6 + x)(7 - x)(x + 5)}$ Ans.: $-\dfrac{x - 5}{x + 5}$

2. $\dfrac{x^2 - x - 12}{20 - x - x^2}$ Ans.: $-\dfrac{x + 3}{5 + x}$

3. $\dfrac{49}{x - 7} - \dfrac{x^2}{x - 7}$ Ans.: $-x - 7$

4. $\dfrac{3x}{4x} - \dfrac{5}{6x} \cdot \dfrac{3x}{2}$ Ans.: $-\dfrac{1}{2}$

Oral Practice problems are helpful the first day.

Second day:
Perform the operations and simplify.

1. $\dfrac{7x + 1}{x - 5} + \dfrac{3x - 4}{5 - x}$ Ans.: $\dfrac{4x + 5}{x - 5}$

2. $\dfrac{x^2 - 10x + 21}{x^2 + x - 2} \cdot \dfrac{4 - x^2}{9 - x^2}$

   Ans.: $\dfrac{x^2 - 9x + 14}{x^2 + 2x - 3}$

3. $\dfrac{3x + 3}{x^2 + x - 2} - \dfrac{2}{x - 1}$ Ans.: $\dfrac{1}{x + 2}$

Third day: Test, or consolidation

Fourth day: Test (if not given previous day).

Assignments:

Day 1: Exercise 11–6, #1–19 odd;
    Exercise 11–1, #6 or 5; and
    Exercise 10–8, #50

There are some special cases you should know about when you simplify rational expressions, such as

$$\frac{5 - x}{x - 5}.$$

Here, the numerator and denominator are *opposites* of each other, as you can see by factoring -1 from the numerator.

$$\frac{5 - x}{x - 5} = \frac{-1(-5 + x)}{x - 5} = \frac{-1(x - 5)}{x - 5} = -1$$

The quick way to get this answer is to reason:

Any number divided by its opposite equals -1.

Caution is required here because some expressions *look* like opposites but really are *not*. For instance,

$$x - 5 \quad \text{and} \quad x + 5$$

are *conjugates,* not opposites. Nothing special happens when you divide two conjugates.

SPECIAL CASES

$\dfrac{x - 5}{5 - x} = -1$ A number divided by its opposite equals -1.

$\dfrac{x + 5}{5 + x} = 1$ A number divided by itself equals 1.
                    ($x + 5$ and $5 + x$ are *equal*.)

$\dfrac{x - 5}{x + 5} = \dfrac{x - 5}{x + 5}$ A number divided by its conjugate
                    is nothing special!

Another special case concerns the *opposite* of a fraction, such as

$$-\frac{7}{9}, \quad \frac{-7}{9}, \quad \text{and} \quad \frac{7}{-9}.$$

The expression $\frac{7}{9}$ means 7 divided by 9. Because negative divided by positive is negative and positive divided by negative is also negative, all three of these fractions are *equal*.

$$-\frac{7}{9} = \frac{-7}{9} = \frac{7}{-9}$$

The $-$ sign can be associated with the numerator, the denominator, or the entire fraction. This fact is called the property of the opposite of a fraction.

PROPERTY

> **OPPOSITE OF A FRACTION**
> For any fraction $\frac{a}{b}$, $b \neq 0$,
> $$-\frac{a}{b} = \frac{-a}{b} = \frac{a}{-b}.$$

Note that $\frac{-a}{-b}$ equals $+\frac{a}{b}$, since negative divided by negative is *positive*.

Objective:
Be able to add, subtract, multiply, and divide rational algebraic expressions, and simplify the answer.

Cover the answers as you work these examples.

EXAMPLE 1

Simplify: $\dfrac{(x + 2)(x - 3)(x - 4)}{(x + 3)(4 - x)(x + 2)}.$

- - - - -   - - - - -

Think These Reasons

$\dfrac{(x + 2)(x - 3)(x - 4)}{(x + 3)(4 - x)(x + 2)}$ Write the given expression.

Day 2: Exercise 11–6, #21–39 odd
Prepare for test if it is to be given the next day.
Day 3: Exercise 11–6, #41–55 odd, if harder problems are desired
Otherwise, in preparation for test:
Exercise 11–6, #20, 30, 32;
Exercise 11–4, #22;
Exercise 11–3, #8; and
Exercise 11–1, #8 or 7
Day 4: Following test, assign Exercise 10–8, #52, 56, 66. It is probably better to present long division (Section 11–7) in class rather than have students read the section on their own.

$$= \frac{(x-3)(x-4)}{(x+3)(4-x)}$$ Cancel the $(x+2)$ factors.

$$= -\frac{x-3}{x+3}$$ $\dfrac{(x-4)}{(4-x)}$ equals -1. $(x-3)$ and $(x+3)$ are conjugates and do *not* cancel.

EXAMPLE 2

Perform the operations and simplify: $\dfrac{2x}{3x} - \dfrac{4}{5x} \div \dfrac{3}{10x}$.

- - - - -   - - - - -

$$\frac{2x}{3x} - \frac{4}{5x} \div \frac{3}{10x}$$ Write the given expression.

$$= \frac{2x}{3x} - \frac{4}{5x} \cdot \frac{10x}{3}$$ Multiply by the reciprocal.

$$= \frac{2x}{3x} - \frac{40x}{15x}$$ Multiply *before* subtracting.

$$= \frac{2}{3} - \frac{8}{3}$$ Cancel the x factors. Cancel 5.

$$= -\frac{6}{3}$$ Subtract the fractions.

$$= \underline{\underline{-2}}$$ Simplify.

EXAMPLE 3

Perform the operations and simplify: $\dfrac{2}{x+7} - \dfrac{1}{x-7}$.

- - - - -   - - - - -

$$\frac{2}{x+7} - \frac{1}{x-7}$$ Write the given expression.

$$= \frac{2}{x+7} \cdot \frac{x-7}{x-7} - \frac{1}{x-7} \cdot \frac{x+7}{x+7}$$ Write the fractions with common denominators.

$$= \frac{2(x-7) - (x+7)}{(x+7)(x-7)}$$ Add the numerators. Use the common denominator.

$$= \frac{2x - 14 - x - 7}{(x+7)(x-7)}$$ Distribute 2 and -1 in the numerator.

$$= \frac{x - 21}{(x+7)(x-7)}$$ Combine like terms in the numerator.

$$= \frac{x - 21}{x^2 - 49}$$ Multiply the denominator factors. (This step is *optional*.)

EXAMPLE 4

Multiply and simplify: $\dfrac{x^2 - 10x + 9}{x^2 + x - 6} \cdot \dfrac{x^2 - 4}{1 - x^2}$.

- - - - -

$\dfrac{x^2 - 10x + 9}{x^2 + x - 6} \cdot \dfrac{x^2 - 4}{1 - x^2}$

Write the given expression.

$= \dfrac{(x - 9)(x - 1)}{(x + 3)(x - 2)} \cdot \dfrac{(x + 2)(x - 2)}{(1 - x)(1 + x)}$

Factor each numerator and denominator *first!* (If you multiply first, you get a *mess*.)

$= \dfrac{(x - 9)(x - 1)(x + 2)(x - 2)}{(x + 3)(x - 2)(1 - x)(1 + x)}$

Use the multiplication property of fractions.

$= -\dfrac{(x - 9)(x + 2)}{(x + 3)(1 + x)}$

Cancel the $(x - 2)$ factors.

$\dfrac{x - 1}{1 - x}$ equals -1.

$= -\dfrac{x^2 - 7x - 18}{x^2 + 4x + 3}$

Do the indicated multiplication.

EXAMPLE 5

Subtract and simplify: $\dfrac{3x - 1}{x^2 + 2x - 15} - \dfrac{2}{x + 5}$.

- - - - -

$\dfrac{3x - 1}{x^2 + 2x - 15} - \dfrac{2}{x + 5}$

Write the given expression.

$= \dfrac{3x - 1}{(x + 5)(x - 3)} - \dfrac{2}{x + 5}$

Factor the denominator.

$= \dfrac{3x - 1}{(x + 5)(x - 3)} - \dfrac{2}{x + 5} \cdot \dfrac{x - 3}{x - 3}$

Write the fractions with common denominators. (You need transform only the *second* fraction.)

$= \dfrac{3x - 1 - 2(x - 3)}{(x + 5)(x - 3)}$

Subtract the numerators. Use the common denominator.

$= \dfrac{3x - 1 - 2x + 6}{(x + 5)(x - 3)}$

Distribute -2. (Be careful not to lose the $-$ sign!)

$= \dfrac{x + 5}{(x + 5)(x - 3)}$

Combine like terms.

$= \dfrac{1}{x - 3}$

Cancel the $(x + 5)$ factors. Do not lose the 1 in the numerator. Also, keep the denominator in *factored* form until the very end to see if any canceling can be done.

ORAL PRACTICE

Tell what each of the following fractions equals.

EXAMPLES

Answers

i. $\dfrac{x-5}{5-x}$ i. -1

ii. $\dfrac{x-5}{x+5}$ ii. $\dfrac{x-5}{x+5}$

iii. $\dfrac{3}{-x}$ iii. $-\dfrac{3}{x}$

A. $\dfrac{x-7}{x-7}$ 1

B. $\dfrac{x-7}{x+7}$ Nothing special

C. $\dfrac{x-7}{7-x}$ -1

D. $\dfrac{x+7}{7+x}$ 1

E. $\dfrac{2x+3}{2x-3}$ Nothing special

F. $\dfrac{3+2x}{2x+3}$ 1

G. $\dfrac{2x-3}{3-2x}$ -1

H. $\dfrac{2x+3}{3x+2}$ Nothing special

I. $\dfrac{-4}{x}$ $-\dfrac{4}{x}$

J. $\dfrac{-x}{5}$ $-\dfrac{x}{5}$

K. $\dfrac{x}{-y}$ $-\dfrac{x}{y}$

L. $\dfrac{-x}{-y}$ $\dfrac{x}{y}$

M. $\dfrac{-(x+3)}{x+3}$ -1

N. $-\dfrac{-(x+2)}{x+2}$ 1

O. $\dfrac{x-5}{-(x-5)}$ -1

P. $\dfrac{-(x+4)}{-(x+4)}$ 1

Q. $\dfrac{-(x+4)}{-(4+x)}$ 1

R. $\dfrac{-(3-x)}{x-3}$ 1

S. $\dfrac{-x+3}{3-x}$ 1

T. $-\dfrac{-(x-6)}{-(x-6)}$ -1

EXERCISE 11-6

Problem Notes:

The problems of this section are designed to tie together the operations with rational expressions. They are designed to force students to distinguish between $(x+y)$ and $(y+x)$, between $(x-y)$ and $(y-x)$, and between $(x+y)$ and $(x-y)$. They also force students

For Problems 1 through 10, simplify the expression.

1. $\dfrac{(x+7)(x-2)}{(x-7)(x-2)}$ $\dfrac{x+7}{x-7}$

2. $\dfrac{(x-8)(x+3)}{(x+8)(3+x)}$ $\dfrac{x-8}{x+8}$

3. $\dfrac{(x+3)(x-6)}{(x+3)(6-x)}$ -1

4. $\dfrac{(x+5)(x-9)}{(x-5)(9-x)}$ $-\dfrac{x+5}{x-5}$

5. $\dfrac{(a+4)(a-3)(2a-1)}{(4+a)(1-2a)(a+3)}$ $-\dfrac{a-3}{a+3}$

6. $\dfrac{(r+6)(r-2)(2r+5)}{(6+r)(2r+5)(2-r)}$ -1

7. $\dfrac{4-x^2}{x^2-4x+4}$ $-\dfrac{2+x}{x-2}$

8. $\dfrac{x^2-6x+9}{9-x^2}$ $-\dfrac{x-3}{3+x}$

9. $\dfrac{x^2-x-12}{6-x-x^2}$ $\dfrac{x-4}{2-x}$

10. $\dfrac{10+3x-x^2}{x^2+3x+2}$ $\dfrac{5-x}{x+1}$

to distinguish between multiplication and addition of fractions by presenting both kinds of problems in the same assignment.

Problems 1–10 are straightforward simplifications involving these concepts.

For Problems 11 through 56, perform the indicated operations and simplify the answer.

11. $\dfrac{5}{7x}+\dfrac{4}{7x}-\dfrac{2}{7x}$ $\dfrac{1}{x}$

12. $\dfrac{4}{3x}-\dfrac{2}{3x}+\dfrac{7}{3x}$ $\dfrac{3}{x}$

13. $\dfrac{x}{5x}+\dfrac{2}{3x}\cdot\dfrac{6x}{5}$ 1

14. $\dfrac{4x}{3x}-\dfrac{14}{9x}\cdot\dfrac{3x}{7}$ $\dfrac{2}{3}$

15. $\dfrac{3r}{r+s}+\dfrac{3s}{r+s}$ 3

16. $\dfrac{5b}{a+b}+\dfrac{5a}{a+b}$ 5

17. $\dfrac{c^2}{c-d}-\dfrac{d^2}{c-d}$ $c+d$

18. $\dfrac{h^2}{h-5}-\dfrac{25}{h-5}$ $h+5$

Problems 17–20 have a minus sign in the denominator to keep students from getting the right answer by wrong methods. For instance, in Problem 17,

$$\dfrac{c^2-d^2}{c-d}$$

becomes $c+d$. One prevalent canceling error would give $c-d$.

In Problems 35 and 36, the denominators are opposites of each other. The fractions can be added immediately if the second fraction is multiplied by $\dfrac{-1}{-1}$.

19. $\dfrac{36}{x-6}-\dfrac{x^2}{x-6}$ $-6-x$

20. $\dfrac{64}{y-8}-\dfrac{y^2}{y-8}$ $-8-y$

21. $\dfrac{2}{a}-\dfrac{3}{a^2}+\dfrac{4}{a^3}$ $\dfrac{2a^2-3a+4}{a^3}$

22. $\dfrac{5}{z^3}-\dfrac{6}{z^2}+\dfrac{7}{z}$ $\dfrac{5-6z+7z^2}{z^3}$

23. $\dfrac{6}{x^2}\cdot\dfrac{5}{2x^3}\div\dfrac{3x^4}{-4}$ $-\dfrac{20}{x^9}$

24. $\dfrac{10}{x^5}\div\dfrac{5x^4}{6}\cdot\dfrac{1}{3x^2}$ $\dfrac{4}{x^{11}}$

25. $\dfrac{6u+12}{5}\cdot\dfrac{15u}{11u+22}$ $\dfrac{18u}{11}$

26. $\dfrac{3v-15}{9v}\cdot\dfrac{v}{6v-30}$ $\dfrac{1}{18}$

27. $\dfrac{13x}{x-2}-\dfrac{26}{x-2}$ 13

28. $\dfrac{7x}{x+5}+\dfrac{35}{x+5}$ 7

29. $\dfrac{25-p^2}{12}\cdot\dfrac{6}{p-5}$ $-\dfrac{5+p}{2}$

30. $\dfrac{4}{1-k^2}\cdot\dfrac{k+1}{4}$ $\dfrac{1}{1-k}$

31. $\dfrac{3}{x+4}+\dfrac{3}{x-4}$ $\dfrac{6x}{x^2-16}$

32. $\dfrac{5}{x-3}+\dfrac{5}{x+3}$ $\dfrac{10x}{x^2-9}$

33. $\dfrac{2}{x-5}-\dfrac{2}{x+5}$ $\dfrac{20}{x^2-25}$

34. $\dfrac{7}{x-8}-\dfrac{7}{x+8}$ $\dfrac{112}{x^2-64}$

35. $\dfrac{7}{x-3}+\dfrac{4}{3-x}$ $\dfrac{3}{x-3}$

36. $\dfrac{10}{x-4}+\dfrac{6}{4-x}$ $\dfrac{4}{x-4}$

Problems 47–56 have been carefully designed so that the numerator and denominator will have a common factor after the fractions have been added or subtracted. However, there are many pitfalls along the way. Any error will probably leave students with numerators and denominators that are relatively prime.

37. $\dfrac{a}{a+3} \cdot \dfrac{3+a}{a^2+2a}$ $\dfrac{1}{a+2}$

38. $\dfrac{m-2}{m^2+5m} \cdot \dfrac{m}{2-m}$ $-\dfrac{1}{m+5}$

39. $\dfrac{r}{r+5} - \dfrac{r^2-2}{r^2+5r}$ $\dfrac{2}{r^2+5r}$

40. $\dfrac{c}{c-2} - \dfrac{c^2-1}{c^2-2c}$ $\dfrac{1}{c^2-2c}$

41. $\dfrac{y}{y+1} \cdot (2y+2) - 2y$ 0

42. $(3z-6) \cdot \dfrac{2z}{z-2} - 5z$ z

43. $\dfrac{x^2-x-12}{x^2-x-30} \cdot \dfrac{x^2-36}{9-x^2}$

44. $\dfrac{x^2-6x+5}{x^2-x-20} \cdot \dfrac{x^2-16}{1-x^2}$

45. $\dfrac{x^2+5x-14}{x^2-49} \div \dfrac{4-x^2}{x^2+9x+14}$

46. $\dfrac{36-x^2}{x^2-4x-12} \div \dfrac{x^2+10x+24}{x^2-4}$

47. $\dfrac{2x-11}{x^2-7x+12} + \dfrac{3}{(x-4)}$

48. $\dfrac{2x-36}{x^2-4x-12} + \dfrac{3}{x-6}$

49. $\dfrac{3x+35}{x^2-25} + \dfrac{2}{x+5}$

50. $\dfrac{5x-27}{x^2-9} + \dfrac{2}{x-3}$

51. $\dfrac{5x+17}{x^2+8x+7} - \dfrac{3}{x+7}$

52. $\dfrac{9x+35}{x^2-49} - \dfrac{7}{x-7}$

53. $\dfrac{2}{x-1} - \dfrac{x+9}{x^2+3x-4}$

54. $\dfrac{2}{x-3} - \dfrac{7x-3}{x^2+3x-18}$

55. $\dfrac{2}{x+6} - \dfrac{5x+28}{x^2+11x+30}$

56. $\dfrac{3}{x-5} - \dfrac{5x-16}{x^2-7x+10}$

Answers to selected problems:

43. $\dfrac{x^2+2x-24}{-x^2-2x+15}$ 44. $-\dfrac{x-4}{x+1}$

45. $-\dfrac{x+7}{x-7}$ 46. $-\dfrac{x-2}{x+4}$

47. $\dfrac{5}{x-3}$ 48. $\dfrac{5}{x+2}$

49. $\dfrac{5}{x-5}$ 50. $\dfrac{7}{x+3}$

51. $\dfrac{2}{x+1}$ 52. $\dfrac{2}{x+7}$

53. $\dfrac{1}{x+4}$ 54. $-\dfrac{5}{x+6}$

55. $-\dfrac{3}{x+5}$ 56. $-\dfrac{2}{x-2}$

57. **a.** Answers may vary. 4.85
  b. Answers may vary. 7.831, 7.833, 7.835, 7.837, 7.839
  c. 379.5, between
  d. $n = \dfrac{x+y}{2}$
  e. $\dfrac{29}{56}$ or 0.517. . . , between
  f. ratio of integers
  g. Any number which can be written in the form $\dfrac{m}{n}$, where m and n are integers, and $n \neq 0$, is called a rational number. The average of two rational numbers, $\dfrac{\frac{a}{b}+\frac{c}{d}}{2}$ or $\dfrac{ad+bc}{2bd}$, lies between them as shown above and is a rational number, since the sums or products of integers are integers.
  h. yes; no; no integer between adjacent integers.

57. ***The Density Property***   The diagram shows a number line. Between 3 and 4 there are many other numbers such as 3.5, 3.79, 3.22861154. . . , etc. If a set of numbers has the property that between any two of them there is another number of that kind, then the set of numbers is said to be *dense*. The work you have been doing with fractions allows you to tell whether or not certain sets of numbers are dense.

There are real numbers between 3 and 4.

Answer the following questions.
  a. Find a real number between 4.8 and 4.9.
  b. Find five real numbers between 7.83 and 7.84.

c. Find the *average* of 378 and 381. Is the average *between* the two numbers, or somewhere else?

d. Explain why the set of real numbers is *dense* by telling how to find a number that is between any two given numbers x and y.

e. Find the average of $\frac{2}{7}$ and $\frac{3}{4}$. Is the answer between $\frac{2}{7}$ and $\frac{3}{4}$?

f. Let $x = \frac{a}{b}$ and let $y = \frac{c}{d}$, where a, b, c, and d stand for integers, and b and d are not zero. Why are x and y *rational* numbers?

g. Prove that the set of rational numbers is dense by showing that there is a rational number between any two given rational numbers.

h. Is there an *integer* between 73 and 76? Does this mean that the set of integers is dense? Explain your answer.

11-7 LONG DIVISION OF POLYNOMIALS

You know how to transform an improper fraction such as $\frac{747}{21}$ into a mixed number. First you long divide 747 by 21.

$$
\begin{array}{r}
35 \\
21\overline{)747} \\
63 \\
\hline
117 \\
105 \\
\hline
12
\end{array}
$$

The answer is the sum of an integer and a proper fraction:

$$\frac{747}{21} = 35\frac{12}{21}.$$

A rational algebraic expression such as

$$\frac{3x^2 + 5x - 9}{x + 2}$$

can be thought of as an improper fraction, too, since its numerator is of higher degree than its denominator. The same long-division process can be used to transform this expression to the sum of a polynomial and a proper fraction. Here, step by step, is how it works.

First, write the fraction in long-division form.

$$x + 2\overline{)3x^2 + 5x - 9}$$

Time: 0 or 1 day

(This section is optional from the standpoint that it is used nowhere else in this text other than indirectly in the integer quotient problems of Section 11–10. However, the topic will appear again in later courses, and the exposure here is good. Students usually enjoy this topic as a welcome relief after the preceding sections.)

Chalkboard Examples:

Present one example, such as the following. Express in mixed-number form:

$$\frac{10x^2 - 26x + 3}{5x - 3} \quad \text{Ans.: } 2x - 4 + \frac{-9}{5x - 3}$$

Then have students work Examples 1–4 on their own before starting the assignment.

Assignment:

Exercise 11–7, #1–17 odd;
Exercise 11–6, #34 or 36; and
Exercise 10–8, #62

Divide $3x^2$ by x, getting $3x$. Write the $3x$ over the x-term in $3x^2 + 5x - 9$.

$$
\begin{array}{r}
3x \\
x + 2\ \overline{)3x^2 + 5x - 9}
\end{array}
$$

Divide.

Now, multiply $3x$ by $x + 2$, getting $3x^2 + 6x$. Write this answer under the like terms in $3x^2 + 5x - 9$.

Multiply.

$$
\begin{array}{r}
3x \\
(x + 2)\overline{)3x^2 + 5x - 9} \\
3x^2 + 6x
\end{array}
$$

Subtract $3x^2 + 6x$ from $3x^2 + 5x - 9$.

$$
\begin{array}{r}
3x \\
x + 2\ \overline{)3x^2 + 5x - 9} \\
\underline{3x^2 + 6x} \\
-x - 9
\end{array}
$$

Subtract.

Then you repeat the process, first dividing $-x$ by x, getting -1.

Multiply.

$$
\begin{array}{r}
3x - 1 \\
x + 2\ \overline{)3x^2 + 5x - 9} \\
\underline{3x^2 + 6x} \\
-x - 9
\end{array}
\qquad
\begin{array}{r}
3x - 1 \\
(x + 2)\overline{)3x^2 + 5x - 9} \\
\underline{3x^2 + 6x} \\
-x - 9 \\
\underline{-x - 2} \\
-7
\end{array}
$$

Divide.   Subtract.

So the answer is

$$
\frac{3x^2 + 5x - 9}{x + 2} = 3x - 1 + \frac{-7}{x + 2}.
$$

The polynomial $3x - 1$ is called the **quotient.** The number -7 is called the **remainder.**

The answer can be checked by multiplication.

$$
(x + 2)\left(3x - 1 + \frac{-7}{x + 2}\right)
$$

$$
= (x + 2)(3x - 1) + (-7) \qquad \text{Distribute } x + 2.
$$

$$
= 3x^2 + 5x - 2 - 7 \qquad \text{Multiply the binomials.}
$$

$$
= 3x^2 + 5x - 9 \qquad \text{Combine like terms.}
$$

This yields the original numerator.

Objective:

Given a rational algebraic expression in which a higher-degree polynomial is divided by a lower-degree polynomial, use long division to transform to mixed-number form—polynomial plus proper fraction.

The following examples help you master this technique. They also show you some tricky special cases. Cover the answer until you have worked the example.

EXAMPLE 1

Express $\dfrac{6x^2 + 8x - 4}{3x - 5}$ in mixed-number form.

- - - - -   - - - - -

$$\frac{6x^2 + 8x - 4}{3x - 5}$$

$$= 2x + 6 + \frac{26}{3x - 5}$$

$$\begin{array}{r} 2x + 6 \\ 3x - 5 \overline{)6x^2 + 8x - 4} \\ \underline{6x^2 - 10x} \\ 18x - 4 \\ \underline{18x - 30} \\ 26 \end{array}$$

Check: $(3x - 5)(2x + 6) + 26$

$$= 6x^2 + 8x - 30 + 26$$

$$= 6x^2 + 8x - 4 \ \ ✔$$

Note: In the long division, $8x - (-10x)$ is $18x$ and $-4 - (-30)$ is 26.

EXAMPLE 2

Express $\dfrac{5x^3 + 7x^2 - 3x + 8}{x + 4}$ in mixed-number form.

- - - - -   - - - - -

$$\frac{5x^3 + 7x^2 - 3x + 8}{x + 4}$$

$$= 5x^2 - 13x + 49 + \frac{-188}{x + 4}$$

$$\begin{array}{r} 5x^2 - 13x + 49 \\ x + 4 \overline{)5x^3 + 7x^2 - 3x + 8} \\ \underline{5x^3 + 20x^2} \\ -13x^2 - 3x + 8 \\ \underline{-13x^2 - 52x} \\ 49x + 8 \\ \underline{49x + 196} \\ -188 \end{array}$$

Check: $(x + 4)(5x^2 - 13x + 49) - 188$

$$= 5x^3 - 13x^2 + 49x + 20x^2 - 52x + 196 - 188$$

$$= 5x^3 + 7x^2 - 3x + 8 \ \ ✔$$

Note: In the check, multiply each term of $x + 4$ by each term of $5x^2 - 13x + 49$. Then combine like terms.

EXAMPLE 3

Express $\dfrac{x^3 - 3x^2 - 23x + 30}{x - 6}$ in mixed-number form.

- - - - -   - - - - -

$$\frac{x^3 - 3x^2 - 23x + 30}{x - 6}$$

$$
\begin{array}{r}
x^2 + 3x - 5 \\
x - 6 \overline{\smash{)}x^3 - 3x^2 - 23x + 30} \\
\underline{x^3 - 6x^2} \\
3x^2 - 23x + 30 \\
\underline{3x^2 - 18x} \\
-5x + 30 \\
\underline{-5x + 30} \\
0
\end{array}
$$

Remainder is zero!

$$= \underline{\underline{x^2 + 3x - 5}}$$

Check: $(x - 6)(x^2 + 3x - 5)$

$= x^3 + 3x^2 - 5x - 6x^2 - 18x + 30$

$= x^3 - 3x^2 - 23x + 30$ ✔

Note: Since the remainder is *zero,* you can conclude that $x - 6$ is a *factor* of $x^3 - 3x^2 - 23x + 30$. As you can see in the check, $x^3 - 3x^2 - 23x + 30$ equals $(x - 6)(x^2 + 3x - 5)$.

EXAMPLE 4

Divide $x^3 + 27$ by $x + 3$, and write the quotient.

- - - - -   - - - - -

$$\frac{x^3 + 27}{x + 3}$$

$$
\begin{array}{r}
x^2 - 3x + 9 \\
x + 3 \overline{\smash{)}x^3 + 0x^2 + 0x + 27} \\
\underline{x^3 + 3x^2} \\
-3x^2 + 0x + 27 \\
\underline{-3x^2 - 9x} \\
9x + 27 \\
\underline{9x + 27} \\
0
\end{array}
$$

Fill in the missing terms.

$$= \underline{\underline{x^2 - 3x + 9}}$$

Check: $(x + 3)(x^2 - 3x + 9)$

$= x^3 - 3x^2 + 9x + 3x^2 - 9x + 27$

$= x^3 + 27$ ✔

Note: In $x^3 + 27$, the x^2-term and the x-term are missing. Before you do the long division, you should put in these missing terms with zeros as their coefficients.

EXAMPLE 5

Express $\dfrac{2x^3 + 7x^2 - 8x - 11}{2x^2 + x - 5}$ in mixed-number form.

- - - - -

$$\frac{2x^3 + 7x^2 - 8x - 11}{2x^2 + x - 5}$$

$$= x + 3 + \frac{-6x + 4}{2x^2 + x - 5}$$

$$\begin{array}{r} x + 3 \\ 2x^2 + x - 5\overline{)2x^3 + 7x^2 - 8x - 11} \\ \underline{2x^3 + x^2 - 5x} \\ 6x^2 - 3x - 11 \\ \underline{6x^2 + 3x - 15} \\ -6x + 4 \end{array}$$

Check: $(2x^2 + x - 5)(x + 3) + (-6x + 4)$

$$= 2x^3 + 6x^2 + x^2 + 3x - 5x - 15 - 6x + 4$$

$$= 2x^3 + 7x^2 - 8x - 11 \quad ✔$$

Note: You can stop dividing when the degree of the remainder is less than the degree of the divisor.

EXERCISE 11-7

For Problems 1 through 24, write the expression in mixed-number form if the remainder is not 0 or as a single polynomial if the remainder is 0. It is advisable to check your answers as shown in the examples.

1. $\dfrac{x^2 + 5x - 11}{x + 3}$

2. $\dfrac{x^2 + 6x - 17}{x + 4}$

3. $\dfrac{6x^2 - 7x + 5}{2x - 1}$

4. $\dfrac{10x^2 - 9x + 7}{2x - 3}$

5. $\dfrac{12x^2 + 13x - 14}{3x - 2}$

6. $\dfrac{6x^2 + 11x - 35}{2x + 7}$

7. $\dfrac{x^3 - 2x^2 - 3x + 12}{x + 2}$

8. $\dfrac{x^3 - 4x^2 - 19x + 9}{x + 3}$

9. $\dfrac{x^3 - 7x^2 + 14x - 8}{x - 4}$

10. $\dfrac{x^3 - 9x^2 + 23x - 15}{x - 5}$

1. $x + 2 - \dfrac{17}{x + 3}$
2. $x + 2 - \dfrac{25}{x + 4}$
3. $3x - 2 + \dfrac{3}{2x - 1}$
4. $5x + 3 + \dfrac{16}{2x - 3}$
5. $4x + 7$ 6. $3x - 5$
7. $x^2 - 4x + 5 + \dfrac{2}{x + 2}$
8. $x^2 - 7x + 2 + \dfrac{3}{x + 3}$
9. $x^2 - 3x + 2$
10. $x^2 - 4x + 3$

Problem Notes:

Problems 13–18, 21, and 22 involve missing terms.

Problems 19–22 involve division by a trinomial.

Problem 25 lays the background for the factor theorem in Problem 26. The fact that the *value* of the polynomial when $x = 3$ is the same as the *remainder* when the polynomial is divided by $(x - 3)$ is called the **remainder theorem.**

In Problem 26, the powers of x (line 60) are found by multiplication rather than by raising to powers. Most computers raise to powers using logarithms. The resulting round-off errors cause the polynomial to be not quite equal to 0, thus causing the computer to overlook a valid answer at line 80.

11. $\dfrac{8x^3 + 10x^2 - 13x - 20}{2x + 3}$

12. $\dfrac{12x^3 - 19x^2 - 25x - 10}{4x + 3}$

13. $\dfrac{x^3 + 7x^2 - 49}{x + 5}$

14. $\dfrac{x^3 + 5x^2 - 20}{x + 3}$

15. $\dfrac{4x^3 - 200x + 28}{x - 7}$

16. $\dfrac{5x^3 + 3x - 8}{x - 1}$

17. $\dfrac{x^3 - 729}{x - 9}$

18. $\dfrac{x^3 + 125}{x + 5}$

19. $\dfrac{x^3 - 4x^2 - x - 1}{x^2 - 2x - 5}$

20. $\dfrac{x^3 - 7x^2 + 10x + 9}{x^2 - 3x - 2}$

21. $\dfrac{2x^3 - 30x - 8}{x^2 + 4x + 1}$

22. $\dfrac{3x^3 - 5x^2 + 20}{x^2 - 3x + 4}$

23. $\dfrac{x^4 + 7x^3 + 5x^2 - 8x - 14}{x + 6}$

24. $\dfrac{x^4 + x^3 - 7x^2 - 2x + 8}{x - 2}$

25. ***Remainders Problem***   In this problem you will learn something about the remainder in a polynomial division problem.
   a. Divide $x^3 - 4x^2 + 9x - 10$ by $x - 3$. What is the remainder? 8
   b. Evaluate $x^3 - 4x^2 + 9x - 10$ if x is 3. How does the answer compare with the remainder in part (a)?   8 Same
   c. Write the polynomial $x^3 - 4x^2 + 9x - 10$ in the form
   $$(x - 3)(\text{quotient}) + \text{remainder},$$
   $(x - 3)(x^2 - x + 6) + 8$
   using the results of parts (a) and (b). Based on the multiplication property of zero, explain why substituting 3 for x leaves only the remainder. $(x - 3)$ is 0 when $x = 3$, leaving 8
   d. Show that the polynomial $x^3 - 4x^2 + 9x - 10$ is zero if x is 2. What would you expect the remainder to be if the polynomial is divided by $x - 2$?   0

26. ***Factor Theorem and the Computer***   From Problem 25 you saw that if you substitute a number n for x in a polynomial such as $x^3 - 4x^2 + 9x - 10$, the *value* of the polynomial equals the *remainder* when the polynomial is divided by $x - n$. If this remainder is 0, then $x - n$ is a *factor* of the polynomial. This conclusion is called the **factor theorem.**

11. $4x^2 - x - 5 - \dfrac{5}{2x + 3}$

12. $3x^2 - 7x - 1 - \dfrac{7}{4x + 3}$

13. $x^2 + 2x - 10 + \dfrac{1}{x + 5}$

14. $x^2 + 2x - 6 - \dfrac{2}{x + 3}$

15. $4x^2 + 28x - 4$

16. $5x^2 + 5x + 8$

17. $x^2 + 9x + 81$

18. $x^2 - 5x + 25$

19. $x - 2 - \dfrac{11}{x^2 - 2x - 5}$

20. $x - 4 + \dfrac{1}{x^2 - 3x - 2}$

21. $2x - 8$

22. $3x + 4 + \dfrac{4}{x^2 - 3x + 4}$

23. $x^3 + x^2 - x - 2 - \dfrac{2}{x + 6}$

24. $x^3 + 3x^2 - x - 4$

26. *Factor Theorem and the Computer*—see Additional Answers.

FACTOR THEOREM

$x - n$ is a *factor* of a polynomial if and only if the polynomial equals 0 when n is substituted for x.

The following computer program evaluates polynomials.

```
10    PRINT "TYPE VALUES OF A, B, C, D"
20    INPUT A,B,C,D
30    PRINT " X      Y"
40    PRINT "---   ---"
50    FOR X =  - ABS (D) TO ABS (D)
60    LET Y =A * X * X * X + B * X * X + C * X + D
70    PRINT X,Y
80    IF Y <  > 0 THEN 100
90    PRINT "***********"
100   NEXT X
110   END
```

For instance, to evaluate $x^3 - 4x^2 + 9x - 10$, you would type in

$$1, -4, 9, -10$$

for A, B, C, and D. Then the computer would evaluate the polynomial for each integer value of x, starting at -10 and ending at 10. The computer would print the value of x and the value of the polynomial. It would also print a row of asterisks, ***********, if the value of the polynomial is 0.

a. Run the program using the polynomial $x^3 - 4x^2 + x + 6$. Use the resulting output to find all factors of the form $x - n$ (such as $x - 3$), where n is a value of x that makes the polynomial equal 0.

b. Run the program again using $x^3 - 5x^2 + 11x - 15$. Write the *one* factor you discover. Then divide the factor into the polynomial to find the other factor.

c. Run the program again to show that there are *no* integer values of x that make $x^3 - 4x^2 + x + 5$ equal 0.

11-8	FRACTIONAL EQUATIONS AND EXTRANEOUS SOLUTIONS

In Section 12.1 you found values of x when you knew the value of a rational expression. For instance, you found x when

$$\frac{x - 5}{x + 4} = 9.$$

Equations like this that have a variable in a denominator are called *fractional equations*.

Assignments:

DEFINITION

> **FRACTIONAL EQUATION**
> A **fractional equation** is an equation that has a variable in at least one denominator.

Now that you know how to operate with rational expressions, you are prepared to solve more complicated fractional equations, such as

$$\frac{3}{x} + \frac{5}{6} = \frac{1}{4x}.$$

The way to work a new problem is to transform it into an old problem. For fractional equations, this means getting rid of the fractions. The technique is to *multiply* each member of the equation by the LCM of the denominators. The LCM of x, 6, and $4x$ is $12x$. So you write

$$12x\left(\frac{3}{x} + \frac{5}{6}\right) = 12x\left(\frac{1}{4x}\right).$$

On the right, $4x$ divided into $12x$ is 3. On the left, you distribute $12x$ to each term.

$$12x\left(\frac{3}{x}\right) + 12x\left(\frac{5}{6}\right) = 3(1)$$

Canceling can now be done in each term on the left, giving

$$12(3) + 2x(5) = 3(1).$$

Multiplying gives

$$36 + 10x = 3.$$
$$10x = -33$$
$$x = -3.3$$
$$\therefore S = \{-3.3\}$$

Check:

$$\frac{3}{-3.3} + \frac{5}{6} \overset{?}{=} \frac{1}{4(-3.3)}$$

$$-0.90909\ldots + 0.83333\ldots \overset{?}{=} -0.07575\ldots$$

$$-0.07575\ldots = -0.07575\ldots \quad ✔$$

Sometimes there are surprises when you solve a fractional equation. For

$$\frac{3}{x - 2} - \frac{6}{x^2 - 2x} = 1,$$

the LCM of the denominators (the LCD) is found by factoring.

$$\frac{3}{x - 2} - \frac{6}{x(x - 2)} = 1,$$

so the LCD is $x(x - 2)$. Multiplying each member by this number gives

$$x(x - 2)\left(\frac{3}{x - 2} - \frac{6}{x(x - 2)}\right) = x(x - 2)(1).$$

Distributing on the left and right gives

$$x(x - 2) \cdot \frac{3}{x - 2} - x(x - 2) \cdot \frac{6}{x(x - 2)} = x^2 - 2x.$$

Canceling on the left leaves

$$3x - 6 = x^2 - 2x.$$

Subtracting $3x$ and adding 6 gives

$$0 = x^2 - 5x + 6.$$

This is now a familiar quadratic equation. In this case the right member *factors*, giving

$$0 = (x - 2)(x - 3).$$

Setting each factor equal to 0 gives

$$x - 2 = 0 \quad \text{or} \quad x - 3 = 0$$

$$x = 2 \quad \text{or} \quad x = 3.$$

The surprise comes when you check the answers.

$x = 2$: $x = 3$:

$$\frac{3}{2 - 2} - \frac{6}{4 - 4} \stackrel{?}{=} 1 \qquad\qquad \frac{3}{3 - 2} - \frac{6}{9 - 6} \stackrel{?}{=} 1$$

$$\frac{3}{0} - \frac{6}{0} \stackrel{?}{=} 1 \quad \text{Does not check!} \qquad\qquad 1 = 1 \quad \text{✔}$$

In this example, 2 satisfies the *transformed* equation, $0 = x^2 - 5x + 6$. But it does *not* satisfy the original equation. Such a number is called an *extraneous solution*.

DEFINITION

> **EXTRANEOUS SOLUTION**
> An **extraneous solution** is a value of the variable that satisfies the *transformed* equation, but *not* the original one.

The difficulty arises because x cannot equal 2 in the original equation. Fractions are *undefined* if their denominators are zero. As soon as you find out that the LCD is $x(x - 2)$, you should state that $x \neq 0$ and $x \neq 2$. These numbers are said to be out of the *domain* of the variable.

DEFINITION

> **DOMAIN**
> The **domain** of a variable is the set of numbers that can be values of the variable.

Note: The domain of the variable must exclude all numbers that make a denominator equal zero.

When you find the LCD for the above equation, you should write

$$\text{LCD:}\quad x(x - 2)$$
$$\text{Domain exclusions:}\quad x \neq 0 \quad \text{and} \quad x \neq 2.$$

At the end of the problem you should *cross out* any extraneous solutions before you write the solution set.

$$\underset{\text{Extraneous.}}{\cancel{x = 2}} \quad \text{or} \quad x = 3$$
$$\therefore S = \{3\}$$

Objective:
Be able to solve a fractional equation, discarding any extraneous solutions.

Cover the answers as you work these examples.

EXAMPLE 1

Solve: $\dfrac{7}{2x} - \dfrac{3}{5} = \dfrac{1}{10}$.

- - - - -   - - - - -

		Think These Reasons

| $\dfrac{7}{2x} - \dfrac{3}{5} = \dfrac{1}{10}$ | LCD: $10x$
 Domain exclusion:
 $x \neq 0$ | Write the given equation.
 Write the LCD and domain exclusion. |

$$10x\left(\frac{7}{2x} - \frac{3}{5}\right) = 10x\left(\frac{1}{10}\right)$$ Multiply each member by the LCD.

$$5(7) - 2x(3) = x(1)$$ Distribute $10x$ and cancel.

$$35 - 6x = x$$ Multiply.

$$-7x = -35$$ Subtract 35 and subtract x.

$$x = 5$$ Divide by -7.

$$\therefore S = \{5\}$$ Write the solution set. (5 is *not* excluded from the domain. So it *is* a solution.)

EXAMPLE 2

Solve: $\dfrac{3}{x - 5} + \dfrac{3}{x + 5} = 7.$

$- - - - -$ $\qquad\qquad$ $- - - - -$

$\dfrac{3}{x - 5} + \dfrac{3}{x + 5} = 7$

LCD: Write the given equation.
$(x - 5)(x + 5)$ Write the LCD and domain
Domain   exclusions.
exclusions:
$x \neq 5, x \neq -5.$

$\left(\dfrac{3}{x - 5} + \dfrac{3}{x + 5}\right)(x - 5)(x + 5)$ Multiply each member by the LCD.
$\qquad = 7(x - 5)(x + 5)$

$3(x + 5) + 3(x - 5)$ Distribute and cancel on the
$\qquad = 7(x^2 - 25)$ left. Multiply on the right.

$3x + 15 + 3x - 15 = 7x^2 - 175$ Distribute.

$6x = 7x^2 - 175$ Combine like terms.

$0 = 7x^2 - 6x - 175$ Make one member equal zero.

$x = \dfrac{6 \pm \sqrt{36 - 4(7)(-175)}}{2(7)}$ Use the Quadratic Formula.

$x = \dfrac{6 \pm \sqrt{4936}}{14}$ Do the computation.

$x \approx 5.45 \quad \text{or} \quad x \approx -4.59$ Round to two decimal places.

$\therefore S = \{5.45, -4.59\}$ Write the solution set. (Neither value of x is excluded from the domain, so both values are solutions.)

EXAMPLE 3

Solve: $\dfrac{2x}{x - 3} - \dfrac{6}{x - 3} = 9.$

$- - - - -$ $\qquad\qquad$ $- - - - -$

$$\frac{2x}{x-3} - \frac{6}{x-3} = 9$$

LCD:
$x - 3$
Domain
exclusion:
$x \neq 3$

Write the given equation.
Write the LCD and
domain exclusion.

$$\left(\frac{2x}{x-3} - \frac{6}{x-3}\right)(x-3) = 9(x-3)$$

Multiply each member
by the LCD.

$$2x - 6 = 9x - 27$$

Distribute and cancel.

$$-7x = -21$$

Add 6: subtract 9x.

Extraneous.

$$x = 3$$

Divide by −7. Discard
the extraneous solution.

$$\therefore S = \emptyset$$

Write the solution set.
(Since the only possible
solution is out of the
domain, the solution set is
empty.)

ORAL PRACTICE

Give the LCD and the restrictions on the domain of x.

EXAMPLE

Answers

$$\frac{3}{x+5} = \frac{7}{x-2}$$

LCD = $(x+5)(x-2)$.
Domain: $x \neq -5, x \neq 2$.

A. $\dfrac{x-4}{x} = \dfrac{5}{x}$ LCD = x
Domain: $x \neq 0$

B. $\dfrac{x}{x-4} = \dfrac{x}{5}$ LCD = $5(x-4)$
Domain: $x \neq 4$

C. $\dfrac{x-7}{2x} = \dfrac{9}{2x}$ LCD = $2x$
Domain: $x \neq 0$

D. $\dfrac{2x}{x-7} = \dfrac{2x}{9}$ LCD = $9(x-7)$
Domain: $x \neq 7$

E. $\dfrac{x+3}{x+4} = 5$ LCD = $x+4$
Domain: $x \neq -4$

F. $\dfrac{x-2}{x+3} = \dfrac{x-5}{x-3}$ LCD = $(x+3)(x-3)$
Domain: $x \neq -3, x \neq 3$

G. $\dfrac{x+3}{x} = \dfrac{6}{x-2}$ LCD = $x(x-2)$
Domain: $x \neq 0, x \neq 2$

H. $\dfrac{x+3}{5} = \dfrac{6}{x-2}$ LCD = $5(x-2)$
Domain: $x \neq 2$

I. $\dfrac{1}{x} + \dfrac{1}{3x} = \dfrac{1}{4}$ LCD = $12x$
Domain: $x \neq 0$

EXERCISE 11-8

For Problems 1 through 24, solve the equation, discarding any extraneous solutions.

Problem Notes:

Extraneous solutions do not appear until Problem 15.

Problems 21–24 require use of the Quadratic Formula. Problem 24 has an empty solution set because the discriminant is negative, not because the solution is extraneous.

1. $\dfrac{4x - 3}{x} = \dfrac{17}{x}$ $S = \{5\}$

2. $\dfrac{3x - 8}{x} = \dfrac{13}{x}$ $S = \{7\}$

3. $\dfrac{11}{r} = \dfrac{7r + 5}{3r}$ $S = \{4\}$

4. $\dfrac{7}{s} = \dfrac{4s - 1}{5s}$ $S = \{9\}$

5. $\dfrac{x - 2}{x} - \dfrac{7}{3x} = \dfrac{3}{4x}$ $S = \{5\frac{1}{12}\}$

6. $\dfrac{x - 3}{x} - \dfrac{6}{5x} = \dfrac{7}{2x}$ $S = \{7.7\}$

7. $\dfrac{1}{7} + \dfrac{1}{x} = \dfrac{1}{5}$ $S = \{17.5\}$

8. $\dfrac{1}{50} + \dfrac{1}{x} = \dfrac{1}{30}$ $S = \{75\}$

9. $\dfrac{1}{5} - \dfrac{1}{20} = \dfrac{1}{x}$ $S = \{6\frac{2}{3}\}$

10. $\dfrac{1}{3} - \dfrac{1}{4} = \dfrac{1}{x}$ $S = \{12\}$

11. $\dfrac{b}{b + 2} = \dfrac{3}{7}$ $S = \{1\frac{1}{2}\}$

12. $\dfrac{a}{a + 4} = \dfrac{8}{3}$ $S = \{-6.4\}$

13. $\dfrac{3}{2x} = \dfrac{5}{x - 7}$ $S = \{-3\}$

14. $\dfrac{7}{3x} = \dfrac{4}{x - 2}$ $S = \{-2.8\}$

15. $\dfrac{x}{x - 3} - \dfrac{3}{x - 3} = 8$ $S = \emptyset$ 3 is extr.

16. $\dfrac{8}{x - 2} - \dfrac{x}{x - 2} = 5$ $S = \{3\}$

17. $\dfrac{4}{x + 2} - \dfrac{x}{x + 2} = 3$ $S = \{-0.5\}$.

18. $\dfrac{x}{x + 6} + \dfrac{6}{x + 6} = 11$ $S = \emptyset$ -6 is extr.

19. $\dfrac{8}{x + 6} + \dfrac{8}{x - 6} = 1$ $S = \{-2, 18\}$

20. $\dfrac{3}{x - 4} + \dfrac{3}{x + 4} = 1$ $S = \{-2, 8\}$

21. $\dfrac{2}{x + 5} - \dfrac{1}{x - 3} = 3$ $S=\{2.63, -4.30\}$

22. $\dfrac{3}{x - 1} - \dfrac{2}{x + 4} = 5$ $S=\{1.56, -4.36\}$

23. $\dfrac{x}{x + 2} - \dfrac{7}{x + 4} = 2$ $S=\{-2.38, -12.62\}$

24. $\dfrac{3}{x - 4} - \dfrac{5}{x + 3} = 2$ $S = \emptyset$ neg. discrim.

For Problems 25 through 34, add or subtract the fractions and simplify the answer. Remember that these are *expressions*, not equations. You cannot get rid of the denominators by multiplying each term by the LCD.

25. $\dfrac{8}{5x} + \dfrac{7}{10x}$ $\dfrac{23}{10x}$

26. $\dfrac{7}{6x} + \dfrac{5}{3x}$ $\dfrac{17}{6x}$

27. $\dfrac{2}{x + 1} + \dfrac{3}{x + 4}$ $\dfrac{5x + 11}{x^2 + 5x + 4}$

28. $\dfrac{5}{x + 3} + \dfrac{2}{x + 1}$ $\dfrac{7x + 11}{x^2 + 4x + 3}$

Problems 25–30 remind students that they cannot multiply each term in an expression the way they multiply each member of an equation.

29. $\dfrac{4}{x+3} + \dfrac{4}{x-3}$ $\dfrac{8x}{x^2-9}$ 30. $\dfrac{6}{x+2} + \dfrac{6}{x-2}$ $\dfrac{12x}{x^2-4}$

31. $\dfrac{x^2}{x-5} - \dfrac{25}{x-5}$ $x+5$ 32. $\dfrac{x^2}{x-4} - \dfrac{16}{x-4}$ $x+4$

33. $\dfrac{5}{x-2} - \dfrac{4}{2-x}$ $\dfrac{9}{x-2}$ 34. $\dfrac{7}{x-5} - \dfrac{4}{5-x}$ $\dfrac{11}{x-5}$

35. See Problem 62, Exercise 6–8, page 247.

35. *General Proof of the Quadratic Formula*—In Section 6.8 you derived the Quadratic Formula by using a specific example, $5x^2 + 13x + 7 = 0$. Now that you have studied operations with algebraic fractions, you should be able to derive the formula in general. Starting with $ax^2 + bx + c = 0$, derive the Quadratic Formula.

11-9	PROBLEMS INVOLVING RATIO AND PROPORTION

Time: 2 days

Chalkboard Examples:

First day:
Work one example, such as the following. A grocer finds that the ratio of apples to oranges sold is 5 : 3. If the fruit display cases have room for a total of 1096 apples and oranges, how many of each should be set out so that the numbers will have this ratio?
Ans.: 685 apples, 411 oranges
Then have students work the three text examples before starting their assignment. The Oral Practice problems are effective here.

Second day:
Homework problems at board.

Assignments:

Day 1: Exercise 11–9, #3–9 odd;
   Exercise 11–8, #11; and
   Exercise 10–8, #6
Day 2: Exercise 11–9, #11–17 odd;
   Exercise 11–8, #8, 26; and
   Exercise 11–6, #40

If somebody says that men and women are in a 3-to-8 ratio, it means that

$$\frac{\text{number of men}}{\text{number of women}} = \frac{3}{8}.$$

There are many ways this equation could be true. For instance, there could be 3 men and 8 women. Or there could be 6 men and 16 women because

$$\frac{6}{16} = \frac{(3)(2)}{(8)(2)} = \frac{3}{8}.$$

The number of men must be a multiple of 3, and the number of women must be the *same* multiple of 8. This means that there is a number x such that

$$3x = \text{number of men},$$

$$8x = \text{number of women}.$$

The number x is a *common factor* of the number of men and the number of women. Suppose that in addition to knowing the ratio 3 : 8 (a short way of writing the ratio 3 to 8), you also know that there is a total of 407 people in the group. How many of each would there be?

Since $3x$ is the number of men and $8x$ is the number of women, you can write

$$3x + 8x = 407$$

$$11x = 407$$

$$x = 37.$$

So there are (3)(37), or 111, men and (8)(37), or 296, women.

In this section you will work more problems involving ratios of two integers.

Objective:
Given two integers, find their ratio in lowest terms; or given information about two integers including their ratio, find the integers.

Cover the answers as you work the examples.

EXAMPLE 1

Fish Problem   Naturalists estimate that there are 3000 fish in Lake Muchimuck. Some are perch and the rest are bass. They drag a fishing net through the lake and catch 24 perch and 21 bass.
a.   What is the ratio of perch to bass caught? Express the answer in lowest terms.
b.   Assuming that the entire lake has this ratio, how many of each kind of fish were there (including those caught)?

– – – – –   – – – – –

a.
$$\frac{\text{number of perch}}{\text{number of bass}} = \frac{24}{21} = \frac{8}{7}$$

Ratio is 8 : 7.

– – – – –   – – – – –

	Think These Reasons

b.   Let x = common factor.   Define a variable.

$8x$ = Number of perch.   Write expressions for the
$7x$ = Number of bass.   numbers of fish.

$8x + 7x = 3000$ Write an equation

(Total number of fish) (is) (3000.)

$15x = 3000$

$x = 200$ Solve the equation.

$\therefore 8x = 1600, \qquad 7x = 1400$ Evaluate the expressions.

1600 perch, 1400 bass.   Answer the question.

Check: $1600 + 1400 = 3000$, and $\dfrac{1600}{1400} = \dfrac{8}{7}$, which checks.

EXAMPLE 2

Triangle Problem   The sides of a triangle have lengths in the ratio 3 : 5 : 7. The perimeter of the triangle is 90 centimeters. Find the lengths of the sides.

- - - - -   - - - - -

Note: The numbers 3 : 5 : 7 mean that sides 1 and 2 are in the ratio 3 : 5, sides 2 and 3 are in the ratio 5 : 7, and sides 1 and 3 are in the ratio 3 : 7.

Let x = common factor.
$\therefore$ $3x$, $5x$, and $7x$ are the lengths of the sides.

$$\underbrace{3x + 5x + 7x}_{\text{The perimeter}} \underset{\text{is}}{=} \underbrace{90}_{90}$$

$$15x = 90$$

$$x = 6$$

$$3x = 18, \qquad 5x = 30, \qquad 7x = 42.$$

$\therefore$ <u>Sides are 18 cm, 30 cm, and 42 cm.</u>

Check: $18 + 30 + 42 = 90$; $18 : 30 = 3 : 5$, $30 : 42 = 5 : 7$, $18 : 42 = 3 : 7$.

EXAMPLE 3

Freshmen and Sophomores Problem   The freshmen at Scorpion Gulch High School outnumber the sophomores 7 : 5. If there are 231 freshmen, how many sophomores are there?

- - - - -   - - - - -

Let x = number of sophomores.   Define a variable.

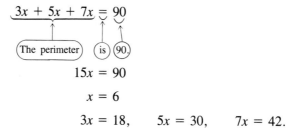

                                                                   Write an equation.

$$5x\left(\frac{231}{x}\right) = 5x\left(\frac{7}{5}\right)$$ Multiply each member by the LCD.

$$5(231) = 7x$$ Cancel.

$$1155 = 7x$$ Multiply.

$$165 = x$$ Divide each member by 7.

<u>165 sophomores.</u>   Answer the question.

Check: $\dfrac{231}{165} = 1.4$, which equals $\dfrac{7}{5}$.

Note: In this problem you already *know* one of the two integers. So it is easier to define the variable to be the *other* integer rather than the common factor.

The equation in Example 3,

$$\frac{231}{x} = \frac{7}{5}$$

is called a **proportion.** It says that two ratios are equal. There is an easy way to solve a proportion. If you look at the third step in the example you see

$$(5)(231) = 7x.$$

This step can be reached by **cross multiplication.**

$$\frac{231}{x} \diagup \frac{7}{5} \qquad \text{Cross multiply.}$$

To find a way to describe cross multiplication, write the fractions in ratio form.

$$231 : x = 7 : 5$$

This equation is read "231 is to x as 7 is to 5." The 231 and 5 are called **extremes** since they are at the two ends of the proportion. The x and 7 are called **means,** since they are in the middle of the proportion.

$$\text{Means.}$$
$$231 : x = 7 : 5 \quad \leftarrow \text{ A proportion.}$$
$$\text{Extremes.}$$

Since this equation is equivalent to $7x = (231)(5)$, you can say that the product of the means equals the product of the extremes. It may be easier for you to remember the cross-multiplying technique, but you should at least remember the words so that you will know what they mean.

DEFINITION

CROSS MULTIPLICATION
In a proportion such as $a : b = c : d$, the product of the means equals the product of the extremes.

That is, if $\dfrac{a}{b} = \dfrac{c}{d}$,

then $ad = bc$.

ORAL PRACTICE

Tell what the ratio would be in lowest terms.

EXAMPLES

Answers

i. $15 : 25$ i.   3 to 5

ii. $15 : 22$ ii. Already in lowest terms.

A. $14 : 35$ $_{2\,:\,5}$ B. $24 : 36$ $_{2\,:\,3}$ C. $12 : 4$ $_{3\,:\,1}$ D. $8 : 48$ $_{1\,:\,6}$

E. $9 : 48$ $_{3\,:\,16}$ F. $10 : 48$ $_{5\,:\,24}$ G. $28 : 21$ $_{4\,:\,3}$ H. $21 : 14$ $_{3\,:\,2}$

I. $21 : 12$ $_{7\,:\,4}$ J. $21 : 10$ $_{21\,:\,10}$

Tell the result of cross multiplication.

EXAMPLE

Answer

$\dfrac{2}{3} = \dfrac{10}{x}$ $2x = 30$

K. $\dfrac{5}{7} = \dfrac{9}{x}$ L. $\dfrac{3}{8} = \dfrac{4}{x}$ M. $\dfrac{5}{x} = \dfrac{10}{27}$ N. $\dfrac{7}{x} = \dfrac{1}{2}$ O. $\dfrac{x}{5} = \dfrac{2}{x}$

$5x = 63$ $3x = 32$ $135 = 10x$ $14 = x$ $x^2 = 10$

EXERCISE 11-9

Problem Notes:

The problems of this section are important background for the ratio and proportion problems that occur in geometry.

Sharper students often figure out shortcuts that allow them to do these problems in their heads. For instance, in Problem 5, $12 + 18 = 30$, so 7200 must be divided into 30 parts of 240 each. One tract has 12(240) or 2880 acres, and the other tract has 18(240) or 4320 acres. The check is that $2880 + 4320 = 7200$. This kind of reasoning should be encouraged when it appears. Real-world problems are solvable many ways—not just algebraically.

1. *Ratio Problem 1*   The ratio of two integers is $13 : 6$. The smaller integer is 54. Find the larger integer.   117

2. *Ratio Problem 2*   The ratio of two integers is $7 : 11$. The larger integer is 187. Find the smaller integer.   119

3. *Ratio Problem 3*   The ratio of two integers is $9 : 7$. Their sum is 1024. Find the two integers.   576 and 448

4. *Ratio Problem 4*   The ratio of two integers is $17 : 13$. Their sum is 390. Find the integers.   221 and 169

5. *Grandchildren Problem*   Mae Berry has 18 grandchildren on her son's side and 12 grandchildren on her daughter's side.

a.   What is the ratio of these numbers, in lowest terms?   3 : 2
b.   The elder Berry divides 7200 acres of land into two tracts,
   whose areas are in this ratio. How many acres are in each tract?

5. b.   4320 acres and 2880 acres

6. *Will Problem*   A. Mann regularly gives $300 a month to charity
   and $800 a month to his grandchildren.
   a.   What is the ratio of these two numbers, in lowest terms?   3 : 8
   b.   Mr. Mann's will specifies that his estate will be divided in the
      same ratio. If his estate contains $104,500, how much will go to
      charity and how much will go to his grandchildren?

6. b. $28,500 to charity,
         $76,000 to grandchildren

7. *Price-to-Earnings Ratio Problem*   The stock of a certain company
   is priced at $18.20 per share. The company's earnings for one year
   amounted to $2.80 per share.
   a.   Find the price-to-earnings ratio. Express it both as a ratio of two
      integers in lowest terms and as a ratio ____ : 1 (as it appears in
      newspapers), where the second number is 1 and the first number
      is not necessarily an integer.   13 : 2, 6.5 : 1
   b.   If the company earned $3,360,000 in that year, what was the
      total value of its stock? $21,840,000

8. *Commission-to-Selling-Price Ratio Problem*   A real estate agent
   sold a house for $84,000. The agent's commission was $5040.
   a.   What was the commission-to-selling-price ratio? Express the an-
      swer both as a ratio of two integers in lowest terms and as a
      percent.   3 : 50, 6%
   b.   What would the commission be for a house that sells for
      $278,000 if the commission-to-selling-price ratio is the same? $16,680

9. *Basketball Tickets Problem*   You are called upon to estimate how
   many of the 12,000 people who attend a professional basketball
   game are women. From a small sample, you determine that the ratio
   of men to women is about 3 : 2. About how many of the people at-
   tending are women?   4800 women

10. *Peanut Contest Problem*   A large jar contains 8400 nuts. You will
   receive a prize if you guess closest to the number of peanuts in the
   jar. From a small sample, you find that the ratio of peanuts to other
   nuts is about 3 : 4. Based on this information, about how many peanuts are in the jar?   3600 peanuts

11. *Milk Stock Problem*   Suppose that you work in a supermarket. The
   milk display case can hold a total of 160 one-gallon containers of
   milk. Sales figures show that the cheaper generic milk outsells the
   national brand milk by 7 : 3. How many containers of each kind
   should you put in the case in order to have this ratio?

11.   112 cartons generic, 48 cartons national

12.   18,000 l unleaded, 8000 l regular

12. *Two Grades of Gasoline Problem*   A local filling station finds that
   unleaded gas outsells regular gas in the ratio 9 : 4. The station's
   monthly quota is a total of 26,000 liters. How many liters of each
   kind should be ordered so that the quota will have this ratio?

13. ***Three Grades of Gasoline Problem*** A local filling station sells regular, unleaded, and super-unleaded gasoline in the ratio 5 : 7 : 2. Their total monthly quota is 28,000 liters of gasoline. How many liters of each kind should be ordered so that the quota will have this ratio? 10,000 l regular, 14,000 l unleaded, 4000 l super unleaded

14. 150 boxes cornflakes, 90 boxes wheat flakes, 270 boxes other cereal

14. ***Cereal Stock Problem*** A supermarket's cereal shelves have room for 510 boxes of cereal. Sales figures show that corn flakes, wheat flakes, and other cereals sell in the ratio of 5 : 3 : 9. How many boxes of each kind of cereal should be put on the shelves so that when the shelves are full the numbers of boxes will be in this ratio?

15. 28 m, 40 m, 44 m

15. ***Triangle Problem 1*** The sides of a triangle are in the ratio 7 : 10 : 11. Its perimeter is 112 meters. How long is each side?

16. 48 furlongs, 56 furlongs, 80 furlongs

16. ***Triangle Problem 2*** The sides of a triangle are in the ratio 6 : 7 : 10. The perimeter is 184 furlongs. How long is each side?

17. ***Rectangle Problem 1*** The length and width of a rectangle are in the ratio 3 : 2. The perimeter is 73 centimeters. Find the length and the width. Length = 21.9 cm, width = 14.6 cm

18. Length = 17.5 ft, width = 10.5 ft

18. ***Rectangle Problem 2*** The length and width of a rectangle are in the ratio 5 : 3. The perimeter is 56 feet. Find the length and the width.

19. ***Fish in the Lake Problem*** Ecologists are trying to determine how many fish there are in a particular lake. They catch 100 fish from the lake, put small tags on their tails, and put them back into the lake. Several days later they catch 15 fish. They find that 2 are tagged and the other 13 are not. Assuming that the tagged to untagged fish are in the ratio 2 : 13, how many fish are in the lake (counting the 15)? 750 fish

20. ***Radioactive Blood Problem*** Researchers are trying to determine how much blood a particular animal has in its body. Since actually draining out the blood to measure it would kill the animal, they withdraw 100 milliliters (ml) of blood and replace it with 100 ml of slightly radioactive blood. They later withdraw a sample and find that the ratio of radioactive to nonradioactive blood is 2 : 34. About how many milliliters of blood does the animal have? 1800 ml

21. ***Age Problem 1*** Clara Fye is 31 years old. Her sister Molly is 47. When will their ages be in the ratio 4 : 5? 33 years from now

22. ***Age Problem 2*** Juan Ting is 23 years old. His sister Tess is 20. When will their ages be in the ratio 3 : 2? Surprising? 14 years *ago*!

23. ***Clock Face Problem*** A clock reads 5:00.
    a. What is the ratio of the area on the clock's face between the two hands to the rest of the area? 5 : 7
    b. If the total area is 132 square centimeters, what is the area between the hands? 55 cm²

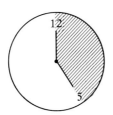

24. ***Similar Rectangles Problem*** The ratio of length to width is 3 : 2 for each of the two rectangles. The length of the larger rectangle is in the ratio 7 : 5 to that of the smaller one. What is the ratio of the *areas* of the two rectangles?   49 : 25

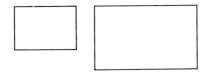

11-10 | PROBLEMS INVOLVING PROBABILITY AND OTHER RATIONAL EXPRESSIONS

The expressions you have been studying in this chapter have variables in their denominators. Such expressions can represent quantities in the real world. For instance, you recall that

$$\text{rate} \times \text{time} = \text{distance.}$$

Dividing each member of this equation by rate or by time gives

$$\text{rate} = \frac{\text{distance}}{\text{time}} \quad \text{or} \quad \text{time} = \frac{\text{distance}}{\text{rate}}.$$

If time or rate are variables, then these expressions will have variables in their denominators. For instance, suppose you travel through the water at x km/h against a current of 5 km/h. Your net speed is

$$x - 5.$$

If you travel a total distance of 10 km at this speed, the time it takes you will be

$$\text{time} = \frac{10}{x - 5}.$$

If x is 7, then

$$\text{time} = \frac{10}{7 - 5} = \frac{10}{2} = 5 \text{ hours.}$$

If x is 25, then

$$\text{time} = \frac{10}{25 - 5} = \frac{10}{20} = \frac{1}{2} \text{ hour.}$$

Time: 4 days

Chalkboard Examples:

First day:
Use Exercise 11–10, Problem 1, as an example.

Second day:
Use one rate-of-work problem, such as the following.
Two neighbor children share a plastic pool. The hose from John's house can fill the pool in 10 minutes. The hose from Theresa's house can fill it in 8 minutes. How long would it take to fill the pool with both hoses running? Ans.: $4\frac{4}{9}$ minutes.
Then have students work text Example 2 before starting their homework.

Third day:
Use one integer quotient problem, such as the following.
If a large positive integer is divided by a smaller one, the quotient is 12 and the remainder is 32. The sum of the integers is 513. Find the two integers.
Ans.: 476 and 37

(This problem is workable by trial and error. The denominator must be 33 or higher, since the remainder is 32. Thus, only 5 trials are needed to discover the answer.)

Then have students work text Example 3 before starting their homework.

Fourth day:
Review in preparation for test.

Assignments:

Day 1: Exercise 11–10, #3, 5, 7;
     Exercise 11–9, #2; and
     Exercise 11–6, #28
Day 2: Exercise 11–10, #9, 19, 21;
     Exercise 11–9, #10; and
     Exercise 11–6, #44
Day 3: Exercise 11–10, #11, 13, 23, 27
Day 4: Selected problems from Exercise 11–11
     in preparation for test.

Suppose that you want to complete a 10-km trip in 3 h. You would write the *equation*

$$3 = \frac{10}{x - 5}.$$

Multiplying each member by $x - 5$ then solving for x gives

$$3(x - 5) = 10$$
$$3x - 15 = 10$$
$$3x = 25$$
$$x = 8\frac{1}{3}$$

$$\underline{\underline{8\frac{1}{3} \text{ km/h}}}$$

In this section you will work more problems in which variables appear in denominators. Some problems will relate to the real world. Others will be contest-type problems designed only to see if you can do the algebra.

Objective:

Be able to write rational expressions involving quantities from the real world, and evaluate these expressions or solve for their variables.

The following examples show you how to do these things. You may like to try them on your own before you uncover the solutions.

EXAMPLE 1

Upstream-Downstream Problem   A boat moves through the water at x km/h. It makes a journey 20 km upstream against a current of 3 km/h and then returns with the current.

a.   Write an expression for the total time for the round trip.
b.   How long will the round trip take if the boat goes 10 km/h through the water?
c.   How fast must the boat travel through the water in order to complete the round trip in 5 hours?

– – – –   – – – –

	Think These Reasons

a. x = number of km/h the boat goes.   Restate the variable.

     $\therefore x - 3$ = number of km/h   boat speed − current speed.
     upstream.

$x + 3$ = number of km/h   boat speed + current speed.
downstream.

$\dfrac{20}{x + 3}$ = number of hours   time = distance/rate.
upstream.

$\dfrac{20}{x + 3}$ = number of hours
downstream.

$\dfrac{20}{x - 3} + \dfrac{20}{x + 3}$ = total time for
round trip.

- - - - -   - - - - -

b.   If $x = 10$, then

$$\dfrac{20}{x - 3} + \dfrac{20}{x + 3}$$ Write the expression.

$$= \dfrac{20}{10 - 3} + \dfrac{20}{10 + 3}$$ Substitute 10 for x.

$$\approx 2.857 + 1.539$$ Do the arithmetic.

$$= 4.396.$$

About 4.4 hours.   Answer the question.

- - - - -   - - - - -

c.   If the time is 5 hours, then

$$\dfrac{20}{x - 3} + \dfrac{20}{x + 3} = 5$$ Write an equation.

$$(x - 3)(x + 3)\left(\dfrac{20}{x - 3} + \dfrac{20}{x + 3}\right)$$

$$= 5(x - 3)(x + 3)$$ Multiply each member by LCD.

$$(x + 3)(20) + (x - 3)(20)$$ Distribute on the left;
$$= 5(x^2 - 9)$$ multiply on the right.

$$20x + 60 + 20x - 60$$ Distribute.
$$= 5x^2 - 45$$

Think These Reasons

$$0 = 5x^2 - 40x - 45$$ Make one member equal 0.

$$0 = x^2 - 8x - 9$$ Simplify (if possible).

$$x = \dfrac{8 \pm \sqrt{64 - 4(1)(-9)}}{2(1)}$$ Use the Quadratic Formula.

$$x = \dfrac{8 \pm \sqrt{100}}{2}$$ Simplify.

$x = 9$ or -1 ↗ Out of domain.   Do the computation.
                                      Discard meaningless solutions.

9 km/h   Answer the question.

Note: In this case, you could also have solved the equation by factoring. Here's how.

$$0 = (x - 9)(x + 1)$$

$$x - 9 = 0 \quad \text{or} \quad x + 1 = 0$$

$$x = 9 \quad \text{or} \quad x = -1$$

EXAMPLE 2

The fill pipe can fill an empty swimming pool in 5 h. With the fill pipe and the garden hose both running, it takes only 3 h to fill an empty pool. How long would it take to fill the pool with just the hose?

- - - - -   - - - - -

Let x = number of hours for hose alone.   Define a variable.

Work = rate × time.   (Similar to $d = rt$.)

∴ Rate $= \dfrac{\text{work}}{\text{time}}$.   Divide by time.

Fill pipe's rate is $\dfrac{1}{5}$ pool per hour.

                                              Rate = work/time.
Hose's rate is $\dfrac{1}{x}$ pool per hour. In this case, the work is 1 pool.

∴ Combined rate is $\dfrac{1}{5} + \dfrac{1}{x}$.   Add the rates.

Combined time is 3 h.   Given

$$\underbrace{\left(\frac{1}{5} + \frac{1}{x}\right)}_{\text{rate}} \underbrace{(3)}_{\text{time}} = \underbrace{1}_{\text{work}}$$ Rate × time = work.

$$\frac{3}{5} + \frac{3}{x} = 1$$ Distribute 3.

$$5x\left(\frac{3}{5} + \frac{3}{x}\right) = 5x(1)$$ Multiply by the LCD.

$$3x + 15 = 5x$$ Distribute 5x.

$$15 = 2x$$

$$7.5 = x$$

| 7.5 h | Answer the question. |

EXAMPLE 3

Integer Quotient Problem   When a certain large positive integer is divided by a smaller positive integer, the integer part of the quotient is 2 and the remainder is 9. The sum of the integers is 48. Find the two integers.

| Let x = larger integer. | Define variables. |
| Let y = smaller integer. | |

$$\frac{x}{y} = 2 + \frac{9}{y} \quad (1)$$ Write an equation.

$$x + y = 48 \quad (2)$$ Write another equation.

Sum   is   48.

$$x = 48 - y \quad (3)$$ From equation (2).

$$\frac{48 - y}{y} = 2 + \frac{9}{y}$$ Substitute $48 - y$ for x in (1).

$$48 - y = 2y + 9$$ Multiply each member by y.

$$39 = 3y$$ Add y; subtract 9.

$$13 = y$$ Divide by 3.

$$\therefore x = 48 - 13$$ Substitute 13 for y in (3).

$$x = 35$$ Do the subtraction.

Integers are 35 and 13.   Answer the question.

EXAMPLE 4

Soup Can Probability Problem   A flood washes all the labels off the soup cans in a grocery store. Inventory records show that there were 300 cans of tomato soup and 500 cans of beef-barley soup before the flood.

a.   If a can is picked at random, what is the probability that it is tomato soup? What is the probability that it is beef-barley?
b.   If 100 cans are picked at random, how many cans of beef-barley soup would you expect to get?
c.   How many cans, total, would you have to take in order for the expected number of cans of tomato soup to be 60?

- - - - -   - - - - -

a.   Total number of cans is
     $300 + 500 = 800.$

Probability for tomato:

$$\frac{300}{800} = \frac{3}{8}$$

Probability equals number of favorable outcomes divided by total number of outcomes.

Probability for beef-barley:

$$\frac{500}{800} = \frac{5}{8}$$

- - - - -   - - - - -

b. Expected number of beef-barley:

$$\left(\frac{5}{8}\right)(100) = 62.5$$

Expected number of favorable outcomes equals probability times total number of outcomes.

<u>About 62 or 63</u>

Round off to an integer.

- - - - -   - - - - -

c. Let x be the total number of cans.

Define a variable.

$$\left(\frac{3}{8}x\right) = 60$$

Write an equation saying the expected number of favorable outcomes equals probability times total number of outcomes.

$$\left(\frac{8}{3}\right)\left(\frac{3}{8}\right)x = \left(\frac{8}{3}\right)(60)$$

Multiply by $\frac{8}{3}$.

$$x = 160$$

Do the computations.

<u>About 160 cans</u>

Answer the question.

ORAL PRACTICE

Tell the quantity asked for.

EXAMPLE

Answer

Distance = 50 mi, time = $x - 5$ min, rate = ?   50 over the quantity $x - 5$ mi/min

A. Distance = 30 ft, time = x sec, rate = ? $\frac{30}{x}$ ft/sec

B. Distance = 20 km, rate = x km/h, time = ? $\frac{20}{x}$ h

C. Distance = 100 yd, rate = $x - 2$ yd/day, time = ? $\frac{100}{x-2}$ days

D.   Distance = 300 in., time = $x + 5$ min, rate = ?. $\dfrac{300}{x+5}$ in/min

E.   Speed through water = 8 ft/sec, current = x ft/sec, speed upstream = ?. $8-x$ ft/sec

F.   Speed through water = 7 mi/h, current = x mi/h, speed downstream = ?. $7 + x$ mi/h

G.   Speed through water = x mi/h, current = 4 mi/h, speed upstream = ?. $x - 4$ mi/h

H.   Work = 1 job, time = 3 h, rate = ?. $\frac{1}{3}$ job/h

I.   Work = 1 lawn, time = x h, rate = ?. $\frac{1}{x}$ lawns/h

J.   Work = 1 tank, time = $x - 3$ min, rate = ?. $\dfrac{1}{x-3}$ tank/min

K.   Work = 1 sink, rate = $\dfrac{1}{5}$ sink per min, time = ?.   5 min

L.   Work = 1 tub, rate = $\dfrac{1}{x}$ tub per min, time = ?. x min

EXERCISE 11-10

1.   **Blimp Problem 1**   A blimp flies through the air at a speed of 120 kilometers per hour (km/h).
   a.   How fast does it fly with respect to the ground if it flies:
      i.   with a tail wind of 30 km/h;   150 km/h
      ii.   into a head wind of 20 km/h;   100 km/h
      iii.   into a head wind of x km/h; $(120 - x)$ km/h
      iv.   with a tail wind of y km/h? $(120 + y)$ km/h
   b.   How long does the blimp take to fly 60 km:
      i.   with no wind blowing;   0.5 h
      ii.   against a head wind of 20 km/h;   0.6 h
      iii.   with a tail wind of 30 km/h;   0.4 h
      iv.   with a tail wind of y km/h? $60/(120 + y)$ h

2.   **Helicopter Problem 1**   A helicopter flies through the air at a speed of 100 km/h.
   a.   How fast does it go with respect to the ground if it flies:
      i.   into a head wind of 40 km/h;   60 km/h
      ii.   with a tail wind of 50 km/h;   150 km/h
      iii.   with a tail wind of x km/h; $100 + x$ km/h
      iv.   into a head wind of y km/h? $100 - y$ km/h
   b.   How long does it take the helicopter to fly 45 km:
      i.   with no wind blowing;   0.45 h
      ii.   into a head wind of 40 km/h;   0.75 h
      iii.   into a head wind of y km/h; $45/(100 - y)$ h
      iv.   with a tail wind of x km/h? $45/(100 + x)$ h

Problem Notes:

Problems 1–12, 17, and 18 are "upstream-downstream" problems. The words ". . . flies through the air with a speed of . . ." are used rather than the more traditional words, ". . . flies in still air with a speed of . . ." for two reasons. First, the air is *not* still. It is *moving*. Second, students should realize that the blimp (plane, etc.) is embedded in the mass of air, and that the whole system is moving with respect to the ground. This is basically different from headwind slowing down a bike rider, for example, in which the vehicle is connected to the ground rather than to the moving air mass.

3. **a.** $\dfrac{60}{120 - x} + \dfrac{60}{120 + y}$

4. **a.** $\dfrac{200}{100 + x} + \dfrac{200}{100 - y}$

5. **a.** $\dfrac{60}{120 - x} + \dfrac{60}{120 + x}$

6. **a.** time $= \dfrac{200}{100 + x} + \dfrac{200}{100 - x}$

   b. With no wind,

   time $= \dfrac{200}{100} + \dfrac{200}{100} = 4$ hr.

   With a wind of, for example, 50 km/h,

   time $= \dfrac{200}{100 + 50} + \dfrac{200}{100 - 50}$

   $= 1.33 + 4$

   $= 5.33$ hr.

   So time when wind blows is *longer* than 4 hours, in this case an hour and 20 min. longer.

7. **c.** Impossible for rowboat to get back to starting point. Algebra says −667 sec.

3. *Blimp Problem 2*   A blimp flies 120 km/h through the air. It goes 60 km into a head wind of x km/h. Later it returns the 60 km with a tail wind of y km/h.
   a. Write an expression for the total time taken for the round trip.
   b. How long will the round trip take if the head wind going is 40 km/h and the tail wind returning is 10 km/h? 1.21 h
   c. If the head wind and the tail wind are equal to x for both parts of the trip and the round trip takes 1.3 hours, how fast is the wind blowing? 57.6 km/h

4. *Helicopter Problem 2*   A helicopter moves through the air at 100 km/h. It flies 200 km with a tail wind of x km/h. On the return trip it flies the 200 km with a head wind of y km/h.
   a. Write an expression for the total time taken for the round trip.
   b. If the tail wind is 20 km/h and the head wind is 30 km/h, how long will the round trip take? 4.52 h
   c. If the tail wind and the head wind both equal x for both parts of the trip and the round trip takes 5 hours, how fast is the wind blowing? 44.7 km/h

5. *Blimp Problem 3*   A blimp moves through the air at 120 km/h. It goes 60 km into a head wind of x km/h and returns with the same wind as a tail wind.
   a. Write an expression for the total time for the round trip.
   b. How much longer does the round trip take when the wind is blowing 30 km/h than it does when there is no wind? 0.07 h longer

6. *Helicopter Problem 3*   A helicopter flies through the air at 100 km/h. It goes 200 km with a tail wind of x km/h and returns with the same wind as a head wind.
   a. Write an expression for the total time for the round trip.
   b. It sounds reasonable that the wind should make no difference in the round trip time, since the speed you gain on the way there is lost on the way back. Show that this conclusion is *false* and that the time with wind blowing is actually *longer* than the time if there is no wind. $1\frac{1}{3}$ h longer

7. *Speedboat Problem*   A speedboat race requires the boat to go 1000 meters down a swiftly moving river and then return upstream to the starting point. The current in the river is known to be 2 meters per second (m/sec).
   a. One boat goes through the water at 5 m/sec. How long will it take for the round trip? 476.19 sec
   b. Another boat takes 300 seconds for the round trip. How fast does it go through the water? 7.22 m/sec
   c. A rowboat enters the race. It can go only 1 m/sec through the water. What does the algebra tell you about its time to complete the race? What *really* happens to the rowboat?

8. *River Swimming Problem*   A race is held, in which swimmers go 100 meters upstream in Rapid River and return downstream to the starting point. The current in the river is known to be 1 meter per second (m/sec).

   a. Flo Tilla swims through the water at 2 m/sec. How long will she take for the round trip?   133.3 sec

   b. Priscilla Goodbody makes the round trip in 80 seconds. How fast does she go through the water?   2.85 m/sec

   c. Phoebe Small takes 5 minutes for the round trip. How fast does she go through the water?   1.39 m/sec

   d. Mae Dupp can swim only 0.5 m/sec, but she enters the race anyway. What does the algebra say her time will be? What *actually* happens to Mae? What must the *domain* of the swimmer's speed variable be in order for the algebra to give reasonable answers to this problem? $x = 0.5$; $t = -133.3$; domain: $x > 1$

9. *Escalator Problem*   Dee Tour runs up the down escalator! After she has gone 13 meters she realizes her mistake, turns around, and runs back down, still going the same speed. The escalator moves at 0.7 meters per second, and the round trip takes a total of 10 seconds. How fast does Dee run?   2.78 m/sec

10. *Popeye and Olive Oyle Problem*   Bluto puts Olive Oyle onto a conveyor belt headed toward a large circular saw at 0.8 meters per second. Popeye jumps on the end of the conveyor belt and runs along it, grabbing Olive in the nick of time. He runs back along the conveyor belt 30 meters to its beginning. Popeye makes the round trip in 17 seconds. How fast does he run?   3.70 m/sec

11. *Pedalboat Problem*   A couple on a picnic rents a pedalboat. They go upstream 600 m, moving 30 m/min through the water. After the picnic they travel back downstream to the starting point. But they are tired and only go 20 m/min through the water. The total time spent pedaling is 75 min. How fast is the current flowing?   20 m/min

12. *Tugboat Problem*   A tugboat pushes a string of barges 200 km up the Mississippi River against a current of 8 km/h. The tug then comes back downstream 50 km, going the same speed through the water. The total time for the two parts of the trip is 52.5 h. How fast does the tug go through the water?   12 km/h

13. *Average Speed Problem 1*   A cyclist rides 5 km at a speed of 20 km/h. She returns at a speed of 10 km/h.

Problems 13–16 have to do with average speeds. The most important conclusion is that the average speed for a trip is seldom equal to the average of the two speeds. For two trips of equal distance at different speeds, the average speed is the *harmonic* mean of the two speeds. This number is always *less* than the arithmetic average of the two speeds, a fact that will serve students well on multiple-choice tests.

a. What is the total time for the round trip?   0.75 h

b. The *average speed* is defined as follows.

DEFINITION

> **AVERAGE SPEED**
>
> The **average speed** for a trip is $\dfrac{\text{total distance}}{\text{total time}}$.

Find her average speed for the round trip. $13\frac{1}{3}$ km/h

c. The average of 20 and 10 is 15. Is the average speed equal to 15, more than 15, or less than 15?   Less

14. *Average Speed Problem 2*   A cyclist rides 5 km at a speed of 20 km/h. How fast must she ride on the return trip to make her average speed equal:

a. 15 km/h;   12 km/h

b. 30 km/h;   60 km/h

c. 40 km/h;   (Surprising?);   Not possible. All time used on trip out.

d. 50 km/h?   (More surprising?)   speed = -100 Impossible!

15. *Average Speed Problem 3*   A cyclist rides d km at a speed of x km/h and returns d km at a speed of y km/h. Write an expression representing the average speed in terms of x, y, and d. Simplify the expression by multiplying by 1 in the form $\dfrac{xy}{xy}$, and thus show that d drops out! $\dfrac{2xy}{x+y}$

16. *Average Speed Problem 4*

a. Use the simplified expression in Problem 15 to find *quickly* the average speed for the following round trips.

  i. Going: 70 km/h;   returning: 90 km/h.   78.75 km/h

  ii. Going: 1000 km/h;   returning: 800 km/h. $888\frac{8}{9}$ km/h

  iii. Going: 2 km/h;   returning: 4 km/h. $2\frac{2}{3}$ km/h

b. Show that in each case above, the average speed is *less* than the average of the speeds.   i. $78.75 < 80$; ii. $888\frac{8}{9} < 900$; iii. $2\frac{2}{3} < 3$

17. *River Rescue Problem*   Susan is stranded in the river near the waterfall. David jumps in and swims 300 feet downstream to rescue her, moving 4 feet per second through the water. With Susan in tow, David manages to move only 2 feet per second through the water on the return trip. They arrive at the starting point, taking a total of 380 seconds for the round trip. How fast is the current?   1.06 ft/sec

18. **Airplane Problem**   Two airplanes start at the same time from airports 500 km apart. Each one flies with an airspeed of 200 km/h directly toward the other airport. But one reaches its airport half an hour before the other plane reaches the other airport. How fast is the wind blowing?   19.80 km/h

19. **Envelope Problem**   Cora Spondence can stuff a pile of letters into envelopes in 3 hours. N. V. Lopes takes 4 hours to do the same job. How many hours would it take to do the job if both of them worked together? $1\frac{5}{7}$ h

Problems 19–26 are rate-of-work problems.

20. **Lawn Mowing Problem 1**   John and Fred must mow the lawn before they can go swimming. By themselves, John would take 30 minutes and Fred would take 45 minutes. How long would it take to mow the lawn with both working together (using two mowers, of course!)?   18 min

21. **Lawn Mowing Problem 2**   Marsha must mow the lawn before she can go swimming. She realizes that it would take her 50 minutes to do it by herself. So she gets Fran to help her. The job is completed in 30 minutes. How long would it have taken Fran to do the job alone?   75 min

22. **Bathtub Problem**   The cold-water faucet can fill the bathtub in 7 minutes. When both the hot and cold faucets are running, the tub is filled in only 5 minutes. How long would it take the hot faucet to fill the tub by itself?   17.5 min

23. **Tank Draining Problem**   The inlet valve on a storage tank in a chemical plant sticks in the open position. The tank is just about to overflow when workmen open the drain valve. To their relief, the liquid level in the tank starts dropping. Company records show that the inlet pipe can fill an empty tank in 7 hours and the drain can empty a full tank in 5 hours. How long will it be until the tank is empty with both inlet and drain open?   17.5 h

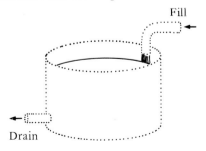

24. **Flood Control Problem**   A torrential rain can fill the basin behind a flood control dam in 5 hours. With the dam's floodgates open, a full basin will drain in 20 hours. How long would it take to fill the basin in a torrential rain with the floodgates open? $6\frac{2}{3}$ h

25. *Sink Draining Problem*   The drain can empty the water from a full sink in 3 minutes. If the water is running while the drain is open, it takes 8 minutes to empty a full sink. How long would it take to fill an empty sink with the drain closed?   4.8 min

26. *Cupcake Problem*   Phoebe Small has baked a large batch of cupcakes. She ices them and sets them on a tray. She knows that it would take her 10 minutes to fill the tray with cupcakes, were it not for the fact that Calvin Butterball is eating them as fast as he can. Calvin eats and Phoebe ices, each at a steady rate. The tray is finally full after 25 minutes. If Calvin continues to eat at the same rate, how long will it take him to eat a tray of cupcakes after Phoebe stops icing? $16\frac{2}{3}$ min

Problems 27–30 are integer quotient problems. Students should work one or two problems from Exercise 11–9 along with these so that they see the similarities and differences.

27. *Integer Quotient Problem 1*   When a large positive integer is divided by a smaller one, the integer part of the quotient is 3 and the remainder is 2. The sum of the integers is 70. Find the two integers.
17 and 53

28. *Integer Quotient Problem 2*   When a large positive integer is divided by a smaller one, the integer part of the quotient is 3 and the remainder is 1. The sum of the integers is 29. Find the two integers.
7 and 22

29. *Integer Quotient Problem 3*   Two positive integers have a sum of 58. If 3 is added to each and then the larger divided by the smaller, the integer part of the quotient is 1 and the remainder is 16. Find the original integers.   21 and 37

30. *Integer Quotient Problem 4*   Two positive integers have a sum of 56. If 6 is subtracted from each and then the larger divided by the smaller, the integer part of the quotient is 43 and the remainder is 0. Find the original integers.   7 and 49

31. **a.** $P(\text{girl}) = \frac{173}{312}$ or 0.554. . . ;

   $P(\text{boy}) = \frac{139}{312}$ or 0.445. . .

   b. 6 or 7 girls (6.653. . .)

31. *Probability Committee Selection Problem*   A committee is to be selected at random from the freshman class. The class has 346 girls and 278 boys.
   a.   If a student is picked at random, what is the probability that it is a girl? a boy?
   b.   If 12 students are to be selected for the committee, approximately how many girls would you expect to be on the committee?

32. **a.** $P(\text{bad}) = \frac{1}{10}$ or 0.1; $P(\text{good}) = \frac{9}{10}$
   or 0.9
   b. 2

32. *Probability Light Bulb Problem*   By accident, 100 defective light bulbs get mixed in with 900 good ones. There is no way to tell just by looking at the bulb whether it is good or bad.
   a.   If a bulb is selected at random, what is the probability that it is bad? that it is good?
   b.   If a sample of 20 bulbs is selected, what number would you expect to be bad?

33. *Probability Dice Problem*

   a. If you roll a die (singular of "dice"), what is the probability that the number comes up 1? What is the probability that the number comes up 5?

   b. If you roll a die 30 times, about how many times would you expect it to come up 1?

   c. Get a die and roll it 30 times. Record the number of times it comes up 1. Were the actual results the same as you expected?

34. *Probability Coin Flip Problem*

   a. If you flip a coin, what is the probability that it lands heads up? Tails up?

   b. If you flip a coin 50 times, how many times would you expect it to land heads up?

   c. Flip a coin 50 times. Record the number of times it lands heads up. Were the actual results the same as you expected?

11-11   CHAPTER REVIEW AND TEST

In this chapter you have refreshed your memory about fractions. If a fraction has a variable in it, then it stands for different numbers depending on the value of that variable. You learned how to evaluate these rational expressions for given values of x, and how to find x when you know the value of the expression. You also learned how to add, subtract, multiply, and simplify rational expressions without actually evaluating them. Finally you worked problems involving ratios and variable rates, in which variables appear in denominators.

Glance through your notes looking for names and definitions before you try the test below. The test may be longer than you would be expected to do in a normal class period.

CHAPTER TEST

  1. What is the difference in each case?

    a. A polynomial and a rational algebraic expression.

    b. The way you add fractions and the way you multiply them.

    c. $3 : 5$ and $3/5$.

    d. A ratio and a proportion.

    e. Net speed upstream and net speed downstream.

33.   **a.** $P(1) = \dfrac{1}{6}$, $P(5) = \dfrac{1}{6}$

    b. 5 times

    c. Answers may vary.

34.   **a.** $P(\text{heads}) = \dfrac{1}{2}$; $P(\text{tails}) = \dfrac{1}{2}$

    b. 25 times

    c. Answers may vary.

Time: 1 day

Test Ideas:

If you have tested earlier in the chapter, this test should concentrate on solving fractional equations and working word problems. You may also wish to include a question or two on concepts students had trouble with in the first part of the chapter.

Assignments:

Following the test assign either
Exercise 11–11, #11,
or
study Section 12–1;
work the three examples; and
work Exercise 12–1, #1–9 odd

Problem Notes:

Problem 3 touches on all the concepts of this chapter as well as on the basic theme of evaluating expressions and solving equations.

1.   **a.** A polynomial has no division by a variable.
     A rational algebraic expression may have division by a variable.

    b. You add fractions by first finding a common denominator.
     You multiply fractions by multiplying their numerators and their denominators.

    c. 3:5 and $\dfrac{3}{5}$ are equivalent. *No* difference.

    d. A ratio is one number divided by another.
     A proportion is an equation stating that two ratios are equal.

    e. Net speed
     upstream = speed − current.
     Net speed
     downstream = speed + current.

2. a. The LCM of positive integers a and b is the smallest positive integer such that LCM = integer × a and LCM = integer × b.

b. Cancelling means dividing the numerator and denominator of a fraction by the same common factor.

c. $-\dfrac{a}{b} = \dfrac{-a}{b} = \dfrac{a}{-b}$

d. An extraneous solution is a value of the variable that satisfies the transformed equation, but not the original one.

e. The domain of a variable is the set of numbers that can be values of the variable.

3. a.

	$\dfrac{x+3}{x-1}$	$\dfrac{x+1}{x-3}$
$x = 0$	-3	$-\dfrac{1}{3}$
$x = 1$	No value	-1
$x = 2$	5	-3
$x = 3$	3	No value
$x = -1$	-1	0
$x = -3$	0	$\dfrac{1}{3}$

Problems 7–10 present one each of the four types of word problems in this chapter.

Problem 11 allows students to apply their knowledge to a new situation. Problems like this are suitable as bonus problems or as after-test homework assignments.

2. Write each of the following.
  a. Definition of least common multiple.
  b. Definition of canceling.
  c. Property of the opposite of a fraction.
  d. Definition of extraneous solution.
  e. Definition of domain of a variable.

3. For the expressions $\dfrac{x+3}{x-1}$ and $\dfrac{x+1}{x-3}$:
  a. evaluate each expression for $x = 0, 1, 2, 3, -1,$ and -3.
  b. find x if the first expression equals 2. $x = 5$
  c. find the product of the two expressions. Simplify if possible. $\dfrac{x^2 + 4x + 3}{x^2 - 4x + 3}$
  d. find the first expression minus the second expression. Simplify if possible. $-8/[(x-1)(x-3)]$
  e. find x if the first expression equals the second one.   No solution possible
  f. find x if the sum of the expressions equals.
    i. 2 $x = 2$
    ii. 1 $x = 2.12$ or -6.12
    iii. 3. $x = 10.12$ or 1.88
  g. find x if the product of the expressions equals 2. $x = 11.74$ or 0.26

4. Simplify.
  a. $\dfrac{24x^4}{32x^7}$ $\dfrac{3}{4x^3}$
  b. $\dfrac{(x+7)(x-5)(x-3)}{(7+x)(5-x)(x+3)}$ $-\dfrac{x-3}{x+3}$
  c. $\dfrac{x^2 + 7x + 10}{x^2 - 25}$ $\dfrac{x+2}{x-5}$
  d. $\dfrac{2x^2 + x - 3}{3x^2 - x - 2}$ $\dfrac{2x+3}{3x+2}$

5. Do the indicated operations and simplify.
  a. $\dfrac{7}{5x} - \dfrac{3}{5x} + \dfrac{1}{5x}$ $\dfrac{1}{x}$
  b. $\dfrac{7}{5x} \cdot \dfrac{3}{5x} \cdot \dfrac{1}{5x}$ $\dfrac{21}{125x^3}$
  c. $\dfrac{6a}{2a-b} - \dfrac{3b}{2a-b}$ 3
  d. $\dfrac{9}{x-3} - \dfrac{x^2}{x-3}$ $-3-x$
  e. $\dfrac{4}{x} + \dfrac{7}{x^2} - \dfrac{2}{x^3}$ $\dfrac{4x^2 + 7x - 2}{x^3}$
  f. $\dfrac{x^2 + x - 6}{x^2 + 3x - 10} \cdot \dfrac{x^2 - 8x + 15}{9 - x^2}$ $-\dfrac{x-5}{x+5}$

6. Use long division, and express your answer in mixed-number form.
  $\dfrac{5x^3 - 13x^2 - 10x + 7}{x-3}$ $5x^2 + 2x - 4 - \dfrac{5}{x-3}$

7. *Television Manufacturing Problem*   The sales department of a television set manufacturing company finds that portables and console models sell in the ratio 7 : 3. The manufacturing department can make 570 sets each week. How many of each kind should be made in a week to have this desired ratio?   399 portables, 171 consoles

8. *Ditch Digging Problem*   Doug Upp can dig a ditch in 3 hours. His brother Phil could dig the same ditch in 5 hours. How long would it take to dig the ditch if both work together? $1\frac{7}{8}$ h

9. *Superman Problem*   Superman flies through the air at 3 miles per second, going 40 miles from Metropolis to Gotham against a head wind of unknown speed. He flies back to Metropolis, moving through the air at 2 miles per second with the same wind as a tail wind. The round trip takes 60 seconds. How fast is the wind blowing?   2.21 miles per second

10. *Integer Quotient Problem*   Two positive integers have a sum of 92. If the larger integer is divided by the smaller one, the quotient is 3 and the remainder is 12. What are the two integers?   20, 72

11. *Peanuts and Popcorn Problem*   A vendor carries 80 bags, total, of peanuts and popcorn. How many of each should she carry for the peanuts-to-popcorn ratio to be 3 : 7?   24 peanuts, 56 popcorn.

12. *Probability Problem:*   The probability of rain is 20% on any one day.
    a.   On how many days would you expect it to rain in a total of five weeks?   7 days
    b.   How long, total, would you expect it to be until it has rained on 40 days?   200 days

13. *Fractional Inequality Problem*   You have studied how to solve inequalities that involve various kinds of expression so far studied, but not rational expressions. In this problem you will solve a fractional inequality and see some of the difficulties involved. The inequality

$$\frac{x + 3}{x - 1} > 4$$

can be solved by multiplying each member by $x - 1$. However, you must consider two possible cases. If $x - 1$ is positive, the order stays the same. But if $x - 1$ is *negative,* the order *reverses.* By considering these two cases, solve the inequality and graph the solution set. $1 < x < \frac{7}{3}$

12

Radical Algebraic Expressions

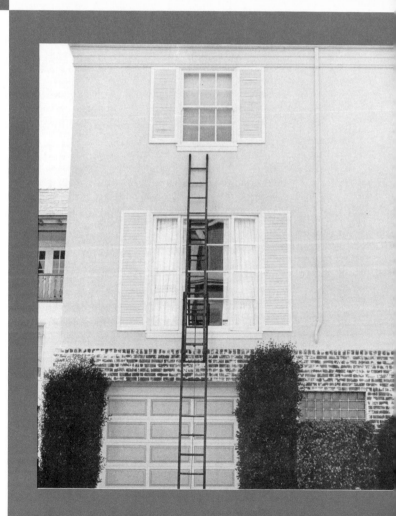

You have already learned how to evaluate radicals by calculator. In this chapter you will learn how to operate with square roots of expressions that have variables. You will evaluate these expressions for given values of the variable and solve equations to find the value of the variable. You will also learn about other kinds of roots such as cube roots and fourth roots. Applications include predicting the weight of a shark from its length and finding the length of the third side of a right triangle when you know the lengths of the other two.

Variables:
H and L

Side lengths in a right triangle

Expression:
$\sqrt{H^2 - L^2}$

Length of third side

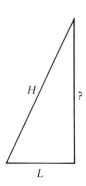

12-1 | INTRODUCTION TO RADICAL ALGEBRAIC EXPRESSIONS

An expression such as $\sqrt{x - 16}$ is called a **radical algebraic expression.** In this section you will learn to evaluate expressions like this when you know what x equals, and vice versa.

Objective:
For radical algebraic expressions such as $\sqrt{x - 16}$, evaluate the expression if x is given, and find x if a value of the expression is given.

Cover the answers as you work the examples.

EXAMPLE 1

Evaluate $\sqrt{x - 16}$ if x is 27.

- - - - -

	Think These Reasons

$$\sqrt{x - 16}$$ Write the given expression.

$$= \sqrt{27 - 16}$$ Substitute 27 for x.

$$= \sqrt{11}$$ Do the arithmetic under the vinculum.

$$\approx \underline{3.32}$$ Find the square root.

Note: The vinculum ("bar") means "Do what is underneath *first,*" just like a pair of parentheses.

Time: $\frac{1}{2}$ day, with Section 12–2

Chalkboard Examples:

Use Problems 1 and 7, if previously assigned. Otherwise, use an example such as the following. For the expression $\sqrt{x - 9}$:
a. evaluate it if $x = 16$;   Ans.: $\sqrt{7}$
b. evaluate it if $x = 5$;   Ans.: No value
c. evaluate it if $x = 54$;   Ans.: $\sqrt{45} = 3\sqrt{5}$
d. find x if the expression
   equals 7.   Ans.: $x = 58$
Use the result of part (c) to introduce the concept of simplifying a radical.

Assignment:

Problems 1–9 odd should have been assigned following your last test on Chapter 11. Problems 2 and 8 are specified in the assignment for Section 12–2.

EXAMPLE 2

Evaluate $\sqrt{x - 16}$ if x is 7.

- - - - -   - - - - -

$\qquad \sqrt{x - 16}$ Write the given expression.

$= \sqrt{7 - 16}$ Substitute 7 for x.

$= \sqrt{-9}$ Do the subtraction.

$\underline{\text{No value}}$ There are *no* real numbers that are square roots of negative numbers.

EXAMPLE 3

Find x if $\sqrt{x - 16}$ is 9.

- - - - -   - - - - -

$\qquad \sqrt{x - 16} = 9$ Write an equation.

$(\sqrt{x - 16})^2 =$ 9^2 Square each member.

$\qquad x - 16 = 81$ Squaring a square root removes the radical sign. Recall from Section 5.9 that $(\sqrt{n})^2$ equals n.

$\qquad \underline{x = 97}$ Add 16 to each member.

In the following exercise you will work more problems like these.

EXERCISE 12-1

Problem Notes:

The problems of this section reinforce the basic theme of this text concerning evaluating expressions and solving equations. The only difference is that the expressions contain radicals.

Problems 3(c) and 4(c) have no value because of the square root of a negative number. Problems 5(d) and 6(d) have no value because of division by zero. It is important for students to realize that there is more than one reason why an expression might be undefined.

For Problems 1 through 6, evaluate the expression for the given values of x. Use a calculator if necessary.

1. Evaluate $\sqrt{3x}$ if:
   a. x is 7;   4.58
   b. x is 27.   9

2. Evaluate $\sqrt{5x}$ if:
   a. x is 8;   6.32
   b. x is 125.   25

3. Evaluate $\sqrt{15 - x}$ if:
   a. x is 6;   3
   b. x is 15;   0
   c. x is 20.   No value

4. Evaluate $\sqrt{x - 11}$ if:
   a. x is 47;   6
   b. x is 11;   0
   c. x is 2.   No value

5. Evaluate $\dfrac{10}{\sqrt{x + 4}}$ if:
   a. x is 96;   1
   b. x is 0;   5

6. Evaluate $\dfrac{24}{\sqrt{x + 9}}$ if:
   a. x is 91;   2.4
   b. x is 0;   8

c. x is -3; 10
d. x is -4. No value

c. x is -5; 12
d. x is -9. No value

For Problems 7 through 10, find x for the given values.

7. Find x if $\sqrt{2x}$ is:
    a. 10; $x = 50$
    b. 3. $x = 4.5$

8. Find x if $\sqrt{3x}$ is:
    a. 12; $x = 48$
    b. 4. $x = 5\frac{1}{3}$

9. Find x if $\sqrt{x + 5}$ is:
    a. 12; $x = 139$
    b. 2; $x = -1$
    c. 0. $x = -5$

10. Find x if $\sqrt{x + 11}$ is:
    a. 5; $x = 14$
    b. 3; $x = -2$
    c. 0. $x = -11$

12-2   SUMS, DIFFERENCES, AND PRODUCTS OF RADICALS

For some uses of radicals it is better *not* to evaluate them on a calculator. In this section you will learn ways to operate on radicals.

There is an easy way to multiply two square roots. For instance,

$$\sqrt{9} \times \sqrt{4} = 3 \times 2 = 6.$$

But 9×4 is 36, and $\sqrt{36}$ is also equal to 6. Thus

$$\sqrt{9} \times \sqrt{4} = \sqrt{9 \times 4}.$$

This example illustrates the fact that the operation square root *distributes* over multiplication.

PROPERTY

> **SQUARE ROOT OF A PRODUCT**
> The square root of a product of two nonnegative numbers equals the product of the square roots of the two numbers. That is, for nonnegative numbers x and y,
>
> $$\sqrt{xy} = \sqrt{x}\sqrt{y}$$
>
> In other words, square root distributes over multiplication.

In Problem 61 of the exercise, you will prove this property.

Time: $\frac{1}{2}$ day, with Section 12–1

Chalkboard Examples:

The calculator can be used to demonstrate the square root of a product property. Have students evaluate:
1. $\sqrt{3} \times \sqrt{5} = (1.73205 \ldots)(2.23606 \ldots) \approx$ 3.8729833
2. $\sqrt{15} \approx 3.8729833$

The fact that the answers are the same to so many decimal places is often more convincing to students than a similar example using perfect squares.

Present an example of a radical to simplify, such as $\sqrt{45} = 3\sqrt{5}$ mentioned in the notes for Section 12–1. Then have students work the three text examples on their own before starting the assignment. If you prefer, the following may be used.
1. Multiply: $\sqrt{7} \times \sqrt{11}$ Ans.: $\sqrt{77}$
2. Multiply: $\sqrt{15} \times \sqrt{10}$ Ans.: $5\sqrt{6}$
3. Multiply: $2\sqrt{7} \times \sqrt{21}$ Ans.: $14\sqrt{3}$
4. Add: $5\sqrt{3} + 7\sqrt{3}$ Ans.: $12\sqrt{3}$
5. Subtract: $10\sqrt{5} - 6\sqrt{5}$ Ans.: $4\sqrt{5}$
6. Subtract: $7\sqrt{2} - 6\sqrt{2}$ Ans.: $\sqrt{2}$
7. Subtract: $5\sqrt{11} - \sqrt{11}$ Ans.: $4\sqrt{11}$
8. Add: $\sqrt{3} + \sqrt{5}$ Ans.: $\sqrt{3} + \sqrt{5}$
    (Does not simplify.)
9. Add: $\sqrt{12} + \sqrt{75}$ Ans.: $8\sqrt{3}$

Assignment:

Exercise 12–2, 3–13 odd or 4–14 even;
21–29 odd or 22–30 even;
41–49 odd or 42–50 even; and
Exercise 12–1, 2, 8

The property is useful in simplifying radicals.

$$\sqrt{75}$$

$= \sqrt{25 \times 3}$ Factor 75.

$= \sqrt{25} \times \sqrt{3}$ Square root of a product property.

$= 5\sqrt{3}$ $\sqrt{25}$ is 5.

The answer, $5\sqrt{3}$, is considered to be simpler than $\sqrt{75}$, because the radicand 3 is *less* than the radicand 75. Note that $5\sqrt{3}$ means 5 *times* $\sqrt{3}$.

Unfortunately, there is *no* similar property for the square root of a sum. For instance,

$$\sqrt{9 + 16}\quad \text{but} \quad \sqrt{9} + \sqrt{16}$$

$= \sqrt{25}$ $= 3 + 4$

$= 5$ $= 7.$

The only way for two square roots to be combined by addition is for the radicands to be equal. Thus

$$5\sqrt{3} + 7\sqrt{3} = 12\sqrt{3}.$$

The process is the same as adding like terms: $5x + 7x = 12x$.

Objective :

Be able to simplify expressions involving sums, differences, and products of square roots, and check by evaluating by calculator.

Cover the answers as you work these examples.

EXAMPLE 1

Simplify: $\sqrt{72}$.

– – – – –   – – – – –

	Think These Reasons
$\sqrt{72}$	Write the given expression.
$= \sqrt{36 \times 2}$	Factor so that at least one of the factors is a perfect square.
$= \underline{6\sqrt{2}}$	Take the square root of 36.

Note: The answer can be checked by calculator.

$$\sqrt{72} \approx 8.4852814$$
$$6\sqrt{2} \approx 8.4852814$$

EXAMPLE 2

Multiply: $\sqrt{15} \times 7\sqrt{20}$.

- - - - -   - - - - -

	$\sqrt{15} \times 7\sqrt{20}$	Write the given expression.
$=$	$7\sqrt{3 \times 5 \times 5 \times 4}$	Factor and multiply the radicands.
$=$	$\underline{70\sqrt{3}}$	Take the square roots of 5×5 and 4.

EXAMPLE 3

Simplify: $4\sqrt{6} - 7\sqrt{6} + \sqrt{6}$.

- - - - -   - - - - -

	$4\sqrt{6} - 7\sqrt{6} + \sqrt{6}$	Write the given expression.
$=$	$\underline{-2\sqrt{6}}$	Combine like terms.

EXAMPLE 4

Simplify: $\sqrt{75} + \sqrt{48}$.

- - - - -   - - - - -

	$\sqrt{75} + \sqrt{48}$	Write the given expression.
$=$	$5\sqrt{3} + 4\sqrt{3}$	Simplify $\sqrt{75}$ and $\sqrt{48}$.
$=$	$\underline{9\sqrt{3}}$	Combine like terms.

ORAL PRACTICE

Give the expression in simple radical form.

A. $\sqrt{12}$ $2\sqrt{3}$ B. $\sqrt{8}$ $2\sqrt{2}$ C. $\sqrt{20}$ $2\sqrt{5}$

D. $\sqrt{9}$ 3 E. $\sqrt{18}$ $3\sqrt{2}$ F. $\sqrt{50}$ $5\sqrt{2}$

G. $\sqrt{2} \times \sqrt{3}$ $\sqrt{6}$ H. $\sqrt{5} \times \sqrt{7}$ $\sqrt{35}$ I. $\sqrt{6} \times \sqrt{3}$ $3\sqrt{2}$

J. $\sqrt{5} \times \sqrt{15}$ $5\sqrt{3}$ K. $6\sqrt{5} + 2\sqrt{5}$ $8\sqrt{5}$ L. $5\sqrt{3} - 2\sqrt{3}$ $3\sqrt{3}$

M. $5\sqrt{3} - \sqrt{3}$ $4\sqrt{3}$ N. $\sqrt{3} - 7\sqrt{3}$ $-6\sqrt{3}$

Problem Notes:

Checking by calculator has the remarkable effect of not only testing for correctness of answers but also emphasizing the fact that the desired answer is to be in radical, not decimal, form.

Students sometimes get lost on these problems because they do not realize that they must collect factors that are *perfect squares* under the radical sign. Once they see this fact, the problems become very easy.

EXERCISE 12-2

1. Evaluate both expressions to show each of the following.

   a. $\sqrt{4 \times 49} = \sqrt{4} \times \sqrt{49}$ b. $\sqrt{3 \times 7} = \sqrt{3} \times \sqrt{7}$
   c. $\sqrt{9 + 16} \neq \sqrt{9} + \sqrt{16}$
   d. $\sqrt{169 - 144} \neq \sqrt{169} - \sqrt{144}$

2. Evaluate both expressions to show each of the following.

   a. $\sqrt{81 \times 4} = \sqrt{81} \times \sqrt{4}$ $18 = 18$
   b. $\sqrt{6 \times 11} = \sqrt{6} \times \sqrt{11}$ $8.1240384 = 8.1240384$
   c. $\sqrt{225 + 64} \neq \sqrt{225} + \sqrt{64}$ $17 \neq 23$
   d. $\sqrt{25 - 16} \neq \sqrt{25} - \sqrt{16}$ $3 \neq 1$

For Problems 3 through 20, simplify the expression as much as possible. Leave the answer in *radical* form. You may check by getting a decimal approximation.

3. $\sqrt{12}$ $2\sqrt{3}$ 4. $\sqrt{20}$ $2\sqrt{5}$ 5. $\sqrt{40}$ $2\sqrt{10}$ 6. $\sqrt{18}$ $3\sqrt{2}$

7. $\sqrt{27}$ $3\sqrt{3}$ 8. $\sqrt{24}$ $2\sqrt{6}$ 9. $\sqrt{45}$ $3\sqrt{5}$ 10. $\sqrt{8}$ $2\sqrt{2}$

11. $\sqrt{32}$ $4\sqrt{2}$ 12. $\sqrt{162}$ $9\sqrt{2}$ 13. $\sqrt{108}$ $6\sqrt{3}$ 14. $\sqrt{80}$ $4\sqrt{5}$

15. $\sqrt{200}$ $10\sqrt{2}$ 16. $\sqrt{300}$ $10\sqrt{3}$ 17. $\sqrt{147}$ $7\sqrt{3}$ 18. $\sqrt{98}$ $7\sqrt{2}$

19. $\sqrt{405}$ $9\sqrt{5}$ 20. $\sqrt{448}$ $8\sqrt{7}$

For Problems 21 through 40, multiply the expressions and simplify the answer. Leave the answer in *integer* or *radical* form.

21. $\sqrt{3} \times \sqrt{15}$ 22. $\sqrt{5} \times \sqrt{30}$ 23. $\sqrt{21} \times \sqrt{7}$
24. $\sqrt{22} \times \sqrt{11}$ 25. $\sqrt{8} \times \sqrt{2}$ 26. $\sqrt{27} \times \sqrt{3}$
27. $\sqrt{3} \times \sqrt{12}$ 28. $\sqrt{7} \times \sqrt{28}$
29. $\sqrt{5} \times \sqrt{30} \times \sqrt{3}$ 30. $\sqrt{35} \times \sqrt{7} \times \sqrt{10}$
31. $7\sqrt{6} \times 3\sqrt{10}$ 32. $3\sqrt{14} \times 5\sqrt{2}$ 33. $8\sqrt{2} \times 5\sqrt{12}$
34. $10\sqrt{3} \times 7\sqrt{15}$ 35. $5\sqrt{9} \times 4\sqrt{11}$ 36. $2\sqrt{25} \times 3\sqrt{6}$
37. $6\sqrt{18} \times 5\sqrt{14}$ 38. $4\sqrt{12} \times 9\sqrt{6}$
39. $7\sqrt{6} \times \sqrt{15} \times 5\sqrt{10}$ 40. $3\sqrt{14} \times 2\sqrt{21} \times 5$

Answers:
1. a. $14 = 14$ b. $4.5825756 = 4.5825756$ c. $5 \neq 7$ d. $5 \neq 1$

21. $3\sqrt{5}$ 22. $5\sqrt{6}$ 23. $7\sqrt{3}$ 24. $11\sqrt{2}$ 25. 4 26. 9 27. 6 28. 14 29. $15\sqrt{2}$ 30. $35\sqrt{2}$ 31. $42\sqrt{15}$ 32. $30\sqrt{7}$ 33. $80\sqrt{6}$ 34. $210\sqrt{5}$ 35. $60\sqrt{11}$ 36. $30\sqrt{6}$ 37. $180\sqrt{7}$ 38. $216\sqrt{2}$ 39. 1050 40. $210\sqrt{6}$

For Problems 41 through 60, simplify each term, if necessary. Then add or subtract. Leave the answer in *integer* or *radical* form.

41. $2\sqrt{5} + 7\sqrt{5}$

42. $6\sqrt{3} + 8\sqrt{3}$

43. $8\sqrt{7} - 3\sqrt{7}$

44. $5\sqrt{11} - 2\sqrt{11}$

45. $13\sqrt{6} - \sqrt{6}$

46. $9\sqrt{5} - \sqrt{5}$

47. $\sqrt{12} + 5\sqrt{3}$

48. $\sqrt{18} + 5\sqrt{2}$

49. $7\sqrt{5} + \sqrt{45}$

50. $5\sqrt{2} + \sqrt{72}$

51. $\sqrt{18} + \sqrt{50}$

52. $\sqrt{12} + \sqrt{75}$

53. $6\sqrt{12} - \sqrt{75}$

54. $4\sqrt{18} - \sqrt{50}$

55. $3\sqrt{7} - \sqrt{175}$

56. $2\sqrt{5} - \sqrt{125}$

57. $3\sqrt{5} - \sqrt{80} + \sqrt{20}$

58. $4\sqrt{6} - \sqrt{150} + \sqrt{24}$

59. $\sqrt{50} - \sqrt{18} - 2\sqrt{12}$

60. $\sqrt{75} - \sqrt{12} - 2\sqrt{8}$

61. *Radicals with Variables Problem*   Square roots containing variables can be simplified by the techniques of this section. For instance, for non-negative values of x,
$$\sqrt{x^7} = \sqrt{x^2 \cdot x^2 \cdot x^2 \cdot x} = x \cdot x \cdot x \cdot \sqrt{x} = x^3\sqrt{x}$$

Simplify the following. Assume non-negative variables.

a. $\sqrt{x^5}$ b. $\sqrt{y^9}$ c. $\sqrt{x^6}$ d. $\sqrt{x^8y^3}$ e. $\sqrt{x^2y^{10}}$

62. *Proof of the Square Root of a Product Property*   Prove that if $z = \sqrt{x}\sqrt{y}$, where x and y are nonnegative numbers, then z is also equal to $\sqrt{xy}$. Do this by squaring each member of the given equation, then distributing the exponentiation over the multiplication.

12-3   QUOTIENTS OF RADICALS

By calculator you can show that
$$\frac{\sqrt{13}}{\sqrt{2}} \approx 2.549509757 \text{ and } \sqrt{\frac{13}{2}} = \sqrt{6.5} \approx 2.549509757$$
The results are the same! So
$$\sqrt{\frac{13}{2}} = \frac{\sqrt{13}}{\sqrt{2}}.$$
This example illustrates that the operation square root distributes over division, just as it does over multiplication.

---

41. $9\sqrt{5}$

42. $14\sqrt{3}$ 43. $5\sqrt{7}$ 44. $3\sqrt{11}$

45. $12\sqrt{6}$ 46. $8\sqrt{5}$ 47. $7\sqrt{3}$

48. $8\sqrt{2}$ 49. $10\sqrt{5}$ 50. $11\sqrt{2}$

51. $8\sqrt{2}$ 52. $7\sqrt{3}$

In Problems 45 and 46, some students may write $13\sqrt{6} - \sqrt{6} = 13$. These problems were written deliberately to call attention to fuzzy thoughts some students may still harbor.

53. $7\sqrt{3}$ 54. $7\sqrt{2}$ 55. $-2\sqrt{7}$

56. $-3\sqrt{5}$ 57. $\sqrt{5}$ 58. $\sqrt{6}$

59. $2\sqrt{2} - 4\sqrt{3}$

60. $3\sqrt{3} - 4\sqrt{2}$

61. a. $x^2\sqrt{x}$
     b. $y^4\sqrt{x}$
     c. x^3
     d. $x^4y\sqrt{y}$
     e. xy^5

62. Prove that if $z = \sqrt{x}\sqrt{y}$, then $z = \sqrt{xy}$, for $x \geq 0$ and $y \geq 0$.
     Proof:

$z = \sqrt{x}\sqrt{y}$	Given
$\therefore z^2 = (\sqrt{x}\sqrt{y})^2$	If two nos. are equal, then their squares are equal.
$z^2 = (\sqrt{x})^2(\sqrt{y})^2$	Exponentiation distributes over mult.
$z^2 = xy$	Definition of square root
$\therefore z = \sqrt{xy}$	Definition of square root

Time: 2 days

Chalkboard Examples:

First day:
Present examples, such as the following.

1. Simplify: $\frac{\sqrt{11}}{\sqrt{3}}$ Ans.: $\frac{\sqrt{33}}{3}$

    Conclusion: Simpler because there is only *one* radical.

2. Simplify: $\dfrac{6}{\sqrt{3}}$ Ans.: $2\sqrt{3}$

Conclusion: Simpler because there is no radical in the denominator.

Oral Practice problems are effective here. Have students work the problems for 5 minutes or so, then call on selected students to tell answers.

Students should work Examples 1, 2, and 3 before starting the assignment.

Second day:

Homework problems at board. Students should work Examples 4 and 5 before starting the assignment.

Assignments:

Day 1: Exercise 12–3, #1–9 odd;
Exercise 12–2, #31–39 odd or 32–40 even; and 51–59 odd, or 52–60 even

Day 2: Exercise 12–3, #11–39 odd or 12–40 even

PROPERTY

SQUARE ROOT OF A QUOTIENT

The square root of a quotient of two positive numbers equals the quotient of the square roots of the numbers. That is, for positive numbers x and y,

$$\sqrt{\frac{x}{y}} = \frac{\sqrt{x}}{\sqrt{y}}$$

In other words, square root distributes over division.

You will prove this property in Problem 49 of the following exercise. The property can be used from right to left to divide two radicals. For instance,

$$\frac{\sqrt{51}}{\sqrt{3}} = \sqrt{\frac{51}{3}} = \sqrt{17}.$$

The answer, $\sqrt{17}$, is simpler than the original expression. However, this technique does not always give a simpler answer. For instance,

$$\frac{\sqrt{2}}{\sqrt{7}} = \sqrt{\frac{2}{7}} = \sqrt{0.285714285\ldots}.$$

If the denominator does not divide the numerator, there is another way to simplify the expression. You can eliminate the radical from either the numerator or the denominator by multiplying the fraction by an appropriate form of 1.

$$\frac{\sqrt{2}}{\sqrt{7}} \qquad \text{or} \qquad \frac{\sqrt{2}}{\sqrt{7}}$$

$$= \frac{\sqrt{2}}{\sqrt{7}} \times \frac{\sqrt{7}}{\sqrt{7}} \qquad = \frac{\sqrt{2}}{\sqrt{7}} \times \frac{\sqrt{2}}{\sqrt{2}}$$

$$= \frac{\sqrt{14}}{7} \qquad = \frac{2}{\sqrt{14}}$$

The expressions $\frac{\sqrt{14}}{7}$ and $\frac{2}{\sqrt{14}}$ are considered to be simpler than $\frac{\sqrt{2}}{\sqrt{7}}$ since they have only *one* radical.

The process of eliminating the radical from the denominator or from the numerator is called *rationalizing the denominator* or *rationalizing the numerator*. For most things you will be doing with radicals it is more convenient to have no radicals in the denominator. So the following definition is made.

DEFINITION

SIMPLE RADICAL FORM
A radical is said to be in **simple radical form** if:

1. There are no radicals in the denominator.
2. The radicand(s) in the numerator are as small as possible.

Objective :
Given an expression involving quotients of radicals, transform it to simple radical form, and check by calculator.

Cover the answers as you work these examples.

EXAMPLE 1

Write in simple radical form: $\dfrac{\sqrt{5}}{\sqrt{7}}$.

- - - - -   - - - - -

> **Think These Reasons**

$\dfrac{\sqrt{5}}{\sqrt{7}}$ Write the given expression.

$= \dfrac{\sqrt{5}}{\sqrt{7}} \times \dfrac{\sqrt{7}}{\sqrt{7}}$ Multiply by a form of 1 to rationalize the denominator.

$= \dfrac{\sqrt{35}}{7}$ Do the multiplication.

Note: The answer can be checked by calculator.

$$\frac{\sqrt{5}}{\sqrt{7}} \approx 0.8451542$$

$$\frac{\sqrt{35}}{7} \approx 0.8451542$$

EXAMPLE 2

Write in simple radical form: $\dfrac{8}{\sqrt{24}}$.

- - - - -   - - - - -

$$\frac{8}{\sqrt{24}}$$ Write the given expression.

$$= \frac{8}{2\sqrt{6}} \times \frac{\sqrt{6}}{\sqrt{6}}$$ Simplify $\sqrt{24}$. Then rationalize the denominator.

$$= \frac{4\sqrt{6}}{6}$$ Cancel. Multiply $\sqrt{6}\,\sqrt{6}$.

$$= \underline{\underline{\frac{2\sqrt{6}}{3}}}$$ Cancel.

Note: Although the given expression has only one radical already, simple radical form requires that any radicals be in the *numerator*, not the denominator.

EXAMPLE 3

Write in simple radical form: $\sqrt{\dfrac{75}{8}}$.

- - - - -   - - - - -

$$\sqrt{\frac{75}{8}}$$ Write the given expression.

$$= \frac{\sqrt{75}}{\sqrt{8}}$$ Square root distributes over division.

$$= \frac{5\sqrt{3}}{2\sqrt{2}} \times \frac{\sqrt{2}}{\sqrt{2}}$$ Simplify $\sqrt{75}$ and $\sqrt{8}$. Then rationalize the denominator.

$$= \underline{\underline{\frac{5\sqrt{6}}{4}}}$$ Multiply the radicals.

Note: The square root of a fraction is considered to have a radical in the *denominator*. To be in simple radical form, the expression must have a *rational* denominator.

EXAMPLE 4

Do the operations and write the answer in simple radical form: $\dfrac{\sqrt{24}}{\sqrt{50}} \div \dfrac{\sqrt{27}}{\sqrt{8}}$.

- - - - -   - - - - -

$$\frac{\sqrt{24}}{\sqrt{50}} \div \frac{\sqrt{27}}{\sqrt{8}}$$ Write the given expression.

$$= \frac{\sqrt{24}}{\sqrt{50}} \times \frac{\sqrt{8}}{\sqrt{27}}$$ Use the definition of division to change to multiplication.

$$= \frac{2\sqrt{6} \times 2\sqrt{2}}{5\sqrt{2} \times 3\sqrt{3}}$$ Multiply the fractions. Simplify the radicals.

$$= \frac{4\sqrt{2}\sqrt{3}}{15\sqrt{3}} \qquad \text{Multiply, and cancel } \sqrt{2}.$$
$$\text{Split } \sqrt{6} \text{ into } \sqrt{2}\sqrt{3}.$$
$$= \frac{4\sqrt{2}}{15} \qquad \text{Cancel } \sqrt{3}.$$

EXAMPLE 5

Do the operations and write the answer in simple radical form:
$$\frac{\sqrt{12}}{\sqrt{50}} - \frac{\sqrt{27}}{\sqrt{8}}.$$

- - - - -   - - - - -

$$\frac{\sqrt{12}}{\sqrt{50}} - \frac{\sqrt{27}}{\sqrt{8}} \qquad \text{Write the given expression.}$$

$$= \frac{2\sqrt{3}}{5\sqrt{2}} - \frac{3\sqrt{3}}{2\sqrt{2}} \qquad \text{Simplify the radicals.}$$

$$= \frac{2\sqrt{6}}{10} - \frac{3\sqrt{6}}{4} \qquad \text{Rationalize the denominators.}$$

$$= \frac{4\sqrt{6}}{20} - \frac{15\sqrt{6}}{20} \qquad \text{Write the fractions with a common denominator.}$$

$$= -\frac{11\sqrt{6}}{20} \qquad \text{Subtract the numerators.}$$

Note: When you are adding or subtracting radical fractions, it is usually easier to *rationalize* the denominators before finding a *common* denominator.

ORAL PRACTICE

Give the expression in simple radical form.

A. $\dfrac{2}{\sqrt{3}} \;\; \dfrac{2\sqrt{3}}{3}$ B. $\dfrac{5}{\sqrt{2}} \;\; \dfrac{5\sqrt{2}}{2}$ C. $\dfrac{1}{\sqrt{5}} \;\; \dfrac{\sqrt{5}}{5}$ D. $\dfrac{3}{\sqrt{7}} \;\; \dfrac{3\sqrt{7}}{7}$ E. $\dfrac{6}{\sqrt{3}} \;\; 2\sqrt{3}$ F. $\dfrac{10}{\sqrt{5}} \;\; 2\sqrt{5}$

G. $\dfrac{\sqrt{2}}{3} \times \dfrac{4}{\sqrt{2}} \;\; \dfrac{4}{3}$ H. $\dfrac{5}{\sqrt{3}} \div \dfrac{10}{\sqrt{3}} \;\; \dfrac{1}{2}$ I. $\dfrac{2}{\sqrt{3}} \times \dfrac{10}{\sqrt{3}} \;\; \dfrac{20}{3}$

J. $\dfrac{\sqrt{5}}{2} \div \dfrac{1}{\sqrt{20}} \;\; 5$ K. $\dfrac{2}{\sqrt{5}} + \dfrac{3}{\sqrt{5}} \;\; \sqrt{5}$ L. $\dfrac{4\sqrt{5}}{7} + \dfrac{3\sqrt{5}}{7} \;\; \sqrt{5}$

M. $\dfrac{8}{\sqrt{7}} - \dfrac{1}{\sqrt{7}} \;\; \sqrt{7}$ N. $\dfrac{3}{\sqrt{4}} - \dfrac{5}{\sqrt{4}} \;\; -1$

EXERCISE 12-3

Problem Notes:

Students should check answers by calculator both to determine correctness and to get experience using the calculator. The value of one expression can be stored in memory while the other is being calculated. The two can be compared by subtraction, although round-off may cause a small difference such as 2E-08 to appear on the calculator.

For Problems 1 through 20, rationalize the denominator and simplify. Leave the answer in *integer, rational,* or *radical* form. You can check your answers by calculator.

1. $\dfrac{\sqrt{3}}{\sqrt{11}}$ $\dfrac{\sqrt{33}}{11}$

2. $\dfrac{\sqrt{13}}{\sqrt{5}}$ $\dfrac{\sqrt{65}}{5}$

3. $\dfrac{\sqrt{12}}{\sqrt{5}}$ $\dfrac{2\sqrt{15}}{5}$

4. $\dfrac{\sqrt{24}}{\sqrt{7}}$ $\dfrac{2\sqrt{42}}{7}$

5. $\dfrac{\sqrt{30}}{\sqrt{6}}$ $\sqrt{5}$

6. $\dfrac{\sqrt{15}}{\sqrt{3}}$ $\sqrt{5}$

7. $\sqrt{\dfrac{3}{13}}$ $\dfrac{\sqrt{39}}{13}$

8. $\sqrt{\dfrac{2}{11}}$ $\dfrac{\sqrt{22}}{11}$

9. $\sqrt{\dfrac{175}{24}}$ $\dfrac{5\sqrt{42}}{12}$

10. $\sqrt{\dfrac{63}{50}}$ $\dfrac{3\sqrt{14}}{10}$

11. $\dfrac{20}{\sqrt{10}}$ $2\sqrt{10}$

12. $\dfrac{40}{\sqrt{20}}$ $4\sqrt{5}$

13. $\dfrac{2\sqrt{5}}{3\sqrt{12}}$ $\dfrac{\sqrt{15}}{9}$

14. $\dfrac{6\sqrt{8}}{5\sqrt{72}}$ $\dfrac{2}{5}$

15. $\dfrac{42\sqrt{15}}{3\sqrt{20}}$ $7\sqrt{3}$

16. $\dfrac{56\sqrt{30}}{7\sqrt{40}}$ $4\sqrt{3}$

17. $\dfrac{150}{\sqrt{300}}$ $5\sqrt{3}$

18. $\dfrac{63}{\sqrt{216}}$ $\dfrac{7\sqrt{6}}{4}$

19. $\dfrac{3\sqrt{35}}{\sqrt{7}\sqrt{45}}$ 1

20. $\dfrac{3\sqrt{22}\sqrt{28}}{\sqrt{8}\sqrt{77}}$ 3

For Problems 21 through 40, do the indicated operations and write the answer in simple radical form.

21. $\dfrac{\sqrt{3}}{\sqrt{5}} \times \dfrac{\sqrt{15}}{\sqrt{8}}$ $\dfrac{3\sqrt{2}}{2}$

22. $\dfrac{\sqrt{7}}{\sqrt{2}} \times \dfrac{\sqrt{14}}{\sqrt{27}}$ $\dfrac{7\sqrt{3}}{9}$

23. $\dfrac{\sqrt{18}}{\sqrt{7}} \times \sqrt{\dfrac{14}{5}}$ $\dfrac{6\sqrt{5}}{5}$

24. $\sqrt{\dfrac{75}{2}} \times \dfrac{\sqrt{15}}{\sqrt{6}}$ $\dfrac{5\sqrt{15}}{2}$

25. $\dfrac{\sqrt{30}}{\sqrt{14}} \div \dfrac{\sqrt{15}}{\sqrt{32}}$ $\dfrac{4\sqrt{14}}{7}$

26. $\dfrac{\sqrt{32}}{\sqrt{24}} \div \dfrac{\sqrt{22}}{\sqrt{3}}$ $\dfrac{\sqrt{22}}{11}$

27. $\sqrt{\dfrac{27}{5}} \div \dfrac{\sqrt{10}}{\sqrt{3}}$ $\dfrac{9\sqrt{2}}{10}$

28. $\dfrac{\sqrt{10}}{\sqrt{6}} \div \sqrt{\dfrac{2}{15}}$ $\dfrac{5\sqrt{2}}{2}$

29. $\dfrac{3}{\sqrt{3}} + \dfrac{18}{\sqrt{27}}$ $3\sqrt{3}$

30. $\dfrac{2}{\sqrt{2}} + \dfrac{12}{\sqrt{8}}$ $4\sqrt{2}$

31. $\sqrt{45} - \dfrac{10}{\sqrt{5}}$ $\sqrt{5}$

32. $\sqrt{28} - \dfrac{21}{\sqrt{7}}$ $-\sqrt{7}$

33. $6\sqrt{\dfrac{2}{3}} + 6\sqrt{\dfrac{3}{2}}$ $5\sqrt{6}$

34. $10\sqrt{\dfrac{2}{5}} + 10\sqrt{\dfrac{5}{2}}$ $7\sqrt{10}$

35. $3\sqrt{3} - \sqrt{48} + 3\sqrt{\dfrac{1}{3}}$ 0

36. $5\sqrt{5} - \sqrt{45} + 10\sqrt{\dfrac{1}{5}}$ $4\sqrt{5}$

37. $6\sqrt{\dfrac{7}{4}} - 14\sqrt{\dfrac{1}{7}} + 3\sqrt{28}$ $7\sqrt{7}$

38. $6\sqrt{\dfrac{5}{3}} - 3\sqrt{60} + 10\sqrt{\dfrac{3}{5}}$ $-2\sqrt{15}$

39. $\sqrt{6}\left(\sqrt{3} - \dfrac{1}{\sqrt{3}}\right)$ $2\sqrt{2}$

40. $\sqrt{15}\left(\dfrac{4}{\sqrt{5}} - \sqrt{5}\right)$ $-\sqrt{3}$

For Problems 41 through 44, rationalize the *numerator*.

41. $\dfrac{\sqrt{3}}{\sqrt{7}}$ $\dfrac{3}{\sqrt{21}}$

42. $\dfrac{\sqrt{7}}{\sqrt{2}}$ $\dfrac{7}{\sqrt{14}}$

43. $\dfrac{\sqrt{6}}{12}$ $\dfrac{1}{2\sqrt{6}}$

44. $\dfrac{\sqrt{15}}{30}$ $\dfrac{1}{2\sqrt{15}}$

45. **Radicals with Variables Problem**   Square roots containing variables can be simplified by the techniques of this section. For instance, for positive values of x,

$$\frac{\sqrt{x^6}}{\sqrt{x^5}} = \sqrt{\frac{x^6}{x^5}} = \underline{\underline{\sqrt{x}}}.$$

Simplify the following. Assume positive values of variables.

a. $\dfrac{\sqrt{x^6}}{\sqrt{x^3}}$ b. $\dfrac{\sqrt{z^5}}{\sqrt{z^8}}$ c. $\dfrac{\sqrt{x^2 y^5}}{\sqrt{x^3 y}}$ d. $\dfrac{1}{\sqrt{x^4 y^{10}}}$ e. $\dfrac{\sqrt{n^7}}{\sqrt{n^{11}}}$

46. **Proof of the Square Root of a Quotient Property**   Prove that if

$$z = \frac{\sqrt{x}}{\sqrt{y}}, \quad \text{then} \quad z = \sqrt{\frac{x}{y}},$$

where x is nonnegative and y is positive. Do this by first squaring each member of the given equation and then distributing the exponentiation over the division.

12-4   BINOMIALS WITH RADICALS

So far you have multiplied and divided radical expressions with only one term, such as

$$\sqrt{12} \times \sqrt{18} \quad \text{or} \quad \frac{\sqrt{12}}{\sqrt{18}}.$$

In this section you do the same operations with *binomial* radical expressions. Multiply each term of one by each term of the other.

Problems 41–44 involve rationalizing the *numerator*. The technique is the same as rationalizing the denominator. The result is used in calculus to find the derivative of the square root function. The result is also useful in solving quadratic equations where b^2 is so large compared to $4ac$ that the numerator rounds off to 0. Rationalizing the numerator avoids this difficulty.

45. a. $x\sqrt{x}$ b. $\dfrac{\sqrt{z}}{z^2}$ c. $\dfrac{y^2\sqrt{x}}{x}$ d. $\dfrac{1}{x^2 y^5}$ e. $\dfrac{1}{n^2}$

46. *Proof:*

$z = \dfrac{\sqrt{x}}{\sqrt{y}}$ Given

$\therefore z^2 = \left(\dfrac{\sqrt{x}}{\sqrt{y}}\right)^2$ If two numbers are equal, then their squares are equal.

$z^2 = \dfrac{(\sqrt{x})^2}{(\sqrt{y})^2}$ Exponentiation distributes over division.

$z^2 = \dfrac{x}{y}$ Definition of square root

$\therefore z = \sqrt{\dfrac{x}{y}}$ Definition of square root

Time: 4 days, including test

Chalkboard Examples:

First day:
Multiply and simplify.
1. $(\sqrt{18} + 3)(\sqrt{18} - 2)$ Ans.: $12 + 3\sqrt{2}$
2. $(\sqrt{23} - \sqrt{5})^2$ Ans.: $28 - 2\sqrt{115}$
3. $(11 + 2\sqrt{3})(11 - 2\sqrt{3})$ Ans.: 109
The Oral Practice problems are effective here.

Second day:
Rationalize the denominator and simplify.

1. $\dfrac{6}{\sqrt{10} - \sqrt{7}}$ Ans.: $2\sqrt{10} + 2\sqrt{7}$

2. $\dfrac{4\sqrt{7} - \sqrt{3}}{\sqrt{7} - \sqrt{3}}$ Ans.: $\dfrac{25 + 3\sqrt{21}}{4}$

Have students work text Example 4 before starting their assignment.

Third day:
Homework on board in preparation for test.

Fourth day:
Test.

Assignments:

Day 1: Exercise 12–4, #1–19 odd or 2–20 even;
Exercise 12–3, #22 or 21, 32 or 31, 41;
Day 2: Exercise 12–4, #25–59 odd or 26–60 even
Day 3: In preparation for test:
Exercise 12–4, #34 or 33, 54 or 53;
Exercise 12–3, #28 or 27;
Exercise 12–2, #18 or 17, 32 or 31,
56 or 55; and
Exercise 12–1, #4, 10
Day 4: (after test): Study Exercise 12–5; work
Exercise 12–5, #1, 3, 5, or Exercise
12–6, #1–9 odd

$$(\sqrt{15} + \sqrt{3})(4\sqrt{15} - \sqrt{3})$$
$$= 4(15) - \sqrt{45} + 4\sqrt{45} - 3$$
$$= 57 + 3\sqrt{45}$$
$$= \underline{57 + 9\sqrt{5}}$$

An important thing happens when you multiply two binomials that are *conjugates* of each other. For instance,

$$(\sqrt{13} + \sqrt{7})(\sqrt{13} - \sqrt{7})$$
$$= 13 - \sqrt{91} + \sqrt{91} - 7$$
$$= \underline{\underline{6.}}$$

The answer is a *rational* number! The two radical terms are *opposites* of each other and thus "drop out."

PROPERTY

> ### PRODUCT OF CONJUGATE RADICAL BINOMIALS
> For any nonnegative rational numbers x and y,
> $$\boxed{(\sqrt{x} + \sqrt{y})(\sqrt{x} - \sqrt{y}) = x - y}$$
> which is a rational number.

Note: This property corresponds to $(a + b)(a - b) = a^2 - b^2$.

This result gives a way to simplify radical expressions involving division by a binomial. For instance, you can rationalize the denominator of

$$\frac{35}{\sqrt{8} - \sqrt{3}}$$

by multiplying by 1 in the form $\dfrac{\sqrt{8} + \sqrt{3}}{\sqrt{8} + \sqrt{3}}$.

$\dfrac{35}{\sqrt{8} - \sqrt{3}} \times \dfrac{\sqrt{8} + \sqrt{3}}{\sqrt{8} + \sqrt{3}}$ Rationalize the denominator—$\sqrt{8} + \sqrt{3}$ is the *conjugate* of the denominator.

$= \dfrac{35(\sqrt{8} + \sqrt{3})}{8 - 3}$ Do the multiplication. Leave the 35 factored out in the numerator.

$= \dfrac{35(2\sqrt{2} + \sqrt{3})}{5}$ Do the arithmetic. Simplify $\sqrt{8}$.

$= 7(2\sqrt{2} + \sqrt{3})$ Cancel.

$= \underline{14\sqrt{2} + 7\sqrt{3}}$ Distribute 7.

Objective :

Be able to multiply or divide binomials containing square roots of constants.

Cover the answers as you work the examples.

EXAMPLE 1

Multiply and simplify: $(\sqrt{12} - 5)(\sqrt{12} + 7)$.

- - - - -   - - - - -

	Think These Reasons
$(\sqrt{12} - 5)(\sqrt{12} + 7)$	Write the given expression.
$= 12 + 7\sqrt{12} - 5\sqrt{12} - 35$	Multiply the binomials.
$= 2\sqrt{12} - 23$	Combine like terms.
$= \underline{4\sqrt{3} - 23}$	Simplify $\sqrt{12}$.

EXAMPLE 2

Multiply and simplify: $(\sqrt{11} - \sqrt{3})^2$.

- - - - -   - - - - -

$(\sqrt{11} - \sqrt{3})^2$	Write the given expression.
$= (\sqrt{11} - \sqrt{3})(\sqrt{11} - \sqrt{3})$	Definition of squaring.
$= 11 - 2\sqrt{33} + 3$	Multiply the binomials.
$= \underline{14 - 2\sqrt{33}}$	Combine like terms.

EXAMPLE 3

Multiply and simplify: $(3\sqrt{5} + 4)(3\sqrt{5} - 4)$.

- - - - -   - - - - -

$(3\sqrt{5} + 4)(3\sqrt{5} - 4)$	Write the given expression.
$= 9(5) - 16$	Multiply conjugate binomials.
$= \underline{\underline{29}}$	Do the computations.

EXAMPLE 4

Rationalize the denominator and simplify: $\dfrac{\sqrt{3} - 2\sqrt{5}}{\sqrt{5} - \sqrt{3}}$.

- - - - -   - - - - -

$\dfrac{\sqrt{3} - 2\sqrt{5}}{\sqrt{5} - \sqrt{3}}$ Write the given expression.

$= \dfrac{\sqrt{3} - 2\sqrt{5}}{\sqrt{5} - \sqrt{3}} \times \dfrac{\sqrt{5} + \sqrt{3}}{\sqrt{5} + \sqrt{3}}$ Rationalize the denominator. $\sqrt{5} + \sqrt{3}$ is the *conjugate* of the denominator.

$= \dfrac{\sqrt{15} + 3 - 2(5) - 2\sqrt{15}}{5 - 3}$ Do the multiplication.

$= \underline{\underline{\dfrac{-\sqrt{15} - 7}{2}}}$ or $\underline{\underline{-\dfrac{\sqrt{15} + 7}{2}}}$ Combine like terms.

ORAL PRACTICE

Give the conjugate.

A. $\sqrt{3} + \sqrt{2}$ B. $\sqrt{5} - \sqrt{7}$ C. $\sqrt{11} - 4$ D. $9 + \sqrt{6}$
$\quad\ \sqrt{3} - \sqrt{2}$ $\qquad\quad \sqrt{5} + \sqrt{7}$ $\qquad\quad \sqrt{11} + 4$ $\qquad\quad 9 - \sqrt{6}$

Give the result of multiplying these conjugates.

E. $(\sqrt{3} + \sqrt{2})(\sqrt{3} - \sqrt{2})$ 1   F. $(\sqrt{7} - \sqrt{5})(\sqrt{7} + \sqrt{5})$ 2
G. $(\sqrt{2} + \sqrt{10})(\sqrt{2} - \sqrt{10})$ −8   H. $(\sqrt{5} + 3)(\sqrt{5} - 3)$ −4
I. $(4 - \sqrt{3})(4 + \sqrt{3})$ 13   J. $(\sqrt{7} + 2)(\sqrt{7} - 2)$ 3

Give the result of squaring these binomials.

K. $(\sqrt{5} + \sqrt{2})^2$ $7 + 2\sqrt{10}$ L. $(\sqrt{3} - \sqrt{2})^2$ $5 - 2\sqrt{6}$
M. $(\sqrt{3} + 2)^2$ $7 + 4\sqrt{3}$ N. $(3 - \sqrt{2})^2$ $11 - 6\sqrt{2}$

EXERCISE 12-4

For Problems 1 through 40, do the multiplication and simplify the answer.

1. $5\sqrt{2} + 7\sqrt{5}$ **2.** $3\sqrt{5} + 8\sqrt{3}$ 1. $\sqrt{5}(\sqrt{10} + 7)$ 2. $\sqrt{3}(\sqrt{15} + 8)$

3. $\sqrt{7}(6 + \sqrt{28})$

4. $\sqrt{5}(13 + \sqrt{45})$

5. $\sqrt{15}(\sqrt{5} - \sqrt{3})$

6. $\sqrt{6}(\sqrt{2} - \sqrt{3})$

7. $\sqrt{3}(\sqrt{12} - \sqrt{75})$

8. $\sqrt{7}(\sqrt{28} - \sqrt{175})$

9. $\sqrt{10}(8\sqrt{5} + 7\sqrt{6})$

10. $\sqrt{15}(7\sqrt{3} + 4\sqrt{5})$

11. $(\sqrt{3} + 5)(\sqrt{3} + 2)$

12. $(\sqrt{5} + 7)(\sqrt{5} + 3)$

13. $(\sqrt{6} - 7)(\sqrt{6} + 4)$

14. $(\sqrt{10} - 6)(\sqrt{10} + 2)$

15. $(\sqrt{7} + 8)(\sqrt{7} - 3)$

16. $(\sqrt{11} + 2)(\sqrt{11} - 9)$

17. $(2 - \sqrt{5})(6 - \sqrt{5})$

18. $(4 - \sqrt{3})(11 - \sqrt{3})$

19. $(\sqrt{5} + \sqrt{2})(\sqrt{5} + 3\sqrt{2})$

20. $(\sqrt{2} + 4\sqrt{3})(\sqrt{2} + \sqrt{3})$

21. $(\sqrt{6} - 2\sqrt{3})(3\sqrt{6} + \sqrt{3})$

22. $(\sqrt{15} - 4\sqrt{5})(2\sqrt{15} + \sqrt{5})$

23. $(2\sqrt{15} - 4\sqrt{5})(6\sqrt{15} - 3\sqrt{5})$

24. $(3\sqrt{10} - 4\sqrt{2})(5\sqrt{10} - 6\sqrt{2})$

25. $(\sqrt{3} - 7)^2$

26. $(\sqrt{7} - 5)^2$

27. $(\sqrt{6} + \sqrt{3})^2$

28. $(\sqrt{10} + \sqrt{5})^2$

29. $(5\sqrt{2} - 3\sqrt{7})^2$

30. $(4\sqrt{2} - 5\sqrt{3})^2$

31. $(\sqrt{5} + 3)(\sqrt{5} - 3)$

32. $(\sqrt{7} + 8)(\sqrt{7} - 8)$

33. $(\sqrt{13} - \sqrt{2})(\sqrt{13} + \sqrt{2})$

34. $(\sqrt{3} - \sqrt{17})(\sqrt{3} + \sqrt{17})$

35. $(5\sqrt{3} - 1)(5\sqrt{3} + 1)$

36. $(1 - 3\sqrt{7})(1 + 3\sqrt{7})$

37. $(3\sqrt{2} + 5\sqrt{3})(3\sqrt{2} - 5\sqrt{3})$

38. $(4\sqrt{5} + 3\sqrt{7})(4\sqrt{5} - 3\sqrt{7})$

39. $(\sqrt{1001} + \sqrt{2001})(\sqrt{1001} - \sqrt{2001})$

40. $(\sqrt{1066} - \sqrt{1776})(\sqrt{1066} + \sqrt{1776})$

3. $6\sqrt{7} + 14$ 4. $13\sqrt{5} + 15$
5. $5\sqrt{3} - 3\sqrt{5}$ 6. $2\sqrt{3} - 3\sqrt{2}$
7. -9 8. -21
9. $40\sqrt{2} + 14\sqrt{15}$ 10. $21\sqrt{5} + 20\sqrt{3}$
11. $13 + 7\sqrt{3}$ 12. $26 + 10\sqrt{5}$
13. $-22 - 3\sqrt{6}$ 14. $-2 - 4\sqrt{10}$
15. $-17 + 5\sqrt{7}$ 16. $-7 - 7\sqrt{11}$
17. $17 - 8\sqrt{5}$ 18. $47 - 15\sqrt{3}$
19. $11 + 4\sqrt{10}$ 20. $14 + 5\sqrt{6}$
21. $12 - 15\sqrt{2}$ 22. $10 - 35\sqrt{3}$
23. $240 - 150\sqrt{3}$ 24. $198 - 76\sqrt{5}$
25. $52 - 14\sqrt{3}$ 26. $32 - 10\sqrt{7}$
27. $9 + 6\sqrt{2}$ 28. $15 + 10\sqrt{2}$
29. $113 - 30\sqrt{14}$ 30. $107 - 40\sqrt{6}$
31. -4 32. -57
33. 11 34. -14
35. 74 36. -62
37. -57 38. 17
39. -1000 40. -710

Problem Notes:

Problems can be checked by calculator.
   Problems 39, 40, 59, and 60 involve historical or otherwise interesting numbers. 1066 was the date of the Battle of Hastings in English history; 1776 is, of course, the date of the signing of the Declaration of Independence; 1001 is the product of consecutive odd primes (7)(11)(13); and 2001 is the beginning of the 21st century. (2001 also has exactly 3 prime factors.)

For Problems 41 through 60, simplify by first rationalizing the denominator.

41. $\dfrac{20}{\sqrt{6} + 2}$ $10\sqrt{6} - 20$

42. $\dfrac{26}{\sqrt{10} + 3}$ $26\sqrt{10} - 78$

43. $\dfrac{24}{\sqrt{15} - 3}$ $4\sqrt{15} + 12$

44. $\dfrac{50}{\sqrt{30} - 5}$ $10\sqrt{30} + 50$

45. $\dfrac{26}{4 - \sqrt{3}}$ $8 + 2\sqrt{3}$

46. $\dfrac{30}{6 - \sqrt{26}}$ $18 + 3\sqrt{26}$

47. $\dfrac{45}{\sqrt{2} + \sqrt{7}}$ $-9\sqrt{2} + 9\sqrt{7}$

48. $\dfrac{48}{\sqrt{3} + \sqrt{5}}$ $-24\sqrt{3} + 24\sqrt{5}$

49. $\dfrac{48}{\sqrt{11} - \sqrt{5}}$ $8\sqrt{11} + 8\sqrt{5}$

50. $\dfrac{36}{\sqrt{19} - \sqrt{10}}$ $4\sqrt{19} + 4\sqrt{10}$

51. $\dfrac{\sqrt{13} + 3}{5 - \sqrt{13}}$ $\dfrac{2\sqrt{13} + 7}{3}$ 52. $\dfrac{\sqrt{31} + 3}{6 - \sqrt{31}}$ $\dfrac{9\sqrt{31} + 49}{5}$

53. $\dfrac{\sqrt{3} + 6}{\sqrt{3} + 5}$ $\dfrac{27 - \sqrt{3}}{22}$ 54. $\dfrac{\sqrt{5} + 7}{\sqrt{5} + 3}$ $4 - \sqrt{5}$

55. $\dfrac{\sqrt{7} + \sqrt{5}}{\sqrt{7} - \sqrt{5}}$ $6 + \sqrt{35}$ 56. $\dfrac{\sqrt{5} + \sqrt{3}}{\sqrt{5} - \sqrt{3}}$ $4 + \sqrt{15}$

57. $\dfrac{\sqrt{10} - \sqrt{6}}{\sqrt{10} + \sqrt{6}}$ $4 - \sqrt{15}$ 58. $\dfrac{\sqrt{12} - \sqrt{3}}{\sqrt{12} + \sqrt{3}}$ $\dfrac{1}{3}$

59. $\dfrac{\sqrt{1776} + \sqrt{1066}}{\sqrt{1776} - \sqrt{1066}}$ $\dfrac{1421 - 4\sqrt{118326}}{355}$ 60. $\dfrac{\sqrt{2001} + \sqrt{1001}}{\sqrt{2001} - \sqrt{1001}}$ $\dfrac{1501 + \sqrt{2003001}}{500}$

12-5 | SQUARE ROOTS OF VARIABLE EXPRESSIONS

Time: 0 or 2 days

Chalkboard Examples:

First day:
Simplify:

1. $\sqrt{x^7}$ Ans.: $|x|^3 \sqrt{x}$
                                  (abs. value *needed*)

2. $\sqrt{a^5}$ Ans.: $a^2\sqrt{a}$
                                  (abs. value *not* needed)

3. $\sqrt{12x^8 y^{11}}$ Ans.: $2x^4|y|^5 \sqrt{y}$

Second day:
Simplify:

1. $\sqrt{x + 5}\,\sqrt{x - 4}$ Ans.: $\sqrt{x^2 + x - 20}$

2. $\sqrt{x^2 - 12x + 36}$ Ans.: $|x - 6|$

3. $\sqrt{(x - 5)^3}$ Ans.: $|x - 5|\sqrt{x - 5}$

Assignments:

Day 1: Section 12–5, #2, 4, 6, and 7–15 odd
        Section 12–4, #42, 44, 46
        Section 12–3, #30, 32
Day 2: Section 12–5, #8–16 even
        Section 12–5, #17–25 odd
        Section 12–4, #48
        Section 12–3, #34

Problem Notes:

Problems 1 through 24 are similar to the text
examples.

Most of the simplifying you have done so far in this chapter has been for radicals with only constants. In this section you will do the same thing with square roots of expressions containing variables.

You recall that the square root of a perfect square is the absolute value of the base. For instance,

$$\sqrt{5^2} = |5| = 5, \quad \text{and} \quad \sqrt{(-7)^2} = |-7| = 7.$$

If the base is a variable, and you do not know beforehand whether it is positive or negative, you must leave in the absolute value sign.

$$\sqrt{x^2} = |x|.$$

Apart from this difficulty, simplifying expressions with variables is done the same way as with only constants.

Objective:
Given an expression containing square roots of variables, simplify it, including rationalizing any denominators.

EXAMPLE 1

Simplify $\sqrt{x^7}$ if x is a positive number.

- - - - -   - - - - -

Think These Reasons

$\sqrt{x^7}$ Write the given expression.

$$= \sqrt{x \cdot x \cdot x \cdot x \cdot x \cdot x \cdot x}$$ Definition of x^7

$$= \sqrt{(x^2)(x^2)(x^2)(x)}$$ Associate the factors in pairs.

$$= |x|\,|x|\,|x|\sqrt{x}$$ Distribute the square root over multiplication.

$$= x \cdot x \cdot x \sqrt{x}$$ x is stated to be positive.

$$= \underline{x^3 \sqrt{x}}$$ Definition of x^3

Problem 25 requires students to think hard about whether or not the absolute value sign is needed, and under what conditions it can be left out.

Problem 26 lets students explore by direct calculation the values of $\sqrt{a} + \sqrt{b}$ and $\sqrt{a+b}$, thus demonstrating that square root does not distribute over addition.

EXAMPLE 2

Simplify $\dfrac{\sqrt{xy^5}}{\sqrt{y}}$. Assume that x and y are positive.

- - - - -   - - - - -

$$\dfrac{\sqrt{xy^5}}{\sqrt{y}}$$ Write the given expression.

$$= \dfrac{\sqrt{xy^5}}{\sqrt{y}} \cdot \dfrac{\sqrt{y}}{\sqrt{y}}$$ Multiply by 1 to rationalize the denominator.

$$= \dfrac{\sqrt{xy^6}}{y}$$ Distribute square root over multiplication.

$$= \dfrac{y^3\sqrt{x}}{y}$$ Take $\sqrt{y^6}$.

$$= \underline{y^2\sqrt{x}}$$ Cancel.

EXAMPLE 3

Simplify $\sqrt{x^2 + 12x + 36}$. Assume that the radicand is a positive number.

- - - - -   - - - - -

$$\sqrt{x^2 + 12x + 36}$$ Write the given expression.

$$= \sqrt{(x + 6)^2}$$ Factor the radicand.

$$= \underline{|x + 6|}$$ Take the square root. Note that although the radicand is stated to be positive, $x + 6$ could be negative. So the absolute value sign is needed.

EXERCISE 12-5

For Problems 1 through 16, simplify the expression. Assume that all variables stand for positive numbers.

1. $\sqrt{x^6}$ 2. $\sqrt{y^4}$ 3. $\sqrt{9a^8}$

1. x^3 **2.** y^2 **3.** $3a^4$

4. $5c$
5. $a^3\sqrt{a}$
6. $z^2\sqrt{z}$
7. $2r^4\sqrt{3r}$
8. $4p\sqrt{3}$
9. $\dfrac{x\sqrt{xy}}{y}$
10. $\dfrac{k^2\sqrt{kp}}{p}$
11. $\dfrac{x\sqrt{xy}}{y}$
12. $\dfrac{x^2\sqrt{y}}{y^2}$
13. $3a^2\sqrt{5}$
14. $6x^3$
15. x^3
16. $\dfrac{6}{5v^2}$
17. $\sqrt{x^2 + x - 6}$
18. $\sqrt{x^2 - 2x - 35}$
19. $|x - 5|$
20. $|x + 4|$
21. $|x + 3|$
22. $|x - 5|$
23. $(x - 7)\sqrt{x - 7}$
24. $(x + 10)^2\sqrt{x + 10}$
25. Both $(x - 3)^4$ and $(x - 3)^2$ must be positive, but $x - 3$ may be negative.
26.
  a. $y = x + 2$
  b. $y = x + 6$
  c. $y = \sqrt{a^2 + 2ab + b^2}$
    $x = \sqrt{a^2 + b^2}$
    $y = x + 2ab$
    so when a and b are positive, $y > x$.
  d. $\sqrt{a^2 + b^2} \neq \sqrt{a^2} + \sqrt{b^2}$

4. $\sqrt{25c^2}$ **5.** $\sqrt{a^7}$ **6.** $\sqrt{z^5}$

7. $\sqrt{12r^9}$ **8.** $\sqrt{48p^2}$ **9.** $\dfrac{\sqrt{x^3}}{\sqrt{y}}$

10. $\dfrac{\sqrt{k^5}}{\sqrt{p}}$ **11.** $\dfrac{\sqrt{x^4 y}}{\sqrt{xy^2}}$ **12.** $\dfrac{\sqrt{x^5 y^7}}{\sqrt{xy^{10}}}$

13. $\sqrt{15a^3}\,\sqrt{3a}$ **14.** $\sqrt{18x}\,\sqrt{2x^5}$ **15.** $\dfrac{3\sqrt{25x^7}}{5\sqrt{9x}}$

16. $\dfrac{12\sqrt{3v}}{5\sqrt{12v^5}}$

For Problems 17 through 24, simplify the expression. Assume that all radicands stand for positive numbers.

17. $\sqrt{x + 3}\sqrt{x - 2}$ **18.** $\sqrt{x + 5}\sqrt{x - 7}$

19. $\sqrt{(x - 5)^2}$ **20.** $\sqrt{(x + 4)^2}$

21. $\sqrt{x^2 + 6x + 9}$ **22.** $\sqrt{x^2 - 10x + 25}$

23. $\sqrt{(x - 7)^3}$ **24.** $\sqrt{(x + 10)^5}$

25. Explain why the simplified form of $\sqrt{(x - 3)^2}$ must have an absolute value sign, but $\sqrt{(x - 3)^4}$ does not need one.

26. Let $x = \sqrt{a^2 + b^2}$. Let $y = a + b$. Assume that a and b stand for positive numbers.
  a. Evaluate x and y if $a = 3$ and $b = 4$. Which is bigger, x or y? How much bigger?
  b. Evaluate x nd y if $a = 15$ and $b = 8$. Which is bigger, x or y? How much bigger?
  c. Explain why y will always be bigger than x if a and b are positive numbers. If you have learned never to forget the middle term when you square a binomial, you have a good chance of being able to answer this question.
  d. Explain how what you have done in this problem proves that square root does *not* distribute over addition.

12-6	RADICAL EQUATIONS

Time: 1 or 2 days

Chalkboard Examples:

Solve and check.

1. $\sqrt{x + 5} = 14$ Ans.: $S = \{81\}$
2. $\sqrt{3x + 4} = 7$ Ans.: $S = \{15\}$

In the last three sections you have operated with radicals that involve only constants. If a variable appears under a radical sign, such as in

$$\sqrt{5x - 7},$$

there are two things you might be expected to do.

1. Evaluate the expression if you know what x equals.

2. Find x if you know what the expression equals.

You did both of these things in Section 12-1. Substituting for x and evaluating the expression involves only arithmetic and is fairly easy. But solving a radical equation for x has some surprises, as you will see in this section.

Suppose you must find x when the expression above equals 3. Setting the expression equal to 3 gives the following *radical equation*.

$$\sqrt{5x - 7} = 3$$

DEFINITION

> **RADICAL EQUATION**
> A **radical equation** is an equation with a variable under the radical sign.

3. $\sqrt{x} + 12 = 8$ Ans.: $S = \emptyset$
   (16 is extraneous.)

4. $3 + \sqrt{4x} = x$ Ans.: $S = \{9\}$
   (1 is extraneous.)

Assignments:

Day 1: Exercise 12–6, #1–9 odd,
       Exercise 12–4, #50,
       Exercise 12–3, #36, 41.
Day 2: Exercise 12–6, #2–10 even,
       Exercise 12–6, #11–19 odd,
       Exercise 12–4, #58.

Squaring each member of this equation removes the radical sign on the left side and gives 9 on the right.

$$(\sqrt{5x - 7})^2 = 3^2 \quad \text{Square each member.}$$
$$5x - 7 = 9 \quad \text{Do the squaring.}$$
$$5x = 16 \quad \text{Add 7 to each member.}$$
$$x = 3.2 \quad \text{Divide each member by 5.}$$

Check:
$$\sqrt{5x - 7} \stackrel{?}{=} 3$$
$$\sqrt{5(3.2) - 7} \stackrel{?}{=} 3$$
$$\sqrt{16 - 7} \stackrel{?}{=} 3$$
$$\sqrt{9} \stackrel{?}{=} 3$$
$$3 = 3 \quad \checkmark$$
$$\therefore S = \{3.2\}$$

For reasons that will soon become obvious, it is advisable to wait until *after* the check to write the solution set!

Some rather innocent-looking radical equations give perplexing results. For instance, solve

$$\sqrt{x} + 2 = x.$$

If you square each member as the equation stands now, the left member becomes

$$(\sqrt{x} + 2)^2, \quad \text{or} \quad x + 4\sqrt{x} + 4.$$

The radical is still there! In order to eliminate the radical you must isolate it on one side of the equation before squaring.

$\sqrt{x} = x - 2$	Subtract 2 from each member to isolate the radical.
$(\sqrt{x})^2 = (x - 2)^2$	Square each member.
$x = x^2 - 4x + 4$	Do the squaring.
$0 = x^2 - 5x + 4$	Make one member equal *zero* since this is a *quadratic* equation.
$0 = (x - 4)(x - 1)$	Factor the right member. (Use the Quadratic Formula, if necessary.)
$x = 4 \quad \text{or} \quad x = 1$	Set each factor equal to 0 and solve.

Before you write the solution set, you should check the answers.

$$x = 4: \qquad\qquad x = 1:$$
$$\sqrt{x} \stackrel{?}{=} x - 2 \qquad \sqrt{x} \stackrel{?}{=} x - 2$$
$$\sqrt{4} \stackrel{?}{=} 4 - 2 \qquad \sqrt{1} \stackrel{?}{=} 1 - 2$$
$$2 = 2 \quad \checkmark \qquad 1 \neq -1 \quad \text{Does not check!}$$

The first answer checks, but the second one does not! This is because there are two different original equations that you could square to get the same transformed equation.

Your equation: Other equation:

$$\sqrt{x} = x - 2 \qquad\qquad -\sqrt{x} = x - 2 \quad \longleftarrow \quad \text{Different!}$$
$$(\sqrt{x})^2 = (x - 2)^2 \qquad (-\sqrt{x})^2 = (x - 2)^2$$
$$x = x^2 - 4x + 4 \qquad\quad x = x^2 - 4x + 4 \quad \longleftarrow \quad \text{Same!}$$

The number 1 satisfies the transformed equation, but not your original equation. As you recall from Section 12.6, such a number is called an *extraneous solution*. So you would label $x = 1$ as extraneous and write only 4 in the solution set.

$$x = 4 \quad \text{or} \quad x = 1 \quad \overset{\text{Extraneous}}{}$$
$$\therefore S = \{4\}$$

Objective:

Be able to solve a radical equation involving square roots, check the answer(s), and discard any extraneous solutions.

Cover the answers as you work these examples.

EXAMPLE 1

Solve and check: $\sqrt{2x + 9} = 6$.

- - - - -

- - - - -

	Think These Reasons

$$\sqrt{2x + 9} = 6$$ Write the given equation.

$$2x + 9 = 36$$ Square each member.

$$2x = 27$$ Subtract 9 from each member.

$$x = 13.5$$ Divide each member by 2.

Check:
Check the solution.

$$\sqrt{2(13.5) + 9} \stackrel{?}{=} 6$$

$$\sqrt{36} \stackrel{?}{=} 6$$

$$6 = 6 \ \blacktriangleright$$

$$\therefore S = \{13.5\}$$ Write the solution set.

EXAMPLE 2

Solve and check: $\sqrt{x} + 32 = 7$.

- - - - -

- - - - -

$$\sqrt{x} + 32 = 7$$ Write the given equation.

$$\sqrt{x} = -25$$ Subtract 32 to isolate the radical.

$$(\sqrt{x})^2 = (-25)^2$$ Square each member.

$$x = 625$$ Do the squaring.

Check: $\sqrt{625} + 32 \stackrel{?}{=} 7$

$$25 + 32 \stackrel{?}{=} 7$$

$$57 \neq 7$$ Extraneous

$$x = 625$$ Discard extraneous solutions.

$$\therefore S = \emptyset$$ Write the solution set.

Notes:

1. The only possible solution is extraneous, so the solution set is empty.

2. You could tell at the second line,

$$\sqrt{x} = -25,$$

that the solution set is empty. Recall that $\sqrt{x}$ means the *positive* square root of x and thus cannot equal -25.

EXAMPLE 3

Solve and check: $5 - \sqrt{3x} = 2x$.

- - - - -   - - - - -

$5 - \sqrt{3x} = 2x$	Write the given equation.
$-\sqrt{3x} = 2x - 5$	Subtract 5 to isolate the radical.
$(-\sqrt{3x})^2 = (2x - 5)^2$	Square each member.
$3x = 4x^2 - 20x + 25$	Do the squaring.
$0 = 4x^2 - 23x + 25$	Make one member equal zero since the equation is quadratic.
$x = \dfrac{23 \pm \sqrt{529 - 4(4)(25)}}{2(4)}$	Use the Quadratic Formula.
$x = \dfrac{23 \pm \sqrt{129}}{8}$	Do the computations.
$x = 4.29\ldots \text{ or } 1.455\ldots$	Finish the computations.

Check:

$x = 4.294\ldots:$	$x = 1.455\ldots:$
$5 - \sqrt{3(4.294\ldots)}$	$5 - \sqrt{3(1.455\ldots)}$
$\qquad \overset{?}{=} 2(4.294\ldots)$	$\qquad \overset{?}{=} 2(1.455\ldots)$
$1.410\ldots \neq 8.589\ldots$	$2.910\ldots \approx 2.910\ldots$

Round solutions.

$\qquad \overset{\text{Extraneous}}{x \approx 4.29} \quad \text{or} \quad x \approx 1.46$ Discard extraneous solutions.

$\qquad \therefore S = \{1.46\}$ Write the solution set.

ORAL PRACTICE

Transform to isolate the radical.

EXAMPLE

$\qquad\qquad$ *Answer*

$5 - \sqrt{x} = 2 \qquad -\sqrt{x} = -3$

A. $\sqrt{x} + 3 = 8$ $\sqrt{x} = 5$ B. $4 + \sqrt{x} = 7$ $\sqrt{x} = 3$

C. $9 - \sqrt{x} = 2$ $-\sqrt{x} = -7$ D. $6 + \sqrt{x} = x$ $\sqrt{x} = x - 6$

Give the result of squaring each member.

EXAMPLE

$$\sqrt{x + 3} = 5 \qquad \overset{Answer}{x + 3 = 25}$$

E. $\sqrt{x} = 9$ $x = 81$ F. $\sqrt{x} = 3x$ $x = 9x^2$ G. $\sqrt{x + 2} = 7$ $x + 2 = 49$

H. $\sqrt{x - 4} = 3$ $x - 4 = 9$ I. $\sqrt{x} = x + 3$ $x = x^2 + 6x + 9$ J. $\sqrt{x} = x - 5$ $x = x^2 - 10x + 25$

K. $\sqrt{x + 9} = x$ $x + 9 = x^2$ L. $\sqrt{x - 1} = x + 4$ $x - 1 = x^2 + 8x + 16$

EXERCISE 12-6

Solve the equations, discarding any extraneous solutions.

1. $\sqrt{x + 3} = 7$ $S = \{46\}$

2. $\sqrt{x + 5} = 3$ $S = \{4\}$

3. $\sqrt{x + 9} = 25$ $S = \{256\}$

4. $\sqrt{x + 7} = 16$ $S = \{81\}$

5. $\sqrt{x + 13} = 9$ $S = \emptyset$

6. $\sqrt{x + 17} = 1$ $S = \emptyset$

7. $\sqrt{3x + 4} = 5$ $S = \{7\}$

8. $\sqrt{5x + 11} = 9$ $S = \{14\}$

9. $\sqrt{7x - 10} = 4$ $S = \{\frac{26}{7}\}$

10. $\sqrt{13x - 3} = 5$ $S = \{\frac{28}{13}\}$

11. $\sqrt{x - 5} + 3 = 10$ $S = \{54\}$

12. $\sqrt{x - 7} - 3 = 5$ $S = \{71\}$

13. $\sqrt{x + 2} + 12 = 7$ $S = \emptyset$

14. $\sqrt{x + 3} + 15 = 8$ $S = \emptyset$

15. $13 - \sqrt{x - 1} = 22$ $S = \emptyset$

16. $11 - \sqrt{x + 4} = 17$ $S = \emptyset$

17. $\sqrt{x + 6} = x$ $S = \{9\}$

18. $\sqrt{2x + 4} = x$ $S = \{8\}$

19. $2 - \sqrt{2x} = 3x$ $S = \{0.38\}$

20. $4 - \sqrt{3x} = x$ $S = \{1.73\}$

Problem Notes:

The problems in this section are similar to those in Exercise 12–1. The only differences are that the radical may have to be isolated first and that solutions may be extraneous. With the background from Section 12–1, students should be able to complete this section in 1 day.

Problems 19 and 20 require use of the Quadratic Formula. Because of the length of the above assignment, it may be better to give these problems along with a later assignment.

Time: 0 or 2 days

Chalkboard Examples:

First day:
1. Find the length of the hypotenuse.
   Ans.: $\sqrt{233} \approx 15.26$

12-7 | **THE PYTHAGOREAN THEOREM AND APPLICATIONS**

In geometry you will learn the properties of triangles. One of the most important properties concerns the lengths of sides of a **right triangle,** in which one angle is a right angle. If you square the lengths of the two shorter sides (the **legs**) and add the two numbers together, you get the square of the length of the longest side (the **hypotenuse**).

2. Find the length
   of the leg.
   Ans.: $\sqrt{50,000} \approx 223.61$

Second day:

3. You walk 75 paces along A Street, turn 90 degrees and walk 100 more paces along First Avenue. If you could walk directly from the starting point to the ending point, about how many
   paces would it be?
   Ans.: $\sqrt{15,625} = 125$ paces (exact answer)

Assignments:

Day 1: Exercise 12–7, #1–19 odd or 2–20 even;
   Exercise 12–6, #12
   Exercise 12–4, #60
Day 2: Exercise 12–6, #21–31 odd or 22–32 even

This property is called the **Pythagorean theorem** in honor of the Greek
mathematician Pythagoras, who lived about 2500 years ago.

PROPERTY

PYTHAGOREAN THEOREM
In a right triangle, the square of the hypotenuse equals the sum
of the squares of the two legs. That is,

$$(\text{hypotenuse})^2 = (\text{leg})^2 + (\text{other leg})^2.$$

More formally, if a and b are the lengths of the legs and c is the
length of the hypotenuse, then

$$a^2 + b^2 = c^2$$

The word *theorem* is another name for a property that can be proved from
properties, definitions, and axioms. One of the easiest ways to see why
this theorem is true is to construct two squares, each with sides of length
$a + b$. Then fill in the squares with *four* right triangles, as shown in the
following diagrams.

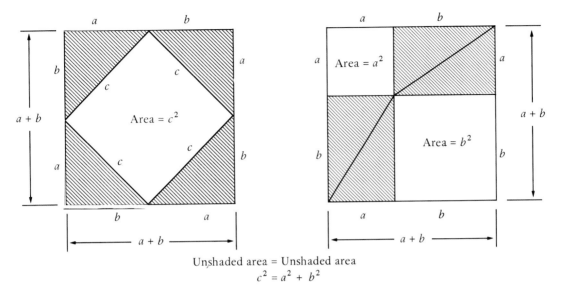

Unshaded area = Unshaded area
$$c^2 = a^2 + b^2$$

In the first diagram, one right triangle goes in each corner. The area of the square in the middle equals c^2, the square of the hypotenuse. In the second diagram, pairs of triangles are put together to form rectangles, and the rectangles are placed in opposite corners. Two squares remain empty, one of area a^2 and the other of area b^2. Since the same-size square is filled with the same four triangles, the unfilled areas must be equal in both figures. Therefore,

$$a^2 + b^2 = c^2.$$

In this section you will use the Pythagorean theorem to compute the length of one side of a right triangle when the lengths of the other two sides are known.

Objective:
Given the lengths of two sides of a right triangle, be able to calculate the length of the third side.

Cover the answers as you work these examples.

EXAMPLE 1

Find the length of the hypotenuse.

	Think These Reasons
$(\text{hypotenuse})^2 = 13^2 + 21^2$	Use the Pythagorean theorem.
$(\text{hypotenuse})^2 = 169 + 441$	Do the squaring.
$(\text{hypotenuse})^2 = 610$	Do the addition.
$\text{hypotenuse} = \sqrt{610}$	Take the square root of each member.
$\text{hypotenuse} \approx 24.70$	Evaluate the square root. Round to two decimal places.

EXAMPLE 2

Find the length of the unknown leg.

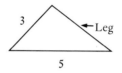

$3^2 + (\text{leg})^2 = 5^2$	Use the Pythagorean theorem.
$(\text{leg})^2 = 25 - 9$	Subtract 3^2; do the squaring.
$(\text{leg})^2 = 16$	Do the arithmetic.
$\text{leg} = \sqrt{16}$	Take the square root of each member.
$\text{leg} = 4$	Evaluate the square root.

Notes:

1. In Example 2 it was necessary to transform the equation from the Pythagorean theorem so that $(\text{leg})^2$ was isolated on one side. Both examples can be worked more quickly if you remember the theorem in this form:

$$\text{hypotenuse} = \sqrt{(\text{leg})^2 + (\text{other leg})^2}$$

$$\text{leg} = \sqrt{(\text{hypotenuse})^2 - (\text{other leg})^2}.$$

2. In Example 2, all three sides (3, 4, and 5) are integers. There are many other such **Pythagorean triples** of integers, as you will see in the following exercise. Most right triangles, however, have at least one side whose length is an *irrational* number, as in Example 1.

EXAMPLE 3

Ship Problem   A ship travels 327 kilometers due east and then turns 90° and travels 193 more kilometers due north. At that point the captain receives a message to return directly to the starting point. How far must the ship travel?

– – – – –   – – – – –

	<div style="border:1px solid;padding:4px">***Think These Reasons***</div>

$d = \sqrt{327^2 + 193^2}$ Draw a picture, look for a right triangle, and label its sides.

$d = \sqrt{327^2 + 193^2}$ Use the Pythagorean theorem (short form).

$= \sqrt{106{,}929 + 37{,}249}$ Do the squaring.

$= \sqrt{144{,}178}$ Do the addition.

$= 379.707\ldots$ Evaluate the square root.

<u>379.71 km</u>   Answer the question. Round to two decimal places.

EXERCISE 12-7

For Problems 1 through 20, find the length of the third side of the right triangle. Round approximate answers to two decimal places.

Problem Notes:

Pythagorean triangles with integer side values can be made up using the fact that if $a^2 + b^2 = c^2$, then there are two integers u and v such that $a^2 = u^2 - v^2$, $b^2 = 2uv$, and $c^2 = u^2 + v^2$. Pick values of u and v that are relatively prime and have opposite parity.

1.

13
17   21.40

2.

15
23   27.46

3.

19
11   21.95

4.

31
14   34.01

5.

8.73   12.96   15.63

6.

71.4   103.8   125.99

7.

8   15   17

8.

7   24   25

9.

1428   1475   2053

10.

1504   1953   2465

11.

19   58   54.80

12.

21   62   58.34

13.

2.27   1.39   1.79

14.
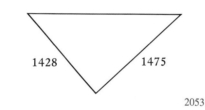
33.5   28.4   17.77

Problems 15 and 16 have answers that are close to but not equal to integers.

In Problem 22 it must be assumed that the guy wires sag a negligible amount and are thus nearly straight lines.[*]

15.

95.01   106   47.00

16.

26.4   29   12.00

17.

18.

19.

20.

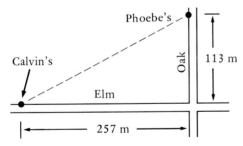

21. **Calvin's to Phoebe's Problem** Calvin Butterball lives on Elm Street 257 meters from its intersection with Oak. Phoebe Small lives on Oak Avenue, 113 meters from its intersection with Elm. How many meters could Calvin save by walking directly to Phoebe's instead of by walking along the roads? 89.25 m

22. **TV Transmitter Problem** A television transmitter is atop an antenna tower 300 meters high. It is held up by guy wires from the top and from the middle, anchored in the ground 160 meters from the base of the antenna. How long is each guy wire? 219.32 m, 340 m

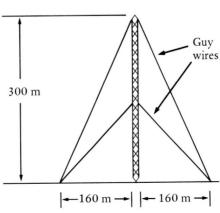

23. *Ladder Problem*   A ladder 5.7 meters long rests against the sill of a second-story window. The base of the ladder is on the ground 2.3 meters from the base of the wall. How far is the window sill above the ground?   5.22 m

5.7 m

|←2.3 m→|

24. *Airplane Problem*   An airplane is flying at an altitude of 3.7 kilometers on a path that will take it directly over the airport. At a certain instant the plane's radar shows that its slant distance from the airport is 14.2 kilometers. How far must the plane travel to be directly above the airport?   13.71 km

3.7 km   14.2 km

Airport

25. *CB Radio Problem*   A CB radio station is located 3 km off the highway. It has a range of 7 km. What length of highway is within its range?   12.65 km

Highway

3 km

7 km

CB

26. *Torpedo Problem*   A submarine lies 2000 meters from the path of a target ship. The sub's torpedoes have a range of 5000 meters. For what distance along its path will the target ship be within range of the torpedoes?   9165.15 m

Target

5000 m

2000 m   Submarine

27. **Pipeline Problem 1**   Oil well 1 is located on a side road 0.9 kilometers from the main road (see the figure). The storage tanks are on the main road, 2.5 kilometers from its intersection with the side road. A pipeline is to be built connecting the well to the tanks. It costs $3000 per kilometer if it is built along the roads or $4000 per kilometer if it is built directly to the tanks. Which way is cheaper? How much cheaper?   Along the roads; $428.26 cheaper

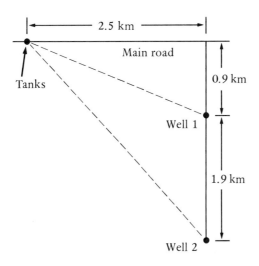

28. **Pipeline Problem 2**   Oil well 2 is located 1.9 kilometers farther down the side road from oil well 1 (see the figure). A pipeline is to be built connecting the well to the tanks on the main road. As in Problem 27, it costs $3000 per kilometer to build pipeline along roads or $4000 per kilometer to build it directly to the tanks. Which way is cheaper? How much cheaper? Figure out an even cheaper way to connect well 2 to the tanks.   Diagonal; $885.34 cheaper; Connect well 2 to well 1. $9,314.66 cheaper!

29. **Rowing versus Walking Problem**   Keri Onward spends two weeks at a summer cottage on the beach. Each day she fishes from the end of the pier. She can either go directly by rowboat or walk 327 meters along the beach and then 204 meters along the pier. She can row 50 m/min and walk 60 m/min. Which way is quicker? How much quicker?   Rowing; 1.14 min. quicker

30. *Shortcut Problem*   Perry Meter can get from Here to There either by going 52 kilometers directly along the Farm Road or by going 43 kilometers down Highway A, turning 90°, and going along Highway B. He can average 1.4 kilometers per minute (km/min) on the highways, but only 0.9 km/min on the Farm Road. Which way is quicker? How much quicker?   Highway; 6.18 min. quicker

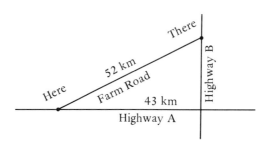

31. *Distance Problem 1*   As a point moves along the *x*-axis, its distance from the point $(0, 20)$ depends on the value of *x*.
   a.   Write an expression representing this distance in terms of *x*. $\sqrt{x^2 + 400}$
   b.   Find the distance when:
      i.   *x* is 37;   42.06
      ii.   *x* is -25;   32.02
      iii.   *x* is 0.   20
   c.   Write an equation stating that the distance is 52. Then solve the equation to find the value(s) of *x*. $\sqrt{x^2 + 400} = 52$; $x = 48$ or -48
   d.   Find the value(s) of *x* when the distance is 15.   Impossible; minimum distance = 20

32. **a.** $d = \sqrt{y^2 + 256}$
   b. $y \approx \pm 19.21$

32. *Distance Problem 2*   As a point moves along the *y*-axis, its distance from the point $(-16, 0)$ depends on the value of *y*.
   a.   Write an expression representing this distance in terms of *y*. $\sqrt{y^2 + 256}$
   b.   Write an equation stating that the distance is 25. Then solve the equation to find the value(s) of *y*. $y = 19.21$ or -19.21
   c.   Find the value(s) of *y* when the distance is 29.   24.19 or −24.19
   d.   Find the distance when:
      i.   *y* is -5;   16.76
      ii.   *y* is 3.5;   16.38
      iii.   *y* is 11.6.   19.76

33. *Proof of the Pythagorean Theorem*   Learn the geometric justification of the Pythagorean theorem well enough so that you could draw the diagram from memory on a classroom quiz and give reasons why $a^2 + b^2 = c^2$.

34. *Spelling Problem*   Learn the spellings of *Pythagoras* and *Pythagorean* well enough that you could write them from memory on a classroom quiz.

12-8 | HIGHER-ORDER RADICALS

You have learned that a square root of x is a number that gives x for the answer when you square it. That is,

$$(\sqrt{x})^2 = x.$$

Using the same reasoning, other roots of a number can be defined. For instance, 5 is a **cube root** of 125, since

$$5^3 = 125.$$

Similarly,

3 is a **fourth root** of 81, since $3^4 = 81$,

2 is a **fifth root** of 32, since $2^5 = 32$.

The symbol for these higher order roots uses the radical sign, $\sqrt{\ }$, with a number outside to tell which root is being taken.

$\sqrt[3]{x}$ is the cube root of x.

$\sqrt[4]{x}$ is the fourth root of x.

$\sqrt[5]{x}$ is the fifth root of x.

The number 3, 4, or 5, above, is called the *root index*. The square root could be written $\sqrt[2]{x}$, but it almost never is written this way.

DEFINITION

> **NTH ROOT**
> An **nth root** of x is a number that, when raised to the nth power, gives x for the answer. That is,
>
> $\sqrt[n]{x}$ is a number such that
>
> $$(\sqrt[n]{x})^n = x.$$
>
> The positive integer n is called the **root index.**

An nth root of x can be evaluated using any scientific calculator. All you have to do is raise x to the power $\frac{1}{n}$. For instance, the cube root of 57 can be found as follows:

$\sqrt[3]{57}$

$= 57^{\frac{1}{3}}$ Write the cube root as a power.

≈ 3.8485011 Press 57 $\boxed{y^x}$ 3 $\boxed{1/x}$ $\boxed{=}$, or press 57 $\boxed{\sqrt[x]{\ }}$ 3 $\boxed{=}$.

You can check this answer by *cubing* it. Since the calculator rounds both in getting the answer and in checking it, you might get a number slightly different from 57, such as 56.999998.

PROPERTY

EXPONENT PROPERTY OF NTH ROOTS

$$\sqrt[n]{x} = x^{\frac{1}{n}}$$

Objective :
Given a higher-order radical, evaluate it by calculator and use the result to work problems.

Cover the answers as you work these examples.

EXAMPLE 1

Evaluate $\sqrt[4]{32.7}$ correct to two decimal places.

- - - - -   - - - - -

	Think These Reasons
$\sqrt[4]{32.7}$	Write the given expression.
$= 32.7^{\frac{1}{4}}$	Write the radical as a power.
$= 2.3913158\ldots$	Press 32.7 $\boxed{y^x}$ 4 $\boxed{1/x}$ $\boxed{=}$
$\approx \underline{2.39}$	Round the answer.

EXAMPLE 2

Evaluate $\sqrt[5]{4,084,101}$ correct to two decimal places.

- - - - -   - - - - -

$\sqrt[5]{4,084,101}$	Write the given expression.
$= 4,084,101^{\frac{1}{5}}$	Write the radical as a power.
$= \underline{21}$	Press 4084101 $\boxed{y^x}$ 5 $\boxed{1/x}$ $\boxed{=}$ (The answer is *exact*.)

EXAMPLE 3

The weight of a diamond is given by

$$w = 0.06 \, d^3,$$

where w is the weight in carats and d is the diameter in millimeters. Find the diameter of a 7-carat diamond.

- - - - -   - - - - -

$w = 0.06\,d^3$	Write the given equation.
$7 = 0.06\,d^3$	Substitute 7 for w.
$\dfrac{7}{0.06} = d^3$	Divide each member by 0.06.
$\sqrt[3]{\dfrac{7}{0.06}} = d$	Take the cube root of each member.
$4.886324 \approx d$	Evaluate the cube root.
<u>About 4.9 m.</u>	Answer the question.

ORAL PRACTICE

Evaluate the radical.

A. $\sqrt[3]{8}$ 2 B. $\sqrt[4]{16}$ 2 C. $\sqrt[3]{27}$ 3 D. $\sqrt[4]{81}$ 3 E. $\sqrt[3]{64}$ 4

F. $\sqrt[6]{64}$ 2 G. $\sqrt[3]{1000}$ 10 H. $\sqrt[3]{1}$ 1 I. $\sqrt[9]{1}$ 1 J. $\sqrt[7]{0}$ 0

Express the radical as a power.

EXAMPLE

$$\sqrt[3]{29} \qquad \overset{\textit{Answer}}{29^{\frac{1}{3}}}$$

K. $\sqrt[3]{42}$ $42^{\frac{1}{3}}$ L. $\sqrt[4]{73}$ $73^{\frac{1}{4}}$ M. $\sqrt[5]{99}$ $99^{\frac{1}{5}}$ N. $\sqrt[6]{309}$ $309^{\frac{1}{6}}$ O. $\sqrt[7]{0.95}$ $0.95^{\frac{1}{7}}$

EXERCISE 12-8

For Problems 1 through 20, evaluate the radical. Round approximate answers to two decimal places.

1. $\sqrt[3]{537}$ 8.13
2. $\sqrt[3]{795}$ 9.26
3. $\sqrt[4]{849}$ 5.40
4. $\sqrt[4]{692}$ 5.13
5. $\sqrt[5]{2478}$ 4.77
6. $\sqrt[5]{9876}$ 6.29
7. $\sqrt[6]{729}$ 3
8. $\sqrt[4]{4096}$ 4
9. $\sqrt[5]{1024}$ 4

10. $\sqrt[5]{3125}$ 5   11. $\sqrt[4]{2401}$ 7   12. $\sqrt[4]{14,641}$ 11

13. $\sqrt[3]{389,017}$ 73   14. $\sqrt[3]{185,193}$ 57   15. $\sqrt[3]{22.79}$ 2.84

16. $\sqrt[3]{13.92}$ 2.41   17. $\sqrt[4]{0.0325}$ 0.42   18. $\sqrt[4]{0.0928}$ 0.55

19. $\sqrt[5]{286.29151}$ 3.1   20. $\sqrt[5]{24.76099}$ 1.9

Problem Notes:

Problems 21–24 are examples of direct cube variation functions. The volumes (and thus weights) of similarly shaped geometrical objects vary directly with the cube of a linear dimension. This is because increasing a length while maintaining the same proportions increases the width and depth, too. If one person is twice as tall as another and both have roughly the same proportions, then the taller person will be *eight* times as heavy as the other!

21. c. About 1650 m

22. a. 7238.23 ≈ 7200 cm³

21. *Cube Problem*   The volume of a cube equals the cube of the length of an edge.
    a.   Find the volume of a cube of edge 3.7 cm.   50.65 cm³
    b.   Find the length of the edge of a cube whose volume is 578 cubic centimeters.   8.33 cm
    c.   A person can fit into a space of about 1 cubic meter. There are approximately 4.5 billion people in the world. Thus a box of volume 4.5 billion cubic meters would hold all the people in the world. If the box were a cube, how long would the edges be?

22. *Sphere Problem*   The volume, V, of a sphere is

$$V = \frac{4}{3}\pi r^3,$$

where r is the radius of the sphere and $\pi \approx 3.14159$.
    a.   Find the volume of a basketball whose radius is 12 cm.
    b.   What radius sphere would hold a liter of water (1000 cubic centimeters)?   6.20 cm
    c.   A spherical water tank is to hold 20,000 cubic feet of water. What must its radius be?   16.84 ft

23. *Shark Problem*   The mass of a great white shark is approximately

$$m = 9.5L^3,$$

where m is its mass in kilograms and L is its length in meters.
    a.   Calculate the mass of a great white shark 2 meters long.   76 kg
    b.   How long would a 200-kilogram shark be?   2.76 m
    c.   The shark in the novel *Jaws* was supposed to have been about 8 meters long. What would its mass have been? Surprising?   4864 kg

24. *Height-Mass Problem*   The mass of a person of average build is approximately

$$m = 11.6h^3,$$

where m is mass in kilograms and h is height in meters.
    a.   What is the mass of a person of average build who is 1.5 meters tall?   39.15 kg
    b.   What is the mass of a very tall person of average build who is 2.5 meters tall?   181.25 kg
    c.   How tall would a 50-kilogram person of average build be?   1.63 m
    d.   What should be the mass of a person of average build who is *your* height?   (Answers will vary.)

25. *Exponent Property of nth Roots Problem*

    a. Show that $\sqrt[3]{8} = 2$ by writing 8 as 2^3 and then raising 2^3 to the $\frac{1}{3}$ power, using the appropriate property of exponentiation.

    b. Show that 3 is a fifth root of 243 by writing 243 as a power and then raising it to the $\frac{1}{5}$ power, using the appropriate property of exponentiation. $\sqrt[5]{243} = \sqrt[5]{3^5} = (3^5)^{\frac{1}{5}} = 3^1 = 3$

    c. Write $\sqrt[n]{x}$ as $x^{\frac{1}{n}}$ and then raise it to the nth power. Explain how this computation shows that $x^{\frac{1}{n}}$ really *is* an nth root of x.
$$\sqrt[n]{x} = x^{\frac{1}{n}}: (x^{\frac{1}{n}})^n = x^1 = x \therefore x^{\frac{1}{n}} = \sqrt[n]{x}$$

25. a. $\sqrt[3]{8} = \sqrt[3]{2^3} = (2^3)^{\frac{1}{3}} = 2^1 = 2$

12-9 | RATIONAL AND IRRATIONAL NUMBERS

In Section 5-10 you learned that *rational* numbers are numbers such as

$$\frac{2}{3}, \quad 5\frac{1}{2}, \quad -\frac{7}{2}, \quad 55,$$

which can be written as ratios of two integers. You also learned that *irrational* numbers are numbers that *cannot* be written as ratios of integers. In this section you will see that repeating decimals represent *rational* numbers and that radicals such as $\sqrt{19}$ represent *irrational* numbers.

To see that rational numbers give repeating decimals, you can evaluate some numbers on a calculator.

$$\frac{2}{3} = 0.66666\ldots$$

$$\frac{3}{11} = 0.272727\ldots$$

$$\frac{2}{5} = 0.4 = 0.400000\ldots$$

You can tell *why* rational numbers give repeating decimals by looking at the long-division process. If you divide a number such as 3 by 11, there are only 11 possible remainders: 0, 1, 2, 3, 4, 5, 6, 7, 8, 9, 10, and 11. If the remainder is ever 0, the decimal terminates. If the remainder is never 0, it is bound to be the same again after at most 10 steps in the division process. Once the remainder repeats, the decimal repeats, too.

It is possible to do the reverse problem and find the fraction equal to a given repeating decimal, such as $0.393939.\ldots$

Let $x =\ 0.393939\ldots$ Write an equation.

$\therefore 100x = 39.393939\ldots$ Multiply each member by 100 to move the decimal point over two places.

Time: 0 or 2 days, with test review

Chalkboard Examples:

1. Write as a repeating decimal.
  a. $\frac{1}{3}$ Ans.: 0.333333 . . .
  b. $\frac{4}{11}$ Ans.: 0.363636 . . .
  c. $\frac{4}{5}$ Ans.: 0.800000 . . .

2. Write as a ratio of integers and simplify.
  0.878787 . . .   Ans.: $\frac{29}{33}$

3. Rational or irrational? Justify your answer.
  a. $\sqrt[5]{243}$ Ans.: Irrational (3.948 . . .)
  b. $\sqrt[5]{243}$ Ans.: Rational (3)
  c. 0.252525 . . .   Ans.: Rational (repeating decimal, $\frac{25}{99}$)
  d. 0.152535 . . .   Ans.: Irrational (non-repeating decimal)

Assignments:

Day 1: Exercise 12–9, #1–59 odd or 2–60 even
Day 2: Selected problems from Exercise 12–10 in preparation for test.

$$99x = 39$$

Subtract the top equation from the bottom one. The decimal parts "drop out."

$$x = \frac{39}{99}$$

Divide each member by 99.

$$x = \frac{13}{33}$$

Do any possible canceling.

This process can be done for *any* repeating decimal. At the second step, just multiply each member by a power of 10 big enough to move the decimal to where the repeating parts again line up. Then subtract the two equations to eliminate the decimal part.

CONCLUSION

> A number is rational *if* and *only* if it can be written as a repeating decimal. (Decimals that *terminate* have repeating zeros.)

With the aid of this conclusion, it is easy to construct a number that is *irrational*. Just write a decimal that clearly does *not* repeat. For instance, these numbers are irrational:

$$0.101001000100001 \ldots$$

$$0.11121314151617. \ldots$$

It turns out that π, the ratio of the circumference to the diameter of a circle, is an irrational number.

$$\pi \approx 3.14159265358979323846264338327950288419716939937510 \ldots$$

Computations of π to over 100,000 decimal places confirm that it does not repeat.

Roots of integers that are not whole numbers are also irrational numbers. For instance, $\sqrt{2}$ is *between* two integers, 1 and 2, and is approximately 1.414. The number 1.414 equals $\frac{1414}{1000}$ and is thus a *rational* number. But 1.414^2 is only 1.999396. So 1.414 is not exactly equal to $\sqrt{2}$.

To see why such radicals are irrational, suppose that $\sqrt{2}$ *did* equal a ratio of two integers such as

$$\frac{1414}{1000}.$$

Factoring the numerator and denominator into primes gives

$$\frac{2 \cdot 7 \cdot 101}{2^3 \cdot 5^3}.$$

Canceling common factors gives

$$\frac{7 \cdot 101}{2^2 \cdot 5^3}.$$

If this fraction is *squared*, the result is

$$\frac{7^2 \cdot 101^2}{2^4 \cdot 5^6}.$$

Squaring a fraction introduces *no* new prime factors into the numerator or denominator. Since no more canceling could be done *before* the squaring, none can be done *afterwards*, either. So $(1.414)^2$ could not possibly be the *integer* 2. The same reasoning can be used to show that *no* rational number that is *between* two integers can possibly turn out to be an integer when it is squared, cubed, or raised to a higher power.

CONCLUSION

> For any integer x, if x is not a perfect n^{th} power, then $\sqrt[n]{x}$ is an *irrational* number.
>
> That is, if x is an integer, then $\sqrt[n]{x}$ is either an *integer* or an *irrational* number.

Objectives :
1. Be able to transform a repeating decimal into a ratio of integers, and

2. Be able to tell whether a given number is rational or irrational, and explain why.

Cover the answers as you work these examples.

EXAMPLE 1

Write $\dfrac{5}{7}$ as a repeating decimal.

_ _ _ _ _   _ _ _ _ _

$$\frac{5}{7} = 0.714285\,714285\,714285 \ldots$$

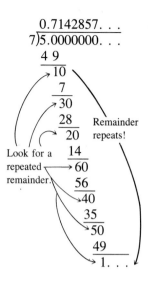

Note: When you divide a number by 7 the decimal will repeat after at most <u>6</u> digits, since there are only 6 possible nonzero remainders.

EXAMPLE 2

Write 0.405405405 . . . as a ratio of two relatively prime integers.

– – – – –   – – – – –

| | Think These Reasons |

$x = \quad 0.405405405 \ldots$ Write an equation.

$\underline{1000x = 405.405405405 \ldots}$ Multiply by 1000 to move the decimal point three places.

$999x = 405$ Subtract top equation from bottom.

$x = \dfrac{405}{999}$ Divide by 999.

$x = \dfrac{45}{111} = \underline{\underline{\dfrac{15}{37}}}$ Do the canceling to get *relatively prime* integers.

EXAMPLE 3

Is $\sqrt[4]{923521}$ a *rational* number or an *irrational* number? Justify your answer.

– – – – –   – – – – –

$\sqrt[4]{923{,}521}$ Write the given expression.

$= 923{,}521^{\frac{1}{4}}$ Write the radical as a power.

$= 31$ Press 923521 $\boxed{y^x}$ 4 $\boxed{1/x}$ $\boxed{=}$.

$\therefore \underline{\sqrt[4]{923521} \text{ is rational.}}$ 31 is a rational number.

EXAMPLE 4

Is $\sqrt[5]{29317}$ a *rational* number or an *irrational* number? Justify your answer.

- - - - -   - - - - -

$$\sqrt[5]{29{,}317}$$ Write the given expression.

$$= 29{,}317^{\frac{1}{5}}$$ Write the radical as a power.

$$\approx 7.8239111$$ Press 29317 $\boxed{y^x}$ 5 $\boxed{1/x}$ $\boxed{=}$.

$$\therefore \underline{\sqrt[5]{29317} \text{ is irrational.}}$$ 7.8239111 is not an integer. The only other choice is "irrational." (See the conclusion.)

EXAMPLE 5

Is 3.21221222122221 . . . a *rational* number or an *irrational* number? Justify your answer.

- - - - -   - - - - -

$\underline{3.21221222122221 \ldots \text{ is irrational.}}$ It is a nonrepeating decimal.

EXERCISE 12-9

For Problems 1 through 20, write the rational number as a repeating decimal or as a terminating decimal.

1. $\dfrac{3}{7}$ $0.\overline{428571}$ 2. $\dfrac{6}{7}$ $0.\overline{857142}$ 3. $\dfrac{9}{11}$ $0.\overline{81}$ 4. $\dfrac{2}{11}$ $0.\overline{18}$

5. $\dfrac{5}{6}$ $0.8\overline{3}$ 6. $\dfrac{1}{6}$ $0.1\overline{6}$ 7. $\dfrac{7}{9}$ $0.\overline{7}$ 8. $\dfrac{4}{9}$ $0.\overline{4}$

9. $\dfrac{3}{16}$ 0.1875 10. $\dfrac{7}{16}$ 0.4375 11. $\dfrac{29}{33}$ $0.\overline{87}$ 12. $\dfrac{32}{33}$ $0.\overline{96}$

13. $\dfrac{49}{66}$ $0.7\overline{42}$ 14. $\dfrac{7}{66}$ $0.1\overline{06}$ 15. $\dfrac{14}{37}$ $0.\overline{378}$ 16. $\dfrac{29}{37}$ $0.\overline{783}$

17. $\dfrac{286}{999}$ $0.\overline{286}$ 18. $\dfrac{985}{999}$ $0.\overline{985}$ 19. $\dfrac{5}{13}$ $0.\overline{384615}$ 20. $\dfrac{9}{13}$ $0.\overline{692307}$

For Problems 21 through 40, write the repeating decimal as a ratio of two relatively prime integers.

21. 0.333333. . . $\frac{1}{3}$ 22. 0.666666. . . $\frac{2}{3}$ 23. 0.777777. . . $\frac{7}{9}$

24. 0.555555. . . $\frac{5}{9}$ 25. 0.565656. . . $\frac{56}{99}$ 26. 0.717171. . . $\frac{71}{99}$

Problem Notes:

For Problems 21–40, students must realize that the number to multiply by (10, 100, 1000, etc.) is determined by the number of places before the decimal repeats. The denominator will always be 9, 99, 999, 9999, etc. Since 37 is a factor of 999, there are relatively simple fractions such as $\frac{19}{37}$ that repeat with a period of 3.

27. 0.151515... $\frac{5}{33}$ 28. 0.454545... $\frac{5}{11}$ 29. 0.909090... $\frac{10}{11}$

30. 0.090909... $\frac{1}{11}$ 31. 0.671671... $\frac{671}{999}$ 32. 0.734734... $\frac{734}{999}$

33. 0.303303... $\frac{101}{333}$ 34. 0.525525... $\frac{175}{333}$ 35. 0.243243... $\frac{9}{37}$

36. 0.675675... $\frac{25}{37}$ 37. 0.037037... $\frac{1}{27}$ 38. 0.370370... $\frac{10}{27}$

39. 0.185185... $\frac{5}{27}$ 40. 0.407407... $\frac{11}{27}$

For Problems 41 through 60, tell whether the given number is *rational* or *irrational*. Justify your answer.

41. $\sqrt{8836}$ 42. $\sqrt{7415}$ 43. $\sqrt{3916}$

44. $\sqrt{2916}$ 45. $\sqrt[3]{7845}$ 46. $\sqrt[3]{2197}$

47. $\sqrt[4]{20{,}736}$ 48. $\sqrt[4]{75{,}802}$ 49. $\sqrt[5]{99{,}248}$

50. $\sqrt[5]{52{,}000}$ 51. 0.371371371...   52. 0.619619619...

53. 0.515115111511115...   54. 0.70200220222022220...

55. 0.005005005...   56. 0.010001000100010001...

57. 0.273   58. 0.195

59. $-\pi$ 60. π

61. **Square Root of 5 Problem**   The square root of 5, $\sqrt{5}$, is approximately equal to 2.236.
   a. Show that 2.236 is a *rational* number by writing it as the ratio of two integers. Do any possible canceling. $\frac{559}{250}$
   b. Factor the numerator and denominator of the simplified fraction in part (a) into primes. (*Clue:* The numerator has exactly two prime factors.) $\frac{13\cdot43}{2\cdot5^3}$
   c. Without actually doing the multiplication, square the factored fraction in part (b). Show that the numerator and denominator of the squared fraction still have no common factors. $\frac{13^2 43^2}{2^2 5^6}$
   d. Explain why the squared fraction in part (c) could not possibly equal 5. $\frac{13^2 43^2}{2^2 5^6} \neq 5$, since numerator and denominator have no common prime factors.
   e. Square 2.236 and show that the answer is *close* to 5. 4.999696

62. **0.999999... Problem**   The number 0.333... represents $\frac{1}{3}$. Also, 2(0.333...), or 0.666... represents $\frac{2}{3}$. So 3(0.333...), or 0.999..., should represent $\frac{3}{3}$, or 1. Show that this is actually true by expressing 0.999... as a ratio of two integers, as in Example 2, and simplifying the result. $\frac{9}{9}=1$

63. **Cube Roots by Trial and Error**   The diagram on the next page is called a **flow chart.** Each rectangular box represents a step to be done in doing a computation. Each diamond-shaped box represents a **branch-point,** at which the flow of the computation could go either of two ways, depending on whether the answer to the question inside is Yes or No. The oval boxes mark the beginning and the end.

---

41. Rational = 94
42. Irrational ≈ 86.1104
43. Irrational ≈ 62.578
44. Rational = 54
45. Irrational ≈ 19.87
46. Rational = 13
47. Rational = 12
48. Irrational ≈ 16.59
49. Irrational ≈ 9.98
50. Irrational ≈ 8.77
51. Rational = $\frac{371}{999}$
52. Rational = $\frac{619}{999}$
53. Irrat., no repeating pattern
54. Irrat., no repeating pattern
55. Rational = $\frac{5}{999}$
56. Rational = $\frac{100}{9999}$
57. Rational = $\frac{273}{1000}$
58. Rational = $\frac{195}{1000}$
59. Irrational, see text
60. Irrational, see text

Problem 61 contains the nucleus of a proof that square roots of integers are either integers or irrational numbers. See, for example, Foerster, *Algebra and Trigonometry: Functions and Applications*, Addison-Wesley, 1980, page 225.

Problem 62 leads to the remarkable fact that 0.999999... is *exactly* equal to 1. It is fun to watch students' reactions as they grasp or resist this fact!

In Problem 63 students are presented with the task of analyzing a flow chart. The process of reading the flow chart is the same as that of tracing a computer program. The steps must be done one at a time, and a simulated memory and output must be shown. Translating the flow chart into BASIC or some other computer language is easier than writing a program from scratch.

63. *Cube Roots by Trial and Error*—see Additional Answers.

This particular flow chart is for a computation of cube roots. At the beginning, a number whose cube root is desired is put in. Then a variable R is started at 1, increased to 2, increased to 3, and so forth, until the *cube* of R becomes greater than N. Next, R is increased by 0.1 each step until R again becomes larger than N. The process is continued until you have a decimal approximation for the cube root of N to two decimal places.

Do the following.

a.   Read through the flow chart one step at a time, doing what it says in each box as you come to it. Write a simulated computer memory, as you would for a program in BASIC, and show the output if 64 is put in for N. At the end you should get the message CUBE ROOT OF 64 IS 4.

b.   Repeat part (a) if 34 is put in for N.

c.   Write a computer program for this flow chart. Test it using 64 and 34 for N, and debug the program if necessary.

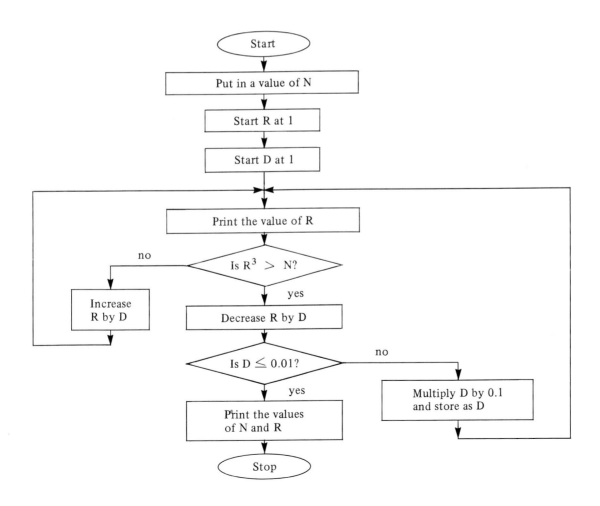

| 12-10 | CHAPTER REVIEW AND TEST |

Time: 1 day

Test Ideas:

Since you may have done only certain parts of this chapter, your test will have to be tailored to suit.

Assignment:

Following the test, assign:
Study Section 13–1;
work Exercise 13–1, #1–9 odd

In this chapter you have taken another look at radicals. Instead of just evaluating square roots on a calculator, you found out their properties when left in radical form. These properties allow you to simplify radicals. The process of rationalizing the denominator allows you to divide by a binomial involving square roots. When a variable occurs under a radical sign, you learned how to solve radical equations, discarding any extraneous solutions. In the real world you found radicals occurring as lengths of sides of right triangles. You learned to transform cube and higher roots to powers with fractional exponents and then evaluate them by calculator. The nth root of an integer was found to be either an integer or an irrational number.

In your review of this chapter you should realize that there are several somewhat separate topics. Unlike prior chapters, not all of these topics are tied together in the problems of the last section. So it is most important for you to look at the objective of *each* section to make sure your review leaves nothing out. The test below touches on each of these topics. If your review has been successful, you should be able to work all the problems *without* looking back in the chapter.

| CHAPTER TEST |

1. **a.** $\text{leg}^2 = \text{hypotenuse}^2 - \text{other leg}^2$
   $\text{hypotenuse}^2 = \text{leg}^2 + \text{leg}^2$.
   b. $\sqrt{64} = 8; \sqrt[3]{64} = 4$.
   c. $8^3_1 = 8 \cdot 8 \cdot 8 = 512$
   $8^{\frac{1}{3}} = \sqrt[3]{8} = 2$.
   d. A rational number *can* be written as a ratio of 2 integers.
   An irrational number *can't* be.
   e. The decimal for π does *not* repeat.
   The decimal for $\frac{22}{7}$ *does* repeat.

2. **a.** An expression is in simple radical form if
   i. The radicand is as simple as possible.
   ii. There are no radicals in denominators.
   b. In a right triangle, $(\text{hypotenuse})^2$
   $= (\text{leg})^2 + (\text{leg})^2$.
   c. $\sqrt[n]{x}$ is a number for which $(\sqrt[n]{x})^n = x$.
   d. $\sqrt[n]{x} = x^{\frac{1}{n}}$

1. Tell the difference in each case.
   a. Finding a leg length by the Pythagorean theorem and finding the hypotenuse length.
   b. The square root of 64 and the cube root of 64.
   c. 8^3 and $8^{\frac{1}{3}}$.
   d. A rational number and an irrational number.
   e. The decimal representation of π and the decimal representation of $\frac{22}{7}$

2. Write each.
   a. Definition of simple radical form.
   b. Statement of the Pythagorean theorem.
   c. Definition of nth root.
   d. Exponent property of radicals.

3. For the expression $\sqrt{3x + 8}$:
   a. Evaluate it in simple radical form if:
   i. x is 4; $2\sqrt{5}$ ii. x is 14; $5\sqrt{2}$ iii. x is 30. $7\sqrt{2}$
   b. Find x if the expression equals:
   i. 7; $x = \frac{41}{3}$ ii. -4;   Not possible $x = -0.38$ or
   iii. $x + 3$.   (Give decimal answers for this part.) $x = -2.62$

4. Simplify. Write the answer in simple *radical* form.
   a. $\sqrt{252}$ $6\sqrt{7}$
   b. $\sqrt{15} \times \sqrt{21}$ $3\sqrt{35}$
   c. $\sqrt{144 + 25}$ 13
   d. $5\sqrt{32} + 7\sqrt{8}$ $34\sqrt{2}$
   e. $9\sqrt{28} - \sqrt{28}$ $16\sqrt{7}$
   f. $\dfrac{\sqrt{10}}{\sqrt{35}}$ $\dfrac{\sqrt{14}}{7}$
   g. $\dfrac{24}{\sqrt{12}}$ $4\sqrt{3}$
   h. $15\sqrt{\dfrac{3}{5}} + 15\sqrt{\dfrac{5}{3}}$ $8\sqrt{15}$
   i. $(2\sqrt{3} + 7)(5\sqrt{3} - 4)$ $2 + 27\sqrt{3}$
   j. $\dfrac{2\sqrt{7} - \sqrt{5}}{3\sqrt{5} + \sqrt{7}}$ $\dfrac{7\sqrt{35} - 29}{38}$

5. Solve: $5 - \sqrt{x} = x$. $S = \{3.21\}$ (7.79 is extr.)

6. Find the length of the third side of these right triangles.
   a.
   261
   503
   429.99

   b.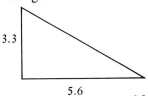
   3.3
   5.6
   6.5

7. Evaluate the radicals. Tell which are rational numbers and which are irrational numbers.
   a. $\sqrt[3]{71}$ 4.14 irrational
   b. $\sqrt[4]{28{,}561}$ 13 rational
   c. $\sqrt[5]{1}$ 1 rational
   d. $\sqrt{4{,}004{,}001}$ 2001 rational

8. *Detour Problem*   Flight 57 normally flies 275 km directly from A to B. One day it detours due to bad weather. It flies 219 km from A and then turns 90° and flies straight to B. How many extra kilometers did it fly because of the detour?   110.32 km

   275 km
   A   *B*
   219 km   90°

9. *Bigger Airplane Problem*   The mass of a particular design of airplane is given by

   $$m = 0.46L^3,$$

   where *m* is mass in kilograms and *L* is the length in meters.
   a.   What is the mass of a plane 20 meters long?   3680 kg
   b.   If a plane were built big enough to have *twice* the mass you calculated in part (a), would it be *twice* as long, *more* than twice as long, or *less* than twice as long? Justify your answer.

   Less than twice as long: at 7360 kg it is 25.2 m long.

Problem Notes:

Problem 9 is an adaptation of the suggested chalk board example for Section 12–9.

13

Inequalities

Solving equations involves finding the value of x *when you know what number an expression equals. In this chapter you will find values of a variable when you know what number an expression is* greater *than or* less *than. The result is called an* inequality. *It could be used to say, for example, that a submarine's hull diameter is within 0.01 foot of the desired value, 33 feet.*

Variable:

x Diameter

Expression:

$|x - 33|$ Difference between x and 33 feet

Inequalities:

$|x - 33| < 0.01$

   Difference is less than 0.01.

$-0.01 < x - 33 < 0.01$

   $x - 3$ is between -0.01 and 0.01.

$32.99 < x < 33.01$

   x is between 32.99 and 33.01.

13-1 | NUMBER-LINE GRAPHS

This section introduces a new concept. However, you should be able to read part or all of it and work the problems without prior instruction from your teacher.

The number 5 is less than the number 8. To say this in a more compact way, people write

$$5 < 8.$$

The symbol $<$ means *is less than*. It is similar to an $=$ sign, but the lines have been pinched together at the smaller number and spread apart at the larger number. A similar symbol, $>$, is used in $13 > 9$, which is read "13 is greater than 9."

Is less than: Is greater than:

$5 < 8$ $13 > 9$

Small end ⟋ ⟍Big end   Big end⟋   ⟍Small end
toward   toward   toward   toward
small number big number   big number   small number

A statement such as $5 < 8$ is called an **inequality.** An inequality with a variable, such as $x < 6$, is true for *many* values of x. The inequality $x < 6$ is true for numbers such as 5, 4, 2, 3.7, 5.99, 0, and all negative numbers. This fact can be shown on a number line.

$x < 6$

0   6

The open circle at 6 shows that x *cannot* equal 6. The shaded part of the line shows numbers that x *can* equal.

The inequality

$$x \geq 2$$

Time: $\frac{1}{2}$ day, with Section 13–2

Chalkboard Examples:

1. Plot: $x > 3$
   Ans.:

   0   3

2. Plot: $x \leq 5$
   Ans.:

   0   5

See Section 13–2 for more examples.

Assignment:

Problems 1–9 odd should have been assigned following your test on Chapter 12. See Section 13–2 for additional problems to be assigned from Section 13–1.

is read "x is greater than or equal to 2." A graph of the inequality looks like this.

$x \geq 2$

The solid dot at 2 shows that x *can* equal 2. The shaded part of the line shows the other numbers that x can equal.

These are the four inequality signs and their meanings.

DEFINITIONS

INEQUALITY SIGNS
$<$ is less than
$>$ is greater than
$\leq$ is less than or equal to
$\geq$ is greater than or equal to

In this section you will draw number-line graphs of inequalities and write inequalities for given graphs.

Objectives:
1. Given an inequality such as $x \leq 7$, draw the graph.
2. Given the graph, write an inequality.
3. Given words, write an inequality and draw its graph.

Cover the answers as you work these examples.

EXAMPLE 1

Sketch the graph of $x \leq 7$.

– – – – –   – – – – –

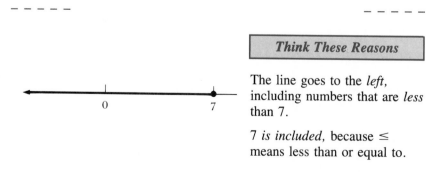

Think These Reasons

The line goes to the *left*, including numbers that are *less* than 7.

7 *is included,* because $\leq$ means less than or equal to.

Note: You should draw a neat sketch, using a ruler if you do not draw well freehand. You do not need to show numbers other than the origin, 0, and the end point, 7.

EXAMPLE 2

Sketch the graph of $x > -3$.

The line goes to the *right*, including numbers that are *greater* than -3.

-3 *is not* included, since the statement $-3 > -3$ is false.

EXAMPLE 3

Write an inequality for the graph.

$\underline{\underline{x \geq 2}}$

The values of x can be *greater* than 2, and 2 *is* included.

EXAMPLE 4

Write an inequality for the graph.

$\underline{\underline{x < -4}}$

The values of x can be *less* than -4, and -4 is *not* included.

EXAMPLE 5

Write an inequality that says x is at least 5, and draw the graph.

$\underline{\underline{x \geq 5}}$

At least 5 means 5 or more. Do not be fooled into thinking that at least means less than.

EXERCISE 13-1

Problem Notes:

In these problems, students sometimes confuse the open and closed end points with the *direction* of the inequality or with the *sign* of the end point. Make sure they understand that it is inclusion or exclusion of the end point that determines this. Also, make sure they realize the open circle includes all numbers up to the end point. Some students think at first that $x > 3$ means that the graph starts at 4.

In this text, students are not asked to show the scale on the number line. The time saved can be used to work more problems. The minimum they should show is the origin, the end point, and the arrow, as in the examples. Arrowheads are left off the number line itself, because they might be mistaken for the graph.

For Problems 1 through 20, draw a number-line graph of the inequality.

1. $x > 8$ 2. $x < 10$

3. $x \leq 2$ 4. $x \geq 4$

5. $x < -7$ 6. $x > -5$

7. $x \geq 9$ 8. $x \leq 12$

9. $x \leq -2.6$ 10. $x \geq -8.3$

11. $x < 0$ 12. $x \geq 0$

13. $y > 100$ 14. $p < 2000$

15. $z \geq -3.146$ 16. $r \leq -1.68$

17. $5 < x$ 18. $3 > x$

19. $-11 \geq x$ 20. $-7 \leq x$

For Problems 21 through 40, write an inequality for the given graph.

37.

$x \geq -13$

38.

$x \leq 55$

39.

$x \leq 0$

40.

$x > 0$

15.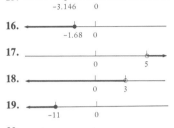

16.

17.

18.

19.

20.

For Problems 41 through 50, write an inequality and draw the graph.

41. *x* is more than 9. $x > 9$ 42. *x* is less than 18. $x < 18$

43. *x* is less than -100. $x < -100$ 44. *x* is more than -5. $x > -5$

45. *x* is at least 10. $x \geq 10$ 46. *x* is at most 13. $x \leq 13$

47. *x* is at most 15. $x \leq 15$ 48. *x* is at least 1. $x \geq 1$

49. *x* is positive. $x > 0$ 50. *x* is negative. $x < 0$

41.–50. See Additional Answers.

Problems 49 and 50 make students stop and think about the definitions of positive and negative numbers.

13-2 | SOLVING INEQUALITIES

The inequality

$$3 < 7$$

tells the *order* in which 3 and 7 appear on the number line.

The number 3 comes first, then the number 7, as you read from left to right. Suppose that you add 2 to each member of the inequality.

$$3 + 2 < 7 + 2$$

$$5 < 9$$

The new inequality is still true. Adding 2 just moves each number an equal distance along the line. The points are still in the same order.

Adding the same negative number (or subtracting the same number) also leaves the points in the same order.

$$3 + (-2) < 7 + (-2)$$

$$1 < 5$$

Time: $1\frac{1}{2}$ days, with Section 13–1

Chalkboard Examples:

First day:
1. Solve and plot: $3x + 7 < 40$
    Ans.: $x < 11$

2. Solve and plot: $9 - 4x \leq 37$
    Ans.: $x \geq -7$

3. Solve and plot: $25 + 2x > 8$
    Ans.: $x > -8.5$

Second day:
Caterer Problem—A caterer has an order to make 100 sandwiches. Their workers can make 3 sandwiches per minute.
a. Write an expression for the number of sandwiches left to be made after *x* minutes.
b. Write an inequality that says that the number of sandwiches left to be made is less than 20. Then solve the inequality to find the range of times when the number is less than 20.

Solution:

a. x = no. of minutes.
   $100 - 3x$ = no. of sandwiches left to be made.

b. $100 - 3x < 20$
   $-3x < -80$
   $x > 26\frac{2}{3}$
   More than $26\frac{2}{3}$ minutes

Assignment:

Day 1: Exercise 13–2, #1–19 odd or 2–20 even (Takes about 20 minutes.)
Exercise 13–1, #31–49 odd or 32–50 even (if no problems like these have yet been worked)

Day 2: Exercise 13–2, #21–45 odd or 22–46 even (Takes about 40 minutes. Start in class, if possible.)

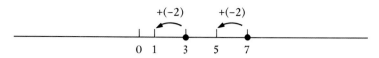

The same thing happens with $>$, $\leq$, and $\geq$. These facts are summarized in the following property.

PROPERTY

ADDITION PROPERTY OF ORDER
Given any real numbers a, b, and c.

$$\text{If } a < b, \text{ then } a + c < b + c.$$
$$\text{If } a > b, \text{ then } a + c > b + c.$$

The order also stays the same if you *multiply* each member by 2.

$$3 < 7$$
$$3 \cdot 2 < 7 \cdot 2$$
$$6 < 14$$

The order stays the same.

But if you multiply by a *negative* number, like -2, the order *reverses!*

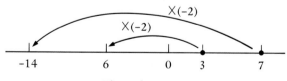

The order *reverses!*

Thus if you want to multiply each member of an inequality by a *negative* number, you must *reverse* the inequality sign.

$$3 < 7$$
$$3(-2) > 7(-2)$$
$$-6 > -14$$

These facts are summarized in the following property.

PROPERTY

> **MULTIPLICATION PROPERTY OF ORDER**
> Given any real numbers a, b, and c.
>
> If $a < b$, then:
> $ac < bc$,   if c is positive;
> $ac > bc$,   if c is negative.
>
> If $a > b$, then:
> $ac > bc$,   if c is positive;
> $ac < bc$,   if c is negative.

These two properties can be used to solve inequalities like

$$5x - 7 > 53.$$

You do whatever is needed to get x by itself. The process is just the same as that for solving equations. But you must remember to *reverse* the inequality signs if you multiply (or divide) by a negative number.

Objective:
For an inequality such as $5x - 7 > 53$, find the values of x that make it true and draw the graph.

EXAMPLE 1

Solve and graph: $5x - 7 > 53$.

- - - - -   - - - - -

	Think These Reasons

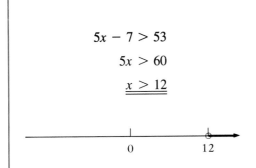

$5x - 7 > 53$ Write the given inequality.

$5x > 60$ Add 7 to each member.

$\underline{x > 12}$ Divide each member by 5. The order stays the same, since you did not multiply by a negative number. (Dividing by 5 is like multiplying by $\frac{1}{5}$.)

Draw the graph.

EXAMPLE 2

Solve and graph: $13 - 2x \geq 22$.

$$13 - 2x \geq 22$$ — Write the given inequality.

$$-2x \geq 9$$ — Add -13 to each member.

$$\underline{\underline{x \leq -4.5}}$$ — Divide each member by -2 and reverse the inequality sign. (The order reverses when you multiply by a negative number. Dividing by -2 is like multiplying by $-\frac{1}{2}$, so you must reverse the inequality sign.)

Draw the graph.

$$-4.5 \quad 0$$

EXAMPLE 3

Solve and graph: $12 - 4(x - 5) < 8 + x$.

$$12 - 4(x - 5) < 8 + x$$ — Write the given inequality.

$$12 - 4x + 20 < 8 + x$$ — Distribute -4.

$$-4x + 32 < 8 + x$$ — Combine like terms.

$$-5x < -24$$ — Add $-x$ and -32 to each member.

$$\underline{\underline{x > 4.8}}$$ — Divide each member by -5 and reverse the inequality sign.

Draw the graph.

$$0 \quad 4.8$$

EXAMPLE 4

Solve and graph: $3x + 11 \leq 3(x + 7)$.

$$3x + 11 \leq 3(x + 7)$$ — Write the given inequality.

$$3x + 11 \leq 3x + 21$$ — Distribute 3.

$$11 \leq 21$$ — Add $-3x$ to each member.

$$\underline{\underline{S = \{\text{real numbers}\}}}$$ — $11 \leq 21$ is *always* true! So you shade in the entire number line.

Draw the graph.

$$0$$

EXAMPLE 5

Appliance Service Problem   If you work as an appliance repair person, you charge a certain amount per hour worked plus a fixed amount for the service call. Suppose that the rate is $20 per hour, plus $25 for the call.

a. Define a variable for the number of hours worked, and write an expression for the total number of dollars the customer would pay you.
b. What range of times could you work to earn up to and including $100?

- - - - -   - - - - -

a.   Let x = number of hours.   Define a variable.

   $\underline{20x + 25}$ = number of dollars. $20x$ for the $20 per hour, plus 25 for the fixed charge.

b. $20x + 25 \leq 100$ The number of dollars is up to and including 100, which means less than or equal to 100.

      $20x \leq 75$ Subtract 25 from each member.

      $x \leq 3.75$ Divide each member by 20.

   $\underline{\text{Up to and including 3 h 45 min.}}$ Answer the question.

ORAL PRACTICE

Tell what you would do to transform the inequality so that x is by itself, and tell whether or not the order reverses.

EXAMPLES

Answers:

i. $x + 3 > 7$ i.   Subtract 3. Order does not reverse.
ii. $-5x > 35$ ii.   Divide by -5. Order does reverse.

A. $x + 2 > 5$ Subtract 2. No   B. $x + 6 < 2$ Subtract 6. No

C. $x - 8 < 7$ Add 8. No   D. $x - 4 > 1$ Add 4. No

E. $2x > 5$ Divide by 2. No   F. $6x < 2$ Divide by 6. No.

G. $-8x < 7$ Divide by -8. Yes   H. $-4x > 1$ Divide by -4. Yes

I. $3x \geq -7$ Divide by 3. No   J. $-5 + x \leq 3$ Add 5. No

K. $-x \leq 3$ Multiply by -1. Yes   L. $6x < -12$ Divide by 6. No

M. $\frac{2}{3}x < 6$ Multiply by $\frac{3}{2}$. No   N. $-\frac{3}{4}x > 24$ Multiply by $-\frac{4}{3}$. Yes

O. $x - \frac{5}{8} \geq \frac{3}{8}$ Add $\frac{5}{8}$. No   P. $x + \frac{2}{3} \leq \frac{5}{3}$ Subtract $\frac{2}{3}$. No

EXERCISE 13-2

Problem Notes:

In problems such as 17, the variable remains on the right side after transformation, $-67 < x$. The safest way to get the graph correct is to realize that x is always the *subject* of the sentence. Thus, $-67 < x$ should be read "x is greater than -67."

In problems such as 29 in which $16x \leq -16$, some fuzzy thinkers will reverse the inequality because "it was negative." They should be made to realize it is the sign of number you multiply or divide by that determines order reversal and not the sign of any particular number in the inequality.

1.–42. See Additional Answers.

For each inequality:

a.   solve it—that is, transform it so that x is by itself;

b.   sketch the graph.

1. $5x + 4 < 39$ $x < 7$

2. $6x + 5 > 53$ $x > 8$

3. $3x - 7 \geq 26$ $x \geq 11$

4. $2x - 13 \leq 95$ $x \leq 54$

5. $13 - 4x < 25$ $x > -3$

6. $5 - 3x > 56$ $x < -17$

7. $\frac{1}{3}x + 5 \leq 7$ $x \leq 6$

8. $\frac{1}{5}x + 3 \geq 9$ $x \geq 30$

9. $-\frac{1}{6}x + 5 > 8$ $x < -18$

10. $-\frac{1}{3}x + 6 < 10$ $x > -12$

11. $\frac{2}{3}x - 4 < 14$ $x < 27$

12. $\frac{3}{4}x - 5 > 7$ $x > 16$

13. $8 - \frac{3}{5}x \leq 23$ $x \geq -25$

14. $6 - \frac{5}{2}x \geq 26$ $x \leq -8$

15. $5x \geq 5x + 11$ $S = \emptyset$

16. $22 \leq 4 + 5x$ $x \geq 3.6$

17. $71 > 4 - x$ $x > -67$

18. $13 < 17 - x$ $x < 4$

19. $16x + 3 + 4x \leq 103$ $x \leq 5$

20. $18x + 7 + 7x \geq 107$ $x \geq 4$

21. $-5x + 17 - 8x > 56$ $x < -3$

22. $-3x + 19 - 5x < 91$ $x > -9$

23. $5(x + 3) - 2x \geq -21$ $x \geq -12$

24. $6(x + 2) - 4x \leq 48$ $x \leq 18$

25. $2(x + 3) - 5(x - 1) > 32$ $x < -7$

26. $3(x + 4) - 5(x - 1) < 5$ $x > 6$

27. $0 < 4(6 - x) + 7x$ $x > -8$

28. $0 > 5(7 - x) + 12x$ $x < -5$

29. $7x \leq -16 - 9x$ $x \leq -1$

30. $11x \geq -400 - 9x$ $x \geq -20$

31. $4x \leq 37 + 4x$ $S = \{\text{real nos.}\}$

32. $5x + 7 \geq 4x + 7$ $x \geq 0$

33. $5x + 8 > 7x + 8$ $x < 0$

34. $5x + 7 > 5x + 8$ $S = \emptyset$

35. $5(9 - x) \leq 4(x + 18)$ $x \geq -3$

36. $7(2 - x) \geq 3(x + 8)$ $x \leq -1$

37. $2[1 - 3(x + 2)] > -x$ $x < -2$

38. $3(1 + x) < 2[3(x + 2) - (x + 1)]$ $x > -7$

39. $6(x + 4) - (x + 3) \geq x - 1$ $x \geq -5.5$

40. $3(3x + 1) - (x - 1) \leq 6(x + 10)$ $x \leq 28$

Two basic problems of algebra are (1) given x, find an expression's value, and (2) given an expression's value, find x. In Problems 41 and 42 you will do these two things with linear expressions.

41. For the linear expression $5x - 7$:
   a. evaluate it if:
      i. x is 6;   23   ii. x is -2; -17
   b. find x if the expression is:
      i. equal to 21; $x = 5.6$ ii. more than 8 (draw the graph); $x > 3$
      iii. at most 17 (draw the graph). $x \le 4.8$

42. For the linear expression $3 - 4x$:
   a. evaluate it if:
      i. x is 7; -25 ii. x is -2;   11
   b. Find x if the expression is:
      i. equal to 19; $x = -4$ ii. less than 23 (draw the graph); $x > -5$
      iii. at least -21 (draw the graph). $x \le 6$

43. ***Plumber's Fee Problem*** Suppose that you go into business doing plumbing repairs. You decide to charge $25 per hour, plus a fixed fee of $30 for the service call.
   a. Define a variable for the number of hours worked, and write an expression for the number of dollars the customer would pay. x = no. of hr. $25x + 30$
   b. Write an inequality which says that your charge is over $100. Solve it to find the range of times for which your charge would be over $100. Over 2.8 h

44. ***Slide Problem*** The amusement park charges 75 cents to rent a mat plus 50¢ each time you ride the big slide.
   a. Define a variable for the number of times you ride. Then write an expression for the total amount you pay x = no. of rides $75 + 50x$
   b. Write an inequality stating that you can afford to pay no more than $6.25. Then solve it to find the range of times you could slide. No more than 11 times

45. ***Phoebe's Loan Problem*** Phoebe Small borrows $50 from her parents to buy a dress she really likes. In return for her painting the garage, her parents agree to subtract $4 from what she owes for each hour she works. For what number of hours will her debt be below $30? Over 5 h

46. ***Desert Travel Problem*** Kara Vann crosses the desert on a camel. She has 200 miles to go, and she travels 30 miles per day. For what range of days will her distance remaining be more than 80 miles? Less than 4 days

Problems 43–46 are quite easy and involve nothing harder than what was involved in the word problems of Chapter 2, except that these involve inequalitites. The word problems are distributed throughout the chapter rather than concentrated at the end of the chapter.

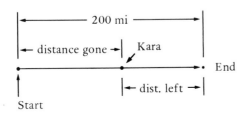

13-3 | COMPOUND INEQUALITIES

Time: 2 days

Chalkboard Examples:

First day:
1. Graph: $x \leq 4$ and $x \geq -2$
   Ans.:

2. Graph: $1 < x < 10$
   Ans.:

3. Graph: $x < -8$ or $x \geq -3$
   Ans.:

Have students work Examples 1–5 while they are still in class.

Second day:
Have students put homework on the board, then do the Oral Practice problems. These work better the second day on this section.

Assignment:

Day 1: Exercise 13-3, #1–23 odd or 2–24 even

Day 2: Exercise 13-3, #25–45 odd or 26–46 even, with 47 optional

You have learned how to graph inequalities like $x > 7$. Suppose that you must graph the values of x for which either

$$x > 7 \quad \text{or} \quad x \leq -2$$

is true. To see what the graph would look like, first draw each part separately.

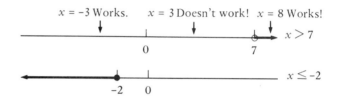

A number such as -3 or 8 *does* satisfy $x > 7$ or $x \leq -2$. Since the conjunction between the two parts is *or*, a value of x need satisfy only *one* part of the inequality. Only numbers like 3, which satisfy *neither* part, are not solutions of $x > 7$ or $x \leq -2$. The graph of this inequality would be the two parts drawn on the *same* number line.

The result is called the *union* of the two graphs, since they have been put together (united). Note, however, that the two intervals are not connected.

DEFINITION

> **UNION**
> The **union** of sets A and B, abbreviated $A \cup B$, is the set of numbers that are either in set A or in set B.

The inequality $x > 7$ or $x \leq -2$ is called a *compound* inequality. Each part is called a *clause*, just like clauses of a compound sentence.

Suppose that the conjunction in a compound inequality is *and*, such as in

$$x > -1 \quad \text{and} \quad x < 5.$$

The graphs of the two clauses are shown.

The conjunction *and* means that *both* clauses must be true. So only numbers like 2, which are *between* −1 and 5, will satisfy the inequality. Numbers like −3 and 6 do not satisfy the compound inequality, even though they do satisfy one clause of it. The graph will be the part of the number line where the two graphs overlap.

Because of this overlapping feature, the result is called the *intersection* of the two graphs. Because of this overlapping feature, the result is called the *intersection* of the two graphs.

DEFINITION

> **INTERSECTION**
> The **intersection** of sets A and B, abbreviated $A \cap B$, is the set of numbers that are in *both* sets.

For your future reference, here are the precise meanings of the words *and* and *or* as used in mathematics.

MEANING

> ***AND* AND *OR***
> The statement A *and* B *are true* means *both* of them must be true.
>
> The statement A *or* B *is true* means at least *one* of them must be true, but not necessarily both.

There is another way to write a compound inequality such as $x > -1$ and $x < 5$. Since x must be *between* −1 and 5, you simply *put* it there:

$$-1 < x < 5.$$

The lesser end point, -1, is on the left and the greater end point, 5, is on the right. The variable x is in between, and both inequality signs have the *same* direction. This inequality can be read:

$$-1 \text{ is less than } x, \text{ which is less than } 5,$$

or, more simply,

$$x \text{ is between } -1 \text{ and } 5.$$

If the end points are included, as in

$$3 \leq x \leq 10,$$

then the inequality is read

"x is between 3 and 10, inclusive."

Its graph would look like this.

For your future reference, here are precise definitions of *between* and *inclusive*.

DEFINITION

> **BETWEEN AND INCLUSIVE**
> x is **between** a and b means
> $$a < x < b.$$
> x is between a and b, **inclusive,** means
> $$a \leq x \leq b.$$

Objectives:
1. Given a compound inequality, solve it and draw the graph.
2. Given a graph or words, write a compound inequality.

Cover the answers as you work these examples.

EXAMPLE 1

Draw the graph of $x > 5$ and $x \leq 8$.

– – – – –

Think These Reasons

Since the conjunction is *and,* draw the intersection—that is, x is *between* the end points 5 and 8, including 8.

EXAMPLE 2

Sketch the graph of $3x + 7 < -8$ or $5 - 2x \leq -9$.

- - - - -

			- - - - -

$3x + 7 < -8 \quad$ or $\quad 5 - 2x \leq -9$ 　　Write the given inequality.

$3x < -15 \quad$ or $\quad -2x \leq -14$ 　　Subtract 7 for the first clause. Subtract 5 for the second clause.

$x < -5 \quad$ or $\quad x \geq 7$ 　　Divide by 3 for the first clause. Divide by -2 and reverse the order for the second clause.

Draw the union of the two graphs.

EXAMPLE 3

Sketch the graph of $-6 < 5x - 2 < 13$.

- - - - -　　　　　　　　　　　　　　　- - - - -

$-6 < 5x - 2 < 13$ 　　Write the given inequality.

$-4 < 5x < 15$ 　　Add 2 to all *three* members.

$-0.8 < x < 3$ 　　Divide all three members by 5.

Shade *between* the end points, because x is between -0.8 and 3.

EXAMPLE 4

Write a compound inequality.

- - - - -　　　　　　　　　　　　　　　- - - - -

$\underline{x < -7 \quad \text{or} \quad x \geq -3}$ 　　Use *or,* since x cannot be on both parts of the graph at the same time. -3 is included; -7 is not.

EXAMPLE 5

If *x* is between −5 and 3, inclusive, write an inequality and draw its graph.

- - - - -

$-5 \leq x \leq 3$ Put *x* between −5 and 3.

−5   0   3   Shade between −5 and 3. Include the end points.

ORAL PRACTICE

Tell whether or not the graph is correct. If not, tell *why* not.

A. $2 < x < 5$
Correct

B. $3 \leq x \leq 7$
Incorrect. End points should be solid.

C. $-2 < x < 3$
Incorrect. Lower end point is −2.

D. $x > 5$ or $x < 2$
Incorrect. Graph should go *outward* from end points.

E. $x < 5$ and $x > 2$
Correct

F. $x > 3$ or $x < -1$
Correct

G. $4 \leq x \leq 6$
Incorrect. Graph should be *between* the end points.

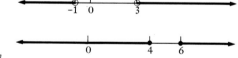

H. $x \leq 4$ and $x \geq 6$
Incorrect. Graph is ∅.

I. $x \leq 4$ or $x \geq 6$
Correct

J.   *x* is between 2 and 5.
Incorrect. There should be *open* circles at the end points.

K.   *x* is between 2 and 5, inclusive.
Correct

L. $9 < x < 10$ (Think!)

Incorrect. Scale puts 9 too close to the origin.

M. $3 > x > 5$

Incorrect. The inequality cannot be $3 > x > 5$ because $3 < 5$.

N. $x < 5$ or $x > 3$

Correct

O. $x < 3$ and $x > 5$

Correct

EXERCISE 13-3

For Problems 1 through 20, transform the inequality (if necessary) and sketch the graph.

1. $x \geq 5$ and $x < 9$

2. $x < -2$ and $x \geq -6$

3. $x < -2$ or $x \geq 6$

4. $x \geq 8$ or $x < 1$

5. $-7 \leq x \leq 2$

6. $-4 < x < 7$

7. $3x + 5 < 20$ or $2x - 1 > 13$

8. $3x - 4 \geq 17$ or $4x + 7 \leq 19$

9. $4 - 5x > -13$ and $3 - x \leq 10$

10. $7 - 2x > 15$ and $5 - x \leq 16$

11. $6x + 7 \leq 1$ or $6x + 7 > 28$

12. $3x + 5 < -13$ or $3x + 5 \geq 2$

13. $5 < x - 7 < 9$

14. $2 < x + 3 \leq 7$

15. $-3 \leq 2x + 11 \leq 9$

16. $-8 \leq 5x + 7 \leq 25$

17. $15 < 6 - 10x \leq 37$

18. $6 < 10 - 2x < 14$

19. $x + 5 > 19$ or $x + 5 < 24$

20. $x - 3 < 7$ and $x - 3 > 13$

For Problems 21 through 32, write a compound inequality for the graph shown.

21.

$-2 < x \leq 3$

23.

$x \leq -3$ or $x \geq 4$

22.

$x < 3$ or $x \geq 7$

24.

$-5 < x < 3$

Problem Notes:

In these problems, a sketch is called for rather than a plot. Thus, no scale need be shown on the number line. The numbers should be placed reasonably, however. For instance, if $-4 < x < 7$, as in Problem 6, then -4 should be closer to the origin than 7. In addition to saving time, this procedure helps increase students' geometric perception of relative length.

1.–20. See Additional Answers.

  7. $x < 5$ or $x > 7$

  8. $x \geq 7$ or $x \leq 3$

  9. $x < 3.4$ and $x \geq -7$

10. $x < -4$ and $x \geq -11$

11. $x \leq -1$ or $x > 3.5$

12. $x < -6$ or $x \geq -1$

13. $12 < x < 16$ **14.** $-1 < x \leq 4$

15. $-7 \leq x \leq -1$ **16.** $-3 \leq x \leq 3.6$

17. $-0.9 > x \geq -3.1$

18. $2 > x > -2$

19. $x > 14$ or $x < 19$, $S = R$

20. $x < 10$ and $x > 16$, $S = \emptyset$

Problems 13–18 have inequalities in which an expression appears between two numbers. Words such as "add 7 to each member" are appropriate here as they have been for earlier equations and inequalities. The word *each* implies three members in this case. The word *members* is used throughout the text rather than *sides*.

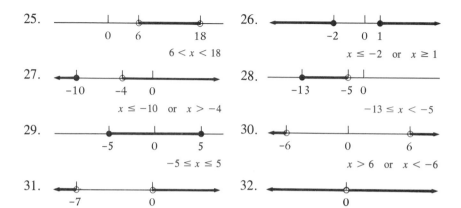

25. $6 < x < 18$

26. $x \leq -2$ or $x \geq 1$

27. $x \leq -10$ or $x > -4$

28. $-13 \leq x < -5$

29. $-5 \leq x \leq 5$

30. $x > 6$ or $x < -6$

31. $x < -7$ or $x > 0$

32. $x > 0$ or $x < 0$

For Problems 33 through 40, write an inequality and draw the graph.

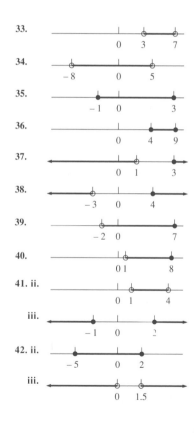

33. x is between 3 and 7. $3 < x < 7$ 34. x is between -8 and 5. $-8 < x < 5$

35. x is between -1 and 3, inclusive. $-1 \leq x \leq 3$

36. x is between 4 and 9, inclusive. $4 \leq x \leq 9$

37. x is at least 3 or x is less than 1. $x \geq 3$ or $x < 1$

38. x is at least 4 or x is less than -3. $x \geq 4$ or $x < -3$

39. x is more than -2 and x is at most 7. $x > -2$ and $x \leq 7$

40. x is more than 1 and x is at most 8. $x > 1$ and $x \leq 8$

41. For the linear expression $5x - 7$:
   a. evaluate it if x is 4;   13
   b. find x if the expression is:
      i. equal to 8; $x = 3$
      ii. between -2 and 13 (draw the graph); $1 < x < 4$
      iii. at least 3 or at most -12 (draw the graph). $x \geq 2$ or $x \leq -1$

42. For the linear expression $3 - 4x$:
   a. evaluate it if x is -9;   39
   b. find x if the expression is:
      i. equal to 31; $x = -7$
      ii. between -5 and 23, inclusive (draw the graph); $2 \geq x \geq -5$
      iii. more than 3 or less than -3 (draw the graph). $x < 0$ or $x > 1.5$

43. **Baby's Weight Problem** Suppose that a baby weighs 7 pounds at birth, and gains 0.3 pound a week thereafter.
   a. Define a variable for the number of weeks and write an expression for the baby's weight. x = no. of weeks; $7 + 0.3x$
   b. For what range of weeks will the baby be between 19 and 28 pounds?   Between 40 and 70 weeks
   c. The family's baby scale goes up to 25 pounds. For what range of weeks will they be able to use this scale?   Up to 60 weeks

44. *Savings Problem*   Penny Pincher gets a present of $100. She puts it
    into a savings account. Thereafter, she adds $4 more at the end of
    each week.
    a. Define a variable for the number of weeks and write an expression
       for the number of dollars she has put into her account. $x =$ no. of weeks
       $100 + 4x$
    b. The savings account pays a certain interest rate when the amount   **44. b.** From 25 up to 100 weeks
       in it is from $200 up to, but not including, $500. For what num-
       bers of weeks will Penny's amount be in this range?
    c. The interest rate is much higher when the balance is over $1000.
       For what range of weeks will the amount be over $1000?
       Over 225 weeks (226 and up)

45. *Car Wash and Fill Problem*   When you fill your gas tank, a car
    wash charges $5 to wash your car. Gas costs $1.50 per gallon. For
    what range of gallons will your total bill be between $11 and $20,
    inclusive?   From 4 to 10 gal, inclusive

46. *Chartered Bus Problem*   A chartered bus travels 60 miles per hour
    as it makes the 500-mile trip from El Paso to Scorpion Gulch. Let t
    be the number of hours since the bus left El Paso. The bus driver
    must contact the bus station when they are between 50 and 100 mi
    from Scorpion Gulch. For what range of values of t will this be?
    Between $6\frac{2}{3}$ h and $7\frac{1}{2}$ h.

47. *Venn Diagrams*   Intersections or unions of sets can be represented   Problem 47 on Venn diagrams is optional.
    by overlapping circles. Suppose that   The topic already may be familiar to your stu-
                                                                              dents.

$$\text{Set } A = \{\text{girls in the school}\}$$

$$\text{Set } B = \{\text{athletes in the school}\}.$$

The following diagrams could be used to represent the two sets.

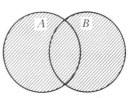

Intersection $A \cap B$. Student   Union $A \cup B$. Student
is a girl *and* an athlete.   is a girl *or* an athlete.

The pictures are called **Venn diagrams.** In this problem, you will
use them to represent unions and intersections of *three* sets. For each
part below, copy the diagram and shade the union or intersection indicated.

a.   **b.**   **c.**   **d.**
$Q \cap R$ $S \cap Q$ $R \cup S$ $(R \cup S) \cup Q$

a. $Q \cap R$ **b.** $S \cap Q$
c. $R \cup S$ **d.** $(R \cup S) \cup Q$
e. $(Q \cap R) \cap S$ **f.** $(Q \cap R) \cup S$
g. $(Q \cup R) \cap S$

e.   **f.**   **g.**

$(Q \cap R) \cap S$ $(Q \cap R) \cup S$ $(Q \cup R) \cap S$

13-4 | **INEQUALITIES CONTAINING ABSOLUTE VALUE**

In the last section you learned that an inequality such as

$$-3 < x < 3$$

can be read "x is between -3 and 3." When a variable or expression is between two numbers that are *opposites* of each other, there is another way of writing the inequality.

Since x is between -3 and 3, its *distance* from the origin is less than 3. This distance is the *absolute value* of x. So the inequality $-3 < x < 3$ is equivalent to

$$|x| < 3.$$

The same thought process can be used in the other direction to transform an inequality with an absolute value sign to one without. For instance,

$$|x - 7| < 5$$

really says that $x - 7$ is between -5 and 5. So you can write

$$-5 < x - 7 < 5.$$

Adding 7 to all three members, as in Section 9.3, gives

$$2 < x < 12.$$

The graph would look like this.

Note that the 5 and 7 in the original inequality also show up on the graph. You can think of $|x - 7| < 5$ as: x is less than 5 units away from 7.

What if the inequality sign had been $>$ instead of $<$? For instance, how would you transform

$$|x + 4| > 6$$

to eliminate the absolute value sign? The inequality says that $x + 4$ is *not* between -6 and 6. So there are two possibilities,

$$x + 4 > 6 \quad \text{or} \quad x + 4 < -6.$$

This is a compound inequality like you solved in the last section. Subtracting 4 from each member of both inequalities gives

$$x > 2 \quad \text{or} \quad x < -10.$$

The graph would look like this.

x is *not* between -10 and 2.

In this section you will solve and graph absolute value inequalities such as these.

Objective:

Be able to solve and graph inequalities such as $|x - 7| < 5$, in which the absolute value of an expression is less than or greater than a constant.

Cover the answers as you work these examples.

EXAMPLE 1

Solve and graph: $|x + 4| < 7$.

$- - - -$ $- - - -$

	Think These Reasons
$|x + 4| < 7$	Write the given inequality.
$-7 < x + 4 < 7$	$x + 4$ is between -7 and 7.
$-11 < x < 3$	Subtract 4 from all three members.

—————————————————
   -11 0   3   Draw the graph.

EXAMPLE 2

Solve and graph: $|4x - 17| \geq 25$.

$- - - -$ $- - - -$

Third day:
More board work is appropriate, especially for Problems 21–30 and for word problems.
Fourth day:
Test.

Assignments:

Day 1: Exercise 13–4, #1–19 odd
Day 2: Exercise 13–4, #12–20 even and 21–33 odd or 22–34 even
Day 3: In preparation for test:
Exercise 13–3, #10, 12, 14, 46 or 9, 11, 13, 45, and Exercise 13–4, #10, 14, 16, 18, 36 or 9, 13, 15, 17, 35
Day 4: After test:
Study Section 13–5.
Work Examples 1 and 2.
Work Exercise 13–5, #1, 3, 5.

$|4x - 17| \geq 25$	Write the given inequality.
$4x - 17 \geq 25$ or $4x - 17 \leq -25$	$4x - 17$ is *not* between -25 and 25. So there are *two* possibilities.
$4x \geq 42$ or $4x \leq -8$	Add 17 to each member of both clauses.
$x \geq 10.5$ or $x \leq -2$	Divide each member by 4.

Draw the graph.

-2 0 .... 10.5

EXAMPLE 3

Solve and graph: $|x + 5| < -9$.

- - - - -   - - - - -

$|x + 5| < -9$ Write the given inequality.

<u>No solutions.</u>   Absolute values are never negative. So $|x + 5|$ cannot be *less* than -9.

                                       $S = \emptyset$

                                            0   Draw an empty number line. Write the empty set symbol.

EXAMPLE 4

Solve and graph: $|x + 7| > -3$.

- - - - -   - - - - -

$|x + 7| > -3$ Write the given inequality.

<u>$S = \{\text{real numbers}\}$.</u>   Absolute values are never negative, so $|x + 7|$ is *always* greater than -3.

                                            0   Fill in the entire number line.

EXAMPLE 5

Gas Station Problem   A driver starts out across the desert, going a steady 1.2 kilometers per minute. Last Chance Gas Station is 70 km from the starting point. The driver is within 5 km of the gas station when the absolute value of the *difference* between this distance from the start and 70 km is *less* than 5 km. For what range of times will the driver be within 5 km of the gas station?

- - - - -   - - - - -

Let x = number of minutes the driver has been going.

$1.2x$ = number of kilometers from start (since $d = rt$).

$|1.2x - 70|$ = number of kilometers from gas station.

$\|1.2x - 70\| < 5$	Write an inequality.
$-5 < 1.2x - 70 < 5$	Transform to remove the absolute value sign.
$65 < 1.2x < 75$	Add 70 to each member.
$54.2 < x < 62.5$	Divide each member by 1.2.
<u>Between 54.2 and 62.5 min.</u>	Answer the question.

From these examples you should be able to understand why the following conclusion is true.

CONCLUSION

TRANSFORMING ABSOLUTE VALUE INEQUALITIES
Assume that c is a positive constant.

The inequality $|\text{expression}| < c$ means:
expression is *between* $-c$ and c; that is,

$$-c < \text{expression} < c.$$

The inequality $|\text{expression}| > c$ means:
expression is *not* between $-c$ and c; that is,

$$\text{expression} > c \quad \text{or} \quad \text{expression} < -c.$$

ORAL PRACTICE

Tell in words what the inequality says.

EXAMPLES

Answers

i. $|x + 3| < 5$ i. $x + 3$ is between -5 and 5.
ii. $|x - 2| > 7$ ii. $x - 2$ is *not* between -7 and 7.

A. $|x - 4| < 9$ B. $|x + 7| > 8$

A. $x - 4$ is between -9 and 9.

B. $x + 7$ is *not* between -8 and 8.

C. $x + 5$ is between -13 and 13, inclusive.

D. $x - 8$ is *not* between -3 and 3, inclusive.

E. $2x - 7$ is between -6 and 6, inclusive.

F. $6x + 2$ is between -5 and 5.

G. $-9 < x - 4 < 9$

H. $x + 7 > 8$ or $x + 7 < -8$

I. $-13 \leq x + 5 \leq 13$

J. $x - 8 \geq 3$ or $x - 8 \leq -3$

K. $-6 \leq 2x - 7 \leq 6$

L. $6x + 2 > 5$ or $6x + 2 < -5$

C. $|x + 5| \leq 13$

D. $|x - 8| \geq 3$

E. $|2x - 7| \leq 6$

F. $|6x + 2| < 5$

Tell the result of transforming the inequality to remove the absolute value sign.

EXAMPLES

		Answers
i.	$|x + 3| < 5$	i. $-5 < x + 3 < 5$
ii.	$|x - 2| > 7$	ii. $x - 2 > 7$ or $x - 2 < -7$

G. $|x - 4| < 9$ H. $|x + 7| > 8$

I. $|x + 5| \leq 13$ J. $|x - 8| \geq 3$

K. $|2x - 7| \leq 6$ L. $|6x + 2| > 5$

The inequality shown came from transforming an absolute value inequality. Tell what that absolute value inequality was.

EXAMPLES

		Answers
i.	$-2 < x + 3 < 2$	i. $|x + 3| < 2$
ii.	$x + 5 \geq 9$ or $x + 5 \leq -9$	ii. $|x + 5| \geq 9$

M. $|x + 8| < 7$ N. $|x - 5| > 10$

O. $|3x + 7| \geq 4$ P. $|2x - 5| \leq 12$

M. $-7 < x + 8 < 7$

N. $x - 5 > 10$ or $x - 5 < -10$

O. $3x + 7 \geq 4$ or $3x + 7 \leq -4$

P. $-12 \leq 2x - 5 \leq 12$

EXERCISE 13-4

Problem Notes:

For Problems 1–20, be sure students show the transformation that removes the absolute value sign. Beware of illegal transformations such as in Problem 5, going from $|x - 3| > 8$ to $|x| > 11$. The numbers inside the absolute value sign are inaccessible via addition or subtraction, because the absolute value of a sum is not equal to the sum of the absolute values. (The triangle inequality would apply.) The other prevalent error is ignoring the absolute value sign completely.

1.–30. See Additional Answers.

For Problems 1 through 20, transform the inequality to eliminate the absolute value signs. Then sketch the graph.

1. $|x| < 7$ $-7 < x < 7$

2. $|x| > 10$ $x > 10$ or $x < -10$

3. $|x| \geq 13$ $x \geq 13$ or $x \leq -13$

4. $|x| \leq 300$ $-300 \leq x \leq 300$

5. $|x - 3| > 8$ $x > 11$ or $x < -5$

6. $|x - 13| < 7$ $6 < x < 20$

7. $|x + 7| \leq 2$ $-9 \leq x \leq -5$

8. $|x + 4| \geq 9$ $x \geq 5$ or $x \leq -13$

9. $|5x - 4| > 34$ $x > 7.6$ or $x < -6$

10. $|2x - 7| < 19$ $-6 < x < 13$

11. $|2x + 15| < 11$ $-13 < x < -2$

12. $|5x + 21| > 34$ $x > 2.6$ or $x < -11$

13. $|9 - 4x| \leq 15$ $6 \geq x \geq -1.5$

14. $|3 - x| \geq 15$ $x \leq -12$ or $x \geq 18$

15. $|7x + 5| < -8$ $S = \emptyset$ 16. $|8x + 1| > -2$ $S = R$

17. $|21x + 4| \geq -2$ $S = \{$real nos.$\}$ 18. $|7x - 4| \leq -5$ $S = \emptyset$

19. $|3x - 12| > 0$ $x > 4$ or $x < 4$ 20. $|4x + 20| > 0$ $x > -5$ or $x < -5$

For Problems 21 through 30, first transform to the form

$$|\text{expression}| < \text{constant}.$$

(The sign could be $>$, $\leq$, or $\geq$.) Then transform and sketch the graph, as in Problems 1 through 20.

For Problems 21–30, be sure students realize that the inequality must be transformed to the form of Problems 1–20 before the absolute value can be removed.

21. $|x| + 3 < 17$ $-14 < x < 14$ 22. $|x| - 4 > 9$ $x > 13$ or $x < -13$

23. $5 + |x - 4| \geq 16$ $x \geq 15$ or $x \leq -7$ 24. $6 + |8 - x| \leq 10$ $12 \geq x \geq 4$

25. $3|x + 8| > 42$ $x > 6$ or $x < -22$ 26. $5|x - 2| < 45$ $-7 < x < 11$

27. $9 - |2x + 1| \leq 3$ $x \geq 2.5$ or $x \leq -3.5$ 28. $8 - |5x + 13| \geq 1$ $-4 \leq x \leq -1.2$

29. $5 \leq |x + 7| - 2$ $x \geq 0$ or $x \leq -14$ 30. $13 \geq |x - 2| - 6$ $-17 \leq x \leq 21$

Two basic problems of algebra are (1) given x, find an expression's value, and (2) given an expression's value, find x. In Problems 31 and 32 you will do these two things with absolute value expressions.

31.   For the expression $|x - 5|$:
   a.   evaluate it when:
      i. x is 13;   8
      ii. x is -2;   7
   b.   find x if the expression is:
      i.   equal to 9; $x = 14$ or $x = -4$
      ii.   less than 11 (draw the graph); $-6 < x < 16$
      iii.   at least 4 (draw the graph); $x \geq 9$ or $x \leq 1$
      iv.   less than or equal to -8 (draw the graph). $S = \emptyset$

32.   For the expression $|17 - 2x|$;
   a.   evaluate it if:
      i. x is -3;   23
      ii. x is 10;   3
   b.   find x if the expression is:
      i.   equal to 13; $x = 2$ or $x = 15$
      ii.   equal to 0; $x = 8.5$
      iii.   greater than 6 (draw the graph); $x < 5.5$ or $x > 11.5$
      iv.   no more than 21 (draw the graph). $19 \geq x \geq -2$

31. ii.

31. iii.

31. iv.

32. iii.

32. iv

33. *Quiz Show Problem*   On a television quiz show, a contestant must guess the price of a new car. To be a winner, the contestant must come within a certain amount of the actual price. Suppose that the actual price is $9826.
   a.   Define a variable for the price the contestant guesses. Then write an absolute value expression for the difference between this guess and the actual price. $x =$ no. of $ guessed $|x - 9826|$

Problems 33–38 show how absolute value inequalities can represent phenomena in the real world in a compact mathematical form.

b. Write an inequality that says the guess must be within $150 of the actual price, inclusive. Solve the inequality to find the range of guesses for which the contestant will win. $|x - 9826| < 150$
Between $9676 and $9976.

34. *Estimated Tax Problem*   People who work for wages have income tax withheld from their paychecks. People who earn money from which tax is not withheld have to pay *estimated tax* during the year. Suppose that Lotta Bucks pays $2400 in estimated tax.

a. At the end of the year, Lotta figures out her *actual* tax bill. Define a variable for this actual tax. Then write an absolute value expression for the difference between the actual tax and the $2400 estimate. x = no. of $ actual tax; $|x - 2400|$

b. How much is 20% of the estimated tax? Write an inequality saying that Lotta's actual tax is within 20% of the estimate, inclusive. Then solve the inequality to find the range of values her actual tax could be. $480; |x - 2400| < 480$ from $1920 to $2880, inclusive.

35. *Submarine Hull Tolerance Problem*   The pressure hull of a submarine should be circular in cross section so that the water pressure will act evenly all the way around. However, the hull cannot be built exactly as a perfect circle. Suppose that the plans for a new submarine call for a diameter of 33 feet, $7\frac{1}{4}$ inches.

a. Define a variable for the actual diameter measured at various places (see the figure). Then write an absolute value expression for the difference between the actual diameter and the 33 ft $7\frac{1}{4}$ in. called for on the plans. x = no. of ft. diameter; $|x - 33'7\frac{1}{4}''|$

b. $|x - 33'7\frac{1}{4}''| \le \frac{1}{8}''$
Between $33'7\frac{1}{8}''$ and $33'7\frac{3}{8}''$, inclusive

b. The plans allow for a *tolerance* of $\frac{1}{8}$ inch in the diameter. This means that the actual diameter must be within $\frac{1}{8}$ inch of 33 feet $7\frac{1}{4}$ inches, inclusive. Write an inequality stating this fact and solve it to find the range of values of the diameter.

36. *Spark Plug Tolerance Problem*   The specifications for a certain type of car state that to be within tolerance, the spark plug gap (see the figure) must be 0.03 ± 0.002 inch. The value ± 0.002 inch is called the *tolerance*.

a. Define a variable for the actual gap width. Then write an absolute value inequality that says the gap is within tolerance.

b. What range of gap widths is within tolerance?

a. x = no. of in. gap width.
$|x - 0.03| \le 0.002$

b. Between 0.028″ and 0.032″, inclusive

37. *Air Traffic Control Problem*   A commercial jet plane flies nonstop from San Francisco to New York at a constant speed of 900 kilometers per hour (km/h). On the way it flies directly over Chicago, 2900 km from San Francisco. Let t be the number of hours since the plane left San Francisco.

a. Write an expression in terms of *t* representing the plane's distance from San Francisco.   900*t*

b. The plane's distance from Chicago is the *absolute value* of the *difference* between its distance from San Francisco and Chicago's distance from San Francisco (2900 km). Write an expression for the plane's distance from Chicago $|2900 - 900t|$

c. The air traffic controllers at Chicago are responsible for the plane when it is within 500 km of Chicago. During what time interval will the Chicago controllers be responsible for it?

    c. Between 2.67 and 3.78 hours

38. **CB Radio Problem**   A trucker starts off from a warehouse and drives at a steady speed of 60 kilometers per hour (km/h). Fifteen minutes ($\frac{1}{4}$ hour) later his buddy starts after him from the same warehouse, going 70 km/h. Let *t* be the number of hours the trucker has been driving.

a. Write expressions in terms of *t* for (i) the number of kilometers the trucker has driven, (ii) the number of hours his buddy has been going, and (iii) the kilometers his buddy has gone.

    a. $60t$, $t - \frac{1}{4}$, $70(t - \frac{1}{4})$

b. The buddy eventually passes the trucker. They are within CB radio range when they are within 5 km of each other. Their distance apart is the *absolute value* of the *difference* between their distances from the warehouse. For what interval of times can they talk to each other by CB radio?   Between 1.25 and 2.25 h.

c. For what *other* time interval are they less than 5 km apart?

    c.   Before $t = \frac{1}{12}$ h (5 min).

13-5 | INEQUALITIES: GIVEN *x*, EVALUATE THE EXPRESSION

You have learned how to evaluate expressions such as

$$11 - 3x$$

when you know what *x* equals. Suppose you must find out what this expression is when *x* is *greater* than or *less* than some given number—for example, *x* > 2. Simply substituting 2 for *x* will not work. There is no good way to tell which way the inequality sign will point. One way to work this problem is to start with the inequality

$$x > 2$$

and transform it until the left member is $11 - 3x$. First, multiply each member by −3, remembering to reverse the inequality sign.

$$-3x < -6$$

Then add 11 to each member, getting

$$11 - 3x < 5.$$

Time: 2 days

Chalkboard Examples:

1. If *x* > 2, what is *x* + 7?
   Ans.: The expression is greater than 9.

2. If *x* ≤ −3, what is 5*x*?
   Ans.: The expression is less than or equal to −15.

3. If *x* < 9, what is 4*x* + 3?
   Ans.: The expression is less than 39.

4. If *x* ≤ 8, what is −7*x*?
   Ans.: The expression is greater than or equal to −56.

5. Do Oral Practice problems.

6. Work Examples 1 and 2.

Assignments:

Day 1: Exercise 13–5, #7–19 odd, Exercise 13–3, #16 or 15 (for review), and Exercise 13–4, #12 or 11 (for review)

Day 2: Exercise 13–5, #12–20 even and 21 and 23 or 22 and 24

So the expression $11 - 3x$ is less than 5 when x is greater than 2.

In this section you will evaluate expressions, finding out what they are greater than or less than. You will also see how this technique can be used in problems from the real world.

Objective :

For linear expressions such as $11 - 3x$, find the range of values of the expression when a range of values of x is given.

Cover the answers as you work these examples.

EXAMPLE 1

Find the values of $16 - 5x$ if $x \leq -3$.

– – – – –   – – – – –

	Think These Reasons
$x \leq -3$	Write the given values of x as an inequality.
$-5x \geq 15$	Multiply each member by -5. (The order reverses.)
$16 - 5x \geq 31$	Add 16 to each member.
Expression is greater than or equal to 31.	Answer the question.

EXAMPLE 2

Find the values of $4x - 7$ if x is between -1 and 5.

– – – – –   – – – – –

$-1 < x < 5$	Write the given values of x as an inequality.
$-4 < 4x < 20$	Multiply each member by 4. (The order does *not* reverse.)
$-11 < 4x - 7 < 13$	Add -7 to each member.
Expression is between -11 and 13.	Answer the question.

Note: If the given values of x had been $-1 \leq x \leq 5$, you would have written "Expression is between -11 and 13, *inclusive.*"

EXAMPLE 3

Hurricane Problem   A hurricane is 250 miles offshore and is
approaching the coast at a rate of 20 miles per hour.

a. Draw a diagram showing the coast, the starting point 250 miles
   offshore, and the hurricane somewhere in between.
b. Let *t* be the number of hours that have passed since the hurricane was
   250 miles offshore. Write an expression in terms of *t* for the distance
   the hurricane is from the coast.
c. If *t* is at least 3 hours, where is the hurricane?
d. For what range of times will the hurricane be between 50 and 150
   miles offshore?

– – – – –   – – – – –

a.

It has *gone* $20t$ miles, so it has
$250 - 20t$ miles left to go.

– – – – –   – – – – –

b. t = number of hours.   Restate the definition of *t*.

   $\underline{250 - 20t}$ = number of miles.   Write an expression. Show it on
                                               the diagram in part (a).

– – – – –   – – – – –

c. $t \geq 3$ Write an inequality: *t* is at least
                                            3.

           $-20t \leq -60$ Multiply each member by -20.
                                            (The order reverses!)

     $250 - 20t \leq 190$ Add 250 to each member.

   <u>Hurricane is at most 190 mi offshore.</u>   Answer the question.

– – – – –   – – – – –

d. $50 < 250 - 20t < 150$ Write an inequality.

     $-200 < -20t < -100$ Subtract 250 from each member.

           $8 > t > 4$ Divide each member by -20.

   <u>Between 4 and 8 h.</u>   Answer the question.

ORAL PRACTICE

Tell in words what the expression is for the given range of *x*.

EXAMPLE

Answer

If $x > 5$, find $x + 3$. $x + 3$ is more than 8.

A. $x + 7$ is more than 11.
B. $x + 2$ is less than 8.
C. $x - 5$ is more than 7.
D. $x - 4$ is less than -3.
E. $3x$ is more than 18.
F. $5x$ is less than 150.
G. $\frac{1}{2}x$ is at least 5.
H. $\frac{1}{3}x$ is at most 4.
I. $-4x$ is less than -80.
J. $-3x$ is more than -90.
K. $-3 + x$ is less than 27.
L. $-x$ is at most -10.
M. $x + 3$ is between 5 and 10.
N. $x - 5$ is between -1 and 3, inclusive.
O. $2x$ is between -12 and 12.
P. $-6x$ is between 0 and -108, inclusive.
Q. $x + 4$ is more than 4.
R. $4x$ is at most 0.

A. If $x > 4$, find $x + 7$.
B. If $x < 6$, find $x + 2$.
C. If $x > 12$, find $x - 5$.
D. If $x < 1$, find $x - 4$.
E. If $x > 6$, find $3x$.
F. If $x < 30$, find $5x$.
G. If $x \geq 10$, find $\frac{1}{2}x$.
H. If $x \leq 12$, find $\frac{1}{3}x$.
I. If $x > 20$, find $-4x$.
J. If $x < 30$, find $-3x$.
K. If $x < 30$, find $-3 + x$.
L. If $x \geq 10$, find $-x$.
M. If $2 < x < 7$, find $x + 3$.
N. If $4 \leq x \leq 8$, find $x - 5$.
O. If $-6 < x < 6$, find $2x$.
P. If $0 \leq x \leq 18$, find $-6x$.
Q. If $x > 0$, find $x + 4$.
R. If $x \leq 0$, find $4x$.

1. $7x + 2 > 93$
    Expr. is more than 93.
2. $5x + 3 < 63$
    Expr. is less than 63.
3. $9x - 4 < 5$
    Expr. is less than 5.
4. $7x - 10 > 4$
    Expr. is more than 4.
5. $9 - 2x \geq -1$
    Expr. is at least -1.
6. $7 - 3x \leq -20$
    Expr. is at most -20.
7. $-8x - 12 \leq 148$
    Expr. is at most 148.
8. $-9x - 1 \geq 53$
    Expr. is at least 53.
9. $17 + 4x < 45$
    Expr. is less than 45.
10. $19 + 6x > 49$
    Expr. is more than 49.
11. $-5x - 8 \leq -18$
    Expr. is at most -18.
12. $-7x - 12 \geq -33$
    Expr. is at least -33.
13. $31 \leq 8x + 7 \leq 47$
    Expr. is between 31 and 47, inclusive.
14. $67 \leq 2x + 37 \leq 77$
    Expr. is between 67 and 77, inclusive.
15. $33 > 13 - 6x > -29$
    Expr. is between -29 and 33.
16. $49 > 17 - 4x > 29$
    Expr. is between 29 and 49.

EXERCISE 13-5

For Problems 1 through 20, find the range of values of the expression that corresponds to the given range of values of x. Write the answer in *words* and as an inequality.

1. If $x > 13$, find $7x + 2$.
2. If $x < 12$, find $5x + 3$.
3. If $x < 1$, find $9x - 4$.
4. If $x > 2$, find $7x - 10$.
5. If $x \leq 5$, find $9 - 2x$.
6. If $x \geq 9$, find $7 - 3x$.
7. If $x \geq -20$, find $-8x - 12$.
8. If $x \leq -6$, find $-9x - 1$.
9. If x is less than 7, find $17 + 4x$.
10. If x is more than 5, find $19 + 6x$.
11. If x is at least 2, find $-5x - 8$.
12. If x is at most 3, find $-7x - 12$.
13. If $3 \leq x \leq 5$, find $8x + 7$.
14. If $15 \leq x \leq 20$, find $2x + 37$.
15. If $-5 < x < 7$, find $13 - 6x$.
16. If $-8 < x < -3$, find $17 - 4x$.

17. If *x* is between 4 and 5, find 19 + 3*x*.

18. If *x* is between 5 and 6.3, find 42 + 10*x*.

19. If *x* is between −3 and 0, inclusive, find −2 − 9*x*.

20. If *x* is between 0 and 4, inclusive, find −11 − 8*x*.

21. *Vacation Financing Problem*   A family goes on vacation. They start with $1500 in traveler's checks and plan to spend $180 per day.
     a.   Define a variable for the number of days they have been on vacation. Then write an expression for the number of dollars they expect to have left.   *x* = no. of days. 1500 − 180*x*
     b.   If they stay at least 5 days, what number of dollars could they expect to have left?   At most $600
     c.   If they want to come home with at least $500 left, what (whole) number of days could they stay?   At most 5 days

22. *Hamburger Help Problem*   A local hamburger establishment takes in $1700 in a day. Some of this is used to pay the employees. The wages are $40 per employee for a day.
     a.   Define a variable for the number of employees hired. Then write an expression for the number of dollars left, out of the $1700, after the employees have been paid.   *x* = no. of employees. 1700 − 40*x*
     b.   The Hamburger Helper's union requires the manager to hire at least 9 employees. What range of dollars will be left?
     c.   The manager wishes to make at least $400 a day after paying the help. What (whole) number of employees could be hired? Is this compatible with union requirements? Explain.

23. *Freight Train Problem*   A freight train leaves the town of Oola, La., and heads for Near, Miss., 200 miles away, at a speed of 40 miles per hour.

     a.   Let *t* be the number of hours that have passed since the train left Oola, La. Write an expression for the distance the train still has to go to get to Near, Miss.   200 − 40*t*
     b.   If the time is greater than 3 hours, how far is the train from Near, Miss.?   Less than 80 miles
     c.   For what range of times will the train be between 30 and 100 miles from Near, Miss.?   Between 2.5 and 4.25 hours

24. *Raft Problem*   A group of campers enters the Colorado River in the morning and travels 50 miles downstream on a raft. The raft floats with the current at 7 miles per hour.

17. 31 < 19 + 3*x* < 34
     Expr. is between 31 and 34.
18. 92 < 42 + 10*x* < 105
     Expr. is between 92 and 105.
19. 25 ≥ −2 − 9*x* ≥ −2
     Expr. is between −2 and 25, inclusive.
20. −11 ≥ − 11 − 8*x* ≥ −43
     Expr. is between −43 and −11, inclusive.

Problem Notes:

The problems of this section usually do not appear in Algebra I texts. They are presented here to carry out the dual theme of this text: Given the value of *x*, find the value of the expression; and given the value of the expression, find *x*. These problems cannot be solved reliably by simple substitution, because the direction of the final inequality is not always the same as that given for *x*.

Problems 21–26 are similar to the problems of earlier chapters but involve inequalities rather than equations.

22. b.   At most $1340

     c.   At most 32 employees. This is compatible, since it is more than 9.

a. Draw a diagram showing the 50-mile stretch of river with the raft somewhere on it. Show the distance the raft has left to go.
b. Let *t* be the number of hours the raft has been floating. Write an expression for the distance it has left to go. $50 - 7t$
c. If the raft has been going for at most 3 hours, what range of distances could it have left to go?   At least 29 mi.
d. For what range of times does the raft have between 8 and 22 miles left to go?   Between 4 and 6 hr.

25. *Calvin's Height Problem*   In his early childhood, Calvin Butterball figured out that his height in inches was always 19 more than 3 times his age in years.
a. In order to sleep comfortably, one's height must be less than the length of the bed in which one sleeps. For what ages will Calvin be comfortable in:
    i.   his bassinet, 31 inches long;   Until he's 4
    ii. his youth bed, 50 inches long?   Until he's $10\frac{1}{3}$
b. During his sixth year (ages 5 to 6, inclusive), what range of heights was Calvin?   Between 34 and 37 in., inclusive
c. To join the Navy, one must be between 5′6″ (66 inches) and 6′4″ (76 inches) tall, inclusive. For what ages will Calvin be eligible to join the Navy?   Between $15\frac{2}{3}$ and 19, inclusive
d. Calvin hopes to reach 7 feet tall and become a professional basketball player. How long would he have to keep growing to be over 7 feet tall? Do you think he will make it?

25. d.   Until he's over $21\frac{2}{3}$. Probably won't grow that long.

26. *Workers and Guards Problem*   A primitive society on a remote tropical island has a rule that the number of people who work in the fields must be three times the number standing guard, minus 1000.
a. If fewer than 5000 people are working, how many can be on guard?   Fewer than 2000
b. If more than 4000 people are on guard, how many must work?
c. Under what conditions will the number of people on guard be more than the number working?   Fewer than 500 on guard
d. If the total number either working or on guard is more than 10,000, what is the minimum number who can be working?   7251

26. b.   More than 11,000

13-6 | LINEAR INEQUALITIES WITH TWO VARIABLES

Time: 2 days

Chalkboard Examples:

First day:
1. Plot: $y > 3/5)x + 4$
   Ans.:

You have been solving inequalities that have *one* variable. In Chapter 8 you studied expressions that have *two* variables. In this section, expressions with two variables are set greater than or less than a specified number. You draw graphs of the resulting two-variable inequalities.

You have plotted graphs of linear equations such as

$$y = 2x - 3.$$

Substituting 2 for x gives

$$y = 2(2) - 3$$
$$y = 1.$$

The point $(2, 1)$ is *on* the line, as shown in the graph.

Suppose that you had the *inequality*

$$y > 2x - 3.$$

Substituting 2 for x gives

$$y > 2(2) - 3$$
$$y > 1.$$

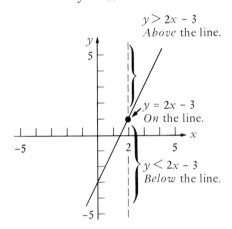

$y > 2x - 3$
Above the line.

$y = 2x - 3$
On the line.

$y < 2x - 3$
Below the line.

As shown in the figure, the points would be *above* the line. For the inequality

$$y < 2x - 3,$$

the points would be *below* the line. The whole graph, for all values of x, would be the entire *region* below the line, as shown in the right-hand figure below.

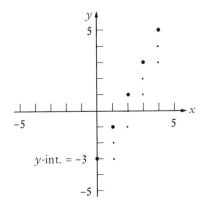

Use rise and run to plot points.

Draw the boundary line.

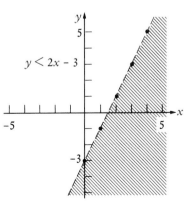

$y < 2x - 3$

Shade the region.

2. Plot the system:
    $2x + 3y < 3$
    $x - y \le 2$
    Ans.: Transform to
    $$y < -\frac{2}{3}x + 4$$
    $$y \ge x - 2$$
    Order reverses in the second inequality.

Second day:
Discuss homework problems. Time can be saved by having overhead projector transparencies prepared beforehand. Students can spend the rest of the period working on homework.

Assignments:

Day 1: Exercise 13–6, #1–9 odd or 2–10 even
Day 2: Exercise 13–6, #11–19 odd or 12–20 even

Once you know what the graph looks like, you can draw it quickly. The line $y = 2x - 3$ forms the **boundary** of the region. Using the rise and run, you can plot points on this line. Then you draw the boundary line, using dashes in this case to show that the line is *not* included. (For the inequalities $\geq$ and $\leq$, you would draw a *solid* line.) Finally, you shade the proper region.

In general, for $y \geq mx + b$ or $y > mx + b$, you shade *above* the line; for $y \leq mx + b$ or $y < mx + b$, you shade *below* the line.

Objective :
Given a linear inequality such as $y < 2x - 3$, draw the graph.

Cover the answers as you work the examples.

EXAMPLE 1

Draw the graph of $2x + 3y \geq 6$.

– – – – –   – – – – –

	Think These Reasons

$2x + 3y \geq 6$ Write the given inequality.

$3y \geq -2x + 6$ Transform so that y is by itself on the left-hand side.

$y \geq -\dfrac{2}{3}x + 2$

Plot the graph as described above.

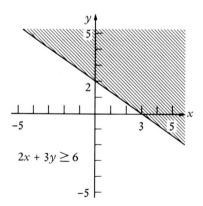

$2x + 3y \geq 6$

Note: The boundary line is *solid*, since the sign is greater than or *equal* to. The region is *above* the boundary line, since the inequality is *greater* than or equal to.

EXAMPLE 2

Draw the graph of the *system* of inequalities

$$x - 3y < -6 \quad \text{and} \quad y \le -\frac{5}{2}x + 1.$$

- - - - -

$x - 3y < -6$

$-3y < -x - 6$

$y > \frac{1}{3}x + 2$

Transform the first inequality to slope-intercept form.

Note that the order *reverses*.

Plot *both* boundary lines, dotted for > and solid for ≤.

Draw small arrows to show which side of the line is shaded.

Shade the *intersection* of the two regions. This is because a solution of a system must satisfy *all* the inequalities.

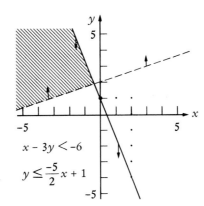

$x - 3y < -6$

$y \le \frac{-5}{2}x + 1$

EXERCISE 13-6

For Problems 1 through 6, plot the graph of the inequality.

1. $y \ge \frac{3}{4}x - 2$

2. $y > \frac{2}{5}x - 4$

3. $3x + 5y > 20$

4. $3x + 4y \le 4$

5. $3x - y \ge -2$

6. $2x - y < -3$

For Problems 7 through 16, plot the graph of the system of inequalities.

7. $y > \frac{2}{5}x + 3$

    $y \le 2x - 1$

8. $y \le \frac{1}{3}x + 5$

    $y > \frac{7}{3}x - 2$

9. $2x + y \ge 1$

    $5x - 3y < 18$

10. $3x - 2y \ge -4$

     $x + 4y < -8$

Problem Notes:

Make sure students use graph paper and do a careful job. Part of the purpose of these problems is to improve drawing skill.

Problems 15 and 16 have parallel boundary lines with the graph between.

Problems 17 and 18 have a closed triangular region for the graph.

Problems 19 and 20 have an open region bounded by three lines for the graph.

1.-20. See Additional Answers.

11. $x + y < 3$
     $2x - 3y < 12$

12. $x - y > -4$
     $4x + y > -3$

13. $3x + y \geq 5$
     $y < -x$

14. $y \geq 3x$
     $3x + y \geq -6$

15. $x - 5y \leq -10$
     $y < \frac{1}{5}x + 4$

16. $2x + y \leq 6$
     $y > -2x + 1$

Problems 17 through 20 are systems with *three* inequalities. Plot the graph of the region that is the intersection of all three.

17. $2x + y > -2$
     $x - y < -2$
     $x - 3y \geq -15$

18. $y > -x$
     $3x + 2y \leq 6$
     $2x - 5y > -20$

19. $2x - 5y > -15$
     $y \leq 2x$
     $x + y \geq -3$

20. $x - 2y < 0$
     $y > x + 1$
     $x + 5y \leq 15$

13-7 | SYSTEMS OF EQUATIONS AND INEQUALITIES

Time: 0 or 3 days (optional section)

Chalkboard Examples:

First day:
For the system
  $2x - 3y < 21$
  $x + y = -2$
a. Solve the system to find the range of values of x.
b. Illustrate the solution by drawing the graph.
Ans.:

In Section 8-7 you graphed systems of equations and found their point of intersection. In the last section you graphed systems of inequalities. In that case, the intersection is a *region* in the Cartesian plane. Suppose that a system has one equation and one inequality, such as

$$2x + 3y > 18$$
$$x - y = -1.$$

The graph of $2x + 3y > 18$ is a region, and the graph of $x - y = -1$ is a line. The intersection is that part of the line in the shaded region.

Two equations

Two inequalities

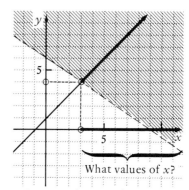

What values of x?

One equation, one inequality

Systems like this sometimes arise in problems from the real world. The values of x or y for the part of the line in the shaded region are easy to find using the substitution technique of Section 8.7. Here is how you would find the values of x for the system above.

	Think These Reasons
$2x + 3y > 18$ $x - y = -1$	Write the given system.
$-y = -x - 1$ $y = x + 1$	Solve the *equation* for y in terms of x.
$2x + 3(x + 1) > 18$	Substitute $x + 1$ for y in the *inequality* to eliminate y. (Now the inequality is just like the inequalities of Section 9.2.)
$2x + 3x + 3 > 18$	Distribute 3.
$5x + 3 > 18$	Combine like terms.
$5x > 15$	Subtract 3 from each member.
$x > 3$	Divide each member by 5.

As you can see from the graph, the line and the region intersect for values of x greater than 3. In this section you will solve systems like this arising in problems from the real world.

Objective:
Given a problem from the real world involving two variables, write a system of one equation and one inequality and solve the system to find a range of values of a variable.

The words *equation* or *inequality* can be shortened to *open sentence*. An open sentence is simply a sentence with a variable in it. The sentence is "open" because its truth or falsity is open to question until someone gives you a value of the variable.

DEFINITION

OPEN SENTENCE
An **open sentence** is a sentence containing a variable.

(Equations and inequalities such as
$$3x + 5 = 7 \quad \text{or} \quad y < 4x - 9$$
are open sentences.)

a. $y > -5$
Note that although the given inequality had $<$, the answer has $>$. This fact has important implications in the word problems that follow.
b. (Graph.)

Second day:
Use Exercise 13–7, 5, as an example.
Third day:
Homework problems at the board

Assignments:

Day 1: Exercise 13–7, #1, 3, 5 and Exercise 13–6, #12 or 11 (for review)
Day 2: Exercise 13–7, #2 and 4 and 7, 9, 11 or 8, 10, 12
Day 3: Exercise 13–8 in preparation for test

Cover the answers as you work these examples.

EXAMPLE 1

a. Solve the system to find the range of values of y.
b. Illustrate your solution by drawing the graph.

$$x + y = 9$$
$$3x - 4y > -8$$

– – – – –   – – – – –

a. $x + y = 9$ Write the given system.

$3x - 4y > -8$

$x = 9 - y$ Solve the *equation* for x in terms of y.

$3(9 - y) - 4y > -8$ Substitute $9 - y$ for x in the *inequality* to eliminate x.

$27 - 3y - 4y > -8$ Distribute 3.

$27 - 7y > -8$ Combine like terms.

$-7y > -35$ Subtract 27 from each member.

$\underline{y < 5}$ Divide each member by -7. (The order reverses.)

b.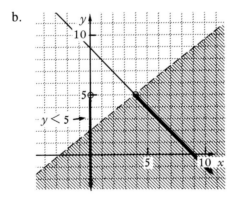

The line has intercepts $x = 9$, $y = 9$.

The inequality transforms to $y < \frac{3}{4}x + 2$.

The boundary line has $m = \frac{3}{4}$, $b = 2$.

The region is *below* the boundary line, since y is *less* than some value.

The values of y actually are less than 5.

EXAMPLE 2

School Faculty Problem   A new elementary school is to have 50 faculty members. Some will be teachers and the rest will be aides. At this school, teachers will earn an average of $20,000 a year and aides an average of $12,000 a year.

a. Define variables for the number of teachers and for the number of aides. Then write an expression for the total amount of money paid in salaries for a year.
b. What total is paid if there are:
   i.   20 teachers and 30 aides;   ii.   30 teachers and 20 aides?
c. Suppose that the total amount to be spent on salaries must be less than \$896,000 a year. Write a system of open sentences, one expressing this fact and the other expressing the fact that there are 50 teachers and aides in all. Then solve the system to find the minimum number of aides that can be hired.

– – – – –   – – – – –

a.   Let x = number of teachers.   Define variables.
        Let y = number of aides.

    $20x + 12y$ = number of thousands   Use *thousands* of dollars to
            of dollars.   simplify the numbers.

b. i. $20(20) + 12(30)$ Substitute 20 for x and 30 for
                                          y and evaluate the expression.

         $= 400 + 360$

         $= 760$

         $\underline{\underline{\$760,000}}$ Answer the question.

    ii. $20(30) + 12(20)$ Substitute 30 for x and 20 for
                                          y and evaluate the expression.

         $= 600 + 240$

         $= 840$

         $\underline{\underline{\$840,000}}$ Answer the question.

– – – – –   – – – – –

c. $20x + 12y < 896$ Write an inequality.

              $x + y = 50$ Write an equation.

                $x = 50 - y$ Solve the equation for y in
                                         terms of x, substitute into the
         $20(50 - y) + 12y < 896$ inequality, and solve for y.

         $1000 - 20y + 12y < 896$

            $1000 - 8y < 896$

               $-8y < -104$

                $y > 13$ (The order reverses!)

    $\underline{\text{Minimum of 14 aides}}$ Answer the question. Since y
                                         is an *integer* and must be
                                         greater than 13, the minimum
                                         is 14.

ORAL PRACTICE

Give the range of values of x and the range of values of y for the part of
the line in the shaded region.

A. $x > 3$ **B.** $x < -1$
   $y > 2$ $y < 2$

A.

B.

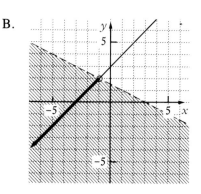

C. $x > 1$ **D.** $x < -2$
   $y < 4$ $y > -3$

C.

D.

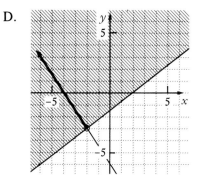

Tell which of the symbols on the right goes with the words on the left.
(You may use a symbol more than once.)

E. is less than 1	**1.** $<$
F. is no less than 4	**2.** $\leq$
G. is at least 4	**3.** $=$
H. is a minimum of 4	**4.** $\geq$
I. is down to 5	**5.** $>$
J. is down to . . . inclusive 4	**6.** $< \cdots <$
K. is up to . . . inclusive 2	**7.** $\leq \cdots \leq$
L. is up to 1	
M. is a maximum of 2	

N.   is at most   2

O.   is more than   5

P.   is no more than   2

Q.   is greater than   5

R.   is between   6

S.   is between . . . inclusive   7

T.   is unsurpassed by   4

U.   is   3

EXERCISE 13-7

For Problems 1 through 4:

a.   find the range of values of x and the range of values of y for which the system is satisfied;
b.   draw the graph of the system.

1. $2x - 3y > -12$ $x > 3$
    $x + y = 9$ $y < 6$

2. $x + y = 13$ $x < 9$
    $4x - 3y < 24$ $y > 4$

3. $x - y = -2$ $x \geq 2$
    $5x + 2y \geq 18$ $y \geq 4$

4. $2x + 3y \leq 15$ $x \leq 6$
    $x - y = 5$ $y \leq 1$

For Problems 5 through 18, answer the questions. Problems 5 and 6 lead you step by step through the solution. For the others, you must think of what to do.

5.   *TV Manufacture Problem*   A manufacturer can produce 40 television sets per day, some color and the rest black-and-white. The color sets sell for $400 each and the black-and-white sets for $100 each.

PRODUCTION SHEET

Kind	Price	No.	$
Color	$400	___	___
B&W	$100	___	___
Totals	. .	40	___

a.   Define variables and write an expression for the total amount of money the manufacturer makes per day.

Problem Notes:

Problems 5–18 are similar to the two-variable problems of Section 8–9. This time, however, one of the two open sentences is an inequality. The result is a *range* of values (an interval) rather than a single value, as in the earlier problems.

Many of the problems have integer domains. For instance, Problem 5 leads to the inequality $x < 5$. Since x stands for a number of TV sets, the maximum number is 4. In Problem 15a, the fraction $33\frac{1}{3}$ must be rounded *up* to 34 because the inequality says $x > 33\frac{1}{3}$.

1.–4. b.   See Additional Answers.

5. a. $x =$ no. of color TV's.
    $y =$ no. of B & W TV's.
    $400x + 100y$

   b.   Evaluate the expression in part (a) if the manufacturer produces:
        i.   25 color and 15 black-and-white per day;   11,500
        ii. 15 color and 25 black-and-white per day.   8500
   c.   The manufacturer wants to make more than $14,500 a day. Write a system of open sentences, one stating this fact and the other stating that the total number of sets is 40. Then solve the system to find the maximum number of black-and-white sets the manufacturer could produce each day.   Maximum number is 4.

6. *Arena Seating Problem*   A new sports arena is being built to seat 10,000 people. Some seats will be reserved and the rest will be general admission. The plan is to charge $10 for a reserved seat and $6 for a general admission seat.

6. a. x = no. of reserved seats.
y = no. of gen. adm. seats.
$10x + 6y$

   a.   Define variables for the numbers of tickets sold and write an expression for the total amount of money received.
   b.   Evaluate the expression in part (a) for sales of:
        i.   3000 reserved and 7000 general admission tickets;   72,000
        ii. 7000 reserved and 3000 general admission tickets.   88,000
   c.   Write a system of open sentences, one saying that sales are more than $68,000, total, and the other saying that all 10,000 tickets are sold. Solve the system to find the maximum number of general admission tickets that could be sold.   Maximum number is 7999.

7. *Condominium Problem*   A developer has space to build 80 condominium units near the beach. Some will be two-bedroom units selling for $100,000 each. The rest will be three-bedroom units selling for $120,000 each. The developer wishes to make more than 9 million dollars selling the condominiums. What number of two-bedroom units could be built?   From 0 through 29 two-bedroom units

8. From 0 through 15 silver bracelets.

8. *Silver and Gold Bracelet Problem*   A jewelry manufacturer can make 20 of a particular design of bracelet each week. Some can be silver, selling for $30 each, and the rest gold, selling for $150 each. If the manufacturer wishes to make more than $1080 a week selling these bracelets, what numbers of silver bracelets could be made?

9. *Lawn Mowing Problem*   A group of 30 students is going to mow grass in the community park as a public service project. Some will use power mowers and the rest will use hand mowers. Moe De-Laune figures that they must mow at least 400 square yards per minute, total, in order to finish by sunset. A person can mow 20 square yards per minute with a power mower, or 8 square yards per minute with a hand mower. What is the minimum number of power mowers they could use and still finish before sunset?   Minimum no. is 14 power mowers.

10. *Hay Bale Problem*   A group of 100 people is hired to load bales of hay. An adult can load 5 bales per minute, and a teenager can load 3 bales per minute. If the group must load more than 328 bales per minute, how many teenagers could be in the group?   From 0 through 85 teenagers

11. *Investment Problem*   Meg A. Bucks has $10,000 to invest. She can put part of it into a certificate of deposit (CD) paying 8% per year interest and the rest into a savings account paying 5%. ("8% of . . ." means "0.08 times . . . .")

   a.   How much interest will Meg get if she puts:
      i. $3000 into the CD and $7000 into savings; $590
      ii. $7000 into the CD and $3000 into savings? $710
   b.   What range of amounts could Meg invest in the savings account and still get over $750 per year interest, total?   From $0 through $1666.66

12. *Milk Mixing Problem*   Cream is 30% butterfat and milk is 4% butterfat. A dairy mixes cream and milk to make 100 pounds of half-and-half.

   a.   How many pounds of butterfat will there be if the dairy uses:
      i.   60 pounds of cream and 40 pounds of milk?   19.6 lb.
      ii.   40 pounds of cream and 60 pounds of milk?   14.4 lb.
   b.   The Dairy Association specifies that 100 pounds of half-and-half must contain no less than 15 pounds of butterfat. What range of pounds of milk could be used?   From 0 through 57.69 lb.

13. *Vitamin Problem*   Suppose that you must take 1000 units per day, total, of vitamins A and B. If the number of units of vitamin A must be at least $\frac{2}{3}$ of the number of units of vitamin B, what are the permissible daily doses of each?   At least 400 units of A; at most 600 units of B

14. *Democrats and Republicans Problem*   The United States Senate has 100 members, Democrats and Republicans. The Democrats figure that to avoid political disaster the number of Democratic senators must be more than $\frac{1}{4}$ of the number of Republican senators. What range of numbers of Democratic senators will avoid disaster?   From 21 through 100

15. *Voting Problem*   In order to defeat a proposed amendment to a constitution, the number of lawmakers voting against it must be more than one-half of the number voting for it. How many lawmakers voting "against" could defeat an amendment in:
   a.   the United States Senate, 100 senators;   Minimum number is 34.
   b.   the United States House of Representatives, 435 representatives;   Minimum number is 146.
   c.   the Texas Legislature, 150 legislators;   Minimum is 51.
   d.   the Kansas Legislature, 125 legislators?   Minimum is 42.

Problem 15 has correct numbers of legislators as of the time the problem was written. You may want to use figures for the legislature in your own state.

Problem 16 specifies the correct relationship that existed between gold and paper dollars when the United States was on the gold standard.

Problem 18 is purely fictitious but contains good mathematical concepts.

16. *Gold and Paper Dollars Problem*   When the United States dollar was backed by gold, the law stated that the number of paper dollars could be no more than four times the number of gold dollars. Let x stand for the number of billions of gold dollars, and let y stand for the number of billions of paper dollars.
   a.   Write an inequality relating x and y. $y \le 4x$
   b.   If there were 40 billion gold dollars, how many paper dollars could there be?   At most $160 billion

c. If there were 200 billion paper dollars, how many gold dollars would be needed?   At least $50 billion

16. d. At least $60 billion gold; at most $240 billion paper

d. If the total number of dollars, gold and paper, were 300 billion, how many of each kind could there be?

17. *Age Problem*   Mona Lott is 5 years younger than her sister Etta. How old will each one be when:

17. a. Mona is at most 26; Etta is at most 31.

b. Mona is at most 50; Etta is at most 55.

c. Mona is less than 95; Etta is less than 100.

a. the sum of their ages is at most 57 years;

b. Etta is at least $\frac{11}{10}$ as old as Mona;

c. Mona's age is less than 95% of Etta's age?

18. *Men Versus Women Problem*   A local chapter of a well-known equal-rights organization specifies that the number of women hired to work in an office must equal 18 plus $\frac{2}{5}$ of the number of men.

a. If the total number of employees is at least 102, how many men can there be? How many women?

18. a. At least 60 men; at least 42 women

b. Total number of employees is less than 60.

b. What total number of employees will make the number of women larger than the number of men?

13-8 | CHAPTER REVIEW AND TEST

Time: 1 day

Test Ideas:

It is suggested that your test go back at least as far as absolute value inequalities, even if you have already tested on this topic. Students often need more contact time with these inequalities to drive home the idea.

In algebra you do three things with expressions.

1. Given a problem, write an expression representing a variable quantity.
2. Given x, find out the value of the expression.
3. Given the value of the expression, find x.

In this chapter you have added greater than and less than to your available symbols. You have evaluated linear expressions for a given range of x-values. You have also solved inequalities that contain linear expressions, absolute value expressions, or two-variable expressions.

You should try to work the following test within the length of time you would have for a classroom test. In order to be able to do this, you might want to look back through your class notes to make sure you are familiar with the techniques before you start the test.

Assignment:

Study Section 14–1.
Work the two examples.
Work Exercise 14–1, #1 and 3.

CHAPTER TEST

Problem Notes:

Problems 2 and 3 touch on the recurring theme of this text: Given x, evaluate the expression; and given a value of the expression (equal, greater than, or less than), find x.

1. What is the difference in each case?
    a. The union of two sets and the intersection.
    b. The graph of $x > 4$ and the graph of $x \geq 4$.

c. Multiplying each member of an inequality by a negative number and adding a negative number to each member.

d. The statements x is less than 7, and x is at least 7.

e. The statements x is between 2 and 5, and x is between 2 and 5, inclusive.

2. For the linear expression $15 - 8x$:

a. evaluate the expression if x is 9; -57

b. find x if the expression is 47;. $x = -4$

c. find x if the expression is less than 71; $x > -7$

d. find x if the expression is at least -577; $x \leq 74$

e. evaluate the expression if x is at least 31.   Expression is at most -233.

3. For the absolute value expression $|5x - 43|$:

a. evaluate the expression if x is 7;   8

b. find x if the expression is 27; $x = 14$ or 3.2

c. find x if the expression is at most 14; $5.8 \leq x \leq 11.4$

d. find x if the expression is less than -13.   No values of x

4. Write an inequality for the graph.

a. $x > -3$
b. $-4 \leq x \leq 6$

5. Graph the system of open sentences.

a. $y \geq \frac{1}{4}x + 2$
    $5x + 2y < 10$

b. $x + y = 2$
    $3x - 5y < 30$

6. *Computer Service Problem*   A national computer service charges a membership fee of $100. Thereafter, you pay $5 per hour while your computer is connected by telephone to theirs.

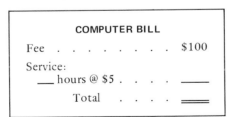

COMPUTER BILL

Fee $100

Service:

___ hours @ $5 . . . . _____

Total . . . . =====

a. Define a variable for the number of hours of "connect time," during which you use the service. Then write an expression for the total number of dollars you pay. $x = $ no. of hr. $100 + 5x$

b. If you pay between $185 and $230, for what range of times could you use the service?   Between 17 and 26 hr.

c. If your connect time is at least 30 yours, what will your bill be?   At least $250

7. *Grade Curving Problem*   Miss Calculate, the math teacher, states that students whose test scores are within 6 points, inclusive, of 73 will get a grade of C.

1. a. The union contains points that are in *at least one* of the sets. The intersection contains points that are in *both* sets.

b. For $x > 4$, the end point is *not* included. For $x \geq 4$, the end point *is* included.

c. Multiplying by a negative number reverses the order. Adding a negative number does not affect the order.

d. "x is less than 7:" $x < 7$
    "x is at least 7:" $x \geq 7$

e. "x is between 2 and 5:" End points are *not* included. "x is between 2 and 5 inclusive:" End points *are* included.

5. See Additional Answers.

Problem 6 reflects actual billing practices of many computer utilities.

a. x = no. of points
$|x - 73|$ or $|73 - x|$

b. From 67 through 79.

8. a. x = no. of hr. walking.
y = no. of hr. riding
$3x + 13y$

9. $x \le 30$ or $x > 30$

0   100

The graph contains *all* values, 0% through 100%.
Therefore, the commercial tells you nothing!
Ridiculous, but they say it every day!

   Problem 9 points out a fallacy of logic that
occurs in many commercials. "Save up to 30
percent or more" says *nothing*!

  a. Define a variable for the test score. Then write an absolute value
         expression for the difference between this score and 73.
  b. Write an inequality that says the student will get a C. For what
         range of test scores will the student get a C?

8. ***Ride and Walk Problem***   A local radio station sponsors a charity
project in which students ride bikes or walk for a total of 8 hours. In return for this, people pledge to pay the students money to be given to the
charity. Jim Shortz can ride at an average speed of 13 miles per hour and
can walk long distances at an average of 3 miles per hour.
  a. Define variables for the numbers of hours Jim walks and rides.
         Then write an expression for the total distance he goes.
  b. The rules specify that each student must go more than 70 miles.
         Write a system of open sentences, one stating this specification
         and the other stating that the total time is 8 hours. Solve the sys-
         tem to find the range of times Jim could spend walking.
         Between 0 and 3.4 hours walking
9. ***Commercial Problem***   On radio and television commercials you often hear statements like, "Save up to 30%, or more!" Let x be the
percent you save. Write a compound inequality corresponding to this
statement. Then draw its graph. Explain why the statement is ridiculous!

14
Functions and Advanced Topics

If y *is equal to an expression containing* x, *then* y *is said to be a function of* x. *For example, the pressure acting on a scuba diver is a function of the depth at which he or she is swimming. In this chapter you will be introduced to the function concept. The things you learn will form a background for your future study of geometry, advanced algebra, trigonometry, and calculus.*

Variables:

x   Depth of diver (feet)

y   Water pressure (pounds per square inch)

Expression:

$0.45x$ Water pressure in terms of x

Function equation:

$y = 0.45x$

Function graph:

14-1	FUNCTIONS

Time: 1 day

Chalkboard Examples:

1. Plot, using integer values, $-2 \leq x \leq 4$:
   $y = x^2 - 2x - 4$
   Ans: (Graph.)
2. Plot, using integer values, $0 \leq x \leq 6$:
   $y = |2x - 6|$
   Ans.: (Graph.)

1.   **2.**

Assignment:

Exercise 14–1, #1 and 3, should have been assigned following the last test on Chapter 13. Assign Exercise 14–1, #2–10 even.

The expression $2x - 3$ is a linear expression. If you set another variable, y, equal to this expression, you get an equation

$$y = 2x - 3.$$

As you recall, the graph of this equation is a straight line with slope 2 and y-intercept -3. For each value of x you pick, you will find that there is one and *only* one value of y. The graph shows this feature.

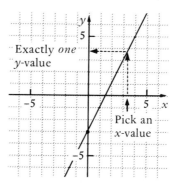

Any time there is exactly *one* y-value as the answer when you pick a value of x, y is said to be a *function* of x. Functions can have curved graphs as well as straight ones. For instance, suppose y equals a quadratic expression such as

$$y = 0.5x^2 - 2x + 1.$$

You can plot the graph by calculating points. For $x = 5$,

$$y = 0.5(5^2) - 2(5) + 1$$

$$y = 12.5 - 10 + 1$$

$$y = 3.5$$

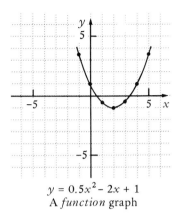

$$y = 0.5x^2 - 2x + 1$$
A *function* graph

Repeating this calculation for other values of x gives the following table of values.

x	y
-1	3.5
0	1
1	-0.5
2	-1
3	-0.5
4	1
5	3.5

The curved graph shown above is called a **parabola.** As you can see, there is still only *one* value of y for any single value of x you might pick, even though there may be two values of x that give the same value of y (such as $x = 0$ and $x = 4$).

There are equations for which there is more than one value of y for the same value of x. For instance, if

$$y = 2 \pm \sqrt{x},$$

then when $x = 9$,

$$y = 2 \pm \sqrt{9}$$

$$y = 2 \pm 3$$

$$y = 5 \quad \text{or} \quad y = -1$$

In this case, y is *not* a function of x.

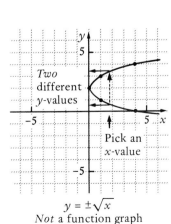

$$y = \pm\sqrt{x}$$
Not a function graph

DEFINITION

> **FUNCTION**
> A **function** is a set of ordered pairs (x, y) for which there is never more than one value of y for any one given value of x.

Objective:
Given the equation for a function, calculate ordered pairs and use them to plot the graph.

Cover the answer as you work this example.

EXAMPLE

For the function $y = |2x - 6|$:

a.   Calculate the value of y for each integer value of x, starting at $x = -1$ and ending at $x = 7$.

b.   Plot the points, determine the pattern, and connect the points appropriately.

— — — — —   — — — — —

x	y
−1	8
0	6
1	4
2	2
3	0
4	2
5	4
6	6
7	8

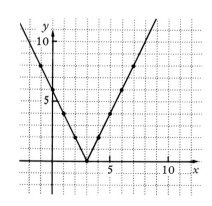

Note: In this case the graph goes down, then up. But the lines are straight, rather than curved as in the quadratic function above.

ORAL PRACTICE

Are these graphs of *functions?* Explain.

A.

Function

B.

Not a function

C.

Not a function

D.

Function

E.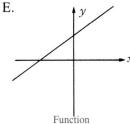

Function

EXERCISE 14-1

For each function:

a.   Calculate the value of *y* for each value of *x* indicated. Use a computer, if you like.

b.   Plot the points and connect them appropriately.

1. $y = 0.3x + 4$, for all integers $-3 \leq x \leq 3$.

2. $y = 2.1x - 7$, for all integers $-3 \leq x \leq 3$.

3. $y = x^2 - 4x + 2$, for all integers $-1 \leq x \leq 5$.

4. $y = x^2 - 2x + 3$, for all integers $-2 \leq x \leq 4$.

5. $y = 0.2x^2 - 1.2x + 1$, for all integers $0 \leq x \leq 6$.

6. $y = 0.4x^2 - 1.6x + 3$, for all integers $-1 \leq x \leq 5$.

7. $y = |2x - 4|$, for all integers $-2 \leq x \leq 6$.

Problem Notes:

Problems 1 and 2 are linear functions. Students should be able to graph these using rise and run.

Problems 3–8 each have a graph with a vertex. A quadratic function (3 through 6) has a rounded vertex, and an absolute value function (7 and 8) has a pointed vertex.

Problems 9 and 10 are inverse variation functions, which students will study in the next section.

1.-10.   See Additional Answers.

8. $y = |3x - 12|$, for all integers $0 \le x \le 8$.

9. $y = \dfrac{12}{x}$, for $x = 1, 2, 3, 4, 6, 12$.

10. $y = \dfrac{10}{x}$, for $x = 1, 2, 4, 5, 10$.

14-2 | **DIRECT AND INVERSE VARIATION FUNCTIONS**

Time: 2 days

Chalkboard Examples:

First day:
1. *Garbage Problem*—The number of tons of garbage generated in a city each day is directly proportional to the number of people who live in that city. Assume that a city of 20 thousand people generates 12 tons of garbage a day.
    a. Find the proportionality constant. Write the particular equation expressing number of tons in terms of number of *thousands* of people.
        Ans.: x = no. of thousands of people
            y = no. of tons
            $y = 0.6x$

    b. How much garbage would be generated in New York, population 9 million?
        Ans.: 5400 tons
    c. What is the population of a city that generates 300 tons of garbage a day?
        Ans.: 500 thousand

2. *Work Crew Problem*—The number of people needed to get a job done varies inversely with the amount of time available to do the job. Suppose that it takes 6 people to do a certain job if 24 hours are available.
    a. Find the proportionality constant. Write the particular equation expressing number of people in terms of time.
        Ans.: x = no. of hours
            y = no. of people
            $y = \frac{144}{x}$
    b. How many people would it take if only 2 hours were available?
        Ans.: 72 people
    c. How long would it take if 18 people work?
        Ans.: 8 hours

Sometimes in the real world two variable quantities are related in such a way that when one of them gets larger, so does the other one. For instance, as you travel in a car, the number of miles you have gone increases as the driving time increases.

In other instances, one variable goes *down* as the other goes up. For example, the length of time needed to do a particular job decreases as the number of workers increases.

The simplest function of the first kind is called a *direct variation function*. It has an equation like

$$y = 3x,$$

where the value of y is found by multiplying the value of x by a constant. In such a function, doubling x also doubles y.

$$x = 10 \xrightarrow{\text{Double } x.} x = 20$$

$$y = 3(10) \qquad\qquad y = 3(20)$$

$$y = 30 \xrightarrow{y \text{ doubles.}} y = 60$$

The simplest function of the second kind is called an *inverse variation function*. It has an equation such as

$$y = \frac{24}{x},$$

where y is found by *dividing* a constant by x. Here, doubling the value of x makes y *half* as big.

$$x = 3 \xrightarrow{\text{Double } x.} x = 6$$

$$y = \frac{24}{3} \qquad\qquad y = \frac{24}{6}$$

$$y = 8 \xrightarrow{y \text{ is halved.}} y = 4$$

For $y = (\text{constant})(x)$, y is said to *vary directly with x*, or to be *directly proportional to x*. For $y = \text{constant}/x$, y is said to *vary inversely with x*, or to be *inversely proportional to x*. In both cases, the constant is called the *proportionality constant*.

DEFINITIONS

DIRECT VARIATION FUNCTION
y varies directly with x, or **y is directly proportional to x,**
if and only if

$$y = kx.$$

where k is the **proportionality constant.**

INVERSE VARIATION FUNCTION
y varies inversely with x, *or* **y is inversely proportional to x,**
if and only if

$$y = \frac{k}{x},$$

where k is the **proportionality constant.**

Second day:
Homework problems at board.
The Oral Practice problems are effective between the first and second assignments for getting students to realize the difference in behavior between direct and inverse variation.

Assignments:

Day 1: Exercise 14–2, #1, 3, 11, 13 or 2, 4, 12, 14;
Exercise 14–1, #5

Day 2: Exercise 14–2, #5, 7, 15, 17 or 6, 8, 16, 18;
Exercise 14–1, #9

An equation such as

$$y = kx \quad \text{or} \quad y = \frac{k}{x}$$

is called a **general equation.** If the value of k is known, such as

$$y = 3x \quad \text{or} \quad y = \frac{24}{x},$$

the equation is called the **particular equation.**

Objective:

Given a situation in which one quantity varies directly or inversely with another, find the proportionality constant, write the particular equation, and use the equation to predict values of variables.

Cover the answers as you work these examples.

EXAMPLE 1

Map Scale Problem   The number of miles represented on a map is directly proportional to the number of centimeters you measure on that map. Suppose that the scale is 2 cm = 15mi.

a. Find the proportionality constant. Write the particular equation expressing miles in terms of centimeters.

b. It is 3.8 cm on the map from Phoenix to Scorpion Gulch. How far apart are the two places?

c. How many centimeters represent 100 mi?

– – – –   – – – – –

	Think These Reasons
a. Let x = no. of centimeters. Let y = no. of miles.	Define variables.
$y = kx$ and $(x,y) = (2, 15)$	Write the general equation and the given ordered pair.
$15 = k(2)$	Substitute (2, 15).
$7.5 = k$	Solve for k.
$\therefore y = 7.5x$	Write the particular equation.
b. $y = 7.5(3.8)$	Substitute 3.8 for x.
$y = 28.5$	Do the arithmetic.
<u>28.5 mi</u>	Answer the question.
– – – –	– – – – –
c. $100 = 7.5x$	Substitute 100 for y.
$13\frac{1}{3} = x$	Solve for x.
<u>About 13.3 cm</u>	Answer the question.

EXAMPLE 2

Time and Speed Problem   The time it takes you to go a certain distance varies inversely with the speed at which you go. Suppose that it takes you 12 minutes to get to school riding your bike at an average speed of 15 miles per hour (mph).

a. Find the proportionality constant. Write the particular equation expressing time in terms of speed.

b. How long will it take you to get to school if you walk at 4 mph?

c. If you must get to school in 5 minutes, how fast must you go?

– – – – –   – – – – –

a.   Let t = number of minutes.   Define variables. You may use
     Let s = number of miles per hour.   letters that sound like *time* and
                                           speed.

$$t = \frac{k}{s}, \text{ and } (s, t) = (15, 12)$$ Write the general equation and
                                                      the given ordered pair.

$$12 = \frac{k}{15}$$ Substitute $(15, 12)$ for (s, t).

$$180 = k$$ Solve for k.

$$\therefore t = \frac{180}{s}$$ Write the particular equation.

- - - - -   - - - - -

b. $$t = \frac{180}{4}$$ Substitute 4 for s.

     $$t = 45$$ Do the arithmetic.

     <u>45 minutes</u>   Answer the question.

- - - - -   - - - - -

c. $$5 = \frac{180}{s}$$ Substitute 5 fot t.

     $$s = \frac{180}{5}$$ Divide each member by 5.
                                           Multiply each member by s.

     $$s = 36$$ Do the arithmetic.

     <u>36 mph</u>   Answer the question.

ORAL PRACTICE

Tell whether each illustrates direct or inverse variation, and why.

EXAMPLES

Answers

i.   Distance gone, and   i.   Direct. Increasing time increases
     time traveled   the distance.

ii. Time to fill the bathtub,   ii. Inverse. The faster the water flows,
     and water flow rate   the *less* time it takes.

A.   Number of left-handed people in a group, and total number of people   A.   Direct. The more people, the more left-
     in the group   handers.

B. Inverse. The more people eating, the less time it takes.
C. Direct. The longer the time, the more money spent.
D. Inverse. The less time you have, the faster you must go.
E. Direct. The taller one is, the greater the arm span.
F. Direct. The more people, the more electricity.
G. Inverse. The more the tank holds, the fewer stops need be made.
H. Direct. The more flour used, the more eggs are needed.
I. Direct. The heavier a person is on earth, the heavier he or she will be on the moon.
J. Inverse. The more people share the rent, the less each must pay.

B. Time taken to consume 100 tangerines and number of people consuming

C. Number of dollars spent on a vacation, and the number of days it lasts

D. Speed you must go, and the number of minutes you have available to get where you are going

E. A person's arm span, and his or her height

F. Electrical power used by a city, and the number of people who live in that city

G. The number of times one must stop for gas on a long trip, and the number of gallons the car's tank holds

H. The number of eggs used in a particular recipe, and the number of cups of flour used

I. The weight of a person on the earth, and his or her weight on the moon

J. The number of people sharing an apartment, and the number of dollars rent each one must pay a month

EXERCISE 14-2

Problem Notes:

Problems 1–10 involve direct variation, and Problems 11–20 involve inverse variation. It is suggested that you give some of each in the same assignment.

1. *Gas Consumption Problem*   The number of gallons of gas a car uses varies directly with the number of miles driven. Suppose that a car uses 3 gallons in going 120 miles.
   a. Find the proportionality constant. Write the particular equation expressing gallons in terms of miles. $g = 0.025$ m
   b. How many gallons would be used in driving 300 miles?   7.5 gals
   c. How far could the car go between fill-ups if the tank holds 11 gals?   440 miles

2. *Batting Average Problem*   The number of hits a particular baseball player is expected to make is directly proportional to the number of times at bat. Suppose that Homer Fly makes 3 hits in 8 times at bat.
   a. Find the proportionality constant. Write the particular equation expressing expected hits in terms of at-bats. $h = \frac{3}{8}b$
   b. How many hits can Homer expect in 24 at-bats?   9 hits
   c. Homer expects to make 33 hits. How many times would he have to be at bat?   88 times

3. *Elephant Ear Problem*   The elephant ear is a semitropical plant that grows near water. The length of a leaf of the elephant ear is directly

proportional to its width. Suppose that a leaf 4 feet long has a width of 3 feet.

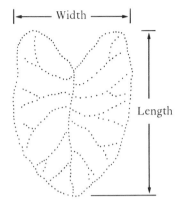

a. Find the proportionality constant. Write the particular equation expressing length in terms of width. $l = \frac{4}{3}w$
b. The end is torn off a leaf, so you cannot measure its length. But it is 5 feet wide. How long was it? $6\frac{2}{3}$ ft
c. A small leaf is 1.3 feet long. How wide is it?   0.975 ft

4. **Similar Triangles Problem**   Two triangles are **similar** if their corresponding angles have equal measures. In such triangles, the altitude is directly proportional to the length of the base. Suppose that one of a set of similar triangles has base 10 cm and altitude 13 cm.

Problem 4 introduces students to similar triangles, a topic they will soon encounter in geometry.

Words such as "*R* varies directly with *S*" imply that the value of *R depends* on the value of *S*. In this case *R* is called a *dependent variable* and *S* is called an *independent variable*. In the real world it is important to distinguish between independent and dependent variables. For this reason an equation relating the variables is called for in each problem. Students can still get correct answers to the other parts of each problem even if the variables are backwards in their equation.

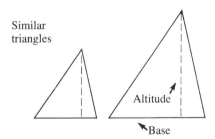

Similar triangles

a. Find the proportionality constant. Write the particular equation expressing altitude in terms of base length. $a = 1.3\ b$
b. What is the altitude of a triangle whose base is 52 cm?   67.6 cm
c. How long is the base of a triangle whose altitude is 130 cm?   100 cm

5. **Scuba Diving Problem**   When you scuba dive, the added pressure due to the water varies directly with your depth. At 20 feet, the added pressure is about 9 pounds per square inch (psi).
a. Find the proportionality constant. Write the particular equation expressing pressure in terms of depth. $p = 0.45d$
b. An amateur diver can safely stand an added pressure of 30 psi. How deep could he or she dive?   About 66 ft

Problem 5—Scuba divers use as a rule of thumb that the pressure increases by about 1 atmosphere for each 33 feet of depth. Normal atmospheric pressure is about 14.7 psi at sea level.

c. A sunken submarine lies in 120 feet of water off Lahaina in Maui, Hawaii. What added pressure would a diver experience in going to the submarine?   54 psi

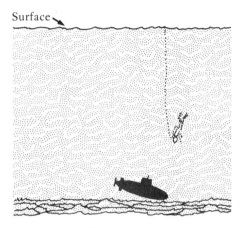

Surface

Problems 6 and 8 provide practical ways to measure lengths of things that are impractical to measure directly.

6. *Tape Recorder Problem*   The number of feet of tape that have gone through a tape recorder varies directly with the number of minutes the recorder has been on. In 3 minutes, 40 feet of tape go through.
a. Find the proportionality constant. Write the particular equation expressing feet in terms of minutes. $f = \frac{40}{3}t$
b. A 90-minute tape plays 45 minutes in each direction. If you unwound a 90-minute tape, how long would it be?   600 ft
c. At how many feet per minute does tape go through the recorder?   13.33 ft/min

7. *Recipe Problem*   Juana Cook has a recipe calling for 3 cups of flour. The recipe serves 5 people. She knows that the number of cups to use is directly proportional to the number of people that are served.
a. Find the proportionality constant. Write the particular equation expressing number of cups in terms of number of people. $C = \frac{3}{5}p$
b. Juana wants to use the recipe in a restaurant, where 100 people will be served. How many cups of flour should be used?   60 cups
c. Juana uses the recipe for company at home. She has 7 cups of flour and hopes to serve 11 people. Does she have enough flour? Justify your answer.   Yes, only needs $6\frac{2}{3}$ cups or can serve $11\frac{2}{3}$ people.

8. *Wire Length Problem*   Millie Watt is an electrical contractor. She needs to find out how many feet of wire are left on a partially used roll, without having to unroll the wire and measure it. So she cuts off a 4-foot piece, weighs it, and finds that it weighs 1.2 pounds. She knows that the length of the wire on the roll is directly proportional to the weight of the wire.

a. Find the proportionality constant. Write the particular equation expressing length in terms of weight. $l = \frac{10}{3} w$

b. The roll of wire remaining weighs 36 pounds. How many feet of wire are there?   120 ft

c. A full roll of the same kind of wire has 200 feet of wire. Millie can lift up to 70 pounds. Can she lift a full roll? Justify your answer. $w = 60$ lbs   Yes! (or she can lift up to $233\frac{1}{3}$ feet)

9. *Thunder and Lightning Problem*   In a lightning storm, the number of seconds between the flash and the bang is directly proportional to the number of miles you are from the lightning. It takes 15 seconds for the thunder sound to reach you from lightning that is 3 miles away.

> Problem 9 leads to a quick way to tell how far away the thunderstorm is. It is a mile for every 5 seconds (a kilometer for every 3 seconds). It is seldom possible to hear thunder from lightning more than 5 miles away.

a. Find the proportionality constant. Write the particular equation expressing time in terms of distance. $t = 5d$

b. How long does it take the sound to reach you from lightning:
    i. 5 miles away;   25s   ii. 2 miles away?   10s

c. How far away is the lightning if the time is only 1 second? $\frac{1}{5}$ mile

10. *Diving Board Problem*   The number of centimeters a diving board bends is directly proportional to the weight of the person standing on it. Phoebe Small, who weighs 90 pounds, bends the board 5 centimeters.

Bend

a. Find the proportionality constant, and write the particular equation, expressing centimeters in terms of pounds. $b = \frac{1}{18} w$

b. Norma Lee weighs 120 pounds. How far will she bend the board?   6.67 cm

c. Calvin Butterball will not tell how much he weighs. But his friends observe that he bends the diving board 15 centimeters. How heavy is he?   270 lbs

11. *Speed versus Time Problem*   The speed you must go to cover a certain distance varies inversely with the time available for the trip. Suppose that you must travel 30 miles per hour (mph) when you have 10 minutes available.

a. Find the proportionality constant. Write the particular equation expressing speed in terms of time. $s = \frac{300}{t}$

b. How fast must you go when there are only 5 minutes available? 60 mph

c. How fast can you go if there is half an hour available?   10 mph

12. ***Book Assembly Problem***   The number of hours it takes to collate the pages for copies of a book is inversely proportional to the number of people doing the collating. Suppose that a crew of 4 people takes a total of 12 hours to do the job.
    a. Find the proportionality constant. Write the particular equation expressing time in terms of number of people. $t = \frac{48}{c}$
    b. How long would it take 10 people to do the job? $t = 4.8$ hrs
    c. How long would it take one person alone to do the job? Where else have you seen this number?   48 hrs The proportionality constant

13. ***Wheel Problem***   The number of times a wheel rotates in going a mile is inversely proportional to the diameter of the wheel. A 27-inch diameter bicycle wheel makes 747 revolutions in going a mile.
    a. Find the proportionality constant. Write the particular equation expressing number of revolutions in terms of diameter. $r = \frac{20169}{d}$
    b. How many revolutions would a locomotive wheel, 80 inches in diameter, take to go a mile?   About 252
    c. How large a diameter wheel would be needed to cover a mile with only 100 revolutions?   About 202 in.

Problem 14—In practice, much of the resistance to heat flow occurs at the glass-to-air boundaries between the window and the surroundings. This is why two $\frac{1}{8}$-inch panes provide much better insulation than one $\frac{1}{4}$-inch pane.

14. ***Heat Loss Problem***   The rate at which heat is lost through a window pane is inversely proportional to the thickness of the pane. Suppose that a normal $\frac{1}{8}$-inch-thick pane loses 400 calories per hour.

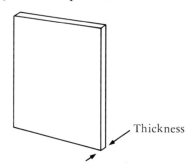

Thickness

    a. Find the proportionality constant. Write the particular equation expressing calories per hour in terms of thickness. $r = \frac{50}{t}$
    b. How many calories per hour would be lost through a $\frac{3}{8}$-inch-thick window pane? $r = 133$ cal/hr
    c. How thick a pane would be needed to make the loss only 50 calories per hour?   1 in.

15. ***Population Problem***   Demographers have a rule of thumb which says that the population of a city in a given region is inversely proportional to the *rank* of that city (largest, second largest, third largest, and so on). Suppose that the fourth-ranked city in a region has a population of 200,000.
    a. Find the proportionality constant. Write the particular equation expressing population in terms of rank. $p = (800,000)/r$

b. What is the population of:
   i. the tenth-ranked city; $p = 80{,}000$ ii. the largest city? $p = 800{,}000$
c. If a city has a population of 4000, what is its rank?   200

16. *What You Can Buy Problem*   A fundamental fact of economics is
that the number of things you can buy with a fixed amount of money
is inversely proportional to the price of each item. Suppose that you
can buy 6 records when the price is $8 each.
   a. Find the proportionality constant. Write the particular equation
       expressing number of records in terms of price. $n = \frac{48}{p}$
   b. If the price increases to $12 each, how many records can you
       buy? $n = 4$
   c. What is the fixed amount of money you have available to spend? $48

17. *Band Formation Problem*   A marching band can make various
rectangular patterns with differing numbers of rows and columns.
The number of columns is inversely proportional to the number of
rows for a band of fixed size. Suppose that a particular band can
form a rectangle with 12 rows and 9 columns.

12 rows

9 columns

   a. Find the proportionality constant. Write the particular equation
       expressing number of columns in terms of number of rows. $c = \frac{108}{r}$
   b. How many columns would there be if there were 6 rows?   18
   c. Could there be 7 rows? Explain.   Yes, but there are extra people.
   d. How many people are in this band?   108

18. *Rectangle Problem*   If rectangles have equal areas, then their
lengths are inversely proportional to their widths. Suppose that one
of these rectangles is 40 meters long and 30 meters wide.

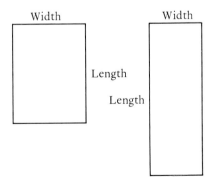

Width   Width

Length

Length

   a. Find the proportionality constant. Write the particular equation
       expressing length in terms of width. $l = \frac{1200}{w}$

b. If another of these rectangles is 20 cm wide, how long must it be?   60 cm

c. How long must one of these rectangles be in order for the length to equal the width?   34.64 m

Problem 19—The properties of levers can be demonstrated in the classroom using a normal meter stick with the pivot at various places.

19. *Prying Problem*   One way to raise a heavy object is to stick a board or crowbar under it to act as a lever and pry it up. The amount of force you must exert on the lever is inversely proportional to the number of centimeters from the pivot at which you push. Suppose that 100 pounds is required at a distance of 20 cm.

a. Find the proportionality constant. Write the particular equation expressing force in terms of distance. $f = \frac{2000}{d}$

b. If you move out to 60 cm from the pivot, how hard would you have to push?   33.33 lbs

c. A small child can exert only 10 pounds of force. Could the child pry up the object? Explain.   Yes. $d = 200$ cm

20. *Truck Speed Problem*   If a truck starts at rest and speeds up under maximum power, its speed after a fixed length of time is inversely proportional to its total weight. Suppose that for a particular truck weighing 3000 pounds empty, the speed is 40 miles per hour (mph) after 20 seconds.

a. Find the proportionality constant and write the particular equation expressing speed in terms of weight. $s = \dfrac{120,000}{w}$

b. The truck is loaded with 5000 pounds of cargo, making its total weight 8000 pounds. What will its speed be after 20 seconds under maximum power?   15 mph

c. When it is partially loaded, the truck's speed is 32 mph after 20 seconds at maximum power.
   i. Find the truck's total weight.   3750 lbs
   ii. Find the number of pounds of cargo.   750 lbs

Problems 21 and 22 present direct and inverse variation as it often appears in science courses. The ideal gas laws are often written in these forms.

21. $y = kx$
$\therefore y_1 = kx_1$ and $y_2 = kx_2$
$\dfrac{y_1}{x_1} = k$ and $\dfrac{y_2}{x_2} = k$
$\therefore \dfrac{y_1}{x_1} = \dfrac{y_2}{x_2}$, which was to be proved.

22. $y = \dfrac{k}{x}$
$\therefore y_1 = \dfrac{k}{x_1}$ and $y_2 = \dfrac{k}{x_2}$
$x_1 y_1, = k$ and $x_2 y_2 = k$
$\therefore x_1 y_1 = x_2 y_2$, which was to be proved.

21. *Proportion Property of Direct Variation*   If (x_1, y_1) and (x_2, y_2) are two ordered pairs in a direct-variation function, $y = kx$, show that

$$\frac{y_1}{x_1} = \frac{y_2}{x_2}$$

22. *Proportion Property of Inverse Variation*   If (x_1, y_1) and (x_2, y_2) are two ordered pairs in an inverse variation function, $y = \frac{k}{x}$, show that

$$x_1 y_1 = x_2 y_2.$$

14-3 | LINEAR FUNCTIONS

Sometimes in the real world two variable quantities are related in such a way that the graph is a straight line. As an example, suppose that a plumber charges $35 to make a house call, plus $25 an hour for the actual work.

Let x be the number of hours the plumber works.

Let y be the total number of dollars charged.

An expression for the number of dollars charges is $25x + 35$. So an equation for y in terms of x is

$$y = 25x + 35.$$

From your work in Chapter 8 you should recognize that this is the equation of a straight line. The slope is 25 and the y-intercept is 35. The figure shows a graph of this equation. Different scales are used on the two axes to make the graph have reasonable proportions.

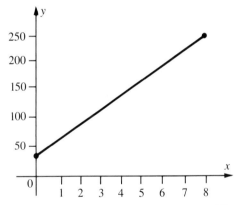

If x and y are related by a linear equation such as $y = 25x + 35$, then y is said to be a *linear function* of x. The following is a formal definition of linear function.

DEFINITION

> **LINEAR FUNCTION**
> A **linear function** is a function in which the ordered pairs (x, y) are related by an equation of the form
>
> $$y = mx + b,$$
>
> where m and b stand for constants, and $m \neq 0$.

Time: 2 days

Chalkboard Examples:

First day:

1. If $y = -3x + 7$,
    a. find y when x is 4.
        Ans.: $y = -3(4) + 7 = \underline{\underline{-5}}$
    b. find x when y is 13.
        Ans.: $13 = -3x + 7$
        $\underline{\underline{x = -2}}$
    c. sketch the graph.

(Note that in the sketch it is *not* necessary to show scales and draw accurately. The y-intercept should be labeled and the slope should be in the right direction and be about the right magnitude.)

2. *Donuts Problem*—At a local donut shop, they charge 20 cents for each donut, plus 15 cents for the box they go in.
    a. Write an equation expressing price of a box of donuts as a function of how many donuts are in the box.
    b. How much would you pay for a box with 12 donuts?
    c. How many donuts would be in a box costing $3.55?
    d. Sketch the graph of this function.

    a. Let x = no. of donuts
        Let y = no. of cents
        $\underline{y = 20x + 15}$
    b. $y = 20(12) + 15 = 255$
        $\underline{\$2.55}$
    c. $355 = 20x + 15$
        $17 = x$
        $\underline{17\ donuts}$
    d.

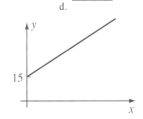

Notes:
1) A different scale can be justified for y since x and y measure different physical quantities.
2) This problem is identical to Problem 1 in Exercise 2–1. Only the terminology has been changed to say "function."

Second day:
Homework problems at the board

Assignments:

Day 1: Exercise 14–3, #1, 3, 5, 7
        Exercise 14–2, #20 (or other review problems)
Day 2: Exercise 14–3, #2, 4, 6, 8, 10

Problem Notes:

Problem 8: Students are usually surprised to learn how much it costs to own a car in excess of the actual driving expenses!

Problem 12: The lower bound of the domain is 2, because 1-story buildings don't need elevators.

The value of one variable in a function often depends on the value of the other. For instance, the number of dollars the plumber makes depends on the number of hours worked. The variable that depends is called the **dependent variable.** The variable it depends on is called the **independent variable.** The dependent variable is usually plotted on the vertical axis, as in the sketch.

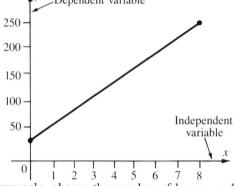

In the plumber example, above, the number of hours worked cannot be negative. if you assume that the plumber would not work more that 8 hours on any one call, the permissible values of x would be all numbers from 0 through 8. These numbers are called the **domain** of the function. The total number of dollars can range from 35 at 0 hours worked to 235 at 8 hours worked. The numbers from 35 through 235 are called the **range** of the function. These sets of numbers are shown in the sketch.

DEFINITION

DOMAIN AND RANGE
The **domain** of a function is the set of permissible values of the **independent variable.**

The **range** of a function is the set of values of the **dependent variable** corresponding to all values of the independent variable in the domain.

Objective:

Given a situation from the real world in which two variables are related by a linear function, find the equation and use it to predict values of the variables.

EXAMPLE 1

For the plumber problem, above,
a. Find the total charge for 5 hours 15 minutes.
b. How long could the plumber work without exceeding a total bill of $120?

– – – – –   – – – – –

	Think These Reasons
a. The equation is $y = 25x + 35$.	From the first of this section
5 hours 15 minutes is 5.25 hours.	60 minutes in an hour
$y = 25(5.25) + 35$	Substitute 5.25 for x.
$y = 166.25$	Do the computations.
$\underline{\$166.25}$	Answer the question.
b. $120 = 25x + 35$	Substitute 120 for y.
$85 = 25x$	Subtract 35.
$3.4 = x$	Divide by 25.
$\underline{3 \text{ hours, } 24 \text{ minutes}}$	Answer the question.

ORAL PRACTICE

State the domain and range of the linear function.

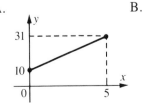

A.

Domain: $0 \le x \le 5$
Range: $10 \le y \le 31$

B.

Domain: $0 \le x \le 200$
Range: $1.7 \le y \le 4.0$

C.

Domain: $2 \le x \le 7$
Range: $3 \le y \le 6$

D.

E.

F.

Domain: $47 \leq x \leq 131$
Range: $28 \leq y \leq 55$

Domain: $-3 \leq x \leq 5$
Range: $10 \leq y \leq 27$

Domain: $-10 \leq x \leq 6$
Range: $-5 \leq y \leq 23$

G.

H.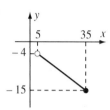

Domain: $-100 < x < 250$
Range: $-3 < y < -1$

Domain: $5 < x \leq 35$
Range: $-15 \leq y < -4$

Tell which variable is independent and which is dependent.

I.

J.

K.

Indep.: Time
Dep.: Distance

Indep.: hours
Dep.: Dollars

Indep.: miles
Dep.: Gallons

L.

Indep.: Temperature
Dep.: Humidity

EXERCISE 14-3

1. If $y = 7x + 3$,
   a. Find y when x is -4. -25
   b. Find x when y is 45. 6

2. If $y = -0.4x + 170$,
    a. Find y when x is 200.   90
    b. Find x when y is 87.   207.5

3.

For Problems 3 through 6, sketch the graph of the linear function described.

3. Slope is positive and y-intercept is negative.

4. Slope is negative and y-intercept is positive.

4.

5. Domain: $2 \le x \le 7$, range: $3 \le y \le 6$

6. Domain: $0 \le x \le 8$, range: $1 \le y \le 9$

7. *Housebuilding Problem*   The cost of building a new house depends on the number of square feet of floor space. Suppose that the builder will charge $60 per square foot, and that the lot on which the house is to be built costs $40,000.
    a. Write an equation expressing total cost as a function of square feet of floor space. $T = 40,000 + 60f$
    b. What will the total cost be for a 2500 square foot house? $190,000
    c. The new owners can afford to pay as much as $220,000, total, for the house and lot. What is the largest house they could build? $f = 3000$ ft^2
    d. Sketch the graph of this linear function. Show clearly the domain and range.

5.   or

6.   or

8. *Owning a Car Problem*   Lisa Carr figures that it costs her 22 cents a mile to drive her car, plus a fixed monthly cost of $230 for car payments, etc. So her total monthly cost for owning the car is a function of the number of miles a month she drives it.
    a. Write an equation expressing total monthly cost in terms of number of miles driven that month. $c = 230 + 0.22m$
    b. How much would it cost Lisa if she drives 1000 miles a month? $450
    c. Lisa can afford no more than $500 a month, total, for car expenses. About how far can she drive each month?   1227 mi.
    d. Sketch the graph of this linear function. Show clearly the domain and range.

7.d.

9. *Tip Money Problem*   Suppose that a waiter makes $40 a day, plus 70% of the tip money he receives.
    a. Write an equation expressing total daily pay as a function of tip money received. $P = 40 + 0.7t$
    b. How much tip money would be needed for the waiter to earn $100 in a day? $85.71
    c. How much would the waiter make in a day if he receives $57 in tip money? $79.90
    d. Sketch the graph of this linear function. Show clearly the domain and range.

8.d.

9.d.

10.d.

11.d.

12.e.

For $s = 2$, $F = 130$
For $s = 23$, $F = 970$

13.   a.   Let w = number of ounces in box.
Let d = cost in dollars for a box (24, 1.95), (18, 1.49).

c. $d - 1.95 = 0.0766 \ldots (w - 24)$
or
$d - 1.49 = 0.0766 \ldots (w - 18)$

d.   Transform the equation to slope-intercept form. The y-intercept is the fixed cost.
$d - 1.95 = 0.0766 \ldots w - 1.84$
$d = 0.0766 \ldots w + 0.11$
The fixed cost is $0.11 or 11¢ per box from d when w is zero.

10.   ***Commission Problem***   Suppose that an insurance agent makes $700 a month base pay. In addition, she makes a commission of 8% of the value of the insurance policies she sells.
a.   Write an equation expressing total monthly pay as a function of number of dollars worth of policies sold. $M = 700 + 0.08v$
b.   How many dollars worth of insurance must she sell to make $2000 in a month? $16250
c.   How many dollars will she get, total, if she sells a million dollars worth of insurance in a month? $80,700
d.   Sketch the graph of this linear function. Show clearly the domain and range.

11.   ***Highway Painting Problem***   The Highway Department estimates that it takes 2.3 hours to paint a mile of center stripe on the highway. In addition, it takes about 45 minutes for the crew to get ready to paint.
a.   Write an equation expressing total time it will take as a function of number of miles to be painted. $T = 0.75 + 2.3m$
b.   How long will it take, total, for the crew to paint 2 miles?   5.35 h
c.   What is the maximum number of miles a crew can paint in a day if they may spend no more than 8 hours, total, that day?   or 5 h 21 min   3.15 mi
d.   Sketch the graph of this linear function. Show clearly the range and domain.

12.   ***Elevator Cable Problem***   The number of feet of cable needed for an elevator in a building is 40 times the number of stories tall the building is, plus 50 feet (used to go into and out of the machinery).
a.   Write an equation expressing total number of feet of cable as a function of number of stories. $F = 50 + 40s$
b.   How much cable would be needed for a 7-story building?   330 ft
c.   A reel of elevator cable contains 1000 feet of cable. What is the tallest building that could be equipped with an elevator without having to splice together pieces of cable?   23 stories
d.   What is the domain of this linear function if the building codes do not allow spliced cable? (Think hard about your answer!)   Domain: $2 \leq s \leq 23$
e.   Sketch the graph of this linear function using the domain in part (d).

13.   ***Corn Flakes Problem***   A 24-ounce box of corn flakes costs $1.95. An 18-ounce box costs only $1.49. Assume that the cost of a box of corn flakes is a linear function of the number of ounces in the box.
a.   Define variables for the number of ounces and the number of dollars. Then write the two given pieces of information as ordered pairs.
b.   Find the slope of this linear function.   about 0.077
c.   Use the point-slope form to write an equation for this function.
d.   How would you find out what they assume as the fixed cost for the box, etc.? What is this fixed cost?

14. *Haircut Problem*   Dan Druff shaved off all his hair some time ago. Presently, his hair is 6 cm long. Three weeks ago it was only 4.8 cm long. Let x be the number of weeks that have elapsed after the present, and let y be the number of centimeters long his hair is.
   a.   Write the two pieces of information about length and time as ordered pairs. You must decide in which order to write the variables. (Think carefully about the correct values of x!)
   b.   Find the slope of this linear function.
   c.   Use the slope-intercept form to write an equation for this function.
   d.   How long ago did Dan shave off his hair?
   e.   Sketch the graph of this linear function. Indicate clearly the domain.

14. a. $(0, 6), (-3, 4.8)$
     b.   0.4
     c. $y = 0.4x + 6$
     d.   15 weeks ago
     e.

14-4 | TRIGONOMETRIC FUNCTIONS

In Section 12-7 you used the Pythagorean theorem to find the length of one side of a right triangle when you knew the lengths of the other two sides. In this section you work similar problems, except you work with the measure of the *angles* in the right triangle, as well as the side lengths.

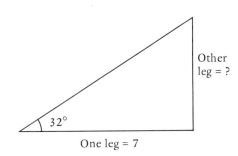

Other leg = ?

32°

One leg = 7

In the right triangle shown, one leg is 7 units long, and an acute angle is of measure 32°. The *ratio* of the legs in a right triangle depends only on the size of the acute angle. You learned this property when you were finding slopes of straight lines. The value of the ratio can be calculated for any angle measure. For 32° it is about 0.6249. So for this triangle,

$$\frac{\text{other leg}}{7} \approx 0.6249.$$

Multiplying each member by 7 gives

$$\text{other leg} \approx 7(0.6249)$$

$$\text{other leg} \approx \underline{4.3743 \text{ units}}$$

Time: 2 days

Chalkboard Examples:

First day:
1. Find x and y.
   Ans.: $x \approx 33.92$
   $\quad\quad\ y \approx 21.20$
   (Answers by calculator.)

2. Find r and s.
   Ans.: $r \approx 60.85$
   $\quad\quad\ s \approx 92.75$
3. Find A.
   Ans.: About 63 degrees.

Have students work text Examples 1, 2, and 3 before starting the assignment.

Second day:
Homework at board if necessary.
Have students work text Example 4 before starting the assignment.

Assignments:

Day 1: Exercise 14–4, #1–19 odd or 2–20 even
Day 2: Exercise 14–4, #21–29 odd or 22–30 even
   Selected problems from 1–20, if needed for consolidation.

By knowing the ratio for any given angle, you can find lengths of legs in *any* right triangle. These values can be found on a calculator or in a table of values if you do not have a calculator.

If *A* is an acute angle in a right triangle, then the side opposite *A* is given the (obvious) name **opposite leg.** The leg next to *A* is called the **adjacent leg.** The word *adjacent* means *next to*. As you recall, the longest side of a right triangle is called the *hypotenuse*.

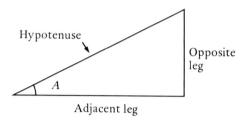

The ratio

$$\frac{\text{opposite leg}}{\text{adjacent leg}},$$

which you were using above, is called the *tangent of angle A,* abbreviated tan *A*. Other sides of a right triangle also have ratios that depend only on the size of the angle. Two of these are named the *sine of A,* (pronounced the same as *sign*) and the *cosine of A*. These are abbreviated sin *A* and cos *A*, respectively, and are defined below. They are called **trigonometric functions** because *trigon* is another name for *triangle,* and *metric* pertains to *measurement*.

DEFINITIONS

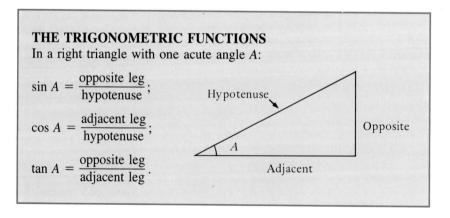

THE TRIGONOMETRIC FUNCTIONS
In a right triangle with one acute angle *A*:

$$\sin A = \frac{\text{opposite leg}}{\text{hypotenuse}};$$

$$\cos A = \frac{\text{adjacent leg}}{\text{hypotenuse}};$$

$$\tan A = \frac{\text{opposite leg}}{\text{adjacent leg}}.$$

Values of these functions can be found most easily on a calculator. You enter the number of degrees, then press the sin, cos, or tan key. There is also a short table of values on page 621 of this book.

Objectives:

1. Given an angle measure and a side length of a right triangle, find the lengths of the other two sides.

2. Given two side lengths of a right triangle, find the measure of an acute angle.

Cover the answers as you work these examples.

EXAMPLE 1

For the right triangle shown, find:

a.   the length of the other leg;

b.   the length of the hypotenuse.

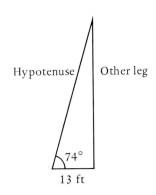

— — — — —   — — — — —

Think These Reasons

a.   Let x = length of other leg in feet.   Define variables.
     Let y = length of hypotenuse in feet.

$$\frac{x}{13} = \tan 74°$$ Use the definition of tangent.

$x = 13(\tan 74°)$ Multiply each member by 13.

$x = 13(3.4874. . .)$ By calculator or tables.

$x = 45.336. . .$ Do the multiplication.

<u>About 45.34 ft.</u>   Answer the question. Round
                                               the answer.

— — — — —   — — — — —

b. $$\frac{13}{y} = \cos 74°$$ Use the definition of cosine.

$13 = y(\cos 74°)$ Multiply each member by y.

$$\frac{13}{\cos 74°} = y$$ Divide each member by
                                               $\cos 74°$.

$$\frac{13}{0.2756\ldots} = y$$ By calculator or tables.

$$47.163\ldots = y$$ Do the division.

<u>About 47.16 ft.</u>   Answer the question. Round.

EXAMPLE 2

The hypotenuse of a right triangle is 50 cm and an acute angle is 19°. Find the measures of the two legs.

– – – – –   – – – – –

Draw a diagram.
Use variables for the un-
known lengths.

$$\frac{y}{50} = \sin 19°$$ Use the definition of sine.

$$y = 50(\sin 19°)$$ Multiply each member by 50.

$$y = 50(0.32556\ldots)$$ By calculator or tables.

$$y = 16.278\ldots$$ Do the multiplication.

<u>About 16.28 cm.</u>   Answer the question. Round.

– – – – –   – – – – –

$$\frac{x}{50} = \cos 19°$$ Use the definition of cosine.

$$x = 50(\cos 19°)$$ Multiply each member by 50.

$$x = 50(0.9455\ldots)$$ By calculator or tables.

$$x = 47.2759\ldots$$ Do the multiplication.

<u>About 47.28 cm.</u>   Answer the question. Round.

EXAMPLE 3

The hypotenuse of a right triangle is 29 inches long and one leg is 17 inches long. Find the measure of the angle opposite the 17-inch side.

– – – – –   – – – – –

Draw a diagram. Use a
variable for the angle
measure.

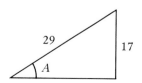

$$\sin A = \frac{17}{29}$$ Use the definition of sine.

$\sin A = 0.5862. . .$ Do the division.

$A = 35.888. . .°$ Leave 0.5862. . . in the calculator. Press $\boxed{\text{inv}}$ $\boxed{\text{sin}}$. Or find the angle in the tables whose sine is closest to 0.5862.

<u>About 35.89°.</u>   Answer the question. Round.

Note: If you use the table of trigonometric functions, find the angle to the nearest degree.

EXAMPLE 4

From a point on the ground, a forester observes that the angle of elevation (see the figure) to the top of a pine tree is 37°. The forester is 123 feet from the base of the tree trunk. About how high is the tree?

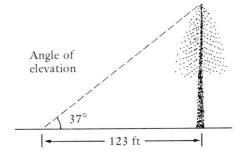

Angle of elevation

37°

|◄——— 123 ft ———►|

— — — — —   — — — — —

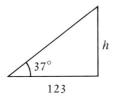

h

37°

123

Draw a diagram. Show the known lengths, and use a variable for the height.

$\dfrac{h}{123} = \tan 37°$ Use the definition of tangent.

$h = 123(\tan 37°)$ Multiply each member by 123.

$h = 123(0.753554. . .)$ By calculator or tables.

$h = 92.687. . .$ Do the multiplication.

<u>About 93 ft high</u>   Answer the question. Round.

ORAL PRACTICE

Tell which lettered side is *opposite* the angle marked, which is *adjacent* to the angle, and which is the *hypotenuse*.

EXAMPLE

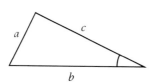

Answers
a is opposite,
c is adjacent,
b is the hypotenuse.

A. *y* is opposite
   x is adjacent
   z is hypotenuse

B. *w* is opposite
   f is adjacent
   p is hypotenuse

C. *r* is opposite
   d is adjacent
   t is hypotenuse

D. *u* is opposite
   c is adjacent
   r is hypotenuse

E. *m* is opposite
   b is adjacent
   y is hypotenuse

F. *j* is opposite
   w is adjacent
   c is hypotenuse

A.

B.

C.

D.

E.

F.

Give sin *A*, cos *A*, and tan *A*.

EXAMPLE

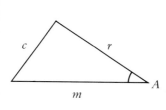

Answers

$$\sin A = \frac{c}{m}$$

$$\cos A = \frac{r}{m}$$

$$\tan A = \frac{c}{r}$$

G.

H.
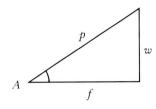

I.

r t d A

J.

A r c u

K. A

b y m

L.

c A w j

G. $\sin A = \dfrac{y}{z}$

$\cos A = \dfrac{x}{z}$

$\tan A = \dfrac{y}{x}$

H. $\sin A = \dfrac{w}{p}$

$\cos A = \dfrac{f}{p}$

$\tan A = \dfrac{w}{f}$

I. $\sin A = \dfrac{r}{t}$

$\cos A = \dfrac{d}{t}$

$\tan A = \dfrac{r}{d}$

J. $\sin A = \dfrac{u}{r}$

$\cos A = \dfrac{c}{r}$

$\tan A = \dfrac{u}{c}$

K. $\sin A = \dfrac{m}{y}$

$\cos A = \dfrac{b}{y}$

$\tan A = \dfrac{m}{b}$

L. $\sin A = \dfrac{j}{c}$

$\cos A = \dfrac{w}{c}$

$\tan A = \dfrac{j}{w}$

Find the following function values by calculator or from the table.

M. $\sin 14°$ 0.2419...   **N.** $\cos 65°$ 0.4226...   **O.** $\tan 38°$ 0.7812...

Find the angle measure to the nearest degree. Use a calculator or the table.

P. $\sin A = 0.8356$ **Q.** $\cos A = 0.8954$ **R.** $\tan A = 1.883$

57°   26°   62°

EXERCISE 14-4

For Problems 1 through 10, find the side lengths indicated in the right triangle.

1.

$x = 16.86$
$y = 30.16$

2.

$x = 19.87$
$y = 43.77$

Problem Notes:

Problems 1–20 present right triangles in various orientations so that students must key on opposite, adjacent, and hypotenuse to get the correct ratio. You can use the Oral Practice problems prior to the first assignment to make sure students have the idea.

3.

x = 22.56
y = 28.25

4.

x = 247.27
y = 263.14

5.
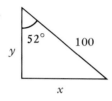

x = 78.80
y = 61.57

6.
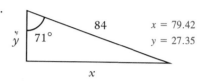

x = 79.42
y = 27.35

7.
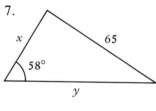

x = 40.62
x = 76.65

8.
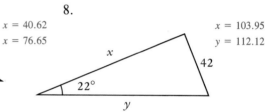

x = 103.95
y = 112.12

9.
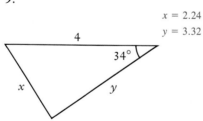

x = 2.24
y = 3.32

10.
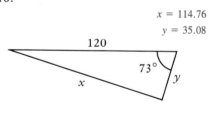

x = 114.76
y = 35.08

For Problems 11 through 20, find the indicated angle measure in the right triangle.

11.

A = 35.54°

12.

B = 36.47°

13.

C = 28.07°

14.
D = 31.10°

15.

E = 44.42°

16.
F = 54.85°

17.

G = 53.13°

18.
H = 16.26°

19.
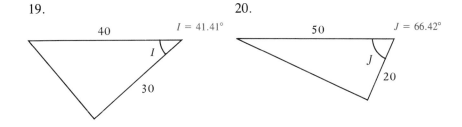
I = 41.41°

20.
J = 66.42°

For Problems 21 through 30, answer the questions.

21. **Building Height Problem**   From a
     point 78 feet from the base of a
     building, the angle of elevation to
     the top of the building is 57°. To
     the nearest foot, how high is the
     building?   About 120 ft

22. *Flagpole Problem*   The sun shines on a flagpole, causing a shadow to be cast on the ground. The distance from the base of the pole to the tip of the shadow is 49 feet. At that time of day, the sun's rays make an angle of 38° with the ground. How tall is the flagpole?   About 38 ft

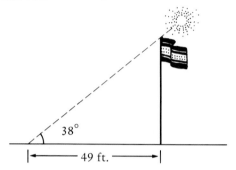

23. *Guy Wire Problem*   A 2000-foot-high television transmitting tower is to be supported by guy wires running from the ground to the top. The wires must make an angle of 63° with the ground.

   a.   How long will each wire be?   2244 ft
   b.   How far from the base of the tower must they meet the ground?   1019 ft

24. *Ship's Path Problem*   Sailors on a ship observe a lighthouse at an angle of 34° to the path of the ship. After the ship has sailed 2000 yards more, the lighthouse is at 90° to the ship's path. How far is the ship from the lighthouse:

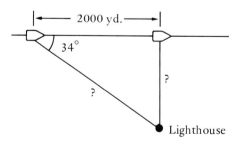

   a.   at the first sighting;   2412 yd   b. at the second sighting?   1349 yd

25. *Submarine Problem*   A submarine starts on the surface, and dives at an angle of 13° to the surface. It goes diagonally a distance of 890 meters before reaching the bottom.

a. How deep is the water where the submarine reaches the bottom?   About 200 m
b. How far is it along the ocean surface from the point where the submarine started to the point directly above where it reached the bottom?   About 867 m

26. *Shortcut Problem*   Calvin Butterball cuts across the field from his house to Phoebe Small's house, going 482 yards along a path that makes an angle of 28° with Alamo Street. Suppose Calvin walked along the streets instead of across the field.

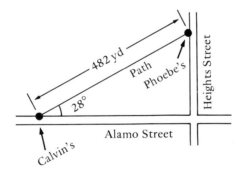

a. How far would he walk along Alamo Street?   426 yd
b. How far would he walk along Heights Street?   226 yd
c. How many yards does he save by using the shortcut?   170 yd

27. *Volcano Problem*   Haleakela (pronounced hallay-ah′-keh-la′) is a 10,000-foot-high dormant volcano on Maui, Hawaii. The peak is a horizontal distance of only about 30,000 feet from the ocean. At what angle would you have to look up to see the peak if you were standing at the edge of the ocean?   18.43°

Problem 27—Haleakela is reputed to be the only place in the world where one can drive from sea level to 10,000 feet in such a short distance. The road is about 40 miles (including hairpin curves) from Kahului on the northwest side of Maui. The 30,000 feet in the problem is measured from Huakini Bay on the southeast side of the island.

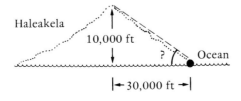

Problem 28—The angle a hill appears to make is an optical illusion. The $11\frac{1}{2}$ degrees of Highland Drive looks like 30 or 40 degrees to the driver or pedestrian. The streets in San Francisco where cable cars travel are only about 8 or 9 degrees.

28. *Hill Angle Problem*   One of the steepest streets in the United States is the 500 block of Highland Drive on Queen Anne Hill in Seattle. If you measure horizontally 70 centimeters from a point on the road surface, you must go down 14.2 centimeters to get back to the surface. What angle does Highland Drive make with the horizontal?   11.47°

29. *Fallen Tree Problem*   A tree is struck by lightning and snaps off 34 feet above the ground. The top part of the tree, 117 feet long, rests with the tip on the ground; the broken end rests on the stump, as shown. What angle does the top part of the tree make with the ground?   16.89°

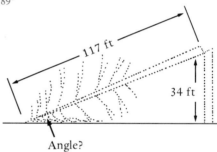

Problem 30—Some grand pianos also have a shorter prop about 32 cm long. You can give students problems such as finding the angle for this prop or finding the length of prop needed to make a specified angle.

30. *Grand Piano Problem*   The lid of a grand piano is held open by a prop, which makes a right angle with the lid. The prop is 71 centimeters long, and its base is 140 centimeters from the lid-to-piano hinge. What angle does the lid make with the piano?   30.47°

14-5 | QUADRATIC FUNCTIONS

In Section 14.1 you learned that a function can have an equation such as

$$y = \text{(an expression involving } x).$$

If that expression is quadratic, as in

$$y = x^2 - 6x + 7,$$

then the function is called a *quadratic function*.

The graph of a quadratic function can be drawn by calculating and plotting points. For the function $y = x^2 - 6x + 7$, if x is 5, then

$$y = 5^2 - 6(5) + 3$$

$$y = 25 - 30 + 3$$

$$y = -2$$

Repeating this calculation for other values of x gives the following table of values.

x	y
-1	10
0	3
1	-2
2	-5
3	-6
4	-5
5	-2
6	3
7	10

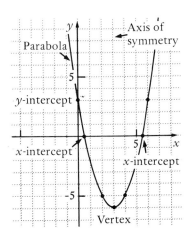

Time: 2 days

Chalkboard Examples:

First day:
For $y = x^2 - 4x - 3$:
a. Calculate points.
   Ans.: (See graph.)

b. Plot the graph.
   Ans.: (Graph.)
c. Find the x- and y-intercepts.
   Ans.: $x \cong 4.65$ or -0.65
          $y = -3$
d. Find the vertex.
   Ans.: $(2, -7)$
Second day:
Homework problems at the board.

Assignments:

Day 1: Exercise 14–5, #1, 3, 5 or 2, 4, 6;
       Exercise 14–4, #22 or 21;
       Exercise 14–2, #9
Day 2: Exercise 14–5, #7, 9, 11 or 8, 10, 12;
       Exercise 14–4, #26 or 25

The graph is a U-shaped figure called a **parabola.** The point at which the graph turns around is called the **vertex.** If you were to fold the graph paper along a vertical line through the vertex, the two halves would fit each other. Another way of saying this is to say that the graph is **symmetric** with respect to a line through the vertex. The word comes from *sym* meaning *same,* and *metric,* meaning *measure.* The vertical line through the vertex is called the **axis of symmetry.** As you can see, there are *two* *x*-intercepts, as well as one *y*-intercept.

In this section you will plot graphs of quadratic functions by calculating points. You will also calculate the *x*- and *y*-intercepts and the vertex.

Objective:
Given the equation of a quadratic function, calculate points, plot the graph, calculate the intercepts, and find the vertex.

For your future reference, here is a formal definition of quadratic function.

DEFINITION

> **QUADRATIC FUNCTION**
> A **quadratic function** is a function with an equation of the form
>
> $$y = \text{a quadratic expression.}$$
>
> That is, the equation has the form
>
> $$\boxed{y = ax^2 + bx + c}$$
>
> for some constants a, b, and c, where $a \neq 0$.

Since the actual computation of points is rather tedious, it makes sense to use a computer for evaluating the *y*-values. The following is a BASIC program that will do the job. You may use this one, or write one of your own.

```
10 PRINT "TYPE A,B,C"
20 INPUT A,B,C
30 FOR X = - 10 TO 10
40 LET Y = A * X * X + B * X + C
50 PRINT X,Y
60 NEXT X
70 END
```

The following are some worked examples that show how to accomplish the objective. You may either try them on your own, or simply read them to get ideas about how to work the problems in Exercise 14-5.

EXAMPLE 1

For the quadratic function $y = x^2 - 4x - 5$:

a. calculate points;
b. plot the graph;
c. find the x- and y-intercepts;

d. find the vertex.

_ _ _ _ _   _ _ _ _ _

	Think These Reasons

a.

x	y
-10	135
-9	112
-8	91
-7	72
-6	55
-5	40
-4	27
-3	16
-2	7
-1	0
0	-5
1	-8
2	-9
3	-8
4	-5
5	0
6	7
7	16
8	27
9	40
10	55

Use the computer program to calculate values.

b. Plot the graph. Note that it is not necessary to plot all the points the computer calculates. Just pick those that fit graph paper.

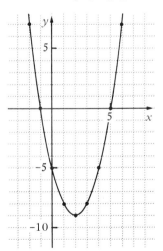

c. x-intercepts are -1 and 5.

The x-intercepts are the values of x when $y = 0$. In this case they can be found in the table.

y-intercept is -5.

The y-intercept is the value of y when $x = 0$. This, too, is in the table.

d.   *x*-coord. $= \frac{1}{2}(-1 + 5)$ The axis of symmetry goes

$= 2$ halfway between the two
                                x-intercepts. So its *x*-coordinate
                                is the *average* of the two
                                intercepts.

y-coord. $= 2^2 - 4(2) - 5$ Substitute 2 for *x* and evaluate
                                y.

$= 4 - 8 - 5$

$= -9$

Vertex: (2, −9)   Write the answer.

EXAMPLE 2

For the quadratic function $y = -x^2 - 3x + 5$:

a.   calculate points;

b.   plot the graph;

c.   find the *x*- and *y*-intercepts;

d.   find the vertex.

– – – – –   – – – – –

a.
x	y
-2	7
-1	0
0	-5
1	-8
2	-9
3	-8
4	-5
5	0
6	7

Use the computer program. Only part of the data is shown.

b.   Plot the graph as in Example 1. Note that when the x^2-coefficient is negative, the graph opens *downward*. In this case the vertex is the *high* point (maximum *y*) instead of the low point.

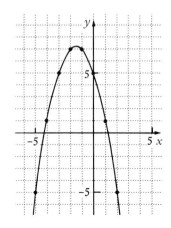

c. $0 = -x^2 - 3x + 5$ Set $y = 0$.

$x = \dfrac{3 \pm \sqrt{9 - 4(-1)(5)}}{2(-1)}$ Use the Quadratic Formula.

$x \approx 1.19$ or -4.19 Do the computations.

x-intercepts are 1.19 and -4.19.   Write the answer.

$y = -0^2 - 3(0) + 5$ Substitute 0 for x and evaluate y.

$y = 5$

y-intercept is 5.   Write the answer.

d. $x = \dfrac{1}{2}(-4.19 + 1.19)$ Average the x-intercepts.

$= -1.5$ Do the computations.

$y = -(-1.5)^2 - 3(-1.5) + 5$ Substitute -1.5 for x and evaluate y.

$y = -2.25 + 4.5 + 5$

$y = 7.25$

Vertex: $(-1.5, 7.25)$ Write the answer.

EXAMPLE 3

For the quadratic function $y = 6x^2 + 15x + 11$:

a.   calculate points;

b.   plot the graph;

c.   find the x- and y-intercepts;

d.   find the vertex.

– – – –   – – – –

a.

x	y	x	y
-8	275	3	110
-7	200	4	167
-6	137	5	236
-5	86		
-4	47		
-3	20		
-2	5		
-1	2		
0	11		
1	32		
2	65		

Use the computer program to calculate points.

b.

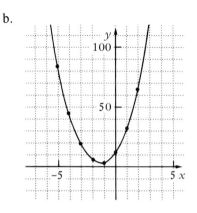

Plot the graph. Since the graph rises so steeply, you might *compress* the vertical scale as shown. Use a normal scale on the x-axis.

– – – – –   – – – – –

c. $0 = 6x^2 + 15x + 11$

Set $y = 0$.

$$x = \frac{-15 \pm \sqrt{225 - 4(6)(11)}}{2(6)}$$

Use the Quadratic Formula.

$$x = \frac{-15 \pm \sqrt{-39}}{12}$$

Do the computations.

<u>No x-intercepts.</u>

Since $\sqrt{-39}$ is not a real number, there are *no* values of x when $y = 0$. This is obvious, because the graph does not cross the x-axis.

$$y = 6(0^2) + 15(0) + 11$$

Substitute 0 for x and evaluate y.

$$y = 11$$

<u>y-intercept is 11.</u>

Write the answer.

– – – – –   – – – – –

d. $x = \dfrac{1}{2}\left(\dfrac{-15 + \sqrt{-39}}{12} + \dfrac{-15 - \sqrt{-39}}{12}\right)$

Average the values of x from part (c).

$$= \frac{1}{2}\left(\frac{-15 + \sqrt{-39} - 15 - \sqrt{-39}}{12}\right)$$

Add the fractions.

$$= \frac{1}{2}\left(\frac{-30}{12}\right)$$

If you treat $\sqrt{-39}$ as a number, the radicals have a sum of 0. See the note at the end of the example.

$$= -1.25$$

Do the computations.

$$y = 6(-1.25)^2 + 15(-1.25) + 11$$ Substitute -1.25 for x and evaluate y.

$$y = 1.625$$

Vertex: $(-1.25, 1.625)$ Write the answer.

Note: From part (d) of Example 3, you can see that for

$$y = 6x^2 + 15x + 11,$$

the vertex is at

$$x = \frac{1}{2}\left(\frac{-30}{12}\right),$$

which reduces to

$$x = \frac{-15}{12}$$

Looking at the original equation, -15 is the *opposite* of the x-coefficient and 12 is *twice* the x^2-coefficient. This pattern is true for *all* quadratic functions.

CONCLUSION

x-COORDINATE OF THE VERTEX
For the quadratic function $y = ax^2 + bx + c$, the x-coordinate of the vertex is

$$x = \frac{-b}{2a}$$

You can use this fact to find the vertex *quickly,* even if there are no x-intercepts.

ORAL PRACTICE

Find the x-coordinate of the vertex using $x = \dfrac{-b}{(2a)}$.

EXAMPLE

$y = 3x^2 + 12x - 13$ $_{-2}$

A. $y = 5x^2 + 30x - 7$ -3 B. $y = 3x^2 - 6x + 4$ 1

C. $y = 2x^2 - 12x + 5$ 3 D. $y = x^2 + 8x + 9$ -4

E. $y = 0.5x^2 + 7x - 3$ -7 F. $y = 0.2x^2 - 20x - 6$ 50

Find the y-intercept.

G. $y = 5x^2 + 30x - 7$ -7 H. $y = 3x^2 - 6x + 4$ 4

I. $y = 2x^2 - 12x + 5$ 5 J. $y = x^2 + 8x + 9$ 9

K. $y = 0.5x^2 + 7x - 3$ -3 L. $y = 0.2x^2 - 20x - 6$ -6

EXERCISE 14-5

Problem Notes:

The problems in Exercise 14–5 are somewhat long. Do not assign too many at one time.

   Problems for which the x^2-coefficient is positive have graphs that open upward. Those with negative x^2-coefficients open downward. The computer program PLOT QUADRATIC on the accompanying disk may be used to draw some of these graphs, but only after students have plotted a few by hand.

See Additional Answers.

For each of the following quadratic functions:

a.   pick values of x and calculate values of $y;$

b.   plot the graph;

c.   find the x- and y-intercepts;

d.   find the vertex.

1. $y = x^2 - 6x + 5$ 2. $y = x^2 - 8x + 7$

3. $y = x^2 + 5x - 2$ 4. $y = x^2 + 3x - 5$

5. $y = -0.4x^2 + 3x + 2$ 6. $y = -0.7x^2 + 2.8x + 4$

7. $y = x^2 - 3x + 5$ 8. $y = x^2 - 5x + 7$

9. $y = -x^2 + 6x - 10$ 10. $y = -x^2 + 4x - 6$

11. $y = 8x^2 - 20x - 37$ 12. $y = 5x^2 + 19x - 41$

14-6 | SOLVING QUADRATIC INEQUALITIES BY COMPLETING THE SQUARE

Time: 1 day

Chalkboard Examples:

1. Solve and graph: $x^2 - 8x - 20 < 0$
   Ans.: $-2 < x < 10$

In Chapter 9 you drew number-line graphs of linear inequalities and absolute value inequalities such as

$$3x + 2 \geq 7 \quad \text{or} \quad |x - 5| < 19.$$

In this and the next section, you will do the same thing for quadratic inequalities such as

$$x^2 - 6x + 4 < 0.$$

The main purpose of these two sections is to give you a review of most of the techniques of algebra while you learn something new.

The inequality above can be solved by completing the square. The first step is to add -4 to each member, leaving a space on the left.

$$x^2 - 6x \qquad < -4$$

To find the number that completes the square, take *half* the coefficient of x, and then *square* it. Half of -6 is -3, and $(-3)^2$ is 9. So you add 9 to each member.

$$x^2 - 6x + 9 < 5$$

The left member equals $(x - 3)^2$. The -3 is half of the x-coefficient: $\frac{1}{2}(-6)$. So you can write

$$(x - 3)^2 < 5.$$

Now you can take the square root of each member. For this, you need to know that taking the square root of each member does not reverse the order of the inequality. The following examples show you why.

$$2 < 7 \qquad\qquad 64 > 25$$
$$\sqrt{2} < \sqrt{7} \qquad\qquad \sqrt{64} > \sqrt{25}$$
$$1.41 < 2.65 \ \ \text{True!} \qquad 8 > 5 \ \ \text{True!}$$

The numbers *do* remain in the same order.

SQUARE ROOT PROPERTY OF ORDER
For any nonnegative numbers a and b,

$$\text{if} \quad a > b, \quad \text{then} \quad \sqrt{a} > \sqrt{b};$$
$$\text{if} \quad a < b, \quad \text{then} \quad \sqrt{a} < \sqrt{b}.$$

That is, you can take the square root of each member of an inequality without changing the order (as long as neither member is negative).

Using this property, you can take the square root of each member of the above inequality.

$$\sqrt{(x - 3)^2} < \sqrt{5}$$

Recalling that $\sqrt{(\text{number})^2}$ equals $|\text{number}|$, you can write

$$|x - 3| < \sqrt{5}.$$

2. Solve and graph: $(x + 3)(x - 9) \le 3x(x + 10)$
   Ans.: $x \ge -0.78$ or $x \le -17.22$

3. Solve and graph: $x^2 - 4x + 13 > 0$
   Ans.: All real numbers. Squares are always greater than negative numbers.

Assignment:

Exercise 14-6, #1–11 odd or 2–12 even; Exercise 14-5, #2 or 1

From here on, it is a problem of the kind you worked in Section 9.4. Since the inequality sign is $<$, the quantity $x - 3$ must be *between* $-\sqrt{5}$ and $\sqrt{5}$.

$$\sqrt{5} < x - 3 < \sqrt{5}$$

Adding 3 to each member gives

$$3 - \sqrt{5} < x < 3 + \sqrt{5}.$$

By calculator, $3\sqrt{5} = 0.763\ldots$. Since x must be *greater* than this number, the rounding must be *upward*. Similarly, $3 + \sqrt{5} = 5.236\ldots$, which must be rounded *downward* since x is *less* than $3 + \sqrt{5}$.

$$0.77 < x < 5.23.$$

The graph is as follows.

Objective:
Given a quadratic inequality such as $x^2 - 6x + 4 < 0$, solve it and graph its solution set.

Cover the answers as you work these examples.

EXAMPLE 1

Solve and graph $x^2 + 10x - 17 > 0$.

– – – – –   – – – – –

	Think These Reasons
$x^2 + 10x - 17 > 0$	Write the given inequality.
$x^2 + 10x \quad\quad > 17$	Make space to complete the square.
$x^2 + 10x + 25 > 42$	Complete the square: $(\frac{1}{2} \cdot 10)^2 = 25$.
$(x + 5)^2 > 42$	Write the left member as a square.
$\|x + 5\| > \sqrt{42}$	Take the square root of each member.
$x + 5 > \sqrt{42}$ or	$x + 5$ is *not* between $\sqrt{42}$ and $-\sqrt{42}$.
$x + 5 < -\sqrt{42}$	

$x > -5 + \sqrt{42}$ or

$\qquad x < -5 - \sqrt{42}$

Add -5 to each member.

$x > 1.49$ or

Do the arithmetic. Round in
the direction of the inequality.

$\qquad x < -11.49$

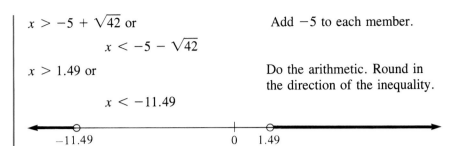

EXAMPLE 2

Solve and graph $x^2 - 13 \leq 8x + 58$.

- - - - -   - - - - -

$\qquad x^2 - 13 \leq 8x + 58$

Write the given inequality.

$\qquad x^2 - 8x \leq 71$

Get variables on the left and
constants on the right.

$x^2 - 8x + 16 \leq 87$

Complete the square (add 16).

$\qquad (x - 4)^2 \leq 87$

Write the left member as a
square.

$\qquad |x - 4| \leq \sqrt{87}$

Take the square root of each
member.

$\qquad -\sqrt{87} \leq x - 4 \leq \sqrt{87}$

$x - 4$ is *between* $\sqrt{87}$ and
$-\sqrt{87}$.

$4 - \sqrt{87} \leq x \leq 4 + \sqrt{87}$

Add 4 to each member.

$\qquad -5.32 \leq x \leq 13.32$

Do the computation. Round in
the direction of the inequality.

EXAMPLE 3

Solve and graph $x^2 + 14x + 60 < 0$.

- - - - -   - - - - -

$x^2 + 14x + 60 < 0$

Write the given inequality.

$x^2 + 14x \qquad < -60$

Make space to complete the
square.

$x^2 + 14x + 49 < -11$

Complete the square (add 49).

$\qquad (x + 7)^2 < -11$

Write the left member as a
square.

$$\therefore S = \emptyset$$

A square is never less than a negative number.

$$S = \emptyset$$

Draw the graph. It is an *empty* number line. Write $S = \emptyset$ on the number line for clarity.

$$\underline{\qquad\qquad\qquad\underset{0}{\vert}\qquad\qquad\qquad}$$

Note: If the inequality were $(x + 7)^2 > -11$, then the graph would be the entire number line. Squares are *always* greater than negative numbers.

ORAL PRACTICE

A. Subtract 2 from each member. Add 9 to each member.

B. Add 7 to each member. Add 16 to each member.

C. Add 3 to each member. Add 25 to each member.

D. Add 3 to each member. Add 4 to each member.

E. Add 5 to each member. Add 1 to each member.

F. Add 7 to each member. Add $\frac{1}{4}$ to each member.

Give the *two* steps that must be done in completing the square.

EXAMPLE 1

Answer:

$x^2 - 12x + 7 > 0$ Subtract 7 from each member. Add 36 to each member.

A. $x^2 - 6x + 2 > 0$ **B.** $x^2 + 8x - 7 \geq 0$

C. $x^2 - 10x - 3 < 0$ **D.** $x^2 + 4x - 3 \leq 0$

E. $x^2 - 2x - 5 < 0$ **F.** $x^2 + x - 7 \geq 0$

Tell what the *right* member should be after the square has been completed on the left.

EXAMPLE 2

Answer:

$x^2 + 12x - 5 < 0$ 41.

G. $x^2 + 6x - 4 \leq 0$ 13   **H.** $x^2 - 8x + 3 < 0$ 13

I. $x^2 + 10x + 6 \geq 0$ 19   **J.** $x^2 - 4x + 13 > 0$ −9

K. $x^2 + 2x + 7 \geq 0$ −6   **L.** $x^2 - x - 1 < 0$ 1.25

EXERCISE 14-6

Transform the inequalities by completing the square, then sketch the graph.

1. $x^2 - 12x + 17 > 0$ **2.** $x^2 - 16x + 41 < 0$

1.-20.   See Additional Answers.

3. $x^2 + 6x + 7 \leq 0$

4. $x^2 + 8x + 9 \geq 0$

5. $x^2 - 10x - 51 \geq 0$

6. $x^2 - 4x - 26 \leq 0$

7. $x^2 - 14x + 33 < 0$

8. $x^2 - 18x + 65 > 0$

9. $x^2 + 2x + 3 \leq 0$

10. $x^2 + 6x + 10 \geq 0$

11. $x^2 - 6x + 12 > 0$

12. $x^2 - 10x + 30 < 0$

13. $x^2 - 5x - 14 < 0$

14. $x^2 - 7x - 30 > 0$

15. $x^2 + 7x - 2 \geq 15$

16. $x^2 + 9x - 5 \leq 30$

17. $x^2 + 3x \leq 5x + 11$

18. $x^2 - 7x \geq 4 - 2x$

19. $6x + 3 < x(5 + x)$

20. $7 - 2x > x(x - 11)$

14-7   SOLVING QUADRATIC INEQUALITIES BY THE QUADRATIC FORMULA

There is a relationship between plotting graphs of quadratic *functions,* as in Section 14-5, and graphing quadratic *inequalities,* as in Section 14-6. To see what the relationship is, first look at the graph of $y = 3x^2 - 7x - 15$. The values of y may be calculated by the computer program of Section 14-5.

x	y
-5	95
-4	61
-3	33
-2	11
-1	-5
0	-15
1	-19
2	-17
3	-9
4	5
5	25
6	51
7	83

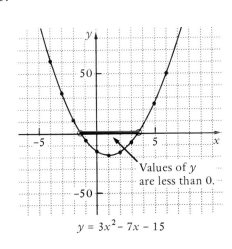

Values of y are less than 0.

$y = 3x^2 - 7x - 15$

From the graph, you can see that when x is between the two x-intercepts, the values of y are *less* than zero. The inequality

$$y < 0$$

is equivalent to the inequality

$$3x^2 - 7x - 15 < 0,$$

because y is equal to $3x^2 - 7x - 15$. The relationship between the two kinds of problem is that the *end points* of the graph of $3x^2 - 7x - 15 < 0$ are the same as the *x-intercepts* of $y = 3x^2 - 7x - 15$.

By considering graphs of quadratic functions, you can discover that there are only four possible ways a quadratic inequality graph could look.

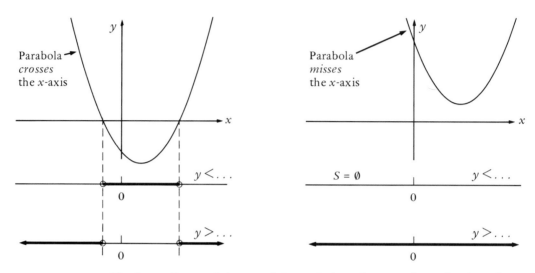

The inequality graph is one of these choices: *between* the end points, *beyond* the end points, *no* values, or *all* values. The particular graph in any given problem depends on whether or not the parabola has x-intercepts and on whether the inequality sign is $<$ or $>$.

CONCLUSION

GRAPHS OF QUADRATIC INEQUALITIES
(*Note:* The x^2-coefficient must be *positive*.)

If $ax^2 + bx + c > 0$, then the graph is *outside* the end points.

If $ax^2 + bx + c < 0$, then the graph is *between* the end points.

There is an easy way to draw the graph of a quadratic inequality without having to draw the parabola or to memorize the conclusion. You simply calculate the endpoints using the quadratic formula (or factoring) and then substitute a value of x to find out which of the four possible graphs it is. The following examples show you how to do this.

Objective:

Given a quadratic inequality, find the end points (if any) and draw the graph.

Study the following examples. If you like, you may try some of them on your own before uncovering the answers.

EXAMPLE 1

Find the end points and draw the graph: $3x^2 - 7x - 15 < 0$.

– – – – –   – – – – –

	Think These Reasons
$3x^2 - 7x - 15 < 0$	Write the given inequality.
$x = \dfrac{7 \pm \sqrt{49 - 4(3)(-15)}}{2(3)}$	Use the quadratic formula to find the end points.
$x = \dfrac{7 \pm \sqrt{229}}{6}$	Do the arithmetic.
$x \approx 3.69$ or -1.36	Finish the arithmetic.
$3(0)^2 - 7(0) - 15 \overset{?}{<} 0$	Substitute a value for x. (0 is the easiest to substitute.)
$-15 \overset{?}{<} 0$ True.	
$\therefore 0$ *is* included.	$-15 < 0$ is a *true* statement.

$$-1.36 \quad 0 \qquad 3.69$$

Draw the end points. Shade the portion *including* 0.

Note: This problem is the same as the one at the beginning of this section.

EXAMPLE 2

Find the end points and draw the graph: $x^2 - 6x + 13 > 0$.

– – – – –   – – – – –

$x^2 - 6x + 13 > 0$	Write the given inequality.
$x = \dfrac{6 \pm \sqrt{36 - 4(1)(13)}}{2(1)}$	Use the Quadratic Formula to find the end points.
$x = \dfrac{6 \pm \sqrt{-16}}{2}$	Do the arithmetic.
<u>*No* end points.</u>	$\sqrt{-16}$ is not a real number.
$0^2 - 6(0) + 13 \overset{?}{>} 0$	Substitute a value for x.
$\qquad\qquad 13 \overset{?}{>} 0 \quad$ True.	
$\therefore$ 0 *is* included.	$13 > 0$ is a *true* statement.

$$S = R$$
$$\mid$$
$$0$$

Draw the graph. Since 0 *is* included and there are *no* end points, the graph is *all* real numbers. Write $S = R$, where R means *real numbers*.

EXAMPLE 3

Find the end points and draw the graph: $x^2 - 6x + 13 < 0$.

– – – – –   – – – – –

This is the same as Example 3, except the sign is $<$.
<u>So there will still be no end points.</u>

Upon substituting 0 for x, you get	
$0^2 - 6(0) + 13 \overset{?}{<} 0$	Substitute a value for x.
$\qquad\qquad 13 \overset{?}{<} 0 \quad$ False.	
$\therefore$ 0 is *excluded*.	$13 < 0$ is a *false* statement.

$$S = \emptyset \qquad \underline{\qquad\mid\qquad\qquad}$$
$$0$$

Draw the graph. Since 0 is *not* included, and there are *no* end points, the graph is the *empty* set. Write $S = \emptyset$ for clarity.

EXAMPLE 4

Find the end points and draw the graph: $2x^2 - 6x + 1 \le 7x^2 - 10$.

– – – – –   – – – – –

$2x^2 - 6x + 1 \le 7x^2 - 10$	Write the given inequality.
$-5x^2 - 6x + 11 \le 0$	Make the right member equal 0.

$$x = \frac{6 \pm \sqrt{36 - 4(-5)(11)}}{2(-5)}$$ Use the Quadratic Formula to find the end points.

$$x = \frac{6 \pm \sqrt{36 - 4(-5)(11)}}{2(-5)}$$ Use the Quadratic Formula to find the end points.

$$x = \frac{6 \pm \sqrt{256}}{-10}$$ Do the arithmetic.

$\underline{x = -2.2 \quad \text{or} \quad 1}$ Finish the arithmetic.

$-5(0)^2 - 6(0) + 11 \overset{?}{\le} 0$ Substitute a value for x in the simplified inequality.

$11 \overset{?}{\le} 0$ False.

$\therefore$ 0 is *not* included. $11 \le 0$ is a *false* statement.

Plot the end points. Shade the portion *excluding* 0.

EXAMPLE 5

Rectangular Building Problem   A rectangular building is to be built on a 30-meter by 50-meter rectangular lot in such a way that there is a path x meters wide all the way around the building. The building can occupy at most 60% of the area of the lot. What is the range of possible values of x?

– – – – –   – – – –

Let L = length of building in meters.
Let W = width of building in meters.

$\therefore LW \le 0.6(30)(50)$ Building area is at most 60% of lot area.

$LW \le 900$ Multiply.

$L = 50 - 2x$
$W = 30 - 2x$ Write L and W in terms of x.

$(50 - 2x)(30 - 2x) \le 900$ Substitute for L and W.

$1500 - 160x + 4x^2 \le 900$ Multiply.

$4x^2 - 160x + 600 \le 0$ Make right member zero.

$$x^2 - 40x + 150 \leq 0$$

Do any obvious simplifications.

Use the Quadratic Formula to find the end points.

$$x \approx 35.81 \quad \text{or} \quad 4.19$$

Do the computations.

$$0^2 - 40(0) + 150 \overset{?}{\leq} 0$$

Substitute a value for x.

$$150 \overset{?}{\leq} 0 \quad \text{False.}$$

$$\therefore 0 \text{ is } excluded.$$

$150 \leq 0$ is a *false* statement.

Plot the end points. Shade the portion *excluding* 0.

$$\underline{4.19 \leq x < 15}$$

Answer the question: x must be less than 15 since the walkway can be no more than half the width of the lot. Also, x cannot *equal* 15, or there would be no building!

ORAL PRACTICE

The graphs show the end points for the given inequalities. Tell in words what the graph will look like. You can do this by substituting 0 for x, as in the examples. Your answer should be one of *between, beyond, all real numbers*, or *empty set*.

Between   A. $x^2 - 3x - 10 \leq 0$

Beyond   B. $x^2 - 3x - 10 \geq 0$

Between   C. $x^2 - 7x + 10 \leq 0$

Beyond   D. $x^2 - 7x + 10 \geq 0$

Between   E. $x^2 + 7x + 10 \leq 0$

Beyond   F. $x^2 + 7x + 10 \geq 0$

Beyond   G. $-x^2 + 3x + 10 \leq 0$

H. $-x^2 + 3x + 10 \geq 0$ Between

I. $-x^2 + 7x - 10 \leq 0$ Beyond

J. $-x^2 + 7x - 10 \geq 0$ Between

K. $x^2 + 3x + 10 \leq 0$ Empty Set

L. $x^2 + 3x + 10 \geq 0$ All real numbers

M. $-x^2 + 3x - 10 \leq 0$ All real numbers

N. $-x^2 + 3x - 10 \geq 0$ Empty set

EXERCISE 14-7

For Problems 1 through 20, find the end points, if any, and sketch the graph.

1.-20.   See Additional Answers.

1. $3x^2 + 5x - 19 > 0$

2. $7x^2 + 10x - 23 < 0$

3. $2x^2 - 7x - 43 \leq 0$

4. $3x^2 - 8x - 87 \geq 0$

5. $x^2 - 9x + 14 > 0$

6. $x^2 - 11x + 24 < 0$

7. $30x - 5x^2 + 47 \leq 0$

8. $79 - 7x^2 - 13x \geq 0$

9. $10x^2 + 11x + 12 \leq 0$

10. $-5x^2 - 11x + 20 \geq 0$

11. $6 + x^2 - 3x > 0$

12. $x^2 + 10 + 3x < 0$

13. $0.3x^2 - 5x - 18.9 < 0$

14. $0.9x^2 - 20x + 98.6 > 0$

15. $4x^2 - 28x + 49 > 0$

16. $25x^2 - 80x + 64 \leq 0$

17. $3x^2 - 20x \leq x^2 - 47$

18. $5x^2 + 22x > 2x^2 + 100$

19. $7x + 30 < x(x + 8)$

20. $4x + 4.8 \geq x(x + 2.3)$

For Problems 21 through 30, work the problem and answer the questions.

21. *Archery Problem*   Mark Wright shoots an arrow into the air with an initial upward velocity of 70 meters per second (m/sec). Let t be the number of seconds since the arrow was shot. You recall that its distance up, d meters is

$$d = rt - 5t^2,$$

Problem Notes:

Problems 21 and 22 review the vertical motion problems of Section 6–9, using inequalities rather than equations.

where r is the initial upward velocity. For what values of t will the arrow be:

a. more than 200 m high; $4 < t < 10$
b. at most 60 m high;   Before 0.75 sec or after 13.25 sec
c. higher than 300 m?   No solution (never happens)

22. *Diving Board Problem*   A diver leaves the 3-meter springboard with an initial upward velocity of 2 meters per second (m/sec). For what range of times will the diver be:

a. above the level of the board;   Between 0 and 0.4 sec
b. less than 5 meters above the board;   No solution (therefore, always)
c. above the water?   Between 0 and 1 sec

Problems 23–28 are similar to the rectangle problems of Section 10–8, using inequalities rather than equations.

Round-off of approximate answers is tricky. For instance, in Problem 27 a solution is $x < 4.3395 \ldots$. This must be rounded off *downward* to $x \leq 4.33$ because x must be less than 4.34. Answers should be rounded in the direction of the inequality rather than to the nearest value.

23. *Rectangle Problem*   The length of a rectangle is 5 meters plus the width. Write an inequality stating that the area of the rectangle is at least 37 square meters. Then solve the inequality to find the range of possible values of the width.   At least 4.08 m

24. *Another Rectangle Problem*   The width of a rectangle is the length minus 3 feet. Write an inequality stating that the area is at most 40 square feet. Then solve the inequality to find the range of possible values of the length.   Between 0 and 8 ft, inclusive

25. *Carpet Problem*   A room 8 meters by 6 meters is to have carpet installed in one corner, leaving a strip of floor x meters wide around the other two sides.

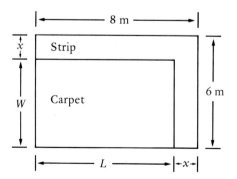

a. Write expressions for the length and for the width of the carpet in terms of x. $L = 8 - x$ $W = 6 - x$

   b.   Write an expression for the area of the carpet in terms of x. $48 - 14x + x^2$
   c.   Write an inequality stating that the area of the carpet is at least
        70% of the area of the room. Solve the inequality to find the
        possible values of x. $0 \le x \le 1.11$
   d.   What values of x make the carpet no more than half of the area
        of the room? $2 \le x \le 6$

26.   **Sidewalk Problem**   A sidewalk of uniform width,
      x, is to be built on two sides of a corner lot, as
      shown. The lot was originally 70 ft by 100 ft.

      a.   Write expressions in terms of x for the length
           and width of the part of the lot remaining.
           $L = 100 - x;\ W = 70 - x$
      b.   Write an expression for the area. $7000 - 170x + x^2$
      c.   The city agrees to leave at least 90% of the
           area of the original lot after the sidewalk is
           built. What is the range of permissible values
           of x? $0 \le x \le 4.22$

27.   **Roadway Problem**   A farmer wishes to leave un-
      plowed a strip of land around the four sides of his
      field. The strip is to be of uniform width, and is to
      leave at least 95% of the area of the 400-m by
      300-m field available for plowing. What is the
      range of permissible strip widths? At most 4.33 m

28.   **Video Game Problem**   A new video game is be-
      ing designed. A red border of uniform width is to
      surround the screen, and any player running into
      this border will be "zapped." The author of the
      game wishes to have at least 90% of the area of
      the 20 cm by 16 cm screen left inside the red bor-
      der. What is the range of possible values for the
      strip width?   At most 0.45 cm

29.   **Parabolas and Quadratic Inequalities Problem**
      a.   Plot the graph of $y = x^2 - 3x - 5$.
      b.   Solve the inequality $x^2 - 3x - 5 \ge 0$. $x \le -1.20$ or $x \ge 4.20$
      c.   Show the solution of the inequality in part (b) on the graph of
           part (a).

Problem 29 shows the relationship between
the parabolas of Section 14–5 and the inequalities of Sections 14–6 and 14–7.

29.   **a-c.** See Additional Answers.

30. a. Shape of parabola stretches in y-direction as absolute value of a increases and is concave upward for positive a, concave downward for negative a.
b. Position of graph varies in y-direction directly as a change in c.
c. Both shape and position vary with b.

30. *Quadratics Computer Graphics Problem*   In this problem you will plot various quadratic functions by computer to see the effects of the coefficients a, b, and c in the equation $y = ax^2 + bx + c$. You may use the program PLOT QUADRATIC on the accompanying disk, or any other suitable graphing program.
 a.   Plot $y = 0.1x^2$ and $y = 0.3x^2$ on the same axes. What is the effect of the coefficient a on the shape of the graph?
 b.   Plot $y = 0.1x^2$ and $y = 0.1x^2 - 5$ on the same set of axes. Does the coefficient c affect the shape of the graph, or just its position? In what way?
 c.   Plot $y = 0.3x^2$ and $y = 0.3x^2 - 3x$ on the same set of axes. Does the coefficient b affect the shape of the graph, or just its position? In what way?

31. a. Plot will be a "V" as described.
b. More steeply sloped "V".
c. Vertex of "V" moves to $(-4, 0)$
d. Vertex of "V" moves to $(0, -5)$
e. As a increases the "V" gets sharper; as b changes the vertex moves in the opposite direction along the x-axis; as c changes the vertex moves in same direction along the y-axis.

31. *Absolute Value Computer Graphics Problem*   An absolute value function has the general equation $y = |ax + b| + c$, where the coefficients a, b, and c stand for constants. Use the program PLOT FUNCTION on the accompanying disk, or similar plotting program.
 a.   Plot $y = |x|$. The BASIC for $|\text{number}|$ is ABS(number). You should find that the graph is a "V" with its point at the origin.
 b.   Plot $y = |3x|$. How does the graph differ from $y = |x|$?
 c.   Plot $y = |x + 4|$. How does the graph differ from $y = |x|$?
 d.   Plot $y = |x| - 5$. How does the graph differ from $y = |x|$?
 e.   Plot $y = |3x + 4| - 5$. By comparing the graph with the others you have plotted, tell how the coefficients a, b, and c influence the graph of $y = |ax + b| + c$.

14-8 | **CHAPTER REVIEW AND TEST**

Time: 1 day

Test Ideas:

Your test should be tailored to those parts of the chapter your students have studied. Since this is the last section of the book, you may wish to include these topics on the final exam rather than give a separate test.

Assignment:

Following the test, study the Final Review. Learn the names and statements of the axioms. Work Final Exam Problems 1, 2, and 3.

In this chapter you have recalled a lot of algebraic techniques from the rest of the course. You used these techniques to analyze problems about functions, direct and inverse variation, triangles, quadratics, and inequalities. In the process, you have both reviewed this course and had a taste of some mathematics yet to come. Functions are important in mathematics. Triangles are analyzed both in geometry and in trigonometry. Even calculus depends on the foundation you have acquired in this beginning algebra course.

The test below touches on materials of this chapter. There is also a problem that lets you extend your knowledge in a new direction—to *fractional* inequalities.

CHAPTER TEST

1. Tell the difference in each case:
   a. Graph of a function and a graph of a non-function.
   b. What y does as x increases in a *direct* variation function and in an *inverse* variation function.
   c. General equation and particular equation.
   d. sin A and cos A.

2. Tell what is meant by each of the following.
   a. Leg *adjacent* to a given angle in a right triangle.
   b. Proportionality constant.
   c. Quadratic function.
   d. Parabola.
   e. Vertex.

3. Plot the graph of the function for the given values of x and connect the points appropriately.
   a. $y = 0.6x + 2$, for all integers $-3 \le x \le 3$.
   b. $y = |x - 2|$, for all integers $-1 \le x \le 5$.
   c. $y = \frac{6}{x}$, for $x = 1, 2, 3$, and 6.

4. *Food Problem*   The number of pounds of food you need to take on a camping trip varies directly with the number of days you will be gone. Suppose that a 10-day trip requires 17 pounds of food.
   a. Find the proportionality constant. Write the particular equation expressing pounds of food in terms of days. $f = 1.7\, d$
   b. How much food should you pack for a 28-day trip?   47.6 lbs.
   c. How many days can you camp if you take 51 pounds of food?   30 days

5. *Music Practice Problem*   Clara Nett figures that the number of mistakes she will make in playing a piece of music varies inversely with the number of minutes she practices that piece. After 20 minutes of practice, she finds that she makes 4 mistakes.
   a. Find the proportionality constant. Write the particular equation expressing number of mistakes in terms of minutes of practice. $m = \frac{80}{t}$
   b. Clara would like to practice long enough so that she makes only *one* mistake. How long would this be?   80 min.
   c. If Clara had had only 5 minutes to practice the piece, how many mistakes might she have made?   16

6. a. Find the length of side x.   b. Find the measure of angle A.

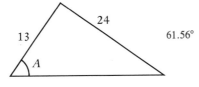

1. a. A function graph has no more than one value of y for each value of x.
   The graph of a non-function has more than 1 y-value for one or more values of x.
   b. For a direct variation function, y *increases* as x increases.
   For an inverse variation function, y *decreases* as x increases.
   c. A general equation has letters to stand for unspecified constants.
   A particular equation has specific values for the constants.
   d. sin A = (opposite)/(hypotenuse).
   cos A = (adjacent)/(hypotenuse).

2. a. The adjacent leg forms one side of the angle.
   b. A proportionality constant is the number k in the equation $y = kx$ or $y = k/x$.
   c. A quadratic function is a function with an equation of the form $y = ax^2 + bx + c$.
   d. A parabola is the graph of a quadratic function.
   e. A vertex is a high or low point on a parabola.

3a.

3b.

3c.

7b. $x \approx 5.35$ or -0.69

-0.69 0 5.35

7c. $x = \dfrac{4 \pm \sqrt{1600}}{6} = 9$ or $-4\frac{1}{3}$

-4.33 0 9

7d. $x = \dfrac{14 \pm \sqrt{-140}}{6}$

No endpoints

$S = R$

0

8. See Additional Answers.

Problem Notes:

Problem 10 is a variation of the rectangular border problems of Section 14–7. The analysis is the same, but x is added to one dimension and subtracted from the other.

7. For the quadratic function $y = 3x^2 - 14x + 8$.
    a. Evaluate y if x is -5. $y = 153$
    b. Solve for x if y is more than 19. Draw the graph.
    c. Solve for x if y is at most 125. Draw the graph.
    d. Solve for x if y is at least -20. Draw the graph.

8. Sketch the graph of a parabola showing how the graph of $ax^2 + bx + c < 0$ could be:
    a. between two end points;   b. beyond two end points;
    c. the empty set;   d. all real numbers.

9. *Baseball Problem*   Pop Dupp hits a baseball with an initial upward velocity of 23 meters per second. The top of the grandstands is 20 meters above where Pop hit the ball. For what time interval will the ball be at least as high as the top of the grandstands?   Between 1.17 and 3.43 seconds, inclusive

10. *Rectangle Problem*   A rectangle is 7 meters by 9 meters. A new rectangle is formed that is x meters longer and x meters narrower than the original one. For what values of x will the new rectangle have less than 80% of the area of the original rectangle? $x > 2.69$

Problem 11 lets students try working a problem they have never seen before. All the concepts are familiar, but they have never been combined in the same problem. The reversal of the inequality sign in part (b) does not change the end points but does change the inequality from "beyond" to "between."

11. a. $x = 3.14$ or -8.28

-8.28 0 2 3.14

11. b. $(x - 2) < 0$
Same end points, but
$0 > x^2 + x - 13$

-8.28 0 2 3.14

11. *Fractional Inequality Problem*   To solve an inequality like

$$\frac{x + 5}{x - 2} < x + 4,$$

you must first multiply each member by $(x - 2)$ to get rid of the fraction. However, when $(x - 2)$ is *negative*, the order will *reverse*, and when $x - 2$ is positive, the order will *not* reverse.
    a. Let x be larger than 2, so that $(x - 2)$ is positive. Solve the above inequality, and plot the graph on that part of the number line for which x is greater than 2.
    b. Let x be less than 2, so that $(x - 2)$ is negative. Solve the above inequality again. Then plot the graph on the rest of the number line, where x is less than 2.

Final Review and Examination

In algebra you have learned to use *variables* to stand for numbers that can take on different values at different times. For instance, if you go on a trip, the number of kilometers you have gone varies. So does the number of minutes or hours you have been going.

The main *use* of algebra in the real world involves expressions that give the value of one variable in terms of a related variable. For instance, if you travel at 80 kilometers per hour, then your distance is given by the expression $80t$, where t is time in hours.

There are two major things you *do* with algebraic expressions. You can use them to find the value of the expression when you know what the variable equals. If distance $= 80t$ and t is 3, then the distance equals $80(3)$, or 240 kilometers. Or you can use them to find the value of the variable when you know what the expression equals. If the distance is 100 kilometers, you would write an *equation*, $80t = 100$, and solve it for t. The answer is 1.25 hours. If the distance is *less* than 150 kilometers, you would write the *inequality* $80t < 150$. Solving gives $t < 1.875$.

To evaluate expressions and solve equations you must often *transform* them in simpler forms. For equations and inequalities you can do the same operation to each member, such as add the same number, multiply by the same number, and so forth. To transform an expression, you can commute and associate terms or factors, distribute multiplication or division over addition or subtraction, multiply by forms of 1, add forms of 0, and so forth. Care is needed, since some tempting transformations do *not* work. For instance, subtracting, dividing, and exponentiating neither commute nor associate.

In algebra, you start with a few rather obvious *axioms*. There are *commutative, associative,* and *distributive* axioms. The facts that $x \cdot 1 = x$ and $x + 0 = x$ are called *identity* axioms, since a number remains identical after you multiply by 1 or add 0. The facts that x and $1/x$ give 1 when multiplied, and that x and $-x$ give 0 when added are called *inverse* axioms. The fact that you get a unique, real number whenever you add or multiply two real numbers is summarized in the closure axioms. Although you have not been told it before, the 11 axioms which apply to addition and multiplication are called the *field axioms*. Any set of numbers that has all 11 of these properties is called a *field*.

Time: 3 days, including examination

Review and Exam Ideas:

Students have been taught to use the words *distribute, commute,* and *associate* as verbs. At the time of the final exam it is appropriate to pull all these ideas together and give formal names to the properties. It is also appropriate to show students that algebra has been a study of expressions and the two major things one does with expressions—evaluate and solve equations.

One way to tie together these ideas is to ask the question, "What do you do in algebra?" Students can give out any answers they can think of. One student can write all the words on the board. They should be able to think of 20 to 40 such items. Then you ask them which of the items are main ideas (expression, equation, etc.), and which are sub-headings under these ideas (simplify, commute, etc.). You will probably be surprised to see how well most students have been able to grasp the big picture about algebra.

The majority of the review should consist of refreshing specific skills. The exam itself provides a reasonably comprehensive review. Students should work on their own as much as possible and look up techniques from the appropriate section or from class notes if necessary. Class time is best spent on individual work with students helping one another over rough spots and you supervising the work.

Assignments:

Day 1: FE, 4–12
Day 2: FE, 13–21
Day 3: Exam.

THE ELEVEN FIELD AXIOMS
For all of these axioms, x, y, and z stand for real numbers.

Closure Axioms
The set of real numbers is *closed* under addition and multiplication. That is,

  1. $x + y$ is a *unique real* number.

  2. xy is a *unique real* number.

Inverse Axioms
The set of real numbers has unique *additive* and *multiplicative inverses* for each of its elements, except that there is no multiplicative inverse for 0. That is,

  3. $x + (-x) = 0$

  4. $x \cdot \dfrac{1}{x} = 1$, provided $x \neq 0$.

Identity Axioms
The set of real numbers has an additive *identity element*, 0, and a multiplicative *identity element*, 1. That is,

  5. $x + 0 = x$

  6. $x \cdot 1 = x$

Associative Axioms
Addition and multiplication are *associative* operations. That is,

  7. $(x + y) + z = x + (y + z)$

  8. $(xy)z = x(yz)$

Commutative Axioms
Addition and multiplication are *commutative* operations. That is,

  9. $x + y = y + x$

 10. $xy = yx$

Distributive Axiom
Multiplication *distributes* over addition.

 11. $x(y + z) = xy + xz$

The other axioms you learned apply to the equality sign. Equality is *reflexive, symmetric,* and *transitive.*

THE THREE EQUALITY AXIOMS
In all of these axioms, x, y, and z stand for real numbers.

1. **Transitive Axiom**
   If one number equals a second number, and the second number equals a third number, then the first number equals the third number. That is,

   $$\text{If } x = y \text{ and } y = z,$$

   $$\text{then } x = z.$$

2. **Symmetric Axiom**
   If one number equals a second number, then the second number equals the first. That is,

   $$\text{If } x = y,$$

   $$\text{then } y = x.$$

3. **Reflexive Axiom**
   A variable stands for the *same* number everywhere it appears in an expression. That is,

   $$x = x.$$

Various *computations* arise in algebra. If an expression such as $5x^2 - 7x + 31$ is evaluated for *many* values of x, a computer is suitable. *Single* calculations involving radicals or many-digit numbers are best done with a calculator. Easy problems like $7x = 56$ should be done in your head.

All the techniques and properties you learn come together in solving *problems* from the real world. Such problems are stated in words. The key to success is translating the words into one or more algebraic expressions. For instance, the words *the perimeter of a rectangle* would become $2L + 2W$, where L and W are the length and width of the rectangle. The two basic questions are: Find the perimeter when L and W are known, and find L and W when the perimeter is known. After you get an answer to these mathematical problems, you write the answer to whatever question was asked. For instance: The perimeter is 35 cm.

In the exam that follows you will demonstrate that you know the properties of numbers, and that you can use these properties to evaluate expressions and to solve equations and inequalities. The exam may take two or three hours. The practice you get should help you on your own final.

Problem Notes:

Problems 1, 2, and 3 may already have been assigned following the last test on Chapter 14. If not, it is probably more efficient to skip directly to Problem 4 and start a review of specific techniques. The names can be learned by students on their own.

    Problems 4–8 address the main theme of this text—given an expression, evaluate it when x is known, or find x when the expression's value is known. The only difference among the problems is the kind of expression.

1.   Field axioms (See text)
2.   Equality axioms (See text)
3.   **a.** Multiplication property of 0:
       For any real number x, $x \cdot 0 = 0$
   b. Multiplication property of -1:
       For any real number x, $-1 \cdot x = -x$
   c. Multiplication property of fractions:
       For any real numbers a, b, c, d, with $b \neq 0$ and $d \neq 0$,
$$\frac{a}{b} \cdot \frac{c}{d} = \frac{ac}{bd}$$
   d. Multiplication property of equality:
       If $a = b$, then $a \cdot c = b \cdot c$
   e. Multiplication property of order for $<$:
       If $a < b$, then
       $ac < bc$ if c is positive
       $ac > bc$ if c is negative
   f. Distributive property of $\div$ over $-$:
$$\frac{a-b}{c} = \frac{a}{c} - \frac{b}{c}$$
   g. Distributive property of exp. over $\times$:
       $(ab)^n = a^n b^n$
   h. Definition of subtraction:
       $x - y = x + (-y)$
   i. Definition of nth root:
       $\sqrt[n]{x}$ is a number such that $(\sqrt[n]{x})^n = x$.
   j. Definition of negative exponents:
$$x^{-n} = \frac{1}{x^n}$$
   k. Property of the power of a power:
       $(x^a)^b = x^{ab}$
   l. Quotient of 2 powers with equal bases:
$$\frac{x^a}{x^b} = x^{a-b}$$
   m. Pythagorean Theorem:
       $(\text{hypot.})^2 = (\text{leg})^2 + (\text{other leg})^2$

FINAL EXAMINATION

1. Name and state the 11 field axioms.

2. Name and state the 3 axioms of equality.

3. State the following properties or definitions.
   a. Multiplication property of 0.
   b. Multiplication property of -1.
   c. Multiplication property of fractions.
   d. Multiplication property of equality.
   e. Multiplication property of order for $<$.
   f. Distributive property of division over subtraction.
   g. Distributive property of exponentiation over multiplication.
   h. Definition of subtraction.
   i. Definition of nth root.
   j. Definition of negative exponents.
   k. Property of the power of a power.
   l. Property of the quotient of two powers with equal bases.
   m. Pythagorean theorem.

4. For the expression $3x + 5$:
   a. Tell what kind of expression it is.   Linear binomial
   b. Evaluate it if $x = 7$ and if $x = -8$. $26, -19$
   c. Find x if the expression equals 9. $x = \frac{4}{3}$
   d. Find x if the expression is greater than -10. Graph the answer. $x > -5$

5. For the expression $|2x - 7|$:
   a. Tell what kind of expression it is.   Absolute value
   b. Evaluate it if $x = 2$ and if $x = 11$. $3, 15$
   c. Find x if the expression equals 13. $x = -3$ or $x = 10$
   d. Find x if the expression is less than 5. Graph the answer. $1 < x < 6$

6. For the expression $x^2 + 3x - 10$:
   a. Tell what kind of expression it is.   Quadratic trinomial
   b. Evaluate it if $x = 2$ and if $x = -3$. $0, -10$
   c. Find x if the expression equals -12. $x = -1, x = -2$
   d. Find x if the expression equals -15.   No values
   e. Find x if the expression is negative. Graph the answer. $-5 < x < 2$

7. For the expression $\dfrac{x + 3}{x - 2}$:
   a. Tell what kind of expression it is.   Rational algebraic
   b. Evaluate it if $x = 5$, if $x = -3$, and if $x = 2$. $\frac{8}{3}$, 0, no value
   c. Find x if the expression equals 4. $x = \frac{11}{3}$
   d. Find x if the expression equals $2x$. $x = -\frac{1}{2}$ or $x = 3$

8. For the expression $\sqrt{3x + 8}$:
   a. Tell what kind of expression it is.   Irrational algebraic

b. Evaluate it if $x = 16$, if $x = -5$, and if $x = \frac{1}{9}$. Write the answers in simple radical form. $2\sqrt{14}$, no value, $\frac{5\sqrt{3}}{3}$

c. Find x if the expression equals 5. $x = \frac{17}{3}$

d. Find x if the expression equals $3x$. $x = 1.12$ $(-0.79$ is ext.$)$

9. For the two-variable equation $x + 5y = 9$:
   a. Find x if y is 4. $x = -11$
   b. Find y if x is -2. $\frac{11}{5}$
   c. Transform it to the slope-intercept form. $y = -\frac{1}{5}x + 1.8$

10. For the system of equations

$$x + 5y = 9 \qquad 3x - 2y = 10$$

   a. Solve the system by the *substitution* method. $(4, 1)$
   b. Solve the system by the *addition-subtraction* method. $(4, 1)$
   c. Plot the graph of the system of *inequalities*

$$x + 5y < 9 \qquad 3x - 2y \le 10.$$

11. Write the simulated computer memory and the output.

```
10   FOR X = 1 TO 10
20   LET R = 17 - X * X
30   IF R < 0 THEN 70
40   LET Y = SQR (R)
50   PRINT X, Y
60   NEXT X
70   PRINT "ENDED WHEN X = "; X
80   END
```

10c.

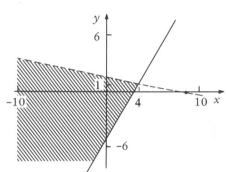

11.

X	$\cancel{1}\cancel{2}\cancel{3}\cancel{4}\,5$
R	$\cancel{1}\cancel{1}\cancel{3}\cancel{8}\cancel{1}\,-8$
Y	$\cancel{4}\,3.6\ldots\,2.8\ldots\,1$

```
Output: 1    4
        2    3.60555
        3    2.82843
        4    1
        ENDED WHEN X = 5
```

12. Do the following.
   a. Multiply: $(3x - 5)(6x + 7)$. $18x^2 - 9x - 35$
   b. Do the squaring: $(4x - 5)^2$. $16x^2 - 40x + 25$
   c. Simplify: $6(3x^2)^4$. $486x^8$
   d. Factor completely: $2x^2 - 98$. $2(x + 7)(x - 7)$
   e. Factor by grouping: $6x^2 + 4ax - 3x - 2a$. $(3x + 2a)(2x - 1)$
   f. Factor by splitting the middle term: $6x^2 - 13x - 8$. $(2x + 1)(3x - 8)$
   g. Subtract and simplify: $\dfrac{x - 21}{x^2 - 2x - 15} - \dfrac{2}{5 - x}$. $\frac{3}{x + 3}$
   h. Add, and write in simple radical form: $\dfrac{18}{\sqrt{3}} + 5\sqrt{12}$. $16\sqrt{3}$
   i. Write in simple radical form: $\dfrac{12}{\sqrt{7} + \sqrt{3}}$. $3(\sqrt{7} - \sqrt{3})$
   j. Solve by completing the square: $x^2 + 6x - 10 = 0$. $S = \{1.36, -7.36\}$
   k. Simplify: $\left(\dfrac{x^3 x^{-5} y^4}{y^{-6}}\right)^{-3}$. $\frac{x^6}{y^{30}}$ or $x^6 y^{-30}$
   l. Divide 2.735×10^{-5} by 3.14×10^{6}. Use scientific notation, and significant digits. 8.71×10^{-12}
   m. Evaluate. Round to two decimal places: $\sqrt[5]{7395}$. 5.94

Problem 12 is a review of the "bread-and-butter" techniques of Algebra I.

Problems 13–21 provide a sampling of the various problem types that appear in this text.

13. ***Lawn Mowing Problem***   Arlene can mow the lawn in 30 minutes. Using the other mower, Bea can mow the same lawn in 60% of this time.
   a. How long would Bea take by herself?   18 min.
   b. How long would it take if both work together?   11.25 min.

14. ***Ball Toss Problem***   You recall that when an object is thrown upward into the air, its distance, d (meters) above the starting point is given by $d = rt - 5t^2$ where t is time in seconds since it was thrown and r is the initial upward speed in meters per second. Suppose that you throw a ball up with an initial speed of 30 meters per second.
   a. How high will it be after 4 seconds?   40 m
   b. To the nearest tenth of a second, what is the first time it reaches a height of 20 meters?   0.76 sec.

15. ***Border Problem***   A strip x cm wide is to be cut from two sides of a 30-cm by 50-cm rectangle. The remaining rectangle is to have 70% of the area of the original one. Find x.   6.09

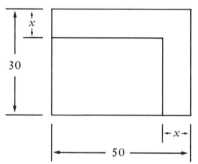

16. ***Income Tax Problem***   The Joneses make $50,000 in a year. They must pay federal income tax equal to 30% of their *net* income (after subtracting state income tax). The state income tax is 10% of their *net* income after subtracting federal tax.
   a. Define variables. Then write two equations representing the above information. $F = 0.3(50.000 - S); S = 0.1(50,000 - F)$
   b. Solve this system of equations to find the amounts of the two taxes, correct to the nearest cent. $F = \$13,917.53; S = \$3,608.25$

17. ***Wheat Shipping Problem***   A shipping company plans to carry wheat from an inland city to a port on the ocean. The ships will go down the river 300 km with the current and then return against the current. The current is 5 km/h.
   a. Write an expression for the total time a ship will take for the round trip in terms of the speed it moves through the water. $\frac{300}{r+5} + \frac{300}{r-5}$
   b. How long will the round trip take if the ship goes 13 km/h through the water? $54\frac{1}{6}$ hr.
   c. The crew must be paid overtime wages if the trip takes more than 40 h. How fast must the ship move through the water for the round trip to take 40 hours?   16.51 km/h

18. *Cars Problem*   There are about 127 million cars in the USA.
    a.   A new car battery costs about $67, on the average. How much could a battery manufacturer make if they sold a battery for each car? Write the answer in scientific notation with the correct number of significant digits 8.5×10^9
    b.   Oil companies sell about 1.07×10^{11} dollars worth of gasoline per year for use in cars in the United States. How many dollars per car is this? Round to the nearest dollar. $843

19. *Roof Problem*   A gable roof rises 4.7 meters above the housetop at its center. The house is 13.8 meters wide.
    a.   What is the slant height of the roof (see sketch)?   8.35 m
    b.   What angle does the roof make with the housetop?   34.26°

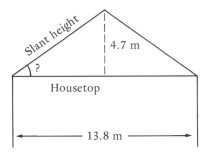

Slant height

4.7 m

?

Housetop

13.8 m

20. *Exhausted Swimmer Problem*   Eileen Dover lost her balance and fell into Rapidan River. In her panic, she started swimming upstream, moving through the water at 72 meters per minute. When she got 120 meters upstream of the point where she fell in, Eileen became exhausted and stopped swimming. As she floated with the current past the place where she fell in, her brother, Ben Dover, bent over and pulled her out. Eileen was in the water a total of 12 minutes. How fast does Rapidan River flow?   12 m/min or 60 m/min

21. *SeeSaw Problem*   The distance a person must sit from the middle of a seesaw is inversely proportional to the person's weight. Phoebe Small, who weighs 90 pounds, must sit 120 inches from the middle.
    a.   Find the proportionality constant, and write the particular equation expressing distance in terms of weight. $d = \frac{10800}{w}$
    b.   How far from the middle must Don Keys sit if he weighs 150 pounds?   72 in.
    c.   Calvin Butterball balances the seesaw when he sits 50 inches from the middle. How heavy is Calvin?   216 lbs.

Distance

TABLE OF SQUARE ROOTS

N	N²	√N	√10N	N	N²	√N	√10N
1.0	1.00	1.000	3.162	5.5	30.25	2.345	7.416
1.1	1.21	1.049	3.317	5.6	31.36	2.366	7.483
1.2	1.44	1.095	3.464	5.7	32.49	2.387	7.550
1.3	1.69	1.140	3.606	5.8	33.64	2.408	7.616
1.4	1.96	1.183	3.742	5.9	34.81	2.429	7.681
1.5	2.25	1.225	3.873	6.0	36.00	2.449	7.746
1.6	2.56	1.265	4.000	6.1	37.21	2.470	7.810
1.7	2.89	1.304	4.123	6.2	38.44	2.490	7.874
1.8	3.24	1.342	4.243	6.3	39.69	2.510	7.937
1.9	3.61	1.378	4.359	6.4	40.96	2.530	8.000
2.0	4.00	1.414	4.472	6.5	42.25	2.550	8.062
2.1	4.41	1.449	4.583	6.6	43.56	2.569	8.124
2.2	4.84	1.483	4.690	6.7	44.89	2.588	8.185
2.3	5.29	1.517	4.796	6.8	46.24	2.608	8.246
2.4	5.76	1.549	4.899	6.9	47.61	2.627	8.307
2.5	6.25	1.581	5.000	7.0	49.00	2.646	8.367
2.6	6.76	1.612	5.099	7.1	50.41	2.665	8.426
2.7	7.29	1.643	5.196	7.2	51.84	2.683	8.485
2.8	7.84	1.673	5.292	7.3	53.29	2.702	8.544
2.9	8.41	1.703	5.385	7.4	54.76	2.720	8.602
3.0	9.00	1.732	5.477	7.5	56.25	2.739	8.660
3.1	9.61	1.761	5.568	7.6	57.76	2.757	8.718
3.2	10.24	1.789	5.657	7.7	59.29	2.775	8.775
3.3	10.89	1.817	5.745	7.8	60.84	2.793	8.832
3.4	11.56	1.844	5.831	7.9	62.41	2.811	8.888
3.5	12.25	1.871	5.916	8.0	64.00	2.828	8.944
3.6	12.96	1.897	6.000	8.1	65.61	2.846	9.000
3.7	13.69	1.924	6.083	8.2	67.24	2.864	9.055
3.8	14.44	1.949	6.164	8.3	68.89	2.881	9.110
3.9	15.21	1.975	6.245	8.4	70.56	2.898	9.165
4.0	16.00	2.000	6.325	8.5	72.25	2.915	9.220
4.1	16.81	2.025	6.403	8.6	73.96	2.933	9.274
4.2	17.64	2.049	6.481	8.7	75.69	2.950	9.327
4.3	18.49	2.074	6.557	8.8	77.44	2.966	9.381
4.4	19.36	2.098	6.633	8.9	79.21	2.983	9.434
4.5	20.25	2.121	6.708	9.0	81.00	3.000	9.487
4.6	21.16	2.145	6.782	9.1	82.81	3.017	9.539
4.7	22.09	2.168	6.856	9.2	84.64	3.033	9.592
4.8	23.04	2.191	6.928	9.3	86.49	3.050	9.644
4.9	24.01	2.214	7.000	9.4	88.36	3.066	9.695
5.0	25.00	2.236	7.071	9.5	90.25	3.082	9.747
5.1	26.01	2.258	7.141	9.6	92.16	3.098	9.798
5.2	27.04	2.280	7.211	9.7	94.09	3.114	9.849
5.3	28.09	2.302	7.280	9.8	96.04	3.130	9.899
5.4	29.16	2.324	7.348	9.9	98.01	3.146	9.950
5.5	30.25	2.345	7.416	10	100.00	3.162	10.000

TABLE OF TRIGONOMETRIC FUNCTIONS

Angle	sin A	cos A	tan A	Angle	sin A	cos A	tan A
1	.0175	.9998	.0175	46	.7193	.6947	1.036
2	.0349	.9994	.0349	47	.7314	.6820	1.072
3	.0523	.9986	.0524	48	.7431	.6691	1.111
4	.0698	.9976	.0699	49	.7547	.6561	1.150
5	.0872	.9962	.0875	50	.7660	.6428	1.192
6	.1045	.9945	.1051	51	.7771	.6293	1.235
7	.1219	.9925	.1228	52	.7880	.6157	1.280
8	.1392	.9903	.1405	53	.7986	.6018	1.327
9	.1564	.9877	.1584	54	.8090	.5878	1.376
10	.1736	.9848	.1763	55	.8192	.5736	1.428
11	.1908	.9816	.1944	56	.8290	.5592	1.483
12	.2079	.9781	.2126	57	.8387	.5446	1.540
13	.2250	.9744	.2309	58	.8480	.5299	1.600
14	.2419	.9703	.2493	59	.8572	.5150	1.664
15	.2588	.9659	.2679	60	.8660	.5000	1.732
16	.2756	.9613	.2867	61	.8746	.4848	1.804
17	.2924	.9563	.3057	62	.8829	.4695	1.881
18	.3090	.9511	.3249	63	.8910	.4540	1.963
19	.3256	.9455	.3443	64	.8988	.4384	2.050
20	.3420	.9397	.3640	65	.9063	.4226	2.145
21	.3584	.9336	.3839	66	.9135	.4067	2.246
22	.3746	.9272	.4040	67	.9205	.3907	2.356
23	.3907	.9205	.4245	68	.9272	.3746	2.475
24	.4067	.9135	.4452	69	.9336	.3584	2.605
25	.4226	.9063	.4663	70	.9397	.3420	2.747
26	.4384	.8988	.4877	71	.9455	.3256	2.904
27	.4540	.8910	.5095	72	.9511	.3090	3.078
28	.4695	.8829	.5317	73	.9563	.2924	3.271
29	.4848	.8746	.5543	74	.9613	.2756	3.487
30	.5000	.8660	.5774	75	.9659	.2588	3.732
31	.5150	.8572	.6009	76	.9703	.2419	4.011
32	.5299	.8480	.6249	77	.9744	.2250	4.331
33	.5446	.8387	.6494	78	.9781	.2079	4.705
34	.5592	.8290	.6745	79	.9816	.1908	5.145
35	.5736	.8192	.7002	80	.9848	.1736	5.671
36	.5878	.8090	.7265	81	.9877	.1564	6.314
37	.6018	.7986	.7536	82	.9903	.1392	7.115
38	.6157	.7880	.7813	83	.9925	.1219	8.144
39	.6293	.7771	.8098	84	.9945	.1045	9.514
40	.6428	.7660	.8391	85	.9962	.0872	11.430
41	.6561	.7547	.8693	86	.9976	.0698	14.301
42	.6691	.7431	.9004	87	.9986	.0523	19.081
43	.6820	.7314	.9325	88	.9994	.0349	28.636
44	.6947	.7193	.9657	89	.9998	.0175	57.290
45	.7071	.7071	1.0000	90	1.0000	.0000	NONE

Glossary

abscissa The first number in an ordered pair as indicated on a number-line graph; the horizontal coordinate on the graph.

absolute value The distance of a number from the origin on a number line; the number itself or the opposite of the number, whichever is positive (or zero).

addition method A method of solving equations in a system by adding.

addition property of equality For real numbers x, y, and z, if $x = y$, then $x + z = y + z$.

addition property of order Given any real numbers a, b, and c; if $a < b$, then $a + c < b + c$; if $a > b$, then $a + c > b + c$.

additive identity axiom For any real number x, $x + 0 = x$.

additive inverse axiom For any real number x, there is a number $-x$ for which $x + (-x) = 0$.

additive inverses Two numbers that add up to zero (for example -3 and 3).

adjacent leg In a right triangle, the leg next to a given angle.

associate To group two of the numbers in parentheses so that the operation between them is done first.

axiom A basic assumption about a mathematical system; a property assumed to be true without proof.

base In an expression requiring multiplication, the constant or variable that tells what number is to be multiplied. In the expression 3^2, 3 is the base.

BASIC A computer language.

binomial A polynomial with two terms.

cancel a fraction To divide the numerator and denominator by the same common factor.

Cartesian coordinate system A system of plotting the values of variables on a graph; named after the French mathematician René Descartes (1596–1650).

Central Processing Unit (CPU) In a computer, the unit that does the work.

closure A given set of given numbers is *closed* under an operation if there is just one answer and the answer is in the given set whenever the operation is performed with the numbers in that set.

coefficient See *numerical coefficient*.

common factor A factor that is in each term of an expression. For example, in $3x + 2x$, x is the common factor.

common multiple A common multiple of a and b is a number that equals (integer) $\times a$ and (integer) $\times b$.

commute To interchange, or reverse, the positions of two numbers.

commutative operation An operation for which commuting the numbers does not change the answer.

completing the square Adding one or more terms to an expression to make it the square of a binomial.

conditional equation An equation that is true for some value(s) of the variable and not true for others.

conjugate binomials Binomials that are the same except for the sign between the terms; for example, $2x + 4$ and $2x - 4$.

constant A symbol (such as 7, 8.9, or $\frac{2}{3}$) which always stands for the same number.

converse of the multiplication property of zero If a product of real numbers equals zero, then one of its factors equals zero.

682

coordinates Numbers corresponding to points on a graph.

cosine A trigonometric function; in a right triangle with acute angle A, cosine $A = \dfrac{\text{adjacent leg}}{\text{hypotenuse}}$.

counter In a computer program, a means of counting the number of times the computer has gone through a loop.

cross-multiplication In a proportion such as $a : b = c : d$, the product of the means equals the product of the extremes; that is, if $\dfrac{a}{b} = \dfrac{c}{d}$, then $ad = bc$.

cubic A word describing a third degree polynomial.

debugging Correcting the errors in a computer program.

degree The highest power of a variable that appears in a polynomial expression. The degree of a polynomial with one variable is the exponent of the highest power of that variable.

denominator In fractions, the number under the vinculum; in $\dfrac{x}{y}$, y is the denominator.

dependent variable Variable dependent on independent variable.

direct variation function y varies directly with x, or y is directly proportional to x, if and only if $y = kx$, where k is the proportionality constant.

discriminant The expression $b^2 - 4ac$ which appears in the quadratic formula $x = \dfrac{-b \pm \sqrt{b^2 - 4ac}}{2a}$. By using the discriminant you can discriminate between quadratic equations that have solutions and those that do not.

distributive axiom For real numbers x, y, and z, $x(y + z) = xy + xz$.

division $x \div y = x \cdot \left(\dfrac{1}{y}\right)$

domain (of a variable) The set of numbers that can be values of the variable.

equation A sentence (such as $x + 7 = 9$) which says that one expression $(x + 7)$ is equal to another expression (9).

evaluating Finding out the value of an expression; finding the number an expression stands for.

exponent In an expression requiring multiplication, the constant or variable that tells how many bases to multiply together. For example, in the expression 3^2, 2 is the exponent.

exponentiation Raising a number to a power; for example, 3^2.

expression A collection of numbers, operation signs, and symbols of inclusion that stands for a number.

extraneous solution The solution that satisfies the transformed equation but not the original one.

extremes In a proportion, the outer terms; for example, in $\dfrac{a}{b} = \dfrac{x}{y}$, a and y are the extremes.

factor a polynomial Transform it to a product of two or more factors.

factor theorem $(x - n)$ is a factor of a polynomial if and only if the polynomial equals zero when n is substituted for x.

factoring by grouping (factoring by associating) Associating pairs of terms and factoring out their greatest common factor.

factors Numbers that are multiplied together.

flag In a computer program, a means of signalling the end of the data.

fractional equation An equation that has a variable in at least one denominator.

function A set of ordered pairs (x, y) for which there is never more than one value of y for any one given value of x.

fundamental theorem of arithmetic Each positive integer has exactly one set of prime factors.

greatest common factor (GCF) The greatest common factor for two positive a and b is the greatest integer for which $a/\text{GCF} = $ integer, and $b/\text{GCF} = $ integer; the greatest factor that is a factor of two or more integers.

hypotenuse In a right triangle, the side opposite the right angle.

identity An equation that is true for all values of the variable.

independent variable Variable that the dependent variable depends on.

inequality A sentence that states one expression is greater than or less than another.

Input/Output Unit (I/O unit) In a computer the means (usually a keyboard) for putting information into the computer and the screen or printer for getting information out.

integers Whole numbers on the number line (for example, $-2, -1, 0, 1, 2 \ldots$), not including the fractions in between.

intersection The intersection of sets A and B is the set of numbers in both sets.

inverse variation function y varies inversely with x, or y is inversely proportional to x, if and only if, $y = \dfrac{k}{x}$, where k is the proportionality constant.

irrational number A real number that cannot be written as a ratio of two integers.

LCD See *least common denominator*.

LCM See *least common multiple*.

least common denominator (LCD) The smallest number that is a multiple of each denominator.

least common multiple (LCM) The least common multiple of integers a and b is the smallest positive number that is a common multiple of a and b.

like terms Two terms in an expression that have the same variable(s) raised to the same powers.

linear A word describing a first degree polynomial.

linear function A function in which the ordered pair (x, y) is related by an equation of the form $y = mx + b$, where m and b stand for constants, and $m \neq 0$.

loop A computer program that goes back and repeats earlier steps is said to have a loop in it.

means In a proportion, the middle terms; for example, in $\dfrac{a}{b} = \dfrac{x}{y}$, b and x are the means.

memory The part of a computer that saves values of variables.

monomial A polynomial with one term.

multiple Integer multiplied by a given number.

multiplication property of equality For real numbers x, y, and z, if $x = y$, then $xz = yz$.

multiplication property of fractions To multiply two fractions, multiply their numerators and multiply their denominators.

multiplication property of -1 For any real number x, $-1 \cdot x = -x$.

multiplication property of order For any real numbers a, b, and c; if $a < b$, then $ac < bc$ if c is positive; and $ac > bc$ if c is negative. If $a > b$, then $ac > bc$ if c is positive; and $ac < bc$ if c is negative.

multiplication property of 0 For any real number x, $0 \cdot x = 0$; that is, if one factor of a product is zero, then the product equals zero.

multiplicative identity axiom Multiplying a number by 1 does not change its value ($x \cdot 1 = x$).

multiplicative inverse axiom For any real number x, there is a number $\dfrac{1}{x}$ for which $x \cdot \left(\dfrac{1}{x}\right) = 1$ (provided $x \neq 0$).

multiplicative inverses (reciprocals) Any two numbers whose product is 1 (for example 4 and $\frac{1}{4}$).

negative exponent For any non-zero number x, and for any integer n, $x^{-n} = \dfrac{1}{x^n}$.

negative number A number less than zero.

n^{th} root An nth root of x is a number that, when raised to the nth power, gives x for the answer.

number line A way of visualizing real numbers, with zero as the origin.

numerator In fractions, the number above the vinculum; in $\dfrac{x}{y}$, x is the numerator.

numerical coefficient In a term, the constant that is multiplied by the variable(s). For example, in $2xy$, 2 is the coefficient of xy.

operation Something that is done to numbers, such as adding, subtracting, multiplying, or dividing.

open sentence A sentence with a variable in it.

opposite leg In a right triangle, the leg not adjacent to a given angle.

ordered pair A symbol that specifies the order in which two numbers occur.

ordinate The second number in an ordered pair; the vertical coordinate on the graph.

origin On a number line, the zero point; on a Cartesian coordinate system, the $(0, 0)$ point.

parabola The graph of a quadratic function.

parallel Lines with equal slopes.

perimeter The sum of the lengths of a figure's sides.

perpendicular Two lines are perpendicular when the slope of one line equals the opposite of the reciprocal of the slope of the other.

point-slope form $y - y_1 = m(x - x_1)$

polynomial An expression that has no operations other than addition, subtraction, and multiplication by or of the variable(s).

positive number A number greater than zero.

power An expression containing a base and an exponent; for example, 3^2 or x^y.

prime number A positive integer that has no positive integers as factors other than 1 and itself. The number 1 is not considered to be a prime.

prime polynomial A polynomial where the only factors are 1 and the polynomial itself.

program A set of instructions for a computer to carry out.

proof A set of steps starting with given information and ending with a conclusion. Each step must be justified with a reason, such as an axiom, a definition, a given piece of information, or a previously proved property.

properties Facts about mathematical processes.

proportion An equation with ratios in which the ratios are equal.

proportionality constant The constant by which two terms are directly or inversely proportional.

Pythagorean Theorem In a right triangle the square of the hypotenuse equals the sum of the squares of the two legs; named after the Greek mathematician Pythagoras.

quadrant One of the four regions in a Cartesian coordinate system.

quadratic A word describing a second degree polynomial.

quadratic equation An equation in which a variable is squared.

Quadratic Formula A formula for solving a quadratic equation. The formula is
$$x = \frac{-b \pm \sqrt{b^2 - 4ac}}{2a}.$$

quadratic function A function with an equation of the form $y = $ (a quadratic expression).

radical An expression that has a root (square root, cube root, etc.); for example $\sqrt{25}$ is a radical.

radical equation An equation with a variable under the radical sign.

radical sign The symbol that shows a number is a radical. For example, in $\sqrt{a}$, $\sqrt{}$ is the radical sign.

radicand The number that appears with a radical sign. For example, in $\sqrt{9}$, 9 is the radicand.

range (of a variable) Set of values of the dependent variable corresponding to all values of the independent variable in the domain.

rational algebraic expressions Fractions that contain variables; a ratio of two polynomials.

rational number A number that can be written as a ratio of two integers.

real numbers All numbers on the number line, including positive numbers, negative numbers, zero, fractions, and decimals.

reciprocals See multiplicative inverses.

reflexive axiom of equality For any real number x, $x = x$; that is, a variable stands for the same number, no matter where it appears in any expression.

relatively prime Integers with no common prime factors and whose greatest common factor is 1 are said to be relatively prime.

rise The change in y in going from one point to another in a Cartesian coordinate system; the vertical change on the graph.

run The change in x in going from one point to another in a Cartesian coordinate system; the horizontal change on the graph.

signed numbers Numbers presented as negative (-3) or positive (3).

simple radical form A radical is said to be in simple radical form if there are no radicals in the denominator, and the radicals in the numerator are as small as possible.

simulated computer memory A list of variables used in simulating the operations of a computer.

simultaneous equations Equations in a system that can be solved at the same time.

sine A trigonometric function; in a right triangle with one acute angle A, sine
$$A = \frac{\text{opposite leg}}{\text{hypotenuse}}.$$

slope-intercept form In graphing an equation, an equation of the form $y = mx + b$, where m and b stand for constants, is in slope-intercept form.

solution (of an equation) A number that can be substituted for the variable in the equation to make the sentence (equation) true.

solution of an equation containing two variables   An ordered pair that makes the equation a true statement.

solution of a system of equations   An ordered pair that satisfies all the equations in the system.

solution set   The set of all solutions to an equation.

solving an equation   Writing the solution set to the equation.

square root n is a square root of x if $n^2 = x$.

square root of a product property   The square root of a product of two nonnegative numbers equals the product of the square roots of the two numbers.

square root of a quotient property   The square root of a quotient of two positive numbers equals the quotient of the square roots of the numbers.

square root property of equality   If two nonnegative numbers are equal, then their positive square roots are equal.

square root property of order   The square root of each member of an inequality can be taken without changing the order, as long as neither member is negative.

string   A computer message (such as *HAVE A NICE DAY*), a string of letters and symbols.

substituting   Replacing a variable (such as x) with a constant (such as 159 or 6.8).

substitution   A method of solving a system of equations by solving one equation to get one of the variables and substituting the result in the other equation.

subtraction   Subtracting a number means adding its opposite. That is, $x - y = x + (-y)$.

system of equations   Two or more equations with the same variables.

symbols of inclusion   Parentheses, brackets, and vinculums which are used in a problem to tell which operation to do first.

symmetric axiom of equality   An axiom that states: for real numbers a and b, if $a = b$, then $b = a$.

tangent   A trigonometric function, in a right triangle with one acute angle A, tangent $A = \dfrac{\text{opposite leg}}{\text{adjacent leg}}$.

terms   Numbers that are added to each other or subtracted from each other.

theorem   A property that can be proved.

tracing a program   The process of reading a computer program step by step and doing what it says.

transforming an equation   Doing the same operation to each member of an equation; a step in solving a set of equations by making the variables have equal or opposite coefficients.

transforming an expression   Commuting, associating, distributing, etc., in such a way that the expression still represents the same number as the original one.

transitive axiom of equality   An axiom that states: if the first number equals a second number, and the second number equals a third number, then the first number equals the third number.

trigonometric functions   The functions of angles in a triangle; *trigonometric* comes from Greek words meaning "measurement of a triangle." See also *sine, cosine,* and *tangent*.

trinomial   A polynomial with three terms.

union   The union of sets A and B is the set of numbers that are either in set A or in set B.

variable   A letter that represents a number. It represents the same number each time it appears in an expression.

vertex   The point at which the graph of a quadratic function turns around.

vertical motion formula   If an object is thrown into the air with an initial upward velocity of r mls then its distance, d m, above its starting point at time t s after it was thrown is approximately $d = rt - 5t^2$.

vinculum   The bar used in fractions and radicals; a symbol of inclusion.

x-intercept   On a graph, the value of x when y is 0.

y-intercept   On a graph, the value of y when x is 0.

zero exponent   For any non-zero number x, $x^0 = 1$.

Problem Title Index

General Index

Additional Answers

(Answers too long to be included on student page)

6-7

61a.

	x	5
x	x^2	$5x$
5	$5x$	25

b.

	x	9
x	x^2	$9x$
9	$9x$	81

c.

	$x-6$	6
$x-6$	$(x-6)^2$	$-6x$
6	$-6x$	36

7-1

1.

K	3	4	5	6	7
Z	79	72	65	58	

OUTPUT:
3	79
4	72
5	65
6	58

2.

D	5	7	9	N	13
E	31	39	47	55	

OUTPUT:
5	31
7	39
9	47
11	55

3.

P	2	3	4	5	6
C	-1	4	N	20	31

OUTPUT:
2	-1
3	4
4	11
5	20
6	31

4.

F	4	5	6	7	8	9
B	84	75	64	51	36	

OUTPUT:
4	84
5	75
6	64
7	51
8	36

5.

A	-3	-2	-1	0	1
B	3	4	1	0	1
C	4	-1	-4	-5	-4

OUTPUT:
-3	4
-2	-1
-1	-4
0	-5
1	-4

6.

X	5	6	7	8	9
Y	-2	-1	0	1	
Z	-8	-1	0	1	

OUTPUT:
5	-8
6	-1
7	0
8	1

7-2

1.

N	3						
X	-2	-1	0	1	2	3	4
Y	4	1	0	1	4	9	

OUTPUT:
?3
-2	4
-1	1
0	0
1	1
2	4
3	9

2.

K	3						
V	-2	-1	0	1	2	3	4
E	-8	-1	0	1	8	27	

OUTPUT:
?3
-2	-8
-1	-1
0	0
1	1
2	8
3	27

3.

L	16					
Z	2	5	8	N	N	17
A	2,3,16...	4,4,69...	5,29...			

OUTPUT:
?16
2	2
5	3.16227766
8	4
11	4.69041576
14	5.29150263

4.

H	29				
L	1	8	15	22	29
R	3.82...	16	25.95...	35.26...	

OUTPUT:
? 29
8	3.82842713
15	16
22	25.9544512
29	35.2664992

5.

U	5					
C	1	2	3	4	5	6
N	6	9	12	15	18	21
P	10	10	14	20	26	

OUTPUT:
?5
1	6	10
2	9	10
3	12	14
4	15	20
5	18	26

6.

T	6
K	1̶ 2̶ 3̶ 4̶ 5̶ 6
F	7̶ 3̶ 1̶ -5̶ -9̶ -13
J	8̶4̶ 2̶4̶ -4̶ 0̶ -36

OUTPUT:
```
?6
1    7    84
2    3    24
3   -1    -4
4   -5     0
5   -9   -36
```

7.

N	7̶ 8̶ 9̶ 1̶0̶ 1̶1̶ 1̶2̶ 1̶3̶ 14
F	1̶.̶7̶5̶ 2̶ 2̶.̶2̶5̶ 2̶.̶5̶ 2̶.̶7̶5̶ 3̶ 3.25
I	1̶ 2̶ 2̶ 2̶ 2̶ 3̶ 3

OUTPUT:
```
7    1.75    1
8    2       2
9    2.25    2
10   2.5     2
11   2.75    2
12   3       3
13   3.25    3
```

8.

U	1̶7̶ 1̶8̶ 1̶9̶ 2̶0̶ 2̶1̶ 22
R	3̶.̶4̶ 3̶.̶6̶ 3̶.̶8̶ 4̶ 4.2
A	3̶ 3̶ 3̶ 4̶ 4

OUTPUT:
```
17   3.4   3
18   3.6   3
19   3.8   3
20   4     4
21   4.2   4
```

9.

C	1̶ 3̶ 5̶ 7̶ 9̶ 11
D	2̶ 0̶ 2̶ 4̶ 6
E	1.73... 1̶ 1.73... 2.23... 2.64...
F	2̶ 1̶ 2̶ 2̶ 3
G	1̶ 3̶ 2̶5̶ 4̶9̶ 729

OUTPUT:
```
1    1
3    3
5    25
7    49
9    729
```

10.

X	-5̶ -1̶ 3̶ 7̶ 11
Y	5̶ 1̶ 3̶ 7
Z	2.23... 1̶ 1.73... 2.64...
W	2̶ 1̶ 1̶ 2
V	2̶5̶ 1̶ 3̶ 49

OUTPUT:
```
-5   25
-1    1
3     3
7    49
```

11.
```
10   LET X = 1
20   LET Y = SQR (X)
30   PRINT X,Y
40   LET X = X + 1
50   IF X < = 10 THEN 20
60   END
1    1
2    1.41421356
3    1.73205081
4    2
5    2.23606798
6    2.44948974
7    2.64575131
8    2.82842713
9    3
10   3.16227766
```

12.
```
10   LET X = 1
20   LET Y = X ^ 2
30   PRINT X,Y
40   LET X = X + 1
50   IF X < = 10 THEN 20
60   END
1    1
2    4
3    9
4    16
5    25
6    36
7    49
8    64
9    81
10   100
```

13.
```
10   LET X = 1
20   LET Y = X ^ 2 - 2 * X + 6
30   PRINT X,Y
40   LET X = X + 1
50   IF X < = 10 THEN 20
60   END
```

```
1     5
2     6
3     9
4    14
5    21
6    30
7    41
8    54
9    69
10   86
```

14.
```
10   LET X = 1
20   LET Y = X ^ 2 - 8 * X + 1
30   PRINT X,Y
40   LET X = X + 1
50   IF X < = 10 THEN 20
60   END
1    -6
2    -11
3    -14
4    -15
5    -14
6    -11
7    -6
8     1
9    10
10   21
```

15.
```
10   INPUT N
20   LET X = 1
30   LET Y = ABS (3 * X - 17)
40   PRINT X,Y
50   LET X = X + 1
60   IF X < = N THEN 30
70   END

]RUN
?10
1    14
2    11
3     8
4     5
5     2
6     1
7     4
8     7
9    10
10   13
```

16.
```
10   INPUT N
20   LET X = 1
30   LET Y = ABS (30 - 5 * X)
40   PRINT X,Y
50   LET X = X + 1
60   IF X < = N THEN 30
70   END
```

```
]RUN
?10
1     25
2     20
3     15
4     10
5     5
6     0
7     5
8     10
9     15
10    20
```

17.
```
10    INPUT N
20    LET X = 1
30    LET Y = 2 ^ X
40    PRINT X,Y
50    LET X = X + 1
60    IF X < = N THEN 30
70    END

]RUN
?10
1     2
2     4
3     8
4     16
5     32
6     64
7     128
8     256
9     512
10    1024
```

18.
```
10    INPUT N
20    LET X = 1
30    LET Y = 0.9 ^X
40    PRINT X,Y
50    LET X = X + 1
60    IF X < = N THEN 30
70    END

]RUN
?10
1     .9
2     .81
3     .729
4     .6561
5     .59049
6     .531441
7     .4782969
8     .43046721
9     .387420489
10    .34867844
```

19.
```
10    LET X = 1
20    LET Y = SQR (3 * X + 5)
30    LET Z = INT (Y)
40    PRINT X,Y,Z
50    LET X = X + 1
60    IF X < = 10 THEN 20
70    END

]RUN
1     2.82842713    2
2     3.31662479    3
3     3.74165739    3
4     4.12310563    4
5     4.47213595    4
6     4.79583153    4
7     5.09901951    5
8     5.38516481    5
9     5.65685425    5
10    5.91607979    5
```

20.
```
10    LET X = 0
20    LET R = 98 - 7 * X
30    IF R < 0 THEN 80
40    LET Y = SQR (R)
50    PRINT X,Y
60    LET X = X + 1
70    GOTO 20
80    END

]RUN
0     9.89949495
1     9.53939202
2     9.16515139
3     8.77496439
4     8.36660027
5     7.93725393
6     7.48331478
7     7
8     6.4807407
9     5.91607979
10    5.29150263
11    4.5825757
12    3.74165739
13    2.64575131
14    0
```

21. *Modifying Existing Programs*
For problems 11 through 14, simply retype line 20 with the new expression. For Problems 15 through 18, retype line 30.

7-3

1.

X	1	2	3	4	5	6
Y	8	13	18	23		28

```
]RUN
PROB. 1
1     8
2     13
3     18
4     23
5     28
DONE!!
```

2.

K	4	5	6	7	8	9
E						-5

```
]RUN
PROB. 2
4     11
5     7
6     3
7     -1
8     -5
FINISHED!
```

3.

N	5			
V	2	3	4	5	6
C			4	7

```
]RUN
PROB. 3
WHAT IS N?5
V     C
2     2
3     1
4     4
5     7
```

4.

L	15			
D				16
S	2.64...	2.82...		3.16...

```
]RUN
PROB. 4
TYPE L-VALUE? 15
D         S
12    2.64575131
13    2.82842713
14    3
15    3.16227766
```

5.

X	1	2	3	4	5	6	7	8
Y	1	4	27	256	3125	46656	823543	16777216

```
]RUN
PROB. 5
1    1
2    4
3    27
4    256
5    3125
6    46656
7    823543
Y IS OVER A MILLION
WHEN X IS 8
```

6.

X	1	2	3	4	5	6	7	8	9	10	11
Y	3	9	27	81	243	729	2187	6561			
Y	19683	59049									

```
]RUN
PROB. 6
1    3
2    9
3    27
4    81
5    243
6    729
7    2187
8    6561
9    19683
10   59049
NEVER OVER A MILLION
```

7.

N	3					
X	0	3	6	9	12	15
Y	0	1.73...	2.44...	3	3.46...	
Z	0	2	2	3	3	

```
]RUN
PROB. 7
WHAT SIZE STEP?3
X = 0    Z = 0
X = 3    Z = 2
X = 6    Z = 2
X = 9    Z = 3
X = 12   Z = 3
```

8.

N	3	8	13	18	23
X	1.5	4	6.5	9	
Y	1	4	6	9	

```
]RUN
PROB. 8
3 IS ODD
8 IS EVEN
13 IS ODD
18 IS EVEN
```

9.
```
10   PRINT "PROB. 9"
20   PRINT " X", "X^2"
30   PRINT "---","---"
40   FOR X = 1 TO 10
50   LET Y = X ^ 2
60   PRINT X,Y
70   NEXT X
80   END

]RUN
PROB. 9
 X        X^2
---       ---
 1         1
 2         4
 3         9
 4         16
 5         25
 6         36
 7         49
 8         64
 9         81
10         100
```

10.
```
10   PRINT "PROB. 10"
20   PRINT " X","SQR(X)"
30   PRINT "---","----------"
40   FOR X = 1 TO 10
50   LET Y = SQR (X)
60   PRINT X,Y
70   NEXT X
80   END

]RUN
PROB. 10
 X        SQR(X)
---       ----------
 1        1
 2        1.41421356
 3        1.73205081
 4        2
 5        2.23606798
 6        2.44948974
 7        2.64575131
 8        2.82842713
 9        3
10        3.16227766
```

11.
```
10   PRINT "PROB. 11"
20   PRINT " X"," Y"
30   PRINT "---","---"
40   FOR X = 1 TO 10
50   LET Y = X ^ 3 - 5 * X
60   PRINT X,Y
70   NEXT X
80   END

]RUN
PROB. 11
 X        Y
---       ---
 1        -4
 2        -2
 3        12
 4        44
 5        100
 6        186
 7        308
 8        472
 9        684
10        950
```

12.
```
10   PRINT "PROB. 12"
20   PRINT " X"," 3^X"
30   PRINT "---","----"
40   FOR X = 1 TO 10
50   LET Y = 3 ^ X
60   PRINT X,Y
70   NEXT X
80   END

]RUN
PROB. 12
 X        3^X
---       -----
 1        3
 2        9
 3        27
 4        81
 5        243
 6        729
 7        2187
 8        6561
 9        19683
10        59049
```

13.
```
10   PRINT "PROB. 13"
20   FOR X = 2 TO 100 STEP 2
30   LET Y = ABS  (X ^ 2 - 10 * X)
40   PRINT X,Y
50   IF Y > 1000 THEN 70
60   NEXT X
70   PRINT "LAST VALUE OF X WAS ";X
80   END
```

```
]RUN
PROB. 13
2      16
4      24
6      24
8      16
10      0
12     24
14     56
16     96
18    144
20    200
22    264
24    336
26    416
28    504
30    600
32    704
34    816
36    936
38   1064
LAST VALUE OF X WAS 38
```

14.
```
10   PRINT "PROB. 14"
20   FOR X = 3 TO 100 STEP 2
30   LET Y = SQR (7 * X - 15)
40   PRINT X,Y
50   IF Y > 10 THEN 70
60   NEXT X
70   PRINT "ENDED WHEN X WAS ";X
80   END

]RUN
PROB. 14
3     2.44948974
5     4.47213595
7     5.8309519
9     6.92820323
11    7.87400788
13    8.71779789
15    9.48683298
17    10.198039
ENDED WHEN X WAS 17
```

15.
```
10   PRINT "PROB. 15"
20   LET S = 0
30   PRINT " X","SUM"
40   PRINT "---","---"
50   FOR X = 2 TO 50 STEP 3
60   LET S = S + X
70   PRINT X,S
80   IF S > 100 THEN 100
90   NEXT X
100  PRINT "FINAL SUM IS ";S
110  END
```

```
PROB. 15
  X      SUM
 ---     ---
  2       2
  5       7
  8      15
 11      26
 14      40
 17      57
 20      77
 23     100
 26     126
FINAL SUM IS 126
```

16.
```
10   PRINT "BRIDGE PROBLEM"
20   LET S = 0
30   PRINT "DIST.","LENGTH"
40   PRINT "----","------"
50   FOR X = 0 TO 1050 STEP 50
60   LET Y = 0.000544 * X ^ 2 -
     0.571 * X + 161
70   LET Y = INT (100*Y+0.5)/100
80   PRINT X,Y
90   LET S = S + Y
100  NEXT X
110  LET T = S * 2
120  PRINT "TOTAL = ";T;"
     FEET."
130  END
```

Lines 20, 90, 110, 120 added for part (b).

```
]RUN
BRIDGE PROBLEM
DIST.    LENGTH
----     ------
0        161.00
50       133.81
100      109.34
150       87.59
200       68.56
250       52.25
300       38.66
350       27.79
400       19.64
450       14.21
500       11.50
550       11.51
600       14.24
650       19.69
700       27.86
750       38.75
800       52.36
850       68.69
900       87.74
950      109.51
1000     134.00
1050     161.21
TOTAL = 2899.82 FEET.
```

7-4

1.

C	~~1~~	~~2~~	~~3~~	~~4~~	5
X	~~7~~	~~15~~	~~20~~	30	
Y	~~19~~	~~35~~	~~45~~	65	

```
Output: PROBLEM 1
         7      19
        15      35
        20      45
        30      65
```

2.

C	~~1~~	~~2~~	~~3~~	~~4~~	5
X	~~2~~	~~8~~	~~6~~	4	
Y	~~17~~	~~47~~	~~37~~	27	

```
Output: PROBLEM 2
         2      17
         8      47
         6      37
         4      27
```

3.

N	~~1~~	~~2~~	~~3~~	4
X	~~3~~	~~0.6~~	~~8~~	20
Y	~~9~~	~~0.36~~	~~64~~	400

```
Output: PROBLEM 3
         3       9
        .6      .36
         8      64
        20      400
        4 NUMBERS
```

4.

N	~~1~~	~~2~~	~~3~~	4
X	~~10~~	~~7~~	~~5~~	3
Y	~~1000~~	~~343~~	~~125~~	27

```
Output: PROBLEM 4
        10      1000
         7       343
         5       125
         3        27
        4 NUMBERS
```

5.

S	~~0~~	~~85~~	~~148~~	~~247~~	337
C	~~1~~	~~2~~	~~3~~	~~4~~	5
X	~~85~~	~~63~~	~~99~~	90	

```
Output: PROBLEM 5
        85      85
        63      148
        99      247
        90      337
```

6.

P	1	2	6	30	210
C	1	2	3	4	5
X	2	3	5	7	

```
Output: PROBLEM 6
        2          2
        3          6
        5          30
        7          210
```

7.

P	1	3	6	-12
C	1	2	3	4
X	2	3	7	
Y	3	2	-2	

```
Output: PROBLEM 7
        2          3
        3          2
        7          -2
        PRODUCT = -12
```

8.

S	0	17	64	101
C	1	2	3	4
X	2	8	6	
Y	17	47	37	

```
Output: PROBLEM 8
        2          17
        8          47
        6          37
        TOTAL = 101
```

9.

S	0	25	42.3	50.7	51.9
C	0	1	2	3	4
L	1	2	3	4	5
N	25	17.3	8.4	1.2	-1

```
JRUN
PROBLEM 9
25
17.3
8.4
1.2
----
51.9
4 NUMBERS
```

10.

S	0	6	10	12	21
C	0	1	2	3	4
X	37	19	8	80	-1
Y	6.08...	4.35...	3	8.94...	
Z	6	4	3	8	

```
JRUN
PROBLEM 10
6.08276254    6
4.35889894    4
3             3
8.94427191    8

4 NUMBERS,
SUM IS 21
```

11.
```
10   PRINT "PROBLEM 11"
20   FOR C = 1 TO 8
30   READ X
40   DATA 27,30,41,29,6,3,-8,0
50   LET Y = 3 * X + 5
60   PRINT X,Y
70   NEXT C
80   END

PROBLEM 11
27      86
30      95
41      128
29      92
6       23
3       14
-8      -19
0       5
```

12.
```
10   PRINT "PROBLEM 12"
20   FOR C = 1 TO 7
30   READ X
40   DATA 4,17,8,-5,-20,6,100
50   LET Y = 6 - 9 * X
60   PRINT X,Y
70   NEXT C
80   END

PROBLEM 12
4        -30
17       -147
8        -66
-5       51
-20      186
6        -48
100      -894
```

13.
```
10    PRINT "PROBLEM 13"
20    LET S = 0
30    FOR C = 0 TO 100
40    READ X
50    IF X < 0 THEN 100
60    DATA 55,73,94,81,-1
70    LET S = S + X
80    PRINT X,S
90    NEXT C
100   PRINT "SUM IS ";S
110   END

PROBLEM 13
55       55
73       128
94       222
81       303
SUM IS 303
```

14.
```
10    PRINT "PROBLEM 14"
20    LET P = 1
30    FOR C = 0 TO 10
40    READ X
50    IF X < 0 THEN 100
60    DATA 3,5.2,7.4,9.8,4.7,-1
70    LET P = P * X
80    PRINT X,P
90    NEXT C
100   PRINT "PRODUCT IS  ";P
110   END

PROBLEM 14
3        3
5.2      15.6
7.4      115.44
9.8      1131.312
4.7      5317.1664
PRODUCT IS 5317.1664
```

15.
```
10    PRINT "PAYROLL PROBLEM"
20    LET T = 0
30    PRINT "DAY HOURS   $"
40    PRINT "--- ----- ----"
50    FOR D = 1 TO 6
60    READ H
70    DATA 2,1.5,.75,2.25,1.8,3.6
80    LET P = 6 * H
90    PRINT D,H,P
100   LET T = T + P
110   NEXT D
120   PRINT "TOTAL IS $";T
130   END
```

```
PAYROLL PROBLEM
DAY   HOURS      $
1     2          12
2     1.5        9
3     .75        4.5
4     2.25       13.5
5     1.8        10.8
6     3.6        21.6
TOTAL IS $71.4
```

16.
```
10   PRINT "BATTING AVERAGE PROBLEM"
20   LET T = 0
30   LET S = 0
40   PRINT "BATS HITS"
50   PRINT "---- ----"
60   FOR N = 1 TO 100
70   READ B,H
80   DATA 3,1,7,3,6,2,4,0,5,1,3,3,-1,-1
90   IF B < 0 THEN 140
100  PRINT B,H
110  LET T = T + B
120  LET S = S + H
130  NEXT N
140  LET A = S / T
150  LET A = INT (A * 1000) / 1000
160  PRINT N; "GAMES, AVERAGE = ";A
170  END
```

```
BATTING AVERAGE PROBLEM
BATS   HITS
3      1
7      3
6      2
4      0
5      1
3      3
7 GAMES, AVERAGE = .357
```

17.
```
10   PRINT "FACTORIALS  PROBLEM"
20   PRINT "TYPE A POSITIVE INTEGER ";
30   INPUT N
40   LET P = 1
50   FOR F = 1 TO N
60   LET P = P * F
70   PRINT F,P
80   NEXT F
90   PRINT N;"! = ";P
100  END
```

```
]RUN
FACTORIALS PROBLEM
TYPE A POSITIVE INTEGER ?12
1          1
2          2
3          6
4          24
5          120
6          720
7          5040
8          40320
9          362880
10         3628800
11         39916800
12         479001600
12! = 479001600
```

8-3

1.

2.

3.

4.

5.

6.

7.

8.

9. c.

$y = -3x + 12$

10. c.

$y = -2x + 10$

11. c.

$y = 2x - 6$

12. c.

$y = 3x - 6$

13. c.

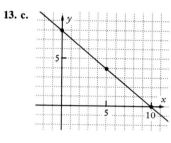

$y = -\frac{4}{5}x + 8$

14. c.

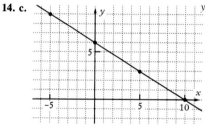

$y = -\frac{3}{5}x + 6$

15. c.

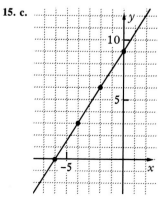

$y = \frac{3}{2}x + 9$

16. c.

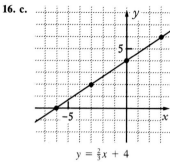

$y = \frac{2}{3}x + 4$

17. c.

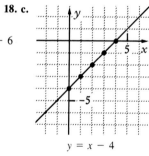

$y = -x + 7$

18. c.

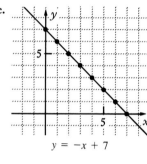

$y = x - 4$

19. c.

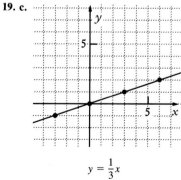

$y = \frac{1}{3}x$

20. c.

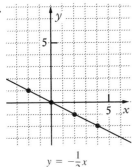

$$y = -\frac{1}{2}x$$

8-4

1.

2.

3.

4.

5.

6.

7.

8.

9.

10.

11.

12.

13.

14.

15.

16.

17.

18.

19.

20.

21.

22.

23.

24.

8-5

3.

4.

5.

6.

7.

8.

9.

10.

11.

12.

13.

14.

15.

16.

17.

18.

19.

20.

21.

22.

25.

28.

23.

26.

29.

24.

27.

30.

8-7

1.

2.

3.

4.

5.

6.

7.

8.

9.

10.

11.

12.

8-11

4., 5.

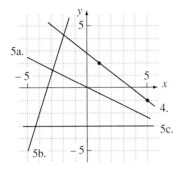

5a.

4.

5c.

5b.

10. a.

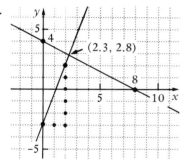

(2.3, 2.8)

9-2

32. a.

X	4			
N	3			
P	~~1~~ ~~4~~ ~~16~~ 64			
C	~~1~~ ~~2~~ ~~3~~ 4			

Output: `4^3 = 64`

b.   i. ```
]RUN
BASE: 8
EXPONENT: 5

8^5 = 32768
```

**ii.**  ```
]RUN
BASE: 5
EXPONENT: 8

5^8 = 390625
```

iii. ```
]RUN
BASE: 7
EXPONENT: 9

7^9 = 40353607
```

**iv.**  ```
]RUN
BASE; 9
EXPONENT: 7

9^7 = 4782969
```

v. ```
]RUN
BASE: 10
EXPONENT: 7

10^7 = 10000000
```

**c.**  ```
]RUN
BASE: 7
EXPONENT: 8

7^8 = 5764801
```

```
]RUN
BASE: 8
EXPONENT: 7

8^7 = 2097152

∴ 7^8 > 8^7
```

d. ```
]RUN
BASE: 10
EXPONENT: 20

10^20 = 1E+20
```

Largest power of 10 will vary depending on the type of computer. Run the program with larger and smaller exponents, thus finding by trial and error the largest power which does not cause "overflow." For a standard Apple II+ computer, the greatest value is 1E+38, or $10^{38}$.

**11-7**

**26. a.**  ```
]RUN
TYPE VALUES OF A, B, C, D
?1,-4,1,6
```

X	Y
-6	-360
-5	-224
-4	-126
-3	-60
-2	-20
-1	0
**********	
0	6
1	4
2	0
**********	
3	0
**********	
4	10
5	36
6	84

Factors:
$(x + 1)$
$(x - 2)$
$(x - 3)$

b. ```
]RUN
TYPE VALUES OF A, B, C, D
?1,-5,11,-15
```

**c.**  ```
]RUN
TYPE VALUES OF A, B, C, D
?1,-4,1,5
```

X	Y
-5	-225
-4	-127
-3	-61
-2	-21
-1	-1
0	5
1	3
2	-1
3	-1
4	9
5	35

12-9

63. (a)

N	64									
R	~~1~~ ~~2~~ ~~3~~ ~~4~~ ~~5~~ ~~4~~ 4.1 ~~4~~ 4.01 4									
D	~~1~~ 0.1 0.01									

```
Output:    1
           2
           3
           4
           5
           4
           4.1
           4
           4.01
Cube root of 64 is 4
```

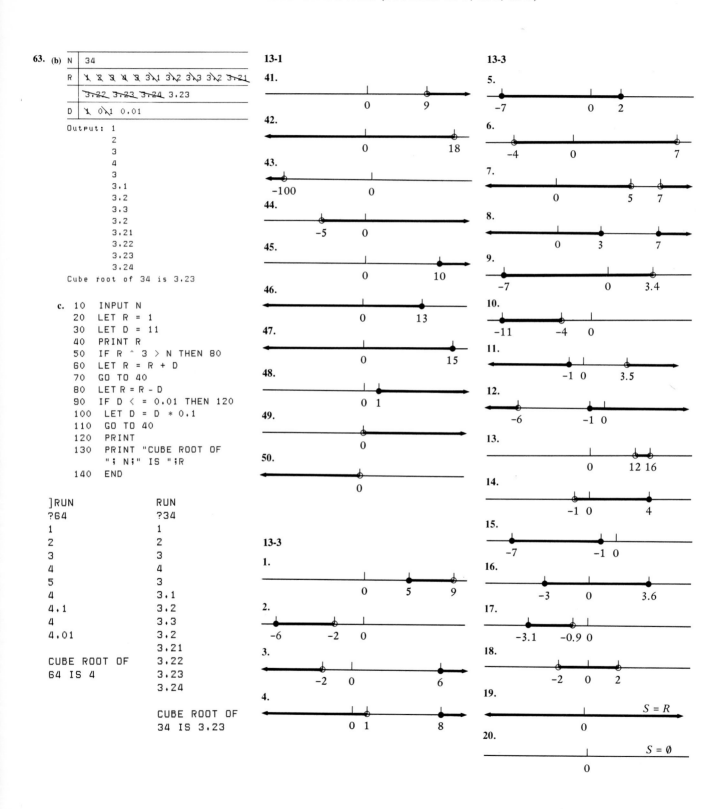

63. (b)

N	34								
R	1̶	2̶	3̶	4̶	3̶	3.1	3.2	3.3	3.2	3.21
	3.22	3.23	3.24	3.23					
D	1̶	0.1	0.01						

```
Output: 1
        2
        3
        4
        3
        3.1
        3.2
        3.3
        3.2
        3.21
        3.22
        3.23
        3.24
Cube root of 34 is 3.23
```

c.
```
10   INPUT N
20   LET R = 1
30   LET D = 11
40   PRINT R
50   IF R ^ 3 > N THEN 80
60   LET R = R + D
70   GO TO 40
80   LET R = R - D
90   IF D < = 0.01 THEN 120
100  LET D = D * 0.1
110  GO TO 40
120  PRINT
130  PRINT "CUBE ROOT OF
     "; N;" IS ";R
140  END
```

```
]RUN          RUN
?64           ?34
1             1
2             2
3             3
4             4
5             3
4             3.1
4.1           3.2
4             3.3
4.01          3.2
              3.21
CUBE ROOT OF  3.22
64 IS 4       3.23
              3.24

              CUBE ROOT OF
              34 IS 3.23
```

13-1

41.

42.

43.

44.

45.

46.

47.

48.

49.

50.

13-3

1.

2.

3.

4.

13-3

5.

6.

7.

8.

9.

10.

11.

12.

13.

14.

15.

16.

17.

18.

19. $S = R$

20. $S = \emptyset$

13-4

1.

13-6

1.
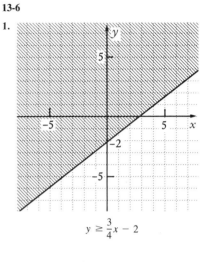
$$y \geq \frac{3}{4}x - 2$$

17.

2.
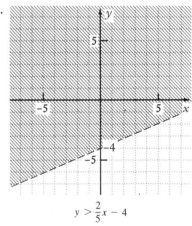
$$y > \frac{2}{5}x - 4$$

3.
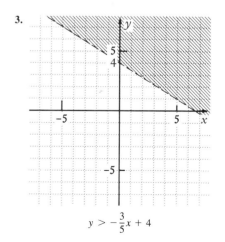
$$y > -\frac{3}{5}x + 4$$

4.

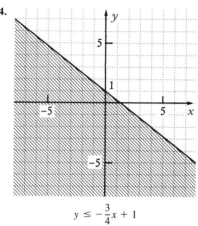

$$y \leq -\frac{3}{4}x + 1$$

7.

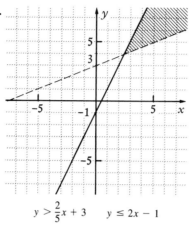

$$y > \frac{2}{5}x + 3 \qquad y \leq 2x - 1$$

10.

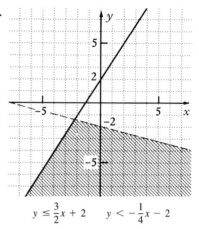

$$y \leq \frac{3}{2}x + 2 \qquad y < -\frac{1}{4}x - 2$$

5.

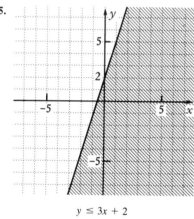

$$y \leq 3x + 2$$

8.

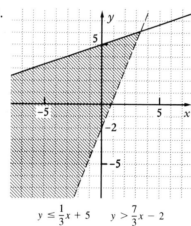

$$y \leq \frac{1}{3}x + 5 \qquad y > \frac{7}{3}x - 2$$

11.

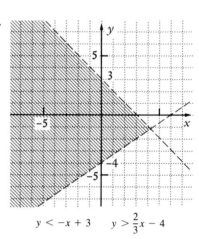

$$y < -x + 3 \qquad y > \frac{2}{3}x - 4$$

6.

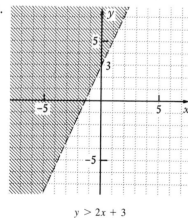

$$y > 2x + 3$$

9.

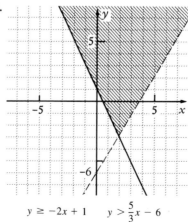

$$y \geq -2x + 1 \qquad y > \frac{5}{3}x - 6$$

12.

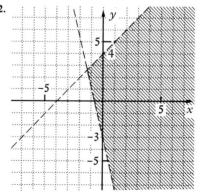

$$y < x + 4 \qquad y > -4x - 3$$

13.

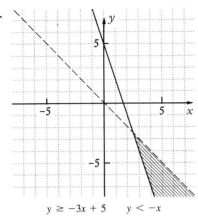

$y \geq -3x + 5 \qquad y < -x$

16.

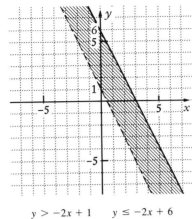

$y > -2x + 1 \qquad y \leq -2x + 6$

19.

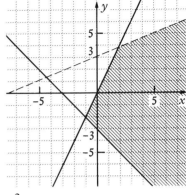

$y < \frac{2}{5}x + 3 \qquad y \leq 2x \qquad y \geq -x - 3$

14.

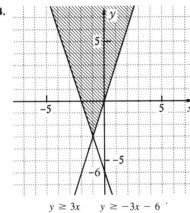

$y \geq 3x \qquad y \geq -3x - 6$

17.

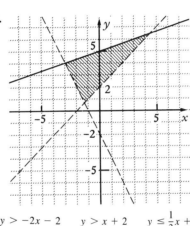

$y > -2x - 2 \qquad y > x + 2 \qquad y \leq \frac{1}{3}x + 5$

20.

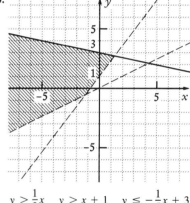

$y > \frac{1}{2}x \qquad y > x + 1 \qquad y \leq -\frac{1}{5}x + 3$

15.

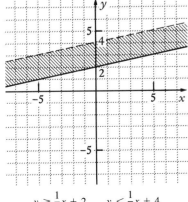

$y \geq \frac{1}{5}x + 2 \qquad y < \frac{1}{5}x + 4$

18.

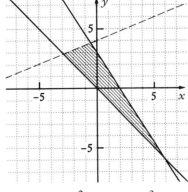

$y \geq -x, \, y < \frac{2}{5}x + 4, \, y \leq -\frac{3}{2}x + 3$

13-7

1.

2.

3.

4.

14-1

1. a.

x	y
-3	3.1
-2	3.4
-1	3.7
0	4
1	4.3
2	4.6
3	4.9

b.

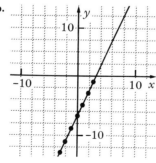

2. a.

x	y
-3	-13.3
-2	-11.2
-1	-9.1
0	-7
1	-4.9
2	-2.8
3	-.7

b.

3. a.

x	y
-1	7
0	2
1	-1
2	-2
3	-1
4	2
5	7

b.

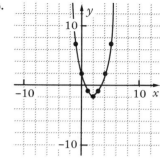

4. a.

x	y
-2	11
-1	6
0	3
1	2
2	3
3	6
4	11

b.

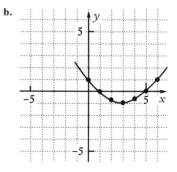

5. a.

x	y
0	1
1	0
2	-.6
3	-.8
4	-.6
5	0
6	1

b.

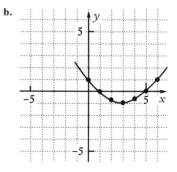

6. a.

x	y
-1	5
0	3
1	1.8
2	1.4
3	1.8
4	3
5	5

b.

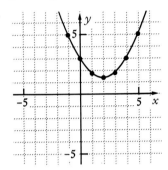

7. a.

x	y
-2	8
-1	6
0	4
1	2
2	0
3	2
4	4
5	6
6	8

b.

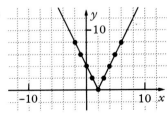

8. a.

x	y
0	12
1	9
2	6
3	3
4	0
5	3
6	6
7	9
8	12

b.

9. a.

x	y
1	12
2	6
3	4
4	3
6	2
12	1

b.

10. a.

x	y
1	10
2	5
4	2.5
5	2
10	1

b.

14-5

1. a.

x	y
-7	96
-6	77
-5	60
-4	45
-3	32
-2	21
-1	12
0	5
1	0
2	-3
3	-4
4	-3
5	0
6	5
7	12
8	21
9	32
10	45

b.

c. $x = 1, 5$
$y = 5$

d. $(3, -4)$

2. a.

x	y
-4	55
-3	40
-2	27
-1	16
0	7
1	0
2	-5
3	-8
4	-9
5	-8
6	-5
7	0
8	7
9	16
10	27

b.

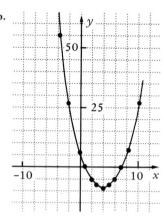

c. $x = 1, 7$
$y = 7$
d. $(4, -9)$

3. a.

x	y
-10	48
-9	34
-8	22
-7	12
-6	4
-5	-2
-4	-6
-3	-8
-3	-8
-1	-6
0	-2
1	4
2	12
3	22
4	34
5	48

b.

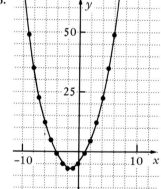

c. $x = \dfrac{-5 \pm \sqrt{33}}{2}$
$x \approx 0.37, -5.37$
$y = -2$
d. $(-2.5, -8.25)$

4. a.

x	y
-9	49
-8	35
-7	23
-6	13
-5	5
-4	-1
-3	-5
-2	-7
-1	-7
0	-5
1	-1
2	5
3	13
4	23
5	35
6	49

b.

c. $x = \dfrac{-3 \pm \sqrt{29}}{2}$
$x = 1.19, -4.19$
$y = -5$
d. $(-1.5, -7.25)$

5. a.

x	y
-3	-10.6
-2	-5.6
-1	-1.4
0	2
1	4.6
2	6.4
3	7.4
4	7.6
5	7
6	5.6
7	3.4
8	.4
9	-3.4
10	-8

b.

c. $x = \dfrac{-3 \pm \sqrt{12.2}}{-0.8}$
$x \approx -.62, 8.12$
$y = 2$
d. $(3.75, 7.63)$

6. a.

x	y
-3	-10.7
-2	-4.4
-1	.5
0	4
1	6.1
2	6.8
3	6.1
4	4
5	.5
6	-4.4
7	-10.7

b.

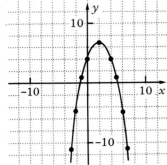

c. $x = \dfrac{-2.8 \pm \sqrt{19.04}}{-1.4}$

$x \approx -1.12, 5.12$

$y = 4$

d. (2, 6.8)

7. a.

x	y
-3	23
-2	15
-1	9
0	5
1	3
2	3
3	5
4	9
5	15
6	23

b.

c. $x = \dfrac{3 \pm \sqrt{-11}}{2}$

x: none

$y = 5$

d. (1.5, 2.75)

8. a.

x	y
-2	21
-1	13
0	7
1	3
2	1
3	1
4	3
5	7
6	13
7	21

b.

c. $x = \dfrac{5 \pm \sqrt{-3}}{2}$

x: none

$y = 7$

9. a.

x	y
-2	-26
-1	-17
0	-10
1	-5
2	-2
3	-1
4	-2
5	-5
6	-10
7	-17
8	-26

b.

c. $x = \dfrac{-6 \pm \sqrt{-4}}{-2}$

x: none

$y = -10$

d. (3, -1)

10. a.

x	y
-3	-27
-2	-18
-1	-11
0	-6
1	-3
2	-2
3	-3
4	-6
5	-11
6	-18
7	-27

b.

c. $x = \dfrac{-4 \pm \sqrt{-8}}{-2}$

x: none

$y = -6$

d. (2, -2)

11. a.

x	y
-3	95
-2	35
-1	-9
0	-37
1	-49
2	-45
3	-25
4	11
5	63
6	131

b.

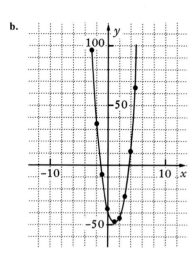

c. $x = \dfrac{20 \pm \sqrt{1584}}{16}$

$x \approx 3.74, -1.24$

$y = -37$

d. $(1.25, -49.5)$

12. a.

x	y
-8	127
-7	71
-6	25
-5	-11
-4	-37
-3	-53
-2	-59
-1	-55
0	-41
1	-17
2	17
3	61
4	115

b.

c. $x = \dfrac{-19 \pm \sqrt{1181}}{10}$

$x \approx 1.54, -5.34$

$y = -41$

d. $(-1.9, -59.05)$

14-6

1. $x^2 - 12x + 17 > 0$
$x^2 - 12x + 36 > 19$
$|x - 6| > \sqrt{19}$
$x > 6 + \sqrt{19}$ or $x < 6 - \sqrt{19}$
$x > 10.36$ or $x < 1.64$*

2. $x^2 - 16x + 41 < 0$
$x^2 - 16x + 64 < 23$
$|x - 8| < \sqrt{23}$
$8 - \sqrt{23} < x < 8 + \sqrt{23}$
$3.21 < x < 12.79$*

3. $x^2 + 6x + 7 \le 0$
$x^2 + 6x + 9 \le 2$
$|x + 3| \le \sqrt{2}$
$-3 - \sqrt{2} \le x \le -3 + \sqrt{2}$
$-4.41 \le x \le -1.59$

4. $x^2 + 8x + 9 \ge 0$
$x^2 + 8x + 16 \ge 7$
$|x + 4| \ge \sqrt{7}$
$x \ge -4 + \sqrt{7}$ or $x \le -4 - \sqrt{7}$
$x \ge -1.35$ or $x \le -6.65$

5. $x^2 - 10x - 51 \ge 0$
$x^2 - 10x + 25 \ge 76$
$|x - 5| \ge \sqrt{76}$
$x \ge 5 + \sqrt{76}$ or $x \le 5 - \sqrt{76}$
$x \ge 13.72$ or $x \le -3.72$

6. $x^2 - 4x - 26 \le 0$
$x^2 - 4x + 4 \le 30$
$|x - 2| \le \sqrt{30}$
$2 - \sqrt{30} \le x \le 2 + \sqrt{30}$
$-3.47 \le x \le 7.47$

7. $x^2 - 14x + 33 < 0$
$x^2 - 14x + 49 < 16$
$|x - 7| < 4$
$3 < x < 11$

8. $x^2 - 18x + 65 > 0$
$x^2 - 18x + 81 > 16$
$|x - 9| > 4$
$x > 13$ or $x < 5$

9. $x^2 + 2x + 3 \le 0$
$x^2 + 2x + 1 \le -2$
$(x + 1)^2 \le -2$
$S = \emptyset$

10. $x^2 + 6x + 10 \ge 0$
$x^2 + 6x + 9 \ge -1$
$(x + 3)^2 \ge -1$
$S = R$

11. $x^2 - 6x + 12 > 0$
$x^2 - 6x + 9 > -3$
$(x - 3)^2 > -3$
$S = \{\text{real nos.}\}$

12. $x^2 - 10x + 30 < 0$
$x^2 - 10x + 25 < -5$
$(x - 5)^2 < -5$
$S = \emptyset$

*Note: All answers are rounded off in the direction of the inequality, not necessarily to the nearest value.

13. $x^2 - 5x - 14 < 0$
$x^2 - 5x + 6.25 < 20.25$
$|x - 2.5| < 4.5$
$-2 < x < 7$

14. $x^2 - 7x - 30 > 0$
$x^2 - 7x + 12.25 > 42.25$
$|x - 3.5| > 6.5$
$x > 10$ or $x < -3$

$\qquad$ -3 $\quad$ 0 $\qquad$ 10

15. $x^2 + 7x - 2 \geq 15$
$x^2 + 7x + 12.25 \geq 29.25$
$|x + 3.5| \geq \sqrt{29.25}$
$x \geq -3.5 + \sqrt{29.25}$ or
$x \leq -3.5 - \sqrt{29.25}$
$x \geq 1.91$ or $x \leq -8.91$

$\qquad$ -8.91 $\qquad$ 0 $\quad$ 1.91

16. $x^2 + 9x - 5 \leq 30$
$x^2 + 9x + 20.25 \leq 55.25$
$|x + 4.5| \leq \sqrt{55.25}$
$-4.5 - \sqrt{55.25} \leq x \leq$
$\qquad -4.5 + \sqrt{55.25}$
$-11.93 \leq x \leq 2.93$

$\qquad$ -11.93 $\qquad$ 0 $\quad$ 2.93

17. $x^2 + 3x \leq 5x + 11$
$x^2 - 2x + 1 \leq 12$
$|x - 1| \leq \sqrt{12}$
$1 - \sqrt{12} \leq x \leq 1 + \sqrt{12}$
$-2.46 \leq x \leq 4.46$

$\qquad$ -2.46 $\quad$ 0 $\qquad$ 4.46

Check: $0 \leq -47$? False. $\checkmark$

18.
$x^2 - 7x \geq 4 - 2x$
$x^2 - 5x + 6.25 \geq 10.25$
$|x - 2.5| \geq \sqrt{10.25}$
$x \geq 2.5 + \sqrt{10.25}$ or $x \leq 2.5 - \sqrt{10.25}$
$x \geq 5.71$ or $x \leq -0.71$

$\qquad$ -0.71 0 $\qquad$ 5.71

19. $6x + 3 < x(5 + x)$
$6x + 3 < 5x + x^2$
$-x^2 + x + 3 < 0$
$x^2 - x - 3 > 0$
$x^2 - x + 0.25 > 3.25$
$|x - 0.5| > \sqrt{3.25}$
$x > 0.5 + \sqrt{3.25}$ or $x < 0.5 - \sqrt{3.25}$
$x > 2.31$ or $x < -1.31$

$\qquad$ -1.31 0 $\quad$ 2.31

20. $7 - 2x > x(x - 11)$
$7 - 2x > x^2 - 11x$
$-x^2 + 9x + 7 > 0$
$x^2 - 9x - 7 < 0$
$x^2 - 9x + 20.25 < 27.25$
$|x - 4.5| < \sqrt{27.25}$
$4.5 - \sqrt{27.25} < x < 4.5 + \sqrt{27.25}$
$-0.72 < x < 9.72$

$\qquad$ -0.72 0 $\qquad\qquad$ 9.72

Exercise 14-7

1. $3x^2 + 5x - 19 > 0$
$x = \dfrac{-5 \pm \sqrt{253}}{6}$
$x \approx 1.82$ or -3.48*

$\qquad$ -3.48 $\quad$ 0 $\quad$ 1.82

Check $-19 > 0$? False. $\checkmark$

2. $7x^2 + 10x - 23 < 0$
$x = \dfrac{-10 \pm \sqrt{744}}{14}$
$x \approx 1.23$ or -2.66*

$\qquad$ -2.66 $\quad$ 0 $\quad$ 1.23

Check: $-23 < 0$? True. $\checkmark$

3. $2x^2 - 7x - 43 \leq 0$
$x = \dfrac{7 \pm \sqrt{393}}{4}$
$x \approx 6.70$ or -3.20

$\qquad$ -3.20 $\quad$ 0 $\qquad$ 6.70

Check: $-43 \leq 0$? True. $\checkmark$

4. $3x^2 - 8x - 87 \geq 0$
$x = \dfrac{8 \pm \sqrt{1108}}{6}$
$x \approx 6.88$ or -4.21

$\qquad$ -4.21 $\qquad$ 0 $\qquad$ 6.88

Check: $-87 \geq 0$? False. $\checkmark$

5. $x^2 - 9x + 14 > 0$
$x = \dfrac{9 \pm \sqrt{25}}{2}$
$x = 7$ or 2

$\qquad$ 0 $\quad$ 2 $\qquad$ 7

Check: $14 > 0$? True. $\checkmark$

6. $x^2 - 11x + 24 < 0$
$x = \dfrac{11 \pm \sqrt{25}}{2}$
$x = 8$ or 3

$\qquad$ 0 $\quad$ 3 $\qquad$ 8

Check: $24 < 0$? False. $\checkmark$

7. $30x - 5x^2 + 47 \leq 0$
$+5x^2 - 30x - 47 \geq 0$
$x = \dfrac{30 \pm \sqrt{1840}}{10}$
$x \approx 7.29$ or -1.29

$\qquad$ -1.29 0 $\qquad$ 7.29

Check: $47 \leq 0$? False. $\checkmark$

8. $79 - 7x^2 - 13x \geq 0$
$7x^2 + 13x - 79 \leq 0$
$x = \dfrac{-13 \pm \sqrt{2381}}{14}$
$x \approx 2.55$ or -4.41

$\qquad$ -4.41 $\quad$ 0 $\quad$ 2.55

Check: $79 \geq 0$? True. $\checkmark$

9. $10x^2 + 11x + 12 \leq 0$
$x = \dfrac{-11 \pm \sqrt{-359}}{20}$
No endpoints. $\qquad\qquad S = \emptyset$

$\qquad\qquad\qquad$ 0

Check: $12 \leq 0$? False. $\checkmark$

10. $-5x^2 - 11x + 20 \geq 0$
$x = \dfrac{11 \pm \sqrt{521}}{10}$
$x \approx -3.38$ or 1.18

$\qquad$ -3.38 $\quad$ 0 $\quad$ 1.18

Check: $20 \geq 0$? True. $\checkmark$

*Note: Answers rounded in the direction of the inequality, not necessarily to the nearest value.

11. $6 + x^2 - 3x > 0$
$x^2 - 3x + 6 > 0$
$x = \dfrac{3 \pm \sqrt{-15}}{2}$
No endpoints $\qquad\qquad S = R$

$\qquad\qquad\qquad$ 0

Check: $6 > 0$? True. $\checkmark$

12. $x^2 + 10 + 3x < 0$
$x^2 + 3x + 10 < 0$
$$x = \frac{-3 \pm \sqrt{-31}}{2}$$
No endpoints.

$\underline{\qquad\qquad\underset{0}{|}\quad S = 0 \qquad\qquad}$

Check: $10 < 0$? False. ✓

13. $0.3x^2 - 5x - 18.9 < 0$
$$x = \frac{5 \pm \sqrt{47.68}}{0.6}$$
$x \approx 19.84$ or -3.17

$\underline{\qquad\underset{-3.17\ \ 0}{\circ\ \ |}\qquad\qquad\underset{19.84}{\circ}\qquad}$

Check: $-18.9 < 0$? True. ✓

14. $0.9x^2 - 20x + 98.6 > 0$
$$x = \frac{20 \pm \sqrt{45.04}}{1.8}$$
$x \approx 14.84$ or 7.38

$\underline{\qquad\qquad\underset{0}{|}\quad\underset{7.38}{\circ}\quad\underset{14.84}{\circ}\qquad}$

Check: $98.6 > 0$? True. ✓

15. $4x^2 - 28x + 49 > 0$
$$x = \frac{28 \pm \sqrt{0}}{8}$$
$x = 3.5$ (only)

$\underline{\qquad\qquad\underset{0}{|}\qquad\underset{3.5}{\circ}\qquad\qquad}$

Check: $49 > 0$? True. ✓

16. $25x^2 - 80x + 64 \le 0$
$$x = \frac{80 \pm \sqrt{0}}{50}$$
$x = 1.6$ (only)

$\underline{\qquad\qquad\underset{0\ \ 1.6}{|\ \ \bullet}\qquad\qquad}$

Check: $64 \le 0$? False. ✓

17. $3x^2 - 20x \le x^2 - 47$
$2x^2 - 20x + 47 \le 0$
$$x = \frac{20 \pm \sqrt{24}}{4}$$
$x \approx 6.22$ or 3.78

$\underline{\qquad\qquad\underset{0}{|}\qquad\underset{3.78}{\bullet}\quad\underset{6.22}{\bullet}\qquad}$

Check: $0 \le -47$? False. ✓

18. $5x^2 + 22x > 2x^2 + 100$
$3x^2 + 22x - 100 > 0$
$$x = \frac{-22 \pm \sqrt{1684}}{6}$$
$x \approx 3.18$ or -10.51

$\underline{\quad\underset{-10.51}{\circ}\qquad\qquad\underset{0}{|}\quad\underset{3.18}{\circ}\qquad}$

Check: $0 > 100$? False. ✓

19. $7x + 30 < x(x + 8)$
$7x + 30 < x^2 + 8x$
$-x^2 - x + 30 < 0$
$x^2 + x - 30 < 0$
$$x = \frac{-1 \pm \sqrt{121}}{2}$$
$x = 5$ or -6

$\underline{\overset{\blacktriangleleft}{\quad}\underset{-6}{\circ}\qquad\underset{0}{|}\qquad\underset{5}{\circ}\overset{\blacktriangleright}{\quad}}$

Check: $30 < 0$? False. ✓

20. $4x + 4.8 \ge x(x + 2.3)$
$4x + 4.8 \ge x^2 + 2.3x$
$-x^2 + 1.7x + 4.8 \ge 0$
$x^2 - 1.7x - 4.8 \le 0$
$$x = \frac{1.7 \pm \sqrt{22.09}}{2}$$
$x = 3.2$ or -1.5

$\underline{\qquad\underset{-1.5}{\bullet}\quad\underset{0}{|}\qquad\underset{3.2}{\bullet}\qquad}$

Check: $4.8 \ge 0$? True. ✓

29. a.

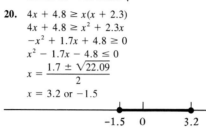

29. b. $x^2 - 3x - 5 \ge 0$
$$x = \frac{3 \pm \sqrt{29}}{2}$$
$x \approx 4.20$ or -1.20

30. a.

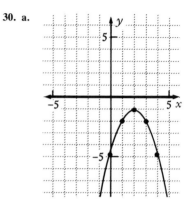

30. b. $-x^2 + 4x - 5 \ge 0$
$$x = \frac{-4 \pm \sqrt{-4}}{-2}$$

$\underline{\qquad\qquad\underset{0}{|}\qquad S = \emptyset \qquad\qquad}$

14-8

8. a. Between:

8. b. Beyond:

8. c. Empty set:

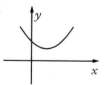

8. d. All real numbers

8-6

1.

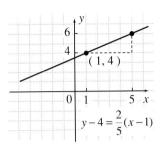

$$y - 4 = \frac{2}{5}(x - 1)$$

2.

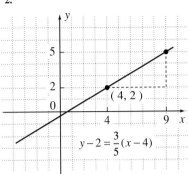

$$y - 2 = \frac{3}{5}(x - 4)$$

3.

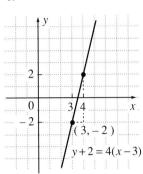

$$y + 2 = 4(x - 3)$$

4.

$$y - 3 = 2(x + 4)$$

5.

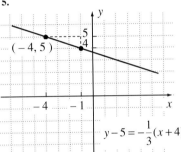

$$y - 5 = -\frac{1}{3}(x + 4)$$

6.

$$(3, -5)$$

7.

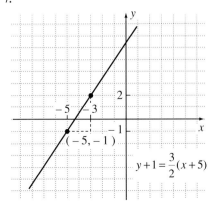

$$y + 1 = \frac{3}{2}(x + 5)$$

8.

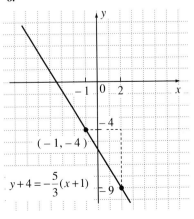

$$y + 4 = -\frac{5}{3}(x + 1)$$

$\mapsto \hbar$